D1496115

The Origin of the Australians

The Origin of
the Australians

edited by R. L. Kirk and A. G. Thorne

Human Biology Series No. 6
Australian Institute of Aboriginal Studies, Canberra
Humanities Press Inc., New Jersey
1976

Papers presented to a symposium at the 1974 Meeting of the Australian Institute of Aboriginal Studies.

The editors wish to express their gratitude to Winifred Mumford and Elizabeth Robertson, who have given invaluable assistance at various stages during the preparation of this book. Shirley Andrew has guided the project throughout and to her must go the major credit for its successful publication.

Library of Congress Catalog number 76 13318
National Library of Australia card number and ISBN 0 85575 053 7   hard cover
    0 85575 052 9   soft cover

U.S.A. edition ISBN 0 391 00 615 0   hard cover
    0 391 00 616 9   soft cover

Typeset in Australia by Dudley E. King Pty Ltd, Melbourne
Printed in Australia by Hedges & Bell, Maryborough, Victoria

8.76.3000

Contents

Introduction

The Pleistocene Background
(Chairman: W. W. Howells)

Aspects of late Quaternary palaeogeography of the Australian-East Indonesian region   J. M. A. Chappell   11
Some biogeographical factors relevant to the Pleistocene movement of Man in Australasia   J. H. Calaby   23
Palaeoenvironments for Man in New Guinea   J. H. Hope and G. S. Hope   29
Recent developments in reconstructing late Quaternary environments in Australia   J. M. Bowler   55

Early Man in Australia
(Chairman: L. Freedman)

Early populations in the Indonesian region   T. Jacob   81
Morphological contrasts in Pleistocene Australians   A. G. Thorne   95
Aboriginal affinities looked at in world context   N. W. G. Macintosh and S. L. Larnach   113
Human remains from Lake Mungo: discovery and excavation of Lake Mungo III   J. M. Bowler and A. G. Thorne   127

Morphological Variation
(Chairmen: N. W. G. Macintosh & D. B. Allbrook)

Metrical analysis in the problem of Australian origins   W. W. Howells   141
Cranial variation in Australia and neighbouring areas   E. Giles   161
Early Man in Tasmania: new skeletal evidence   A. G. Wallace and G. A. Doran   173
Aboriginal palaeophysiology   W. V. Macfarlane   183
Head size increases in Australian Aboriginals: an example of skeletal plasticity   T. Brown   195

Morphological variation in the adult Australian Aboriginal
   A. A. Abbie   211
Australian Aboriginals and the outer world: dermatoglyphical
   evidence   *M. Prokopec and V. Šedivy*   215
Variability of anthropometric traits in Australian Aboriginals
   and adjacent populations: its bearing on the biological
   origin of the Australians   *P. A. Parsons and N. G. White*   227
Ossification variation in two populations from Papua New
   Guinea   *W. B. Wood*   245
Evolutionary process and semantics: Australian prehistoric
   tooth size as a local adjustment   *R. V. S. Wright*   265

Genetic Patterns
(Chairman: N. E. Morton)

Genetic relationships of several aboriginal groups in South
   East Asia   *L. E. Lie-Injo*   277
The biological origin of Australian Aboriginals: an examina-
   tion of blood group genes and gene frequencies for possible
   evidence in populations from Australia to Eurasia
   R. T. Simmons   307
Serum protein and enzyme markers as indicators of population
   affinities in Australia and the Western Pacific   *R. L. Kirk*   329
Immunoglobulin markers as indicators of population affinities
   in Australasia and the Western Pacific   *C. C. Curtain,*
   E. van Loghem and M. S. Schanfield   347
The genetic relations of the Ainu   *K. Omoto and S. Misawa*   365

Genetics and Evolutionary Relationships
(Chairman: J. H. Bennett)

Human microdifferentiation in the Western Pacific   *N. E.*
   Morton and B. Keats   379
Comparative genetic studies between some groups of Australian
   Aboriginals and certain tribal peoples of India   *L. D.*
   Sanghvi   401
Genetic distance analysis of some New Guinea populations: an
   evaluation   *P. B. Booth and H. W. Taylor*   415

List of Authors   431
Index: Persons   433
   Subject   443

Introduction

SPECULATION concerning the origin of the Australian Aboriginals has occurred since the earliest times. Such speculation by Aboriginals themselves is embodied in a variety of 'origin' legends, some of which record progenitors coming from the sea and peopling the country with both human and animal forms. Since the time of European contact the world-view of Aboriginal origins has widened and increasingly sophisticated methods of study have been focused on this problem.

During the last one hundred years many writers have expressed views on the origin of the Australian Aboriginals. Some have theorised that Aboriginals evolved entirely from Neanderthal forms within Australia, and proponents of such theories have included Schoetensack (1901), Klaatsch (1908), Basedow (1925), Sollas (1911) and Hrdlicka (1926, 1928).

Most other writers, including all recent workers, believe we must look outside the Australian continent for traces of the ancestors of present-day Aboriginals. Two general classes of theory have been proposed, one that modern Aboriginals are descendants from a single introduction of people at some time in the past, the other that two or more waves of immigrants arrived at different periods. The demonstrable variation in genetic, anthropometric and anthroposcopic traits in the living full-blood Aboriginals has arisen, according to the proponents of the first theory, as a result of local, internal adaptation to specific environmental pressures and to a range of random genetic processes, including mutation and drift. According to proponents of the second theory some at least of the demonstrable variation present today reflects the different physical and genetic types of the various founding populations, modified by hybridisation of their descendants in various parts of the continent. Amongst those who have supported the theory of a unitary origin are Turner (1884), Keith (1925), Wood-Jones (1934), Campbell et al (1936), Howells (1937), Abbie (1951, 1960, 1963, 1966) and Macintosh (1963). Supporters of the theory of multiple origins have included Topinard (1872), Davis (1874), Lesson (1880), Fenner (1939), Wunderly (1943), Hooton (1947), Tindale and Birdsell (1941) and Birdsell (1949, 1950 and 1967), Gates (1960) and Morrison (1967).

Many of the workers cited above supported their views with limited studies of museum skulls or anthropometric studies on selected groups of living Aboriginals. Only Abbie on the one hand and Tindale and Birdsell on the other have attempted a systematic survey in different parts of the continent in studies sustained over a long period.

During the last decade however Australian and overseas scholars have been engaged in wide-ranging investigations not only in Australia but also in New Guinea and other parts of south and south-east Asia and the western Pacific: these studies have an important bearing on the interpretation of evidence relating to the evolution of Man in Australia. Recent archaeological finds have pushed the antiquity of human activity in Australia to approximately 40,000 years, and to a comparable time in New Guinea. For much of that period Australia, New Guinea and Tasmania were a single landmass and newer studies are revealing some of the climatic and biogeographic features which would have predominated during the time Man was occupying and adapting himself to the varied ecological zones in the continent. Much evidence has accumulated also on the genetic similarities and differences between Aboriginals and neighbouring populations and new theoretical insights have been developed to help interpret such genetic information in a biologically meaningful way. Finally, fresh data has been accumulated on the plasticity of human morphology in relation to environmental variables, data which is of great importance in making deductions based on comparisons of anthropometric and other physical anthropological traits.

The desire to bring together some of the results of research having a direct or potential bearing on the biological origin of the Australians was the basis of a symposium held in Canberra on May 21–22, 1974, during the Biennial General Meeting of the Australian Institute of Aboriginal Studies. The papers delivered at the symposium, some of them in revised form, constitute the present volume. There is one additional paper, by Bowler and Thorne, describing the new human skeletal remains from Lake Mungo, which were announced at the meeting.

Apart from the presentation of new data it was hoped that the symposium would result in some airing of a number of problems associated with the multidisciplinary approach to the question of Aboriginal origins. Although not unique to this part of the world there has been some compartmentalisation, leading to relative isolation, of human biology and other disciplines, and more particularly within the general field of human biology. The peculiarities of specific sorts of data-gathering, as well as the seemingly inevitable development of specialised research interests and problems, tend to disguise mutual interests in and approaches to particular problems. It was felt the symposium might redefine at least some points of contact, both geographic and problematic, leading to a more co-ordinated attack on human biological questions, by human biologists and other specialists. One concern is the need to appreciate the limitations of particular lines of research—the chronological limits to genetic analysis and the sampling problems associated with human palaeontology being two that are crucial in any approach to Aboriginal origins. Another consideration for human biologists, in the light of sea-level, geomorphological and environmental data, is the need to view Australia, Tasmania and New Guinea as a single and constantly changing landmass having a continuous population in the late Pleistocene, and thus avoid general conclusions based on the analysis of data from any one area in isolation.

Many of these issues were explored during the two-day meeting, particularly in the terminal session of the symposium where chairmen of several of the sessions presented their own interpretations and summaries.

Professor Howells pointed out that in the first session of the symposium the climatologists had shown that there were fluctuations, though not very extensive, in the Pleistocene and that it was necessary to consider the bearing which this had on biological origins and continuities, on population size and distribution. For instance, when Australia-New Guinea was a single continent the inviting upland-scrub grassland described by the Hopes would have been the logical place for the largest population. What is not clear is how separate such a population would have been from other inhabited parts of New Guinea or Australia. Was there another zone where the New Guinea-Australia population was continuous? Such a zone might account for the present day blood genetic and morphological picture, where in north Australia we have a population somewhat closer to New Guinea than to those in the centre and other parts of the continent.

Another view which emerged was that during the Pleistocene the distribution of Man in the southern part of Australia must have been a good deal more 'spotty' than thought previously. It was suggested that Aboriginals at that time would not have favoured the highlands and would have tended to remain in the more well-watered valleys, so that, here again, population distribution would have been different. It is still necessary to solve whether the main part of the continent was fairly arid, or was more lushly vegetated, as might be suggested by Professor Macfarlane's views on water turnover. The likely distribution on entry into the country and subsequent separation into different climatic zones, which might have led to physical differentiation, is an important question. One other important problem, which Professor Howells pointed out was still unresolved, was the linguistic differentiation: the Papuan languages are still a valid group quite distinct from the Australian languages. By implication this suggests a long period of separation between the speakers.

Several chairmen discussed the implications of the variation in Australian fossil skull morphology, a problem to which considerable attention was given following the sessions on early man and morphological variation. Professor Howells recalled that it was Professor Macintosh who had noted first the extremes represented by the Keilor and Cohuna crania; the latter is robust and exhibits features of heaviness, large size of the face and flatness of the forehead that are uncommon or absent in demonstrably recent Aboriginal crania. The two explanations of the characteristics of the Cohuna and Kow

Swamp crania that have been put forward are that:

1. They are *heritage* traits from *Homo erectus*, that is, they represent the persistence of genetic elements in the earliest Australians, from Java, perhaps through Solo Man, or
2. They are *habitus* traits, the expression of morphological patterns developed within Australia.

Following his first examination of the Kow Swamp material, Professor Howells said he thought it reinforced the notion of two prehistoric populations about 10,000 years ago. For several reasons this was a position he would now abandon. On the expanded evidence available Macintosh now felt the range of variation prehistorically was at all times the same as in modern populations and Thorne agreed that no non-metrical feature lay outside the modern range. More importantly, the papers by Wright and Brown pointed to significant mechanisms of change operating under conditions of environmental stress.

As noted earlier it was hoped to bring together the divergent aims and methodologies of those concerned, directly or indirectly, with studies of early man in Australia. However no consensus emerged. Perhaps this was inevitable, particularly given the rarity of actual fossil materials and the assumptions that need to be made about the relevance of studies of living people to the biology of past populations. Opinions tended to reflect relatively fixed positions and no suggestions emerged, for example, as to whether *both* habitus and heritage traits were involved and if so how these might be separated and unravelled. As Dr Freedman pointed out the studies by Macintosh and Larnach, and by Thorne, came to the similar conclusion that there was considerable variation in Australian crania—possibly representing two main groups, one gracile and one robust—from at least 30,000 to 10,000 years BP. Future research will have to try and discover the origin and basis of the variation (or dichotomy), why it persisted and why it apparently later disappeared.

The sessions devoted to analysis of the genetic patterns in living populations and their interpretation introduced some of the newer mathematical tools. Professor Bennett in discussing the use which had been made of these in several papers cautioned against the uncritical acceptance of the results. He pointed out that if we have a set of related populations with known pedigree connections, then the mean coefficients of kinship will provide measures of the relative genetic differences between these populations. This is an example of what might properly be described as microdifferentiation. However, if an attempt is made to reverse this process of reasoning and to see whether, given populations with no known pedigree relationship, estimates of kinship (or genetic distance) derived by comparing their gene pools or phenotypic resemblances can be used for estimating their biological relationship, then other possibly far-reaching assumptions are involved. Professor Bennett asked is it valid to assume, for example, that the populations being compared are derived from a common ancestral population and that the mean frequency of any gene over all populations is the same as it was in the (hypothetical) common ancestral population? Can one properly assume that at any locus, alleles of the same state which are present in the different populations concerned are identical by descent, or in other words that every such allele has arisen only once (in the hypothetical ancestral population) and that all alleles of the same state now present in the different populations have been derived from those original ones? These assumptions may be not unreasonable for the case of closely related populations known from pedigree data to have been derived from a common ancestral population but in other circumstances, as for example those considered by Morton and Keats, we would do well to question whether the validity of this approach has been properly demonstrated.

He questioned also the approach of those who say essentially that present day populations have been derived from a common ancestral population by a series of splits or fissions, indicated by a simple branching process. There must have been much fusion and hybridisation, as well as fission, in human evolution and models must take this into account.

Summarising the session on the distribution of blood genetic markers in Australia and neighbouring areas Professor Morton made the following points.

Over a long period of time, geographic location is more important than gross appearance in specifying the gene pool of a population. The group called Negrito are polyphyletic, and their gene pools are no more similar than two random populations of the Western Pacific, and the Malay aborigines are similarly derived from various ancestral stocks. The populations of the Western Pacific differ considerably among themselves, and there is no close affinity between the gene pools of two ethnic groups within the region. In addition, none of the populations of the Western Pacific, including Ainu, Australian Aboriginals, and Negritos, differs from the others in such a way as to suggest close relationship to any population outside the region.

Genetic contact with remote populations at some time in the past is suggested by such observations as $Gm^{1,5,6}$ in the Senoi and Gc^{Ab} in Australians and Melanesians: both genes may be identical by descent with African genes. However, the possibility of polyphyletic descent of these alleles cannot be excluded. Not only their amino acid sequences, but also the base sequences of their messengers, are unknown. Even identical base sequence would not prove common ancestry.

There is a small probability that a nearly neutral mutant will drift to polymorphic frequency in a local population. The chance of achieving polymorphism is greater for a locally advantageous mutant, but present information suggests that such mutations are much rarer than the nearly neutral class. In either event, local polymorphism constitutes a marker for population movement, study of which is often more interesting than a global measure of genetic distance, as the dynamics and history of genetic patterns are far more significant than microtaxonomy. Since the gene frequency variance among small populations is large, the evidence for drift is unequivocal.

The gene frequency pattern does not speak clearly for or against selection unless securely related to some environmental factor, such as malaria. The statistical significance of associations between unlinked genes (as A_2 and Rh–) is not amenable to precise test, since local populations are not independent replicates.

Professor Morton pointed out that microdifferentiation allows tests of consistency among indices of population structure. Predictions from genealogy and migration may be compared with estimates from gene frequencies, anthropometrics, isonymy, shared cognates, and ethnohistory. On the other hand, macrodifferentiation among groups long separated in time and space provides no credible predictions. Reliance has to be placed on consistency of different kinds of evidence and methods of analysis. Failure of consistency casts doubt on the evidence, methods, or both.

In conclusion, data on genetic patterns can be summarised topologically as a scatter diagram or a tree. This facilitates comparison of different methods and kinds of evidence, but detail is necessarily lost. Morton agreed with Bennett in adopting caution by stating that a phylogenetic interpretation is suspect when applied to populations connected by migration and/or with considerable drift.

A number of questions were raised in discussion:

a.   What is the relative value of genetic, anthropometric, linguistic, and other evidence on population origin? Genetic markers have the highest heritability, and may be less affected by selection than most anthropometric traits, but they are generally inapplicable to archaeological material.

b.   Given that differentiation involves migration and drift, and selection for some genes, when did these factors operate? On the one hand, if we accept that genes from *Homo erectus* are present in modern man, and that there were geographic races before *Homo sapiens*, it would be surprising if racial variation today did not reflect in some degree this ancient differentiation.

c.   How did gene flow occur? Undoubtedly land contacts, passive and deliberate ocean travel, small and large groups of migrants, intermarriage and displacements played different roles in different areas. Ecological pressures from unfavourable habitats, especially due to drought, may have favoured unidirectional gene flow, as perhaps from the Australian desert toward the sea.

Finally, growing contact with social anthropology and linguistics was implicit in several areas. The geneticists wondered how understanding of kinship systems might be affected by precise specification of genealogy and migration. While comparison of genetic and linguistic differentiation has become common in terms of shared cognates, linguists have methods to study even more shallow changes that take place in the course of a few generations or centuries, which could be applied to microdifferentiation. Perhaps the preoccupation of geneticists with spatial variation would give more rigour to glottochronology, since linguistic divergence can hardly be independent of contact. By estimating a genetic covariance matrix in relatives, measures of affinity from anthropometrics could be converted into estimates of genetic kinship, neglecting environmental differences among populations. Possibly this would make for more meaningful comparisons of genetic and anthropometric evidence, especially with regard to the role of selection.

It may be expected that the next discussion of human differentiation in the Western Pacific will have an even greater wealth of evidence to consider.

R. L. Kirk
A. G. Thorne
Canberra, May 1975

References

ABBIE, A. A.   1951   The Australian Aborigine. *Oceania*, 22:91–100.
——   1960   Doctor Ruggles Gates and the Aboriginal Australian. *Nature*, 187:375–76.
——   1963   Physical characteristics of Australian Aborigines. In *Australian Aboriginal Studies*, Helen Shiels (ed), pp. 89–107. Oxford University Press, Melbourne.
——   1966   Physical characteristics. In *Aboriginal Man in south and central Australia*, B. C. Cotton (ed), part 1, pp. 9–45. Government Printer, Adelaide.
BASEDOW, H.   1925   *The Australian Aboriginal*. F. W. Preece, Adelaide.
BIRDSELL, J. B.   1949   The racial origin of the extinct Tasmanians. *Records of the Queen Victoria Museum*, 2:105–22.
——   1950   Some implications of the genetical concept of race in terms of spatial analysis. *Cold Spring Harbor Symposia on Quantative Biology*, 15:259–311.
——   1967   Preliminary data on the trihybrid origin of the Australian Aborigines. *Archaeology and Physical Anthropology in Oceania*, 2:100–55.
CAMPBELL, T. D., J. H. GRAY and C. J. HACKETT   1936   Physical anthropology of the Aborigines of central Australia. *Oceania*, 7(1):106–261.
DAVIS, J. B.   1874   On the osteology and peculiarities of the Tasmanians, a race of man recently become extinct. *Natuurkundige verhandelingen van de Hollandsche maatschappij der wetenschappen 3 de Verz.* 2(4).
FENNER, F. J.   1939   The Australian Aboriginal skull; its non-metrical morphological characters. *Transactions of the Royal Society of South Australia*, 63(2):248–306.
GATES, R. R.   1960   Racial elements in the Aborigines of Queensland, Australia. *Zeitschrift fur Morphologie und Anthropologie*, 50:150–66.
HOOTON, E. A.   1947   *Up from the ape*. 2nd edition. Macmillan, New York.
HOWELLS, W. W.   1937   *Anthropometry of the natives of Arnhem Land and the Australian race problem*. Papers of the Peabody Museum, 16.
HRDLICKA, A.   1926   The peopling of the earth. *Proceedings of the American Philosophical Society*, 65:150–56.
——   1928   Catalogue of human crania in the United States National Museum collections. (Australians, Tasmanians, South African Bushmen, Hottentots, and Negro). *Proceedings of the United States National Museum*, 71(2696) article 24:1–40.
KEITH, A.   1925   *The antiquity of man*. 2nd edition, London.
KLAATSCH, H.   1908   The skull of the Australian Aboriginal. *Report from the pathological laboratory of the lunacy department, New South Wales*, 1(3):43–167.
LESSON, A.   1880   *Les Polynesiens*. Vol. 1, Paris: Libraire de la Société Asiatique de Paris.
MACINTOSH, N. W. G.   1963   Origin and physical differentiation of the Australian Aborigines. *Australian Natural History*, 14:248–52.
MORRISON, J.   1967   The biracial origin of the Australian Aborigines. *Medical Journal of Australia*, 2:1054–6.

SCHOETENSACK, O.   1901   Die Bedeutung Australiens fur die Heranbildung der Menschen aus einer niederen Form. *Zeitschrift für Ethnologie* 33:127–54.

SOLLAS, W. J.   1911   *Ancient hunters and their modern representatives*. Macmillan, London.

TINDALE, N. B. and J. B. BIRDSELL   1941   Tasmanoid tribes in north Queensland. *Records of the South Australian Museum*, 7(1):1–9.

TOPINARD, P.   1872   Étude sur les Tasmaniens. *Memoirs of the Society of Anthropology of Paris*, Ser. 1, 3:307–29.

TURNER, W.   1884   Report on the human crania and other bones of the skeletons collected during the voyage of H.M.S. *Challenger*, in the years 1873–1876. Part 1— The crania. In *Report of the scientific results of the exploring voyage of H.M.S. Challenger 1873–1876 zoology*, 10:1–130.

WOOD-JONES, F.   1934   *Australia's vanishing race*. Angus and Robertson, Sydney.

WUNDERLY, J.   1943   The Keilor fossil skull: anatomical description. *Memoirs of the National Museum of Victoria*, 13:57–69.

The Pleistocene Background

Aspects of late Quaternary palaeogeography of the Australian-East Indonesian Region

J. Chappell

THE PRINCIPAL geographic factors likely to have influenced prehistoric Man's migration into Australia and New Guinea, are the breadth of sea passages, the patterns of winds and currents, and, more generally, the patterns of climate. All of these have varied in upper Quaternary times. The task of identifying the past patterns rests with analysis of the geologic record in the long run; but at the present stage our field studies are not sufficiently comprehensive to enable adequate palaeogeographic reconstructions to be made over the period of interest. Theoretical speculations thus have a place in preliminary reconstructions, to a greater or lesser extent according to the physical factor and geographic region under consideration.

The quite large variations of coastline geography, which have occurred as a result of glacio-eustatic sea-level changes accompanying the waxing and waning of Pleistocene icecaps, can in principle be established as there are nowadays numerous estimates of Quaternary palaeo sea-levels from many parts of the world. There are large disparities between many such results, however, arising from radiometric dating errors, on one hand, and tectonic and isostatic movements on the other. It is now possible to reckon with these complicating factors, and this has been done in the preparation of the palaeocoastline maps in this paper.

Patterns of past ocean currents and climates, at either regional or local scales, are more difficult to identify. Ocean palaeo currents in particular are potentially less recordable geologically than either past sea levels or climates. A few estimates of Pleistocene currents have been made elsewhere in the world; for the east Indonesian and Australian region, however, the discussion in this paper of past currents is mainly theoretical. As to climates during the time of Man's early occupation of this region, the identification of these from geologic, geomorphologic, and palaeobotanical records is the subject of other papers in this Symposium, and I shall only outline certain broad-scale aspects of atmospheric circulation, as they apply to past climates of this region. My first concern is to establish patterns of changing coastline geography over the last 55,000 years, for which purpose the history of eustatic changes must first be set out.

Upper Quaternary sea-levels

Migrations through Wallacea into New Guinea and Australia were facilitated by, or at least influenced by, the emergence of continental shelf areas during low sea-levels of the Last (Wisconsin or Wurm) Glaciation. The evidence for sea-levels lower than the present is more difficult to collect, to date, and to interpret, than for interglacial strands at or above the present sea-level.

Palaeo sea-levels during the last glaciation may be estimated in two ways: either from ice volume estimates based on the continental glacial record, or from dated strandlines, usually submerged. There is now fair concordance between modern estimates of ice volumes at the climax of the last glacial advance (late Wisconsin or Wurm III), which occurred between 16,000 and 20,000 years ago, and the absolute range of corresponding sea-level lowering is from 95 m (Patterson, 1972) to 130 m (Flint, 1971). Estimates of ice volumes prior to this last maximum are less satisfactory as the icecap margins are much less well known. The records of interstadial periods of 28,000 BP and about 42,000 to 45,000 BP are instructive: these are respectively the Paudorf and later Brorup of Europe (Woldstedt, 1967; Andersen, 1965), and the Plum Point and Port Talbot in The Great Lakes area (MacDonald, 1971; Dreimannis and Karrow, 1972). Such sources show that ice retreat was extensive, especially around 40,000 to 45,000 BP, although deglaciation was never complete. Satisfactory ice volume estimates at these times have not yet been made, partly because the glacial geologic record is fragmentary and partly because detailed synchroneity of such interstadials has yet to be proven, between Fennoscandian and Laurentide icecaps. The direct evidence of marine strandlines thus potentially is important. However, studies of late Pleistocene strandlines have been handicapped by the problem of achieving satisfactory dating. This is principally because the dateable material in such sediments is mostly shell carbonate, which becomes increasingly suspect for C^{14} dating as sample age goes beyond 20,000 years (Olsson and Blake, 1962; Chappell and Polach, 1972). Attempts to demonstrate high sea-levels around the times of the 28,000-year and 42,000-year interstadials have been frustrated by the fact that very many such C^{14} age estimates reported from strandlines at or near present sea-level have proven to be quite unreliable (Thom, 1973).

Our basis for knowing the record of upper Quaternary sea-level changes has improved markedly in recent years with the advent of Th^{230}/U^{234} dating of fossil shorelines in coral reef areas. The salient results come from areas of rapid tectonic uplift where successions of offlapping reefs provide records of well-dated marine transgressions and regressions, superimposed on steady uplift of the land. These records, coming from Barbados (Broecker et al, 1968; James et al, 1971; Steinen et al, 1973) New Guinea (Veeh and Chappell, 1970; Chappell, 1974a; Bloom et al, 1974), and the Ryukyu Islands (Konishi et al, 1970, 1974), have been tied to the internationally recognised high sea-level of 3 to 6 m above present, which occurred 120,000 years ago (Veeh, 1966; Broecker and van Donk, 1970; Ku, 1974). This reference point allows the tectonic factor to be eliminated from the relative sea-level records of these rising islands, and a high level of agreement has been found between absolute palaeo sea-level estimates from the three places (Chappell, 1974a; Bloom *et al*, 1974). Figure 1 shows the now well-accepted resultant sea-level curve for the last 125,000 years. This provides the primary basis for the palaeo shoreline reconstructions given below.

The low sea-levels of about 20,000 and 53,000 years ago are probably of more interest than any other single points on Figure 1, because land areas were maximal and sea passages were minimal at these times. There is considerably more evidence for the absolute level of the 16,000–20,000 BP low sea-level than for earlier minima, and yet there exist wide disparities between results from different parts of the world. Emery *et al* (1971), summarising international evidence from dated submerged strandlines on continental shelves, set this last sea-level minimum between −70 m and −145 m. Such an uncertainty, if realistic, would make palaeo shoreline reconstruction quite problematic. It is possible, however, greatly to reduce this uncertainty, once dating errors and isostatic movements of continental shelves and ocean basins are identified.

Isostatic movements in late Quaternary times, resulting from offloading of ice from Fennoscandia and the Laurentide area and consequently increased water loading of the ocean basins, have affected the course of sea-level rise relative to landmass throughout the world. The magnitude of such movement varies globally, so that the absolute depth below present sea-level of strandlines formed at the last glacial maximum must vary from place to place. The changing ice and water loads induce displacements of the earth's surface of two kinds: rapid elastic displacement, and slow visco-elastic movement (it is the latter kind of movement which is observable today as continuing uplift of the Fennoscandian and Laurentide areas). Recent analyses of these deformations, especially those induced by changing oceanic water loads, are given by O'Connell (1971), Walcott (1972a, 1972b), and Chappell (1974b). Figure 2 shows the global elastic deformation since the last glacial maximum (after Walcott, 1972a), and results of slow visco-elastic creep of broad and narrow continental shelves, over the same period.

The elastic deformation produces very broad global effects, so that the post-glacial relative rise of sea-level in the southwest Pacific will be about 25 per cent greater than in the north Atlantic. A principal effect of the slow visco-elastic deformation on the other hand, is that the course of sea-level rise relative to continental margins will vary with location, according to shelf geometry and the physical structure of the underlying mantle.

The exact reconciliation of uppermost Quaternary palaeo sea-level estimates from different parts of the world, in terms of isostatic displacements, is given in detail by Chappell (1974b). It is sufficient here to make a summarising statement. Various estimates exist for a low sea-level around 15,000 to 18,000 BP which are based on apparently reliable radiometric dates, and which range from as low as −160 m (e.g. from the Arafura Sea, and the Great Barrier Reef: Jongsma, 1970; Veeh and Veevers, 1970), through −140 to −130 m (e.g. Northwest Atlantic shelf, and the Yucatan shelf:

Emery and Garrison, 1967; Logan *et al*, 1970), up to −90 m (e.g. Texas: Curray, 1960). Many other estimates, ranging up to −65 m, such as are noted by Milliman and Emery (1968) and Emery *et al* (1971), appear to be founded on unreliable C^{14} dates, either because of sample mixing or recrystallisation. Reduction of the apparently reliable data, by eliminating all isostatic effects, has yielded an estimate for absolute eustatic lowering at the last glacial maximum of 105 ± 5 m (Chappell, 1974b).

The sea-level curve in Figure 1 shows the 18,000 BP low sea-level as −130 to −140 m. The basis is a submerged terrace in the type section (Huon Peninsula), younger than the dated 28,000 BP reef and predating the Holocene transgression (Chappell, 1974). This low level reflects the regional elastic depression induced by post-glacial water loading (Figure 2a). Visco-elastic effects are likely to be negligible in the Huon Peninsula area, where the sea floor descends abruptly into narrow Vitiaz Strait. Figure 1 is thus applicable as an 'absolute' eustatic curve for the Australian-south Indonesian region, because elastic displacement is regionally very nearly constant (Figure 2a). However, visco-elastic displacement effects must be assumed for broad shelves, as suggested by Figure 2b. Such corrections are subject to uncertainty about physical parameters of the upper earth in the region (i.e. lithosphere flexural rigidity; asthenosphere viscosity), but a depression of 20 m of the outer margin of broad continental shelves, since the last glacial maximum, is a conservative estimate. These isostatic movements thus account for the low sea-level of around −160 m, 15,000 to 17,000 BP, identified from the Arafura Sea (Jongsma, 1970), and Great Barrier Reef (Veeh and Veevers, 1970).

Before passing on to discuss uppermost Quaternary shoreline palaeo-geography, in the light of Figures 1 and 2, two other points should be

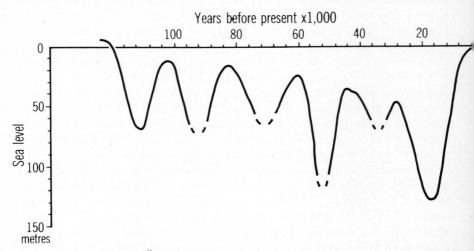

Figure 1 Eustatic changes for the southwest Pacific region during the past 125,000 years. From Chappell (1974); Bloom *et al* (1974)

discussed: (i) the sea-level curve, 18,000 to present, and (ii) the possibility that tectonic movements substantially affected the palaeogeography in the last 60,000 years.

The course of post-glacial sea-level change is of particular interest, as shoreline geography was changing rapidly during the period for which the archaeological record is comparatively rich. The record shown in Figure 1 from 18,000 BP to the present has not been determined in the same area as the rest of the curve, but is based on closely agreeing evidence of two types from the northern hemisphere. Firstly, the course of the last deglaciation is now well known (Bryson *et al.* 1967; Flint, 1971), and on this basis, Bloom (1971) has estimated the corresponding course of sea-level rise. Bloom's curve, secondly, is consistent with direct drillhole records of the post-glacial transgression, from Panama (Bartlett *et al*, 1969), and from Bermuda (Neumann, 1972), as well as with the Atlantic shelf data of Emery and Garrison (1967) when the latter is corrected for isostasy (Chappell, 1974b).

The question of tectonism influencing palaeogeography of the region may be answered in the negative on general grounds. The extension or diminution of straits by horizontal crustal movement is likely to be unimportant. Plate convergence along northern New Guinea is more rapid than identified elsewhere, amounting to 10 cm/year (Le Pichon, 1968). This is very much an upper limit for horizontal motion between any two adjacent landmasses in the island chains from Malaya to Australia, and widths of straits will not have altered, therefore, by more than a few kilometres at the very most, over the last 60,000 years. The matter of vertical movements can also be discounted for the broad shelf regions. Rapid uplift certainly occurs along the major tectonic sutures: rates of 3 mm/year have been well proven at Huon Peninsula, New Guinea (Chappell, 1974), and of 10 mm/year has been suggested for Aitape, New Guinea (Gill, 1967), and comparable rates are likely to be discovered at other high terraced islands adjacent to plate convergence zones, such as Timor. However, the sea floor descends steeply in such places and palaeo shoreline changes over the last 60,000 years will have been small. Such high uplift rates are likely to be at least an order of magnitude greater than any rates of continuing uplift or subsidence on broad shelves in the region. The most debatable such area is the periorogenic trough immediately south of the central cordillera of New Guinea; however, rapid sedimentation from the rising cordillera is thought likely to keep pace with any trough subsidence, preventing the development of an alternative passage north of the present Torres Strait. An example of apparent stability, in the Arafura Sea, is proved by the evidence for a low sea-level at −200 m prior to 170,000 years ago (Jongsma, 1970), as such is likely to have occurred during the Illinoisan-Riss or an earlier glaciation when ice volumes substantially exceeded those of the Wisconsin-Wurm (Flint, 1971). Putative evidence for substantial late Quaternary vertical movements of north Australian shelves, such as from the Gulf of Carpentaria (Phipps, 1970), has been re-interpreted and discounted (Jennings, 1972b).

a. Elastic warping (Walcott, 1972a)

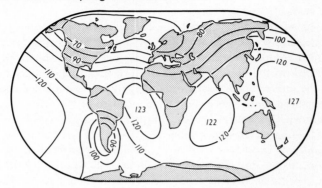

b. Visco-elastic shelf warping

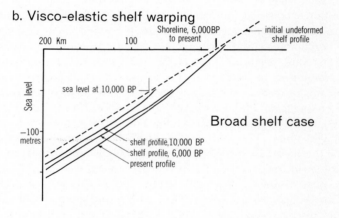

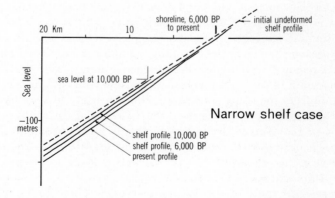

Figure 2 Illustrating displacements of the earth's surface induced by redistribution of water masses from Pleistocene icecaps to the oceans: (a) instantaneous elastic effects; numbers refer to percentages of absolute eustatic change that will occur across the globe (after Walcott, 1972a); (b) slow visco-elastic warping of typical simple continental shelves (from Chappell, 1974b).

Shoreline palaeogeography of the last 60,000 years: Discussion

Using Figure 1, with visco-elastic displacement corrections where necessary, the shoreline for 18,000 ± 2,000 years ago, over the east Indonesian-New Guinea-north Australia region is mapped in Figure 3. The primary data sources used for bathymetry were Admiralty charts. The shoreline lies close to the 150 m isobath—somewhat deeper than this around broad shelves, and close to −140 m where shelves are narrow or absent. Because the submarine slope in most places steepens markedly at or above 130 m, the overall pattern is not very different from the mapping obtained by Doutch (1972), or Webster and Streten (1972), who used the 200 m isobath to approximate to the palaeogeography of glacial low sea-level times.

Also mapped in Figure 3 is the shoreline of 10,000 BP, when eustatic lowering, relative to central and outer zones of the shelves in the region, is estimated to have been 45 to 50 m (Figure 1). This provides a useful reference for discussing coastline positions in the last 60,000 years. The 28,000 BP shore lay slightly landwards of this, and that of 42,000 to 45,000 yet further landwards, although at no time in at least the last 60,000 years has Torres Strait landbridge been submerged (conjectured also by Jennings, 1972a,b). The shoreline of about 33,000 BP was somewhat seawards of the 10,000 strand, and that of about 53,000 lay close to the 18,000 BP line. It is interesting to note that the depth zone from about −30 to −50 m has been more frequently occupied by shorelines in the last 60,000 years, than levels higher or lower (cf. Figure 1). The 10,000 BP coastline defines the seaward margin of this 'most frequently occupied' shore zone.

Certain general remarks can be made in the light of this shoreline reconstruction. For the region shown in Figure 3, the broad Torres Strait landbridge is the most salient palaeogeographic change engendered by glacio-eustatic lowering, and the results given here confirm Jennings' (1972a) suggestion that this isthmus persisted from at least 80,000 BP until about 8,000 BP. An important direct effect is on ocean currents. Wintertime westward flow through Torres Strait was blocked during this upper Pleistocene interval. Whether northward flow of the cool current bordering West Australia was consequently stronger, as Webster and Streten (1972) suggest, is debatable. The West Australian boundary current is a weak component of the Indian Ocean system, apparently with minimal upwelling (Wooster and Reid, 1963). In this ocean the low latitude circulation is determined by the annually-reversing trade winds (Knauss, 1963), and West Australian palaeo currents are likely to have been influenced by relative strengths of the trades and the mid-latitude westerlies, rather than by closure of Torres Strait. The manner in which the strengths of these major wind systems changed in the southern hemisphere, in late Pleistocene times, is uncertain (Kraus, 1973), and reconstruction depends heavily on evidence.

Interest in palaeo currents and ocean palaeo temperatures largely stems from their effect on climates. Cyclogenesis—a major element in climates of Timor Sea region and tropical Australia—is likely to be significantly reduced if seawater temperatures are several degrees lower (Webster and Streten,

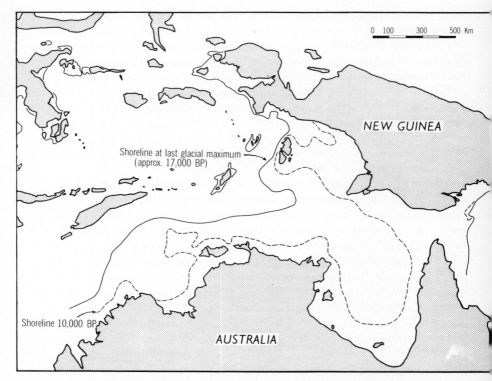

Figure 3 Palaeo shorelines for east Indonesia—New Guinea—north Australia, at 18,000 BP and 10,000 BP. The shoreline at 28,000 BP lay near the 10,000 BP line. For position at other times, see text.

1972). It can be noted that Jennings (1976) has inferred from ancient dunes near Derby a reduction of cyclonic influence and a relative strengthening of the trade winds around the time of the last glacial maximum. Whether this effect near the modern northwest Australian coast reflects exposure as land of the Sahul Shelf and Arafura Sea, or lower ocean temperatures, cannot at the moment be resolved. The latter explanation is somewhat paradoxical: while lower ocean temperatures would reduce cyclogenesis, the same is unlikely to strengthen trade winds in the region (*v.* Kraus, 1973). It should be stated that the oft-used estimates of tropical seawater temperatures by Emiliani (1955, 1966), based principally on oxygen isotopes in deep sea cores, must be treated with caution. This is because the effect of Pleistocene diminutions of ocean volumes on ocean water O^{18} enrichment is debated, and Olausson (1965) and Shackleton (1973) interpret the effect as being twice as important as does Emiliani. The result is that palaeo temperature swings corresponding to deep sea core O^{18} changes are liable to be less than suggested by Emiliani. Recent results suggest surface water temperature changes in equatorial Pacific were less than 1°C, from glacial maximum to present (Shackleton, 1973). Project 'Climap' results for parts of the central Atlantic show surface waters 17,000 years ago as having temperatures similar to the present (Kraus, 1973). These facts show, once again, the importance of acquiring evidence before attempting oceanographic reconstructions. Investigations of two kinds would be useful: (i) palaeo-ecologic analysis of deep sea cores from the region shown in Figure 3, after the fashion of Imbrie and Kipp (1971) in the Caribbean context, and (ii) oxygen isotope analyses of the same cores. Also useful in this connection would be oxygen isotope analyses of littoral molluscs from archaeological sites, especially of summer and winter mollusc growth bands to estimate seasonal contrasts, as achieved from Mediterranean sites by Emiliani et al (1963).

Late Pleistocene glaciation in New Guinea was accompanied by lowering of the snowline by 700 m to 1000 m, identified on geomorphic grounds (Löffler, 1970), and palaeobotanical evidence (Hope, 1973), at about the time when southeast Australia was changing from relatively more humid than present to more arid (Bowler, 1971). During this time, Torres Strait appears to have been more arid (Jennings, 1972b). The facts are developed by other authors, (Bowler, 1976; Hope and Hope, 1976); at this juncture the importance must be emphasised of the issue of timing of such past different climates in different parts of the region. The matter can be highlighted by drawing attention to the changing pattern of solar radiation received, in late Quaternary times, as a result of orbital perturbations (van Woerkom, 1953; Broecker and van Donk, 1970). A major obliquity minimum at 25,000 BP, coupled with small orbital eccentricity, reduced the meridional insolation gradient and is likely to have diminished summer to winter temperature contrasts in the Australian region. The obliquity then increased rapidly, to a maximum at 11,000 BP. Changing insolation over the relatively cloudless central and West Australian region and adjacent east Indian Ocean must have had climatic significance, affecting amongst other factors the character and persistence of the thermal low pressure systems of the Australian desert. The interaction of these insolation effects with globally cooler atmosphere during glaciation is difficult to assess, when local ocean palaeotemperatures are unknown. Hence, no tentative palaeo climatic reconstruction is attempted here, and the foregoing serves to amplify the earlier statement that more benchmark data is required.

This paper is concluded with brief observations about the variations in ease of migration into Australia and New Guinea associated with upper Quaternary changes of land area. The most radical diminutions of straits are between Borneo and Sulawesi, Sulawesi and the Sula Islands, Timor and northwest Australia, Tanimbar and New Guinea, and, more modestly, between both Halmahera and Ceram, and the Vogelkop of Irian. Straits within the Sunda Arc were only very modestly altered in width and intervisibility, except for Java-Bali and Sumbawa-Flores passages. The ease of accidental crossings may have been greater for certain passages, such as Lombok Straits, with reduced tidal flows resulting from the Java Sea becoming land. However, at places other than the Timor Sea crossing, and from Sulawesi through Sula Island and Ceram to New Guinea, the probabilities of accidental migration into Australia-New Guinea appear to have been little affected.

Acknowledgement: I wish sincerely to thank Professor J. N. Jennings, Department of Biogeography and Geomorphology, A.N.U., for substantial discussions, and for presenting the paper at the symposium in the author's absence, and Mrs P. Quiggin, Department of Geography, A.N.U., for compiling the bathymetric data and base map, on which Figure 3 is founded.

References

ANDERSEN, B. G.　　1965　The Quaternary of Norway. In *The Quaternary*, vol. 1, K. Rankama (ed), pp. 91–138. Interscience, New York.

BARTLETT, A. S., E. S. BARGHOORN and R. BERGER　　1969　Fossil maize from Panama. *Science*, 165:389–90.

BLOOM, A. L.　　1967　Pleistocene shorelines: a new test of isostasy. *Geological Society of America Bulletin*, 78:1477–94.

——, W. S. BROECKER, J. CHAPPELL, R. S. MATTHEWS and K. J. MESOLELLA　　1974 Quaternary sea level fluctuations on a tectonic coast: new Th^{230}/U^{234} dates from the Huon Peninsula, New Guinea. *Quaternary Research*, 4:185–205.

BOWLER, J. M.　　1971　Pleistocene salinities and climatic change: evidence from lakes and lunettes in southeastern Australia. In *Aboriginal man and environment in Australia*, D. J. Mulvaney and J. Golson (eds), pp. 47–65. Australian National University Press, Canberra.

BROECKER, W. S. and J. VAN DONK　　1970　Insolation changes, ice volumes, and the 0^{18} record in deep sea cores. *Review Geophysics and Space Physics*, 8:169–98.

——, D. L. THURBER, J. GODDARD, T-L KU, R. K. MATTHEWS and K. J. MESOLELLA 1968　Milankovitch hypothesis supported by precise dating of coral reefs and deep-sea sediments. *Science*, 159:297–300.

BRYSON, R. A., W. M. WENDLAND, J. D. IVES and J. T. ANDREWS　　1967　Radiocarbon isochrons on the disintegration of the Laurentide ice sheet. *Arctic and Alpine Research*, 1:1–14.

CHAPPELL, J.　　1974a　Geology of coral terraces on Huon Peninsula, New Guinea: a study of Quaternary tectonic movements and sea level changes. *Geological Society of American Bulletin*, 85:553–70.

——　　1974b　Late Quaternary hydro- and glacio- isostasy, on a layered visco-elastic earth with loads varying spatially and temporally. *Quaternary Research* 4:405–28.

—— and H. A. POLACH　　1972　Some effects of partial recrystallisation on C^{14} dating late Pleistocene corals and molluscs. *Quaternary Research*, 2:244–52.

CURRAY, J. R.　　1961　Late Quaternary sea level: a discussion. *Geological Society of America Bulletin*, 72:1707–12.

DOUTCH, H. F.　　1972　The paleogeography of northern Australia and New Guinea and its relevance to the Torres Strait area. In *Bridge and barrier: the natural and cultural history of Torres Strait*, D. Walker (ed), pp. 1–10. Australian National University Press, Canberra.

DREIMANNIS, A. and P. F. KARROW　　1972　Glacial history of the Great Lakes-St Lawrence region, the classification of the Wisconsin(an) Stage, and its correlatives. *International Geological Congress, 24th Session, Section* 12:5–15.

EMERY, K. O. and L. E. GARRISON　　1967　Sea Levels 7000 to 20000 years ago. *Science*, 157:684–87.

——, H. NIINO and B. SULLIVAN　　1971　Post-Pleistocene levels of the East China sea. In *Late Cenozoic Glacial Ages*, K. Turekian (ed), pp. 381–90. Yale University Press, New Haven.

EMILIANI, C.　　1955　Pleistocene paleotemperatures. *Journal of Geology*, 63:538–78.

—— 1966 Paleotemperature analysis of Caribbean cores P6304–8 and P6304–9 and a generalised paleotemperature curve for the past 425000 years. *Journal of Geology*, 74:109–26.

——, L. CARDINI, T. MAYEDA, C. B. M. McBURNEY and E. TONGIORGI 1963 Paleotemperature analysis of fossil shells of marine molluscs from the Arene Candide cave, Italy, and the Haua Fteah cave, Cyrenaica. In *Isotopic and cosmic chemistry*, H. Craig (ed), p. 133. North-Holland, Amsterdam.

FLINT, R. F. 1971 *Glacial and Quaternary Geology*. Wiley, New York.

GILL, E. D. 1967 Significance of Aitape (New Guinea) radiocarbon dates for eustasy and tectonics. *Australian Journal of Science*, 30:142.

HOPE, G. 1973 *The vegetation history of Mt Wilhelm*. Ph.D. Thesis, Australian National University Library.

IMBRIE, J. and N. G. KIPP 1971 A new micropaleontological method for quantitative paleoclimatology: application to a Late Pleistocene Caribbean core. In *Late Cenozoic Glacial Ages*, K. Turekian (ed), pp. 71–182. Yale University Press, New Haven.

JAMES, N. P., E. W. MOUNTJOY and A. OMURA 1971 An early Wisconsin reef terrace at Barbados, West Indies, and its climatic implications. *Geological Society of America Bulletin*, 82:2011–18.

JENNINGS, J. N. 1972a Some attributes of Torres Strait. In *Bridge and barrier: the natural and cultural history of Torres Strait*, D. Walker (ed), pp. 29–38. Australian National University Press, Canberra.

—— 1972b Discussion on the physical environment around Torres Strait and its history. In *Bridge and barrier: the natural and cultural history of Torres Strait*, D. Walker (ed), pp. 93–108. Australian National University Press, Canberra.

—— 1976 Desert dunes and estuarine fill in the Fitzroy Estuary, N.W. Australia. *Catena*, (in press).

JONGSMA, D. 1970 Eustatic sea level changes in the Arafura Sea. *Nature*, 228:150-51.

KNAUSS, J. A. 1973 Equatorial current systems. In *The Sea*, M. N. Hill (ed), pp. 235–52. Interscience, New York.

KONISHI, KENJI, S. O. SCHLANGER and AKIO OMURA 1970 Neotectonic rates in the central Ryukyu Islands derived from ^{230}Th coral ages. *Marine Geology*, 9:225–40.

—— and AKIO OMURA 1974 In *Proceedings of the 2nd International coral reef Symposium*, University of Queensland. (in press).

KRAUS, E. B. 1973 Comparison between Ice Age and present general circulations. *Nature*, 245:129–33.

KU, T. L. 1974 Eustatic sea level 120000 years ago on Oahu, Hawaii. *Science*, 183:959–62.

LÖFFLER, E. 1970 Evidence of Pleistocene glaciation in East Papua. *Australian Geographic Studies*, 8:16–26.

LE PICHON, X. 1968 Sea floor spreading and continental drift. *Journal of Geographical Research*, 73:3661–99.

LOGAN, B. W., *et al* 1969 Carbonate sediments and reefs, Yucatan Shelf, Mexico. *American Association Petrological Geology Memoir II*: 1–198.

McDONALD, B. C. 1971 Late Quaternary stratigraphy and deglaciation in eastern Canada. In *Late Cenozoic Glacial Ages*, K. Turekian (ed), pp. 331–54. Yale University Press, New Haven.

MILLIMAN, J. D. and K. O. EMERY 1968 Sea levels during the past 35000 years. *Science*, 162:1121–22.

NEUMANN, A. C. 1972 Quaternary sea level history of Bermuda and the Bahamas. *American Quaternary Association 2nd National Conference, Miami, Florida (Abstracts)*:41–4.

O'CONNELL, R. J. 1971 Pleistocene glaciation and the viscosity of the lower mantle. *Geophysical Journal of the Royal Astronomical Society*, 23:299–327.

OLAUSSON, E. 1967 Climatological, geoeconomical and paleooceanographic aspects on carbonate deposition. In *Progress in Oceanography*, M. Sears (ed), pp. 245–65. Pergamon Press, Norwich.

OLSSON, I. U. and W. BLAKE 1962 Problems of radiocarbon dating of raised beaches, based on experience in Spitsbergen. *Norsk Geografisk Tidsskrift*, 13:47–64.

PATERSON, W. S. B.   1972   Laurentide ice sheet: estimated volumes during Late Wisconsin. *Review of the Geophysical Space Physics*, 10:885–912.

PHIPPS, C. V. G.   1970   Dating of eustatic events from cores taken in the Gulf of Carpentaria and samples from the New South Wales continental shelf. *Australian Journal of Science*, 32:329–30.

SHACKLETON, N. J. and N. D. OPDYKE   1973   Oxygen isotopes and paleo-magnetic stratigraphy of equatorial core V28–238: oxygen isotope temperatures and ice volumes on a 10^5 and 10^6 year scale. *Quaternary Research*, 3:39–55.

STEINEN, R. P., R. S. HARRISON and R. K. MATTHEWS   1973   Eustatic tow stand of sea level between 125000 and 105000 B.P.: evidence from the sub-surface of Barbados, West Indies. *Geological Society of America Bulletin*, 84:63–70.

THOM, B. G.   1973   The dilemma of high interstadial sea levels during the last glaciation. *Progress in Geography*, 5:170–245.

VEEH, H. H.   1966 Th^{230}/U^{238} and U^{234}/U^{238} ages of Pleistocene high sea level stand. *Journal of Geographical Research*, 71:3379–86.

—— and J. M. A. CHAPPELL   1970   Astronomic theory of climatic change: support from New Guinea. *Science*, 167:862–65.

—— and J. J. VEEVERS   1970   Sea level at -175 m off the Great Barrier Reef 13600 to 17000 years ago. *Nature*, 226:536–37.

WALCOTT, R. I.   1972a   Past sea levels, eustasy, and deformation of the earth. *Quaternary Research*, 2:1–14.

——   1972b   Late Quaternary vertical movements in eastern North America: quantitative evidence of glacio-isostatic rebound. *Review of Geophysical Space Physics*, 10:849–84.

WEBSTER, P. J. and N. A. STRETEN   1972   Aspects of Late Quaternary climates in tropical Australia. In *Bridge and barrier: the natural and cultural history of Torres Strait*, D. Walker (ed), pp. 39–60. Australian National University Press, Canberra.

WOERKOM, VAN A. J. J.   1953   In *Climatic change*, H. Shapley (ed), pp. 147–56. Harvard University Press, Cambridge.

WOOSTER, W. S. and J. L. REID   1963   Eastern boundary currents. In *The sea*, M. N. Hill (ed), pp. 253–96. Interscience, New York.

WOLDSTEDT, P.   1967   The Quaternary of Germany. In *The Quaternary*, 2, K. Rankama (ed), pp. 239–300. Interscience, New York.

Some biogeographical factors relevant to the Pleistocene movement of Man in Australasia

J. H. Calaby

RHYS JONES (1973) has outlined the dramatic increase in knowledge over the past ten years, of the occupation of Australia by Man during the Pleistocene. Man was well established in many areas of Australia and New Guinea between 25,000 and 30,000 years ago, the earliest unequivocal date being approximately 32,000 years BP for a southern Australian site. There is no reason to believe that the flood of new information has ebbed and in the next few years even earlier dates may be anticipated. Jones also pointed out that Man was present in Java for several hundred thousand years, and together with extinct elephantids, had managed to cross substantial water barriers to reach the Philippines, Flores and Timor in ancient times.

It is a customary assumption that Man had to await the invention of suitable water craft before he made the final crossing of the roughly 100 km wide straits between the nearest Indonesian islands and the enlarged Pleistocene Australo-Papuan continent. It is possible however that water craft were not necessary and the original Australians were unwilling castaways carried off in floods, clinging to the branches of uprooted trees. Salt water gaps represent the most effective barriers to dispersal of mammals (other than bats). Nevertheless mammals have succeeded in crossing substantial gaps, including the Asian ancestors of the native Australo-Papuan rodents that arrived at various times during the late Tertiary and early Pleistocene. Probably the most interesting examples of oversea dispersal of mammals are found in the Wallacean islands, particularly Sulawesi. The mammal fauna of that island consists of a number of species that were presumably carried there by Man in fairly recent times, together with a suite of endemic genera and species that certainly pre-date the arrival of Man. These include two cuscuses (*Phalanger*), primates, civets, rats, squirrels, a pig (*Babyrousa*), a small bovid (*Anoa*), and a small Pleistocene elephantid (Darlington, 1957; Laurie and Hill, 1954). All except the Australo-Papuan *Phalanger* are of Asian origin. Broadly speaking the endemic mammals of Sulawesi can be classified into two adaptive types. Most of them are arboreal, the kinds one would expect to have the greatest capacity for dispersal over salt water barriers, on fallen trees or rafts of vegetation carried off in floods. The remainder are large or fairly large ungulates, the kinds of mammals that would have the physiological stamina to stay afloat and alive for a fairly lengthy period if caught in floods and swept out to sea.

Man has something of the characteristics of both types. He is essentially arboreal and in all ages and cultures has climbed trees for food and shelter and to escape floods. He is also large enough to have the physiological resources to survive long periods of exposure and deprivation. Even if water craft were available it is possible and even likely that the earliest immigrants did not deliberately embark on a voyage of colonisation but were carried off accidentally during storms. The literature contains many accounts of seemingly miraculous survival of castaways, among the best known examples from different parts of the cultural spectrum are Pacific islanders, carried off in canoes in violent storms, and William Bligh and his comrades. The Sundaland castaways would not have the knowledge of navigation out of sight of land enjoyed by the Micronesians and Polynesians and Bligh, and it would not be expected that they would deliberately embark on such journeys. Such accidental voyages as envisaged above would happen at rare intervals and most would not have a happy ending, but given the long time interval involved a few might have been successful. As with most mammals the founding population need not have amounted to many individuals. Perhaps even one young pregnant female was sufficient. However new individuals may have been added to the population at intervals.

Chappell (1976) has given well-founded estimates of sea-level changes in the late Quaternary. However, if accidental voyages were the means by which Australia was originally colonised, the earliest people could have arrived at any time since Man became *Homo sapiens*. Nevertheless the chances of a successful landfall would be greatly enhanced at times of lowest sea-level. At such times land would be visible ahead across most or all water gaps, depending on the route (Birdsell, 1958). The most likely points of entry to Australia were on the shore of the exposed Sahul Shelf, possibly in the vicinity of the Aru Islands or opposite Timor (Birdsell, 1958). Reconstructions of climate and vegetation of the exposed Sahul Shelf area at times of low sea-level during glacial periods have been given by Webster and Streten (1972) and Nix and Kalma (1972). Rainfall was lower, and average temperatures were a few degrees lower with consequent lessening of evaporation. The vegetation of the exposed shelf consisted of open forest and there was a migration coastwards of the arid vegetation of inland Australia. Such open vegetation would have facilitated the movements of human groups.

Taking the Australian fauna as a whole the earliest Pleistocene immigrants would have found a fauna not greatly different from that of modern Australia, and most of the species would have been at least as abundant as they are today. The major difference would have been that there was a greater variety of species, as some Pleistocene forms now extinct still existed. I have discussed this aspect in more detail on a previous occasion (Calaby, 1971). Of course the geographical ranges and relative abundance of many species would have changed markedly as a result of environmental changes brought about by the waning of glacial conditions.

The fauna of the Sahul Shelf would have been rather similar to that found in the present day northern Australian woodlands, open forests and sedgelands. Small mammals and some large ones were common. Waterbirds were abundant in association with seasonal or permanent swamps, or waterholes and billabongs along the prolongations of rivers that currently flow into the Arafura and Timor Seas. There were a number of species of grasses with seeds suitable for harvesting. Available marine food along the shoreline was abundant then as now. One important problem would have been the lack of stone for implements on the Sahul Shelf. However shell, wood and bone were readily available. The nearest good quality stone was in the quartzite and sandstone ranges of the Kimberleys and western Arnhem Land; these areas would have been reached soon after the original people became established.

It is reasonable to assume, following Birdsell (1958), that all of Australia was rapidly invaded by the descendants of the first handful of immigrants, probably in less than 2000 years. Most ecological regions were occupied by at least 20,000 years ago (Jones, 1973). Although there have been few studies and much contradictory argument, a convincing picture of environmental conditions during the later Pleistocene is beginning to emerge. The extent of glaciation in southeastern Australia was small and only the tablelands and higher parts of that region would have been uninhabitable (Costin, 1971). A considerable part of Tasmania also would have remained uninhabited. In southern Australia the climate was cooler and more humid than at the present time. Bowler (1971, 1976) has given a detailed review of late Quaternary environmental conditions in southern Australia, including much new information, to which the reader is referred. In the overall picture the later Pleistocene climatic and vegetational zonation was much the same as today. However the woodland belts were wider and had more surface water. It is to be expected that these zones were occupied first in the waves of population expansion, because of ease of movement and because they were richest in numbers of larger mammal and bird species. The desert and periglacial regions would have been the last to be invaded.

The site reports on which Jones' review is based (references listed in his paper) include what is known of the food of the Pleistocene Australians. As could be predicted they were opportunists who were well adapted to the zones in which they lived, and exploited most of the available food sources.

An important problem that has been discussed for a number of years and in my view remains unsolved, concerns Man's role in the extinction of the Pleistocene giant fauna. Jones (1973) believes that Man with his fires and hunting economy had 'an immense ecological impact', and stated that there is 'accumulating evidence that man was partially or decisively responsible for the rapid extinction of a large number of "giant" marsupial and other animals'. There is no doubt that at least some Pleistocene giant species were in existence when Man arrived. The evidence for this lies chiefly in the fact that some bones from dated contexts were apparently deposited later in time than the earliest dated Pleistocene archaeological sites. However in the considerable number of Pleistocene sites reported to date (locations and references cited by Jones) the majority of faunal remains, when they occur, are of modern species. Records of giant fauna have been claimed for three sites. Tedford (1967) reported a few charred bones of *Procoptodon* and charred *Macropus ferragus* teeth from a partially deflated site at Lake Menindee, among a large number of bones collected. The site also contains implements. Marshall (1973) speaks of a charred *M. ferragus* fourth metatarsal reported by Tedford from an 'Aboriginal oven at Lake Menindee' and then goes on to state that metatarsals referred to *M. ferragus* by Tedford are indistinguishable from *M. titan* bones from Keilor. I can find no reference to charred metatarsals in Tedford's paper which adds further confusion to the problem. It is clear from Marshall's (1973, 1974) papers that he believes that Tedford misunderstood the large *Macropus* species. Both *M. ferragus* and *M. titan* occur at Lake Menindee but Tedford does not record *M. titan* and describes a new species, *M. birdselli*, that Marshall (1973) considers to be identical with *M. cooperi*, the large Pleistocene forerunner of the modern euro (*M. robustus*). Marshall (1974) also states that one of the jaws figured by Tedford as *M. birdselli* is a specimen of *M. titan*. Some of the marsupial bones are in the form of partial skeletons and articulated parts of limbs, and it seems clear that some at least of the animals were killed by predators whose bones also occur on the site, and others possibly died from natural causes. The *Procoptodon* bones could have been burnt in a natural fire.

Marshall (1973, 1974) points out that the confusion in the determination of extinct species is important when considering the effect of Man on the giant fauna. Some of the Pleistocene giant forms are in fact direct lineal ancestors of modern species. The modern *M. giganteus* is the direct lineal descendant of *M. titan* which can thus be considered to be still in existence. *M. ferragus* however has left no descendants and is certainly an extinct Pleistocene giant kangaroo.

Bowler (1976) refers to Marshall's (1974) study of the Pleistocene giant fauna collected by Dr A. Gallus from a deposit at Keilor that also contains artifacts above and below the bones, and claims that the occurrence provides the 'clinching evidence' of Man's coexistence with the giant fauna. Unfortunately, so far as I am aware the critical archaeological and stratigraphical details which would enable one to comment on the nature of the association of Man and fauna have not been published. Glennie and Macumber (1974) have recently recovered a large quantity of bones, chiefly jaws of *M. titan* but also a few specimens of *Protemnodon* and *Diprotodon*, and some stone artifacts, in a Pleistocene deposit at Lancefield, Victoria. This is a preliminary announcement only and an evaluation of the association must await the publication of further details. The presence of occasional isolated teeth in archaeological contexts should be treated with caution as even modern Aboriginals have carried teeth of Pleistocene giant marsupials as 'charms' (Akerman, 1973).

One aspect of the problem that has not received much attention to date is the historical adaptive evolution of the Australian flora and fauna. In the mid-Tertiary and later, cool temperate rainforest was widespread and there seems to have been a gradual desiccation extending from the later Tertiary to recent times. The rainforests were slowly replaced by the distinctive Australian woodland and grassland flora. Schodde and Calaby (1972) have indicated that many groups of the bird and mammal faunas and the flora of the dry woodlands have been derived from less specialised forms in the subtropical montane rainforests.

Several authors (Gardner, 1957; Mount, 1964, 1969; Cochrane, 1968) have produced evidence that many elements of the distinctive Australian flora are adapted to fire and indeed some species and vegetation communities apparently need periodic fires to keep them in existence. Such adaptations presuppose that the flora was subject to fairly frequent fires since at least the later part of the Tertiary and long before the coming of Man.

The large browsing diprotodontids had proliferated in the Tertiary but were declining by the beginning of the Pleistocene. The great radiation of grazing macropodids was a feature of the late Pliocene and Pleistocene (Bartholomai, 1972) and a considerably smaller proportion of grazing kangaroos became extinct than browsing forms. The chief species in the Pleistocene that became extinct were the large browsing diprotodontids and macropodids.

The radiation of the extinct giant ratite bird family Dromornithidae occurred in the Tertiary and only one species of *Genyornis* survived into the Pleistocene (P. Vickers Rich, pers. comm.). Several genera and species of flamingoes were present in Australia in the Tertiary and Pleistocene (Miller, 1963; G. F. van Tets, pers. comm.) but the family disappeared in the late Pleistocene. The species that survived longest (*Phoenicopterus ruber*) still exists in both the Old and New Worlds, and nobody has doubted that its disappearance from Australia followed habitat deterioration caused by climatic change.

We still need Pleistocene sites with abundance of bones, with unequivocal evidence of butchering and charring. Even when sites are discovered with such clear evidence of the hunting and butchering of giant fauna by Pleistocene Man will it mean much? Before it can be said with confidence that predation or habitat alteration or any other ecological factor has an effect on populations of organisms it is necessary to have a measure of those populations and other biological information, something that is scarcely possible with the extinct Pleistocene fauna. Whether one believes or not that Man was a major factor in the extinction of the fauna will always remain a matter of personal prejudice. The only evidence in favour of his drastic intervention is a supposed coincidence in time of the arrival of Man and the extinction of the fauna. So far there is little evidence in support of the supposed coincidence. A great deal more information is required on the time of extinction of most species. I think that the weight of evidence favours climatic changes as the ultimate major cause of extinction and the most that Pleistocene Man may have done was to hasten the extinction of the remaining already doomed species that were still around when he arrived.

References

AKERMAN, L.   1973   Two Aboriginal charms incorporating fossil giant marsupial teeth. *Western Australian Naturalist,* 12:139–41.

BARTHOLOMAI, A.   1972   Aspects of the evolution of the Australian marsupials. *Proceedings of the Royal Society of Queensland,* 82:v-xviii.

BIRDSELL, J. B.   1958   Some population problems involving Pleistocene man. *Cold Spring Harbor Symposia on Quantitative Biology,* 12:47–69.

BOWLER, J. M.   1971   Pleistocene salinities and climatic change: evidence from lakes and lunettes in southeastern Australia. In *Aboriginal man and environment in Australia,* D. J. Mulvaney and J. Golson (eds), pp. 47–65. Australian National University Press, Canberra.

——   1976   Recent developments in reconstructing Late Quaternary environments in Australia. In *The biological origin of the Australians,* R. L. Kirk and A. G. Thorne (eds), pp. 55–77. Australian Institute of Aboriginal Studies, Canberra.

CALABY, J. H.   1971   Man, fauna, and climate in Aboriginal Australia. In *Aboriginal man and environment in Australia,* D. J. Mulvaney and J. Golson (eds), pp. 80–93. Australian National University Press, Canberra.

CHAPPELL, J.   1976   Aspects of Late Quaternary palaeogeography of Australian-east Indonesian region. In *The biological origin of the Australians,* R. L. Kirk and A. G. Thorne (eds), pp. 11–21. Australian Institute of Aboriginal Studies, Canberra.

COCHRANE, G. R.   1968   Fire ecology in southeastern Australian sclerophyll forests. *Proceedings of the Annual Tall Timbers Fire Ecology Conference,* 8:15–40. Tall Timbers Research Station, Tallahassee.

COSTIN, A. B.   1971   Vegetation, soils and climate in Late Quaternary southeastern Australia. In *Aboriginal man and environment in Australia,* D. J. Mulvaney and J. Golson (eds), pp. 26–37. Australian National University Press, Canberra.

DARLINGTON, P. J.   1957   *Zoogeography: the geographical distribution of animals.* Wiley, New York.

GARDNER, C. A.   1957   The fire factor in relation to the vegetation of Western Australia. *Western Australian Naturalist,* 5:166–73.

GLENNIE, R. and P. MACUMBER   1974   (Note) *Australian Quaternary Newsletter,* 3:8.

JONES, R.   1973   Emerging picture of Pleistocene Australians. *Nature,* 246:278–81.

LAURIE, E. M. O. and J. E. HILL   1954   *List of land mammals of New Guinea, Celebes and adjacent islands 1758–1958.* British Museum, London.

MARSHALL, L. G.   1973   Fossil vertebrate faunas from the Lake Victoria region, S.W. New South Wales, Australia. *Memoirs of the National Museum of Victoria,* 34:151–71.

——   1974   Late Pleistocene mammals from the 'Keilor Cranium Site', southern Victoria, Australia. *Memoirs of the National Museum of Victoria,* 35:63–86.

MILLER, A. H.   1963   The fossil flamingos of Australia. *Condor,* 65:289–99.

MOUNT, A. B.   1964   The interdependence of eucalypts and forest fires in Southern Australia. *Australian Forestry,* 28:166–72.

——   1969   Eucalypt ecology as related to fire. *Proceedings of the Annual Tall Timbers Fire Ecology Conference,* 9:75–108.

NIX, H. A. and J. D. KALMA   1972   Climate as a dominant control in the biogeography of northern Australia and New Guinea. In *Bridge and barrier: the natural and cultural history of Torres Strait,* D. Walker (ed), pp. 61–91. Australian National University Press, Canberra.

SCHODDE, R. and J. H. CALABY   1972   The biogeography of the Australo-Papuan bird and mammal faunas in relation to Torres Strait. In *Bridge and barrier: the natural and cultural history of Torres Strait,* D. Walker (ed), pp. 257–300. Australian National University Press, Canberra.

TEDFORD, R. H.   1967   The fossil Macropodidae from Lake Menindee, New South Wales. *University of California Publications in Geological Sciences,* 64:1–165.

WEBSTER, P. J. and N. A. STRETEN   1972   Aspects of late Quaternary climate in tropical Australasia. In *Bridge and barrier: the natural and cultural history of Torres Strait,* D. Walker (ed), pp. 39–60. Australian National University Press, Canberra.

Palaeoenvironments for Man in New Guinea

J.H. and G.S. Hope

DURING GLACIAL PERIODS of the late Pleistocene, lower sea levels resulted in amalgamation of many of the islands of Indonesia and Malaya with the Asian mainland, and the connection of New Guinea and Australia by a broad low plain. Between these two land masses lay the islands of Wallacea, cut off from both by deep sea channels. That this separation of the two land areas by the intervening channels and islands persisted is attested by the distinct fauna of the Australian region. Man, however, was able to cross the island-channel barrier and establish himself in Australia and New Guinea in the late Pleistocene.

It seems most probable that man first moved through Wallacea during a time of low sea level, when the water barriers were narrowest and land would be visible ahead from one island to the next (Howells, 1973). Since he was well established in southeastern Australia by 30,000 years ago, he probably made the initial water crossing by 50,000 years ago. Several routes through Wallacea were possible: along the Lesser Sunda Islands, through Timor to the coast of the Sahul Shelf off northwestern Australia; or through the more northerly islands either to the coast of the Arafura Shelf near the Aru Islands, or to the northwest tip of New Guinea. It may be that more than one migration took place, over some or all of these routes.

For a tropical, coastal, maritime people the most familiar environment would have existed along the coast of New Guinea. The north coast may have been much as it is today, as little additional land was exposed here by the fall in sea level. Although large rivers cut the coast line, there are sandy beaches and embayments, rather than mangrove or cliffs.

For those moving south into Australia, the familiar coastal environments would have given way inland to a vegetation gradient resembling that inferred by Nix and Kalma (1972) from a theoretical palaeoclimatic reconstruction. They suggest that the vegetation graded from dense closed forest on the precipitous southern face of the central mountain chain of New Guinea, through more open forest on the lower slopes at the north of the Arafura Shelf, to open woodlands and finally to the relatively dry to arid savannahs of central Australia. Major rivers would have run south from the mountains to empty into the Banda Sea. The gradient of the Arafura Shelf was so gentle that freshwater swamps could have been extensive (Golson, 1972). The environments encountered and adapted to by the south-moving migrants were basically Australian in character and are not further discussed here.

This paper considers movement into montane New Guinea. At first glance, a high, cold area with scattered ice caps might not seem to be a particularly favourable environment for people moving from a tropical maritime life. Yet the earliest archaeological site known in New Guinea is in high country. Kosipe, occupied by man 26,000 years ago (White *et al*, 1970), is situated at 2000 m in the Owen Stanleys, less than 10 km from the present subalpine grasslands on Mt Albert Edward (3990 m). It lies at the far southeastern corner of New Guinea, at least 1400 km from the western Pleistocene coastline. If man was established there 26,000 years ago, with a specialised toolkit, he must have been living and adapting to life in New Guinea for some considerable time beforehand.

The central cordillera is the dominant physical feature of New Guinea. In Irian Jaya*, the Merauke Range forms an almost complete chain from the Paniai Lake area to the Star Mountains with only one narrow gap, cut by the Baliem River. The Arfak Mountains in the northwest peninsula of New Guinea are much lower and isolated from the main chain. The highest peaks, some snow clad, lie along the southern face of the Merauke Range, which rises from near sea level to above 4000 m over a distance of 15–30 km. A mountain complex with valleys and high plateaux extends 30–80 km to the north. In Papua New Guinea the cordillera continues as the Star Mountains at somewhat lower altitudes, then broadens in the Western Highlands to form a series of roughly parallel ranges (Bismarck, Kubor, Kratke, etc.) and extends as the Owen Stanleys to the southeast tip of New Guinea. The Finisterre and Saruwaged Ranges in the northeast are isolated from the main chain by the intermontane trough carrying the valleys of the Sepik, Ramu and Markham Rivers. Lower ranges follow the north coast line, but the remainder of the island is at very low altitude and generally swampy in character. Winding rivers cross most of these plains and empty into the sea without large deltas, except on the southern Papuan Gulf. Figure 1 shows the extent of areas above 2000 and 3000 m and indicates places discussed in the text.

Within the mountain ranges of the main cordillera lie the high intermontane basins of the eastern, western and southern highlands of Papua New Guinea, and the Baliem and Paniai Lakes regions of Irian Jaya. Today these

---

* In this paper the name New Guinea refers to the whole island, Papua New Guinea to the eastern half of the island and Irian Jaya to the western half. Many geographical names in Irian Jaya have changed recently and the following are used in this paper with the earlier names in brackets: Merauke or Moake Range (Snow or Sneeuw Mountains), Mt Jaya (Carstensz), Mt Trikora (Wilhelmina), Mt Mandala (Juliana), Sudirman Range (Nassau), Jayawijaya Range (Tinne), Paniai Lake (largest of the Wissel Lakes).

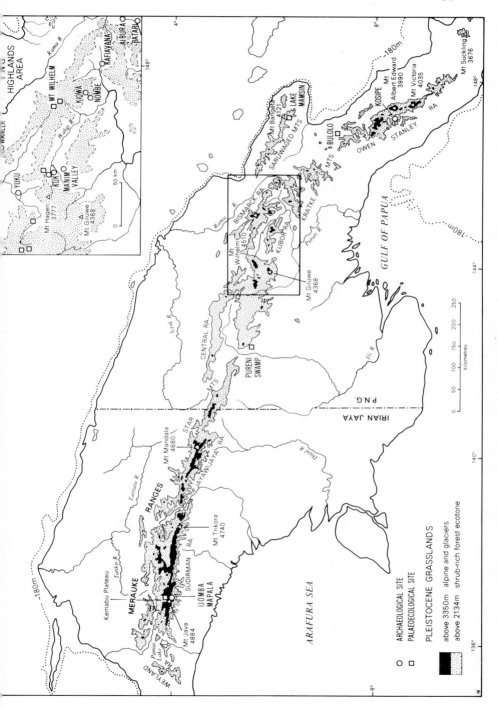

Figure 1   New Guinea. Location of sites mentioned in the text.

support the densest populations in New Guinea. The basins are at altitudes of 1300–2200 m, but in some areas subsistence agriculture may extend up to 2750 m. On the outer flanks of the ranges, populations are more scattered and the upper limits of cultivation tend to occur below 2000 m. Brookfield (1964) has suggested that this may be due to the excessively cloudy, wet climate of the outer flanks, whereas the intermontane basins have a climate controlled more by local circulation, and experience relatively fine weather for much of the year.

Dense montane and subalpine forests extend from the cultivated areas to the treeline at 3850–4000 m, above which alpine grasslands occur on the higher peaks. Very large areas of subalpine, shrub-rich tussock grassland also occur down to 3000 m on most mountains, and parts of these are clearly of anthropogenic origin. Below 1000 m the montane forests are replaced by lowland tropical forests which are almost uninhabited in most areas, except near the coast. In the more seasonal climates of southern New Guinea, a *Eucalyptus* savannah replaces the rainforest (Walker, 1972).

Pleistocene palaeoenvironments

Evidence from pollen analyses and radiocarbon dating of Pleistocene and postglacial deposits in montane New Guinea enables a preliminary recon-struction of the climatic and vegetational history to be made. No data are yet available for lowland regions; any speculation about these derives from general climatic reconstruction (e.g. Nix and Kalma, 1972), or by extra-polation from high altitudes.

During the last 50,000 years the high peaks of New Guinea have been glaciated. It is not known when the ice advance commenced but pollen analyses in the Western Highlands suggest that cold conditions continued from before 38,000 years to about 10–11,000 years BP. (Williams *et al*, 1972; Flenley, 1972; Walker, 1970, 1973; Powell, 1970). Glaciers probably fluctuated to some extent, but would have been present throughout this time.

Glaciers occurred on all mountains above 3,800 m during the late Pleistocene. The Sudirman Range supported the largest ice cap with valley glaciers, but substantial ice areas also occurred on Mt Mandala, Giluwe, Wilhelm, Albert Edward and Bangeta. The highest plateau areas around some of these mountains had thin but extensive ice sheets which left series of moraines up to 200 m high across the ground. Deep valleys, such as those on Mt Wilhelm, were filled with up to 1000 m of ice which eroded U-shaped valleys and deep cirques and left cirque lakes and massive end moraines at 2900–3200 m. Below these flat-floored glacially eroded valleys, the topography is typically steeper, with V-shaped valleys and razor crested interfluves. The upper limits of the large moraines indicate that the snowline at the time of maximum glacier extension was about 3500–3600 m (Löffler, 1972; Galloway *et al*, 1973; Hope and Peterson, 1975).

The pollen analyses referred to above, as well as those from four sites on Mt Wilhelm (Hope, 1976) and one on Mt Jaya (Hope and Peterson, 1976) suggest that at the time of maximum ice extent the regional treeline stood between 2000 and 2400 m. Table 1 shows the ice extent and area of grassland that would have existed below it, calculated on an estimated treeline elevation of 2134 m (7000 ft) throughout the island. (It should be pointed out that this estimate is based on very few data; in particular we do not know yet if the treeline lay at different altitudes on the outer flanks of the cordillera. Fluctuations in the altitude of the grassland and glaciers probably occurred during the cold period but there is no doubt that mountain grasslands formed a major environment in New Guinea during the late Pleistocene.)

The depression of the treeline by about 1700 m to an altitude of 2100–2300 m contrasts with the maximum snowline depression by only 1100 m to 3550–3750 m. Thus the zone of non-forest mountain vegetation was not only lower during the glacial phases but also extended over about 1400 m, twice the present altitudinal range.

The subalpine forest zone appears to have been extremely narrow and instead, perhaps below 3000–3200 m, there was a broad zone of shrub-rich tussock grasslands with groves of *Cyathea* tree ferns. Such a zone is virtually absent above the treeline today, but it is analogous to the subalpine shrub zone with pachycauls found above the forest limits on East African and Andean mountains (Coe, 1967; Coetzee, 1967; Hedberg, 1964; Wardle, 1971). The Pleistocene grasslands in New Guinea probably resembled closely the wide expanses of anthropogenic grasslands occurring below forest limits today, and many of the species found in the latter may have developed in the earlier grassland (Figure 2).

Above the shrub-rich grasslands grew alpine grasslands and heaths without any tall woody plants, giving way finally to open ground and tundra at the ice edge. Because the area above 3000 m decreases rapidly with altitude, the shrub-rich mountain grassland and treeline vegetation covered most of the non-forested area. The treeline was probably not abrupt, but would have consisted of tall, closed forest giving way to lower forest patches and shrublands on sheltered ridge slopes, extending over 200–500 m altitude, as is seen today on the relatively undisturbed Mt Mandala (Verstappen, 1964).

The forest boundaries below 2000 m appear to have been depressed by 500–700 m, again on evidence from only one area. If there was a narrow subalpine forest zone it was presumably like that of the present, being less than 10 m in height, dense, and carpeted with a mat of mosses and liverworts. The dominant species varied on different mountains, but *Dacrycarpus compactus*, *Rapanea* sp., and large *Rhododendron* species were always present. Below this was the complex microphyllous montane forest, dominated by tree species of Elaeocarpaceae, Myrtaceae and Cunoniaceae (the lower mountain forest of Walker, 1973). *Nothofagus* spp. today form almost pure stands in the forest, although the highest altitude at which they occur varies across the island. When the treeline was lower these forests may have been rather different from their present forms, but *Nothofagus* was certainly an

Table 1: Major mountain areas in New Guinea

Major peaks	Altitude Metres	Location °S	Location °E	Mountain areas — Range	Present Ice extent sq km	Present Mountain Grassland sq km*	35,000 – 14,000 yrs Ice extent sq km†	35,000 – 14,000 yrs Mountain grassland sq km‡
Kwoka	3000	1	132	Arfak Mountains		<2	5	1400
Kobowre	3890	4	136	Weyland Mountains				1050
Jaya	4884	4	137	Sudirman Range ⎫	8	3900	980	16100
Trikora	4730	4	139	⎭				
Mandala	4702	5	140	Jayawijaya Range		250	390	7300
Antares	4120	5	141	Star Mountains (PNG & IJ)	<2	<2	25	2550
Burgers	3690	5	143					
Giluwe	4368	6	144	Western Highlands of PNG		320	225	14000
Hagen	3800	6	144	⎭				
Kubor	3900	6	145	Kubor Range		20	27	1000
Wilhelm	4510	6	145	Bismarck Range ⎫		90	108	3200
Michael	3647	6	145	⎭				
Tabletop	3600	7	146	Kratke Range		40	4	3300
Bangeta	4121	6	147	Saruwaged Mountains		120	92	1750
Albert Edward	3990	8	147	Owen Stanley Range ⎫		240	133	6450
Suckling	3660	10	149	⎭				
				Total	8	5000	2000	57,200

* Estimated from field and air photo observations, correlated with map areas above 3050 m altitude. Proportion of grassland to forest varies for different mountain areas.

† Other authors (e.g. Verstappen 1964) estimate 5–6000 sq km ice, but field observations in the Merauke Range suggest that much of the high plateau of Irian Jaya was not glaciated during the last major advance. Figures given here are based on map area above 3600 m snowline, plus an estimate of glacier tongue area. Figures for PNG are those of Löffler (1972) and are based on air photographs.

‡ Map area above the postulated treeline. The estimate is a maximum as it includes rock and ice areas and possible scattered forest outliers.

Figure 2a Open mountain grasslands at 3,600 m on the Kemabu Plateau, Irian Jaya. These open treefern grasslands with scattered forest patches probably resulted from burning by man. They resemble the Pleistocene mountain grasslands that extended across the island before 10,500 years BP.

Figure 2b Mt Wilhelm, P.N.G., from the east. Mountain grasslands below Brass Tarn (arrow) have probably been formed in the last 800 years. Although Pleistocene glaciers did not extend beyond the large moraine (dotted line), the treeline was well below the area under forest shown here.

important element. The presently cultivated intermontane valleys were mainly covered with forest, perhaps also with some grassed frost hollows, swamp and open riverine plains. The lower limit of montane forest in the Pleistocene is not known, but its boundary with the tropical rainforest may have been depressed by a few hundred metres. It seems to have formed a continuous zone along the southern mountain slopes. Still further south, Nix and Kalma (1972) hypothesise that the tropical rainforest would have been greatly restricted to the foothills and as a gallery forest due to dry, seasonal conditions (Figure 3). A savannah woodland and grasslands similar to those found on the Oriomo Plateau today would have extended over the Arafura Shelf plains to Australia. An area presently occupied by rain forest in north Queensland previously supported a more arid vegetation, especially after 30,000 years ago (Kershaw, 1973). The swamp forests of the Sepik and Taritatu Rivers would not have changed greatly, but dry areas in the Upper Markham and Ramu Valleys and east of Wewak may have been more extensive.

The climate during the glacial period is presumably reflected by growth of the montane forests at a lower altitude, compared to the present. The lowering of both snowline and forest boundaries is consistent with temperatures 5–8°C colder than present. Conditions below the treeline must have resembled those of the montane forests today, with mean annual temperature exceeding 10°C, more than 1200 mm of effective precipitation spread throughout the year and no long dry periods. The climate in the mountain grasslands can be extrapolated from short term records on Mt Wilhelm (McVean, 1968). Mean air temperatures decreased with altitude from about 8°C at the treeline to 1°C at the glacier snouts, the 0°C isotherm lying at 3650–3750 m, a little above the Pleistocene snowline. Frost frequency increased rapidly with altitude; today 88 per cent of nights bring frost at 4320 m compared to 72 per cent at 3510 m (R. Hnatiuk, pers. comm.).

A possible explanation for the wide expanses of shrub-rich grassland is that intense frost periods occurred every few years, preventing forest establishment. This implies somewhat drier conditions than present, producing a climate similar to that of the African high mountains today. There the thin dry air allows quick heat loss by radiation and cold air drainage, giving lower surface minima at any elevation, in contrast to the very humid New Guinea mountains. Nix and Kalma (1972) postulate a general rainfall reduction during the Pleistocene in New Guinea, due to a cooler ocean surface and the extensive dry land of the Arafura Shelf. The level of persistent cloud may have been lower too, giving misted humid conditions to the forests area around 1500 m, rather than 2700 m as at present. The orographic increase in rainfall in this case would have ceased above 2000 m and rainfall totals may even have fallen with increasing altitude above 2000 m, as occurs today on the African high mountains (Coetzee, 1967). However, the widespread occurrence of alpine bog plants such as *Astelia* in pollen diagrams shows that the mountain grasslands were far from arid. The greater specialisation for frost resistance of the African alpine megaphytes, compared to

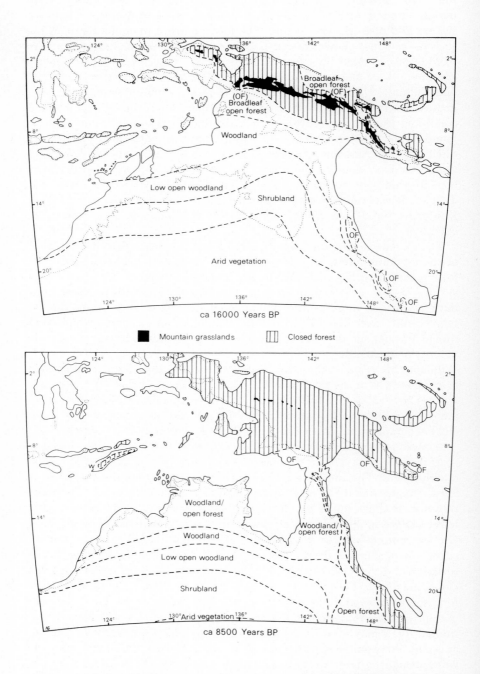

Figure 3 Vegetation in late Pleistocene New Guinea. (Adapted from Nix and Kalma 1972).

Cyathea, suggests that the New Guinea shrub-rich grasslands were less frosty in the Pleistocene than is the above-treeline shrub zone on the African mountains today.

Man in the Pleistocene grasslands

Several environments were available for man on his arrival in New Guinea. The southern savannah was ecologically part of Australia and is not considered here, nor are the lowland swamp environments whose Pleistocene history is unknown. In montane New Guinea there were two alternatives, the forested mountain slopes and basins, and the higher ecotone made up of the treeline and the subalpine grasslands. S. and R. Bulmer (1964) have suggested that the lower montane forest would have offered richer possibilities than higher areas to the pre-agricultural people of New Guinea. However the new evidence for the great extent of the treeline-grassland ecotone suggests to us that early colonists could have established themselves more easily there than in the forests. Modern usage of treeline areas for hunting and travel, although marginal to the present horticultural societies, indicates that climate is not a severely limiting factor, for although it can be unpleasant, cold or wet conditions never persist for a long period.

Trade routes   Today high altitude tracks cross many of the mountains of New Guinea. In the immediate area of Mt Jaya live about 15,000 Damal (Uhunduni) people, more or less evenly divided north and south of the range (Ellenberger, 1962). Although the Damal live at lower altitudes (below 2500 m), concentrated at Beoga and Ilaga, to the north of the Kemabu Plateau, high altitude tracks crossing the Sudirman Range link the scattered population. Other tracks pass from west to east, linking the Paniai Lake region across the Kemabu Plateau to the Baliem Valley.

The main purpose of these tracks is trade, and Ellenberger (1962) has summarised the trading patterns of the Damal of Beoga and Ilaga, who live in the centre of the east-west trade route. However, one of us (GSH) was told by the Damal he met at Mt Jaya that the east-west trade routes went up to very high altitudes to avoid enemy villages. Nevertheless, travel in the high grasslands of the plateau is easier and faster than through the montane forest in the steeper, non-glaciated valleys to the north. The north-south tracks of Irian Jaya, through geographic necessity, reach very high altitudes. The 1938–39 Archbold expedition travelled between Lake Habbema and Mt Trikora along a track which reached an altitude of 3800 m. In places it was worn shoulder deep into the ground by continual usage and water erosion (Brass, 1941). The expedition met several parties of people moving over the track, the largest of which numbered 100 and included whole families. Heider (1967) records that Grand Valley Dani reach Ilaga by means of this route. Hughes (1971) has described tracks passing from the Jimi Valley across the northern slope of Mt Wilhelm to Bundi, and another track leads from the head of the Chimbu Valley to Kerowagi across subalpine grassland south of Mt Wilhelm. Ryan (1959) describes a journey across the Saruwageds

in 1943, following a trading route from south to north. This crossed a
10–13 km wide plateau on the top of the range. The track passed a boulder
under which were the skeletons of a group of people who died during a
previous crossing. Champion (1940) followed tracks from the southern
highlands to Ialibu over the summit plateau (3820 m) of Mt Giluwe.

Rockshelters, common in the limestone of the high country of Irian Jaya,
are used for overnight campsites on the high tracks. Archaeological deposits
in the Mapala rockshelter, 3996 m, near Mt Jaya, and the Hamid rockshelter, 3420 m, are described below. Harrer (1964) camped in others at
similar altitudes. Archbold *et al* (1942) noted that on the track from Lake
Habbema via Mt Trikora, rockshelters became more common as the forest
thinned (within the forest, shelters were built of *Papuacedrus* bark) and were
used exclusively above 3500 m. In one such rockshelter at 3560 m, charred
fragments of human bones were found, and in a niche in the rock were burned
pieces of human skull and femur wrapped in bark (Brass, 1941). R. Mitton
(pers. comm.) photographed rock paintings in a shelter at about 3200 m
near Mt Mandala in 1972, but he suggests that this region is not traversed
often now, as thick *Coprosma* shrubland occurs at altitudes vegetated by
grassland on the other high mountains in Irian Jaya.

Hunting   Hunting has probably been the most important reason for
visits to or occupation of the treeline ecotone, both now and in the past.
Ecotones, the transition zones between diverse communities, such as forest
and grassland, often have a greater absolute number of species, and greater
population densities of those species, than do the flanking communities
(Odum, 1959). Today the forest-grassland transition is an optimal place for
hunting. Burning of forest maintains edge communities and produces a
greater amount of grassland/forest mosaic. Gillison (1969) summarised the
benefits in the Tari Gap area: 'Hunting tracks are usually present within
the forest margin and collection of *Pandanus* fruit is common along grassland/
forest transitions where *Pandanus* largely occurs. The higher incidence of
fauna occurring along the transition also attracts hunters'.

Near Mt Jaya, people travel long distances to hunt on the high plateaux,
although the populations within a 50 km radius of the mountains are sparse
and would not appear to be placing significant pressure on forest game. One
of us (GSH) was shown a photograph taken by workers at the Ertsberg
Mine (at 3600 m on the south of Mt Jaya) of a group of hunters returning
south from higher altitudes with eight dead anteaters (*Zaglossus*). It is likely
that these animals were caught on the Kemabu Plateau; to reach this from
the villages south of the mountain entails a journey of at least 25 km,
climbing from 2000 m to more than 4500 m through alpine passes, then down
to 4000 m. In fact, when GSH crossed onto the Kemabu Plateau for the
first time, he saw bare human footprints in snow at 4540 m in New Zealand
Pass, which has become ice-free within the last 30 years.

The rich mammalian fauna found at the Mapala rockshelter suggests it
was used as a hunting camp (it is on a minor north-south track across Mt

Jaya). Included were grassland species such as *Mallomys rothschildi* (giant rat), *Peroryctes longicauda* (bandicoot), and *Thylogale* spp. (wallabies) and forest species such as *Phalanger* sp. (cuscus), *Pseudocheirus cupreus* (ringtail possum) and *Dendrolagus* sp. (tree kangaroo). These latter species probably lived in small patches of forest or shrubland within the subalpine grassland.

On Mt Wilhelm, hunters from the Upper Chimbu Valley travel into the subalpine grasslands at least 1000 m above the garden limits specifically for the ringtail possum, *Pseudocheirus cupreus*. Hunting occurs in both grassland and forest islands in the grassy valleys, but in less disturbed, heavily forested valleys, tracks and hunting are restricted to the forest-grassland edge. Newsome (1970) described the capture of wallabies (*Thylogale bruijni*) by men from Palnil village in a patch of forest at about 3800 m, close to the summit area of Mt Giluwe. He comments that people from Mendi, Palnil and Ialibu regularly travel to the grasslands of Giluwe to hunt, and that small 'kapul' traps are set in large numbers across rat pads in the grass.

Brass (1941) considers that hunting was not a major reason for people crossing the high tracks near Mt Trikora, but ducks were shot with bow and arrow on the lakes, and from Lake Habbema up to about 3600 m deadfalls to catch bandicoots and rats were found.

However, it is possible that hunting is less important now than it has been in the past because of the reduction in the numbers of game animals through hunting pressure (from both men and dogs). Little data are available on this subject, but it is interesting to compare isolated mountains where human activity is minimal and those where hunting has had a long history. Mt Suckling, in eastern Papua New Guinea is isolated from the nearest villages and apparently little affected by man. The subalpine grassland and forest shows no signs of burning or other disturbance (Stevens and Veldkamp, in press). The mountain has very high populations of mammals, especially wallabies, which are often seen during the daytime. There are also signs of grazing and other disturbance of wallabies and anteaters. In contrast, although two species of *Thylogale* are present in older levels of the Mapala rock shelter, they have never been recorded by expeditions to the montane areas of Irian Jaya, although some reasonable collections and observations of fauna are available, especially those from the Mt Trikora area, made by the 1938 Archbold Expedition (Brass, 1941).

Pleistocene game The mammalian fauna of New Guinea was once more extensive, and included several large marsupials that are now extinct. The oldest and best known fossil marsupials are from the Pliocene Otibanda Formation (K/Ar dates of $5\cdot7$ and $7\cdot6$ million years) exposed in the alluvial gold mines of the upper Watut River near Bulolo (Plane, 1967a and b). Three diprotodonts occur in the Awe Fauna collected here, *Nototherium watutense*, *Kolopsis rotundus* and *Kolopsoides cultridens*. Although smaller than the giant Pleistocene Australian form *Diprotodon optatum*, all three were quadrupeds, perhaps as large as modern buffalo. Extinct macropods represented in this fauna are *Protemnodon otibandus* and *P. buloloensis*, both as large or larger than the modern grey kangaroo, and a wallaby similar to but much larger than the modern *Dorcopsis*. The fauna also includes a small dasyurid, a rodent, cassowary and crocodile.

Little information is available about the Pleistocene fauna. In the Tari-Koroba district in western Papua, vertebrate fossils have been recovered from Pureni Swamp (1500 m) (Williams *et al*, 1972). These include a diprotodont probably different from any of those at Watut, as well as phalangerids and rodents (M. Plane, pers. comm.). The fossils were associated with a C^{14} date with a range of 41,000 to 36,700 years BP (ANU-231). Pollen analyses from related sites suggest that the vegetation between about 50,000 and 30,000 years ago consisted of local bog forest of *Dacrydium*, *Podocarpus* and Myrtaceae, with beech and oak forest on the slopes. The subalpine grasslands were present on higher areas nearby. *Protemnodon otibandus* has since been found in similar Pleistocene deposits near Koroba (M. Plane, pers. comm.). A fragmentary tooth belonging to this genus has also been discovered in pre-occupation deposits at Kafiavana, certainly more than 10,000 years old (Plane, 1972). The marsupial carnivore *Thylacinus* has been recovered from a 10,000 year old level in Kiowa rock shelter (Van Deusen, 1963; Bulmer, 1964).

Future discoveries will no doubt confirm that during the Pleistocene, New Guinea, like Australia, had a more extensive mammal fauna, much of which may have become extinct within the last 50,000 years. Although the fragmentary records so far available all come from sites below the postulated Pleistocene treeline, it is probable that the extinct marsupials were widespread through both grasslands and forests of the mountain region.

Plant resources   In contrast to animal resources, there appear to be no significant plant foods available in the grasslands or subalpine forests. Although the fruits of *Astelia papuana*, *Styphelia suaveolens* and *Coprosma* spp. are common and edible they are not of great food value. The Chimbu visit the subalpine forest margins on Mt Wilhelm to collect *Pipturus* stems from which string fibre is made and prize the local alpine fern *Papuapteris linearis*. Within the subalpine grasslands, the tussock grasses and tree ferns are used for thatch, and the very common tree-shrub *Rapanea* sp. will burn even when green and wet, due to its oil glands.

On some mountains, the cypress *Papuacedrus papuana* is common up to 3500 m, and its bark, which can be stripped as a single sheet from the trunk, is widely used for house building. Bark collected at 3100 m on Mt Giluwe has been used for house building material at villages at 2200 m. The upper montane forests include *Pandanus guilianetti* and *Elaeocarpus* spp. which have edible nuts. *Pandanus* fruits seasonally but the nuts can be smoked and stored.

The montane forests and natural clearings contain a number of wild plant food species, although present day usage is minimal, presumably due to the availability of garden cultivars. S. and R. Bulmer (1964) and Clarke (1971) provide detailed surveys of the possibilities of the lower montane forest of the

Bismarck Ranges. Little is known of the resource potential of these food plants in a pre-agricultural context, particularly in higher forests in other areas of New Guinea. Possible important wild species include some *Ficus* species, wild Araceae, *Castanopsis acuminatissima*, tree ferns (*Cyathea* spp.) and the grasses *Saccharum officianale, S. edule, Setaria palmifolia*, and *Coix lachryma-jobi*, the last a possible cereal producer.

The plant foods of importance in the montane areas at present have nearly all been introduced from lower altitudes, and display extreme frost sensitivity. Varieties of some species, such as bananas, have become acclimatised to particular altitudinal zones, but there is no reason to suppose that the initial domestication took place in montane New Guinea (Powell *et al*, 1975).

Archaeological record   Archaeological evidence is still very sparse. Kosipe, the oldest known site, is situated at about the presumed Pleistocene treeline (Figure 1). White *et al* (1970) suggest that it might have been seasonally occupied for the collection of *Pandanus*, which now grows 200 m north of the site in the Kosipe Swamp. Kosipe, situated on the ecotone between forest and grassland 26,000 years ago, would have offered easy access to hunting grounds above and *Pandanus* and other forest vegetation resources below, if the montane forests lay closer to the treeline than they do today.

Other possible Pleistocene sites in New Guinea are as yet inadequately dated. Table 2 lists all the archaeological sites yet investigated in the Highlands, excluding those connected only with recent horticulture. Most of these are from a small area of the Papua New Guinea Highlands (inset, Figure 1). They are in the altitude range of 1300–1700 m, somewhat lower than the Pleistocene treeline, but never far from it. The majority of the sites seem to have been occupied after the glaciers retreated and the treeline had begun to rise. This period is discussed below.

In all archaeological sites where bone is preserved, both 'forest' and 'grassland' species are represented. If in fact hunting has always been concentrated by preference along forest/grassland transitions (whether natural in the Pleistocene or man-made in recent times), it will be difficult to use the relative proportions of forest and grassland species in a site at any given time to indicate the kind of environment nearby. Nevertheless, disappearance of forest species from a site well below the treeline and within the last few thousand years would indicate complete deforestation. Another complicating factor in interpreting faunal remains is that people today travel long distances to hunt at the treeline. Paleoenvironmental interpretations are also hindered by our knowledge of the distributions and habits of many species. For example *Zaglossus*, the large mountain anteater, has been regarded as 'strictly a forest dweller' by Van Deusen (1972), who gives its altitudinal range as 1200–3000 m. However, *Zaglossus* is common today in the grasslands of the Kemabu Plateau and one was living at 3996 m beneath a boulder near the Mapala rock shelter in January 1972. Apart from those

Table 2: Archaeological sites in montane New Guinea

Site	Altitude	Locality	Maximum Date BP (Approx.)	Ecological Significance	Reference
Kosipe	2000 m	Southern Slopes Mt Albert Edward, PNG	26,000	Open site at Pleistocene treeline. No plant or animal remains	White *et al* 1972
Nombe (Niobe)	1660 m	2 km from Kiowa, Eastern Highlands District PNG	Late Pleistocene	Rockshelter below treeline. Grass and forest species	White 1972 Bulmer 1974
Yuku	1300 m	Near Lai River, Western Highlands District, PNG	12,000	Rockshelter below treeline. Grass and forest species	Bulmer 1974
Kafiavana	1350 m	20 km S. Goroka, Eastern Highlands District, PNG	11,000	Rockshelter below treeline. Grass and forest species. *Protemnodon* below occupation levels.	White 1972

Site	Altitude	Location	Date	Description	Reference
Kiowa	1600 m	Near Chuave, Chimbu District, PNG	10,000	Rockshelter below treeline. Grass and forest species. *Thylacinus* in occupation level.	Bulmer 1974
Manim Valley	1760–2440 m	8 km SE Mt Hagen, Western Highlands District, PNG	10,000	Series of rockshelters. Hunting and settlement.	Christensen 1975
Batari	1300 m	30 km S. Kainantu Eastern Highlands District, PNG	8000 (?16,000)	Rockshelter below treeline. Grass and forest species.	White 1972
Wanlek	1680 m	Kaironk Valley Madang District, PNG	5500	Open site, forest clearance. No fauna.	Bulmer 1973
Mapala	3996 m	Near Mt Jaya, Paniai Division, Irian Jaya	5500	Rockshelter at Modern treeline. Grass and forest species.	this paper
Aibura	1640 m	15 km S. Kainantu Eastern Highlands District, PNG	4000	Rockshelter below treeline. Grass and forest species.	White 1972

seen near the Ertsberg mine, as mentioned earlier, Harrer (1964) has also recorded the species at 4000 m in Discovery Valley, to the west of the Mapala rockshelter.

In concluding this section on man in the Pleistocene grasslands we suggest that the lower subalpine grasslands and the forest edge within the altitude range 1800–2500 m may have been an important zone for the Pleistocene population of montane New Guinea. Perhaps between 50,000 and 10,000 years BP it may have been relatively easier to move through the mountain grasslands along the spine of the island, rather than from high to low altitudes through the dense forests on the mountain slopes.

Conditions during this 40,000 year period cannot, of course, have been static. When people first moved from the lowland coasts and tropical savannahs into montane New Guinea, they would have entered unfamiliar environments. However, in the upper mountain forests and grasslands large Pleistocene marsupials, probably unafraid of man in the absence of prior hunting, may have provided a food source exploitable by known methods, thus giving the people time to gain knowledge of the plant resources available. We do not yet know the causes, timing or pattern of extinction of marsupials, but their disappearance would have completely altered the itinerant hunting lifestyle envisaged for the earliest inhabitants. The increasing knowledge of the forest environment and hence access to it would have led to progressive changes in the balance between hunting and gathering. Most of the archaeological sites so far known in montane New Guinea record only the final stages of this process of adaptation.

It follows that a search for archaeological sites in the altitudinal zones of the Pleistocene treeline could be rewarding. The most promising areas are those closest to the Pleistocene coastline, where the belts of closed forest on the mountain flanks would have been narrow. Figure 2 suggests that the Paniai Lake region in the west and the Albert Edward region of the Owen Stanley Range in the east are good possibilities. The dun coloured grasslands and the gleaming icecaps of these mountain areas would have been clearly visible from the open woodlands on the Arafura Plains.

Holocene environments

After the long period of relatively stable conditions in the Pleistocene, major environmental changes began. The large glaciers of the last ice advance began to retreat 14–15,000 years ago (based on ten C^{14} dates from Mt Wilhelm, Mt Jaya and the Saruwaged Range) and had probably melted completely by 9000 years ago. The sea flooded the Arafura Shelf over the same period, and Nix and Kalma (1972) postulate sharp increases in rainfall after 11,000 years BP, especially for areas now subject to rain from the south-east. This probably caused a rise in the altitude of daily cloud formation, and generally increased cloudiness and reduced frost.

For about 4000 years after glacial retreat commenced, the forest seems to have remained at low elevations. In the Pindaunde Valley of Mt Wilhelm

(Figure 4), forest migrated upwards after 10,500 years, reaching 3500 m about 9000 years ago. It persisted as high as 4000–4100 m until 5000 years ago, when the treeline retreated below a site at 3910 m. Since then vegetation boundaries have remained stable. It is not known whether the 3000 year period of higher treeline on Mt Wilhelm, perhaps reflecting milder conditions, applied elsewhere in New Guinea, but it does coincide with an apparent absence of glaciers, in addition to a record of forest development at lower altitudes, on Mt Jaya and in the Saruwageds.

Conditions have been generally cooler over the last 5000 years. On Mt Jaya, ice readvances have occurred at least four times in the last 3500 years, with recessions 3000–2400 years BP, 1600 years BP, and during the last century (Galloway et al, 1973). Minor icecap formation postulated for Mt Wilhelm within the last 7000 years (Hope and Peterson, 1975) may correlate with these advances. The generally cooler conditions, indicated by the ice advances, the Mt Wilhelm treeline depression, and a change from grassland to tundra on the summit of Mt Wilhelm do not seem to have affected vegetation below the treeline directly.

This preliminary palaeoclimatic evidence broadly parallels that from other high equatorial areas (e.g. Gonzales, van der Hammen and Flint, 1966; Livingstone, 1967 and Coetzee, 1967) in the timing of deglaciation and upward migration of the treeline. The recent glacial readvances are in agreement with 'little ice age' chronologies from elsewhere in the world (e.g. Denton and Karlen, 1973). In north Queensland, Kershaw (1970, 1971, 1973) has found evidence for a savannah-*Eucalyptus* forest phase from before 30,000 years BP until 6–8000 BP, at which time a rainforest community indicating warmer and wetter conditions than present replaced the earlier more arid community. The present community, a rainforest indicative of slightly cooler conditions became established about 2000 years ago. Although this cannot be directly extrapolated to New Guinea, it is possible that the lowland New Guinea rainforest experienced similar changes, particularly in marginal areas such as the rainforest-savannah boundary. Kershaw's evidence broadly supports the climatic reconstruction of Nix and Kalma.

The disappearing grasslands   Over the period 10,500 to 8000 years BP, the treeline climbed from 2200 m to 4000 m (representing forest encroachment of about 8 m per year in the Upper Chimbu Valley). If these results from the Papua New Guinea Highlands again apply to the whole island, then the total area of mountain grasslands shrank from 50000 sq km to about 800 sq km, mainly around the rocky summit areas. (The total area of the five major intermontane agricultural areas today is about 12,000 sq km.)

The initial extension of forest must have affected rapidly the entire shrub-rich treefern grassland zone. If limiting factors on tree growth, such as frost, ceased abruptly, some species would have been free to grow into low trees and coalesce to form a simple forest in which seedlings from other forest species at lower altitudes would slowly appear. Colonisation of the

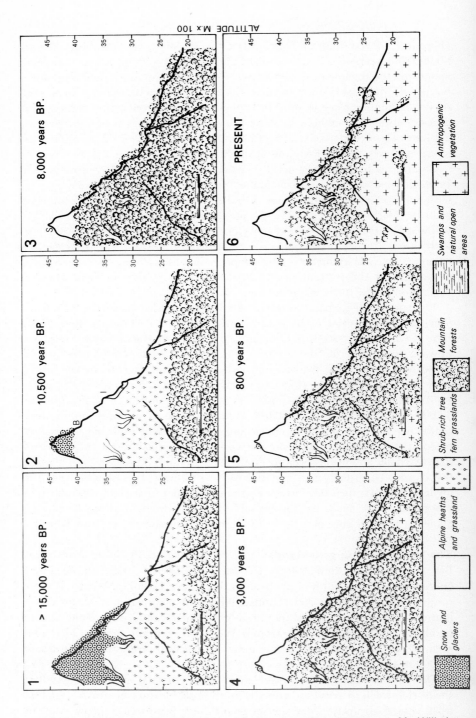

Figure 4 Inferred late glacial and postglacial vegetation changes on Mt Wilhelm, P.N.G. Pollen analytical sites are Komanimambuno (K), Imbuka (I), Brass Tarn (B) and Summit Bog (S).

shrub-free grasslands would then take place gradually, although low woody plants such as *Styphelia suaveolens*, growing within the alpine grasslands, would form robust shrubs over 1 m in height in a warmer climate. On Mt Wilhelm the forest that advanced onto the previously glaciated area was dominated by *Rapanea* shrubs, but on Mt Jaya *Coprosma* and *Rhododendron* also contributed.

By 9000 years ago the nearly continuous expanses of grassland stretching along the length of the island would have dwindled to small patches around the highest peaks (Figure 2). The large Pleistocene marsupials apparently died out much earlier than this, as in Australia, since they have not been recorded in early archaeological sites in New Guinea, though the thylacine, at least, survived until 10,000 years ago. However if any mammals adapted to the grasslands did exist in New Guinea in the Pleistocene, they may have disappeared finally at this time due to the shrinking of the grasslands, possibly combined with increased hunting pressure. If so, the cessation of grazing may have affected vegetation development. Fire, which may have been used as a hunting technique in the Pleistocene grasslands, would have been less effective as conditions became wetter.

The disappearance of the grasslands must have thrown their inhabitants onto greater dependence on forest resources, particularly vegetable sources such as *Pandanus*. Initial forest clearance may have been made in an attempt to replicate the grassland-shrubland ecotone of the Pleistocene environment. Disappearance of larger game, sporadic clearing to open up grasslands, a greater dependence on vegetable resources would set the stage for the development or adoption of agriculture.

Generally milder weather between 9000 and 5000 years BP, indicated by the high treeline altitude on Mt Wilhelm, may have favoured garden development, and it is in this period that the extensive swampland agriculture of the Upper Wahgi Valley commenced (Powell *et al*, 1975). The spread of warm, wet rainforest in north Queensland at about this time could indicate that the New Guinea lowland rainforest also reached its greatest extent at this time. This would have combined with the final rise in sea-level to decrease the area of savannah on the south coast, and result in even higher rainfall than at present on the mountains. Although small areas of savannah clearly survived in Papua, to later expand to their present extent, populations oriented to a savannah life may have experienced difficulties similar to the mountain grassland groups.

It is likely that by 5000 years BP clearance was already extensive on the slopes of the Upper Wahgi, so that the initial disturbance of the forest at altitudes below 2000 m must predate this (Powell *et al* 1975; Allen, 1972). However, there is now some evidence to indicate disturbance above the present zone of agriculture up to the modern treeline 5000 years ago. The present extent of mountain grasslands (about 5000 sq km) appears to have been caused by expansion of about 800 sq km of grasslands that occupied the rocky and boggy areas of the high peaks, following forest burning (e.g. Paijmans and Löffler, 1972; Brass, 1941, 1964).

Positive evidence of human presence at very high altitudes in New Guinea about 5000 years ago comes from Mapala rockshelter, at 3996 m, 1 km north of Mt Ngga Pulu (4860 m), and close to the southern shore of Lake Larson. It consists of a large block of limestone ($15 \times 15 \times 8$ m) perched by retreated ice onto lateral moraines, to give a deep overhang on its southern side. The shelter lies just above the treeline in shrub-rich subalpine tussock grassland. Large shrubs of *Rhododendron culminicolum* and *Rapanea* sp. occur in sheltered spots, so firewood is available. Heavy frosts and light snow occurred there a few times during February 1972.

The deposit in this cave is rich in bone and charcoal. A fragment of a stone scraper has been recovered, as well as estuarine shell. No systematic excavation has been carried out; the site was discovered when the floor was dug out by an Indonesian climbing party. However a C^{14} date of 5440 ± 130 BP (ANU–1015) has been obtained from charcoal about 30 cm below the surface.

Let. Kol. Hadji Aswar Hamid rockshelter, lies at an altitude of 3450 m near the swallet of the Asair River about 20 km north of Mt Jaya. A date of 820 ± 65 years BP (ANU–1014) was obtained on wood charcoal from about 35 cm below the surface of an ashy hearth deposit.

Circumstantial evidence for human activity at high altitudes at about the same time comes from other areas of New Guinea. In the Saruwaged Mountains, Costin *et al* (in press) found a deposit of forest tree remains, including leaves and fruits, on the bank of Lake Mamsin (3550 m). This was dated at 5660 ± 80 (Y–1619) and 6420 ± 80 years BP (Y–1620). The lake area today is almost devoid of forest so the dates are maximum ages for complete clearance. Löffler (1971) reports a date of 4320 ± 100 years BP (Gak–2164) for charcoal in a soil on moraine, overlain by two younger soils. The moraine, to the southeast of Lake Mamsin, must have supported forest originally, but is now covered by tussock grassland. The forest was probably removed by burning and the slope instability that followed may have been the result of further burning. Although dated charcoal from such a fire cannot be absolutely attributed to human action, natural fires would probably have been too infrequent to have had such a pronounced effect on completely forested, very wet terrain. Thus the date provides circumstantial evidence for the presence of man in the Saruwaged Mountains.

Blake and Löffler (1971) discovered two layers of wood charcoal buried beneath 2 m of alluvium at 3200 m elevation on the southwest flank of Mt Giluwe, again in a grassland area that presumably had been almost completely forested at an earlier time. The dates 3780 ± 140 (GaK–2524) and 1810 ± 150 (GaK–2523), indicate slope instability that followed forest fires, and may again implicate man by recording a minimal age for forest disturbance.

On Mt Wilhelm, two pollen analytical sites, Imbuka and Lower Pindaunde Lake, at 3550 m and 3510 m respectively, lie within an area of partial deforestation in the Pindaunde Valley (Hope, 1976). Both pollen diagrams show that undisturbed forest was present in the area until about 800 years ago; less than 980 ± 110 (ANU–1007B), and more than 600 ± 145 (ANU–819). From this time the local forest opened up and grassland widened, with a subsequent increase in *Cyathea* tree ferns. A higher site shows no evidence of treeline change over this period, so forest clearance can be definitely attributed to man.

The five pollen diagrams from Mt Wilhelm show that silviculture of *Casuarina* started about 1200 years ago in the Upper Chimbu Valley, and slowly increased until about 200–300 years ago, when a rapid expansion, following increasing destruction of the lower forest, must have taken place. The disturbance of the subalpine forests apparently occurred when increasing garden areas and population at lower altitudes placed growing pressure on the mountain resources.

It is probably too early to say whether these dates from widely separated mountain areas reflect a general increase in human activity from about 6–4000 years. The continuing destruction of the subalpine forests above 3000 m may have been facilitated by change in climate. They became established at higher altitudes on Mt Wilhelm, probably at a time of slightly milder climates between 8–5000 years ago, and may have been particularly sensitive to disturbance over the last 5000 years of cooler, frostier conditions, which may tend to suit the shrub-rich treefern grassland flora that was so extensive during the Pleistocene. At the same time the higher mountain areas may have become more important for hunting because of the increasing populations at lower altitudes. The evidence from Mt Wilhelm suggests that an increase in human activity in this area occurred only within the last 1000 years, whereas the important trade routes in the Merauke Range may be older than 5000 years.

Conclusions

The palaeoenvironments of montane New Guinea over the last 50,000 years can be summarised as follows:

50,000–10,500 years Extensive glaciation, possibly fluctuating. Cold, possibly drier climate. Extensive shrub-rich grasslands down to 2200 m. Large marsupial fauna, becoming extinct.

10,500–8000 years Glaciers melting. Climate warms rapidly, possibly with increasing rainfall. Treeline rises and grassland shrinks to islands around the highest peaks. Last Pleistocene marsupials disappear.

8000–5000 years Glaciers absent. Climate milder than present. Forest reaches highest altitudes, mountain grasslands form smallest area.

5000 years to present Slight glacial readvances. Climate deteriorates to present fluctuating conditions.

As already noted, this speculative framework requires testing in every palaeoenvironmental aspect, in all areas of New Guinea. This paper is intended to show that interpretation of archaeological sites should take into account the likelihood that a major Pleistocene environment, of unknown but possibly great economic potential, virtually disappeared around 10,000 years ago.

Acknowledgements: The authors thank Jim Allen, Sue Bulmer, Ole Christensen, Jack Golson, Alan Thorne and Donald Walker for reading the manuscript and for their critical discussion.

References

ALLEN, J.   1972   The first decade in New Guinea archaeology. *Antiquity*, 46: 180–90.

ARCHBOLD, R. A., A. L. RAND and L. J. BRASS   1942   Results of the Archbold Expeditions. No. 41. Summary of the 1938–1939 New Guinea expedition. *Bulletin of the American Museum of Natural History*, 89:197–288.

BLAKE, D. H. and E. LÖFFLER   1971   Volcanic and glacial landforms on Mount Giluwe, Territory of Papua and New Guinea. *Bulletin of the Geological Society of America*, 82:1605–14.

BRASS, L. J.   1941   The 1938–1939 expedition to the Snow Mountains, Netherlands New Guinea. *Journal of the Arnold Arboretum, Harvard University*, 22:271–342.

——   1964   Results of the Archbold Expedition 86. Summary of the Sixth Archbold Expedition to New Guinea. *Bulletin of the American Museum of Natural History*, 127:145–216.

BROOKFIELD, H. C.   1964   The ecology of Highland settlement: some suggestions. *American Anthropology*, 66(2):20–38.

BULMER, S.   1964   Radiocarbon dates from New Guinea. *Journal of the Polynesian Society*, 73:327–28.

——   1973   Notes on 1972 Excavations at Wanlek. Working Paper in Archaeology No. 29. Department of Anthropology, University of Auckland.

——   1974   Settlement and economy in prehistoric Papua New Guinea: a review of the archaeological evidence. Working Papers in Anthropology, Archaeology, Linguistics and Maori Studies No. 30. Department of Anthropology, University of Auckland.

—— and R. BULMER   1964   The prehistory of the Australian New Guinea Highlands. *American Anthropology*, 66(2):39–76.

CHAMPION, I.   1940   The Bamu-Purari Patrol, 1936. *Geographical Journal*, 96:243–57.

CHRISTENSEN, O. A.   1975   Hunters and horticulturalists: a preliminary report on the 1972–4 excavations in the Manim Valley, Papua New Guinea. *Mankind*, 10:24–36.

CLARKE, W. C.   1971   *Place and people. An ecology of a New Guinea community.* Australian National University Press, Canberra.

COE, M. J.   1967   *The ecology of the alpine zone of Mt Kenya.* Junk, The Hague.

COETZEE, J. A.   1967   *Pollen analytical studies in East and Southern Africa.* Balkema, Cape Town.

COSTIN, A. B., R. D. HOOGLAND and C. LENDON (in press) Vegetation changes in the Lake Mamsin area, Saruwaged Plateau, New Guinea. *Bulletin of the American Museum of Natural History*.

DENTON, G. H. and W. KARLEN   1973   Holocene climatic variations—their pattern and possible cause. *Journal of the Quaternary Research*, 3:155–205.

ELLENBERGER, J. D.   1962   On leadership among the Damals (Uhundunis) north of the Carstensz Mountain Range. *Working Papers in Dani ethnography No. 1.* pp. 10–15. Bureau of Native Affairs, Hollandia.

FLENLEY, J. R.   1972   Evidence of Quaternary vegetational change in New Guinea. In *The Quaternary era in Malesia*, P. and M. Ashton (eds), pp. 98–108. University of Hull, Hull.

GALLOWAY, R. W., G. S. HOPE, E. LÖFFLER and J. A. PETERSON   1973   *Late Quaternary glaciation and periglacial phenomena in Australia and New Guinea.* Balkema, Cape Town.

GILLISON, A. N.   1969   Plant succession in an irregularly fired grassland area—Doma Peak region, Papua. *Journal of Ecology*, 57:415–27.

GOLSON, J.   1972   Land connection, sea barriers and the relationship of Australian and New Guinean prehistory. In *Bridge and Barrier*, D. Walker (ed), pp. 375–97. Australian National University Press, Canberra.

GONZALEZ, E., T. VAN DER HAMMEN and R. F. FLINT   1966   Late Quaternary glacial and vegetational sequence in valle de Lagunillas, Sierra Nevada del Cocuy, Colombia. *Leidsche geologische mededelingen*, 32:157–82.

HARRER, H.   1965   *I come from the Stone Age*. Dutton, New York.

HEDBERG, O.   1964   Features of Afroalpine plant ecology. *Acta phytogeographica suecica*, 49:1–144.

HEIDER, K. G.   1970   *The Dugum Dani*. Viking Fund Publications in Anthropology, No. 49.

HOPE, G. S.   1976   *The vegetational history of Mt Wilhelm Papua New Guinea*. *Journal of Ecology*, 64:627–64.

—— and J. A. PETERSON   1975   Glaciation and vegetation in the high New Guinea Mountains. *Bulletin of the Royal Society of New Zealand*, 13:155–62.

HOPE, G. S. and J. A. PETERSON   1976   Palaeoenvironments. In *Gunung Es: results of the Australian Universities' expeditions to the glaciers of Irian Jaya, 1971–1973*. G. S. Hope, J. A. Peterson and U. Radok (eds), A. A. Balkema, Rotterdam. In press.

HOWELLS, W. W.   1973   *The Pacific Islanders*. Weidenfeld and Nicholson, London.

HUGHES, I. M.   1971   *Recent neolithic trade in New Guinea: the ecological basis of traffic in goods among stone age subsistence farmers*. Ph.D. thesis, Australian National University.

KERSHAW, A. P.   1970   A pollen diagram from Lake Euramoo, northeast Queensland, Australia. *New Phytologist*, 69:785–805.

——   1971   A pollen diagram from Quincan Crater, northeast Queensland, Australia. *New Phytologist*, 70:669–81.

——   1973   *Late Quaternary vegetation of the Atherton Tableland, Northeast Queensland, Australia*. Ph.D. thesis, Australian National University.

LIVINGSTONE, D. A.   1967   Postglacial vegetation of the Ruwenzori mountains in equatorial Africa. *Ecological Monographs*, 37:25–52.

LÖFFLER, E.   1971   The Pleistocene glaciation of the Saruwaged Range, Territory of New Guinea. *Australian Geographer*, 11:463–72.

——   1972   Pleistocene glaciation in Papua and New Guinea. *Z. Geomorphologie Supplement*, 13:46–72.

MCVEAN, D. N.   1968   A year of weather records at 3,480 m on Mt Wilhelm, New Guinea. *Weather*, 23:377–81.

NEWSOME, A.   1970   A collection of mammals from Mt Giluwe, 5–8 September, 1970. In Tambul Patrol Report No. 1–1970/71.

NIX, H. A. and J. D. KALMA   1972   Climate as a dominant control in the biogeography of northern Australia and New Guinea. In *Bridge and barrier: the natural and cultural history of Torres Strait*, D. Walker (ed), pp. 61–92. Australian National University Press, Canberra.

ODUM, E. P.   1959   *Fundamentals of Ecology*. 2nd Edition, W. B. Saunders, London.

PAIJMANS, K. and E. LÖFFLER   1972   High-altitude forests and grasslands of Mt Albert Edward, New Guinea. *Journal of Tropical Geography*, 34:58–64.

PLANE, M. D.   1967a   Two new Diprotodontids from the Pliocene Otibanda Formation, New Guinea. *Bulletin. Bureau of Mineral Resources, Geology and Geophysics, Australia*, 85:105–28.

——   1967b   Stratigraphy and vertebrate fauna of the Otibanda Formation, New Guinea. *Bulletin. Bureau of Mineral Resources, Geology and Geophysics*, Australia, 86:1–64.

——   1972   Fauna from the basal clay at Kafiavana. Appendix 5 in White, J. P. 1972.

POWELL, J. M.   1970   The history of agriculture in the New Guinea Highlands. *Search*, 1:199–200.

——, A. KULUNGA, R. MOGE, C. PONO, F. ZIMIKE and J. GOLSON   1975   *Agricultural traditions of the Mt Hagen area*. Occasional Paper 12. Department of Geography, University of Papua New Guinea, Port Moresby.

RYAN, P.   1959   *Fear drive my feet*. Melbourne University Press, Melbourne.

STEVENS, P. F. and J-F. VELDKAMP   1976   The Mount Suckling Expedition, 1972, with notes on the flora and vegetation of the subalpine region. Bulletin. Division of Botany, Department of Forests, Papua New Guinea. In press.

VAN DEUSEN, H. M.   1963   First New Guinea record of Thylacinus. *Journal of Mammalogy*, 44:279–80.

——   1972   Some comments on the ecology of some highland mammals. Appendix 1 in White, J. P. 1972.

VERSTAPPEN, H. T.   1964   Geomorphology of the Star Mountains, *Nova Guinea. Geology*, 5:101–58.

WALKER, D.   1970   The changing vegetation of the montane tropics. *Search*, 1:217–21.

——   1972 (ed)   *Bridge and barrier: the natural and cultural history of Torres Strait*. Australian National University Press, Canberra.

——   1973   Highlands vegetation. *Australian Natural History*, 17(12):410–19.

WARDLE, P.   1971   An explanation for alpine timberline. *New Zealand Journal of Botany*, 9:371–402.

WHITE, J. P.   1972   *Ol tumbuna. Archaeological excavations in the eastern Central Highlands, Papua New Guinea*. Terra Australis 2, Canberra.

——, K. A. W. CROOK and B. P. RUXTON   1970   Kosipe: a late Pleistocene site in the Papuan Highlands. *Proceedings of the Prehistoric Society*, 36:152–70.

WILLIAMS, P. W., I. McDOUGALL and J. M. POWELL   1972   Aspects of the Quaternary geology of the Tari-Koroba area, Papua. *Journal of the Geological Society of Australia*, 18:333–47.

Recent developments in reconstructing late Quaternary environments in Australia

J.M. Bowler

THE RELEVANCE OF late Quaternary environmental history to the study of Man requires little emphasis. The rhythmic advance and retreat of the northern hemisphere ice caps with their complementary global oscillations of sea-level have long been recognised as powerful agencies or catalysts directing Man's evolutionary paths. By their alternate opening and closing of climatic and physiographic barriers they have controlled migration routes and helped determine the morphologic evolution of specific groups by enforced isolation. An understanding of these and many other aspects of Quaternary environmental influences are essential to our knowledge of Man.

Not only did the physical environment operate on Man, but only now are we beginning to realise that Man, through his use of fire, through his clearing of forests for agriculture and in other subtle ways exerted an important modifying influence on the physical surroundings whose forces were actively shaping his own destiny.

The extent to which we can understand either of these aspects of Man's operations and conditions basically depends on our having an accurate knowledge of the sequence of physical changes in each geographic region and on having an adequate understanding of the complex processes that caused them. In Australia, we are still in the early phases of developing this understanding. Even some of the simple aspects of late Quaternary environmental history remain to be explored. However, significant advances have been made since 1969 when it could be said of our knowledge of late Quaternary climates 'it is painfully clear that we really know very little' (Galloway, 1971). In recent years we have experienced a burgeoning of activity and interest in the often dramatic events expressed in the Quaternary history of this land.

The complexities of climatic variation that this continent experienced during the Pleistocene period can be glimpsed only through the methodical analysis of evidence preserved in landforms and sediments formed at that time. Before discussing these in detail it is appropriate to scan briefly some of the recent developments that have contributed substantially to the quickening of interest that many of us have shared in recent years.

Ongoing studies of glacial and periglacial environments continue to provide new information of the extent and nature of processes involving conditions of severe cold in those small but important southern regions of the continent that preserve the mark of Pleistocene ice viz. the south-eastern highlands and Tasmania. The application of new techniques of proven value such as extensive radiocarbon dating and reconstruction of vegetation histories by pollen analysis hold out much promise in these as well as other areas of the continent. In northern Australia, Kershaw's (1974) detailed and chronologically well-controlled account of vegetation history from lakes on the Atherton Tableland stretches back beyond 50,000 years, providing the first reliable account of environmental changes from the inter-tropical zone. Concerted attempts of a similar nature on sediments derived from swamps, lakes and caves from southern Australia have already begun to yield important new information (Martin, 1973; Dodson, 1974; Dodson and Wilson, 1974).

In the area of geomorphic and sedimentary analysis of landform history, the development of new integrated departments such as the School of Earth Sciences of Macquarie University has provided additional momentum to Quaternary studies. In South Australia a combination of geomorphic techniques, combined with interpretation of sedimentary and pedologic facies, has been used by Williams (1973) to provide an important new account of the evolution and palaeoclimates of the Lake Torrens area. In Western Australia, an area comprising almost one third of the continent, few reliable reconstructions of Quaternary changes are yet available. However, extension of important work associated with archaeological sites such as at Devil's Lair (Dortch and Merrilees, 1973) provides important new evidence with added promise of things to come. Similarly, although we have a detailed relative sequence of landform evolution from Central Australia (Litchfield, 1969) we still know little about the detailed chronology and impact of Quaternary oscillations in the history of that important region.

Zoological evidence is becoming increasingly available. Vertebrate sequences from Lake Victoria (Marshall, 1973), Cloggs Cave (Hope, 1973) and McEachern's Cave (Wakefield, 1967, 1972) are now redressing a long felt deficiency in this part of the record.

These and other developments represent work carried out within the past ten years. Although the workers remain few in number their results have proved substantial. We can now freely contemplate whether glacial phases may have been times of reduced rather than increased rainfall (Galloway, 1965); acceptance of the more orthodox chronology which equates glacial with pluvial periods is regarded with apprehension (cf. Dury, 1973). The deficiencies of the Australian Arid Period of mid-Holocene age have become apparent from a record that shows greatest aridity around 15,000 years BP rather than the 5000 to 7000 BP dry period as previously widely maintained. The demise of these and other shibboleths has provided an intellectual atmosphere in which it is just as exciting to discover a new hypothesis that replaces an old one as it is reassuring to find in the observations and descriptions of the early pioneers a meticulous attention to field detail that we, often more quantitative and laboratory oriented analysts of today, would do well to emulate.

Perhaps the most significant element in this exciting phase of discovery of Australia's late Quaternary history stems from the interaction between those studies directed specifically at Man and those whose constraints involve them with the physical environment. This multi-disciplinary approach to historic analysis is providing us with a new, dynamic and rapidly evolving view of ancient Man-land relationships in this continent, an account which in the detail and diversity of environmental situations it records has already brought us to the frontiers of historic synthesis. This is a matter of profound importance not only to the scientific body but also to the community at large. That this land and its Aboriginal inhabitants can demonstrate to us, and indeed to the rest of the world, a history involving intimate reactions between Man and land for more than 30,000 years, bears directly on our ability to understand and hence conserve that land today as it does to remind us of the tragic record of our relationships with its original occupants.

The vitality of the subject and its new momentum pose special problems for the reviewer. Not only is it impossible to provide a comprehensive account of the field in a short statement but even by adopting a policy of deliberate selectivity in evidence cited (many will recognise a bias towards data of my own interest) I am aware that much of this account may be superseded in a few years or even by the time this paper goes to press.

General principles
In considering major environmental changes that might have affected Man and his adaptation to this continent we are concerned with the type, magnitude, age and duration of those changes.

The major features of Australia's climatic system were initiated at the end of the Tertiary period, long before the arrival of Man. Throughout the past two million years of the Pleistocene period, the climate has undergone systematic variations, the scope and magnitude of which we are only now beginning to comprehend. The events of the past 50,000 years, in kind and in dimension, are probably representative of earlier Pleistocene variations.

The diversity of changes recorded in environmental history may be considered in terms of variations in two basic climatic parameters: (a) changes in temperature regimes; and (b) variations in humidity.

Although it is convenient to treat both separately these two parameters are to a large degree interdependent—a small decrease in temperature will result in reduced water loss through evaporation with a concomitant increase in run-off inducing increases in stream discharges, rises in lake and ground-water levels and increased water available for plant growth. Whilst any change in temperature brings its own change in humidity, the reverse is not necessarily true. Humidity variations may be caused by changed precipitation patterns independent of temperature variations, although a significant change in precipitation with its attendant changes in cloud cover and latent

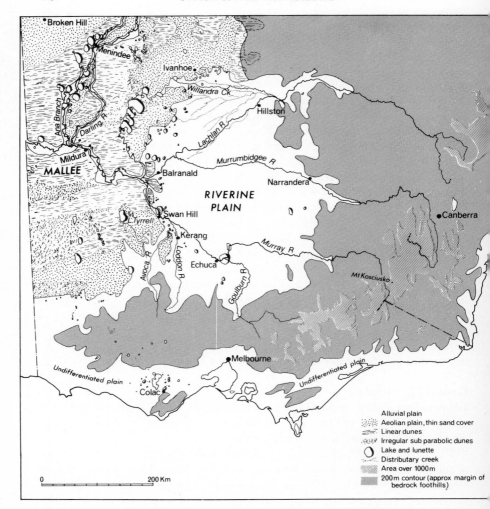

Figure 1   Regional map of south east Australia showing the area above 1000 m being
approximate area affected by intense periglacial activity about 30,000 BP. In the far
west the semi-arid dunefields and lakes experienced substantial stress during the later
period of major aridity about 15,000 BP.

heat of condensation will often be accompanied by some change in the
temperature regime.

If precipitation remains constant during a period of reduced temperature
the resultant decrease in evaporation loss results in increased humidity. Thus
the precipitation is said to be more *effective* and it is this effective precipitation
reflected as changes in humidity that we see in the record of increased stream
flows, higher lake level and groundwater variations during the cold phases
of late Quaternary time. Thus changes in humidity may be due either to
changes in precipitation or temperature, or a combination of both. But
because of the interdependence of these variables, unless we can isolate the

effect of one, we cannot evaluate the other in absolute terms. In reconstructing the Quaternary environmental record, the evidence we see is largely the
effect of changes in humidity. For this exercise then, we shall be concerned
primarily with periods of hydrologic change; our ability to reconstruct the
controlling climatic parameters, temperature or precipitation, will depend
on the nature of the evidence. But since humidity is perhaps the most
important single element in the complex factors controlling variation in
ecologic systems, evidence of a palaeohydrologic kind provides one of the best
means of evaluating the stresses that have operated on both Man and his
environment in late Quaternary time.

Let us begin by considering the climatic situation that existed in Australia
when men first arrived. Firstly, we must make some estimate, however
tentative, of the duration of Man's presence in this continent. To do so we
shall consider the positive evidence of his presence using the known age of
artifacts or other evidence of his activities. We shall then discuss his apparent
absence from potentially favourable occupational sites of known age, thereby
arguing that men had not arrived in the area at the time these habitats were
in existence.

Man's antiquity in Australia

Recent reviews have dealt adequately with the large body of evidence
obtained in recent years. Barbetti and Allen (1972) have summarised the
evidence from the Willandra lakes (Figures 1 and 2), where Aboriginal
hearths have been dated consistently at between 26,000 and 31,000 in a
stratigraphic unit from which transported unionid shells date back to
32,000 BP (Bowler, 1971). A site of charred plant remains within dark sandy
sediment of the same unit has provided a date of 35,300 (ANU–687, Barbetti
and Polach, 1973) providing possible though unconfirmed evidence of
occupation of Lake Mungo (Figure 3) at this time. This possibility is strengthened by an identical date we have obtained recently from a layer of transported
unionid shells near Lake Mungo (N–1665, 34,100–37,400 BP). The
concentration of disarticulated shells along a horizontal bedding plane,
intimately associated with charcoal fragments over a 6 m horizontal bedding
plane, provides strong presumptive evidence of shell harvesting at that
time. Man's presence in western New South Wales at least by 35,000 BP
seems assured.

Elsewhere in southern Australia, important evidence of human antiquity
has been derived from the terraces of the Maribyrnong River near Keilor
(Figure 1). Here, as at Lake Mungo we have an example of a site that continues to yield evidence as remarkable for its diversity as it is for its antiquity.
Deposits from the second youngest alluvial terrace, the Keilor terrace,
have yielded the Keilor cranium dated at about 15,000 BP (Gill, 1966), the
Green Gully skeleton of 7000 BP (Bowler et al, 1967) and a wealth of artifacts
through this sequence. At Dry Creek, the site of the original cranium, the
efforts of Dr A. Gallus in exploring the sedimentary unit below that of the
Keilor terrace continue to provide new evidence bearing on the earliest phases
of the occupational record.

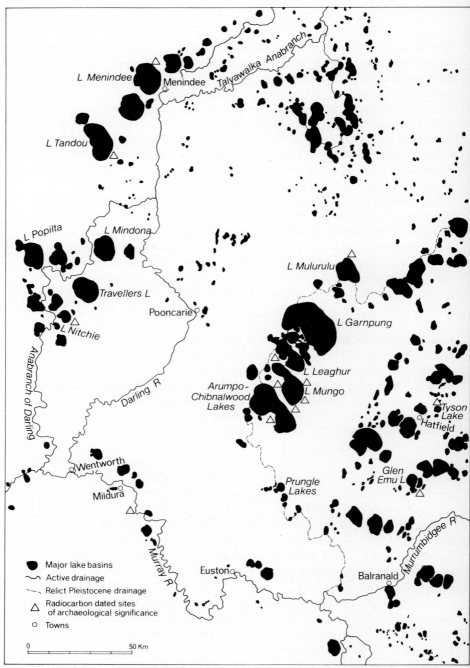

Figure 2 Lake basins in western New South Wales which are thought to have been maintained at high levels for substantial periods in late Quaternary time. Many acted as focal points for human occupation preserving a wealth of archaeological data. Most dried during the onset of aridity and, apart from ephemeral flooding, have remained dry throughout the past 15,000 years.

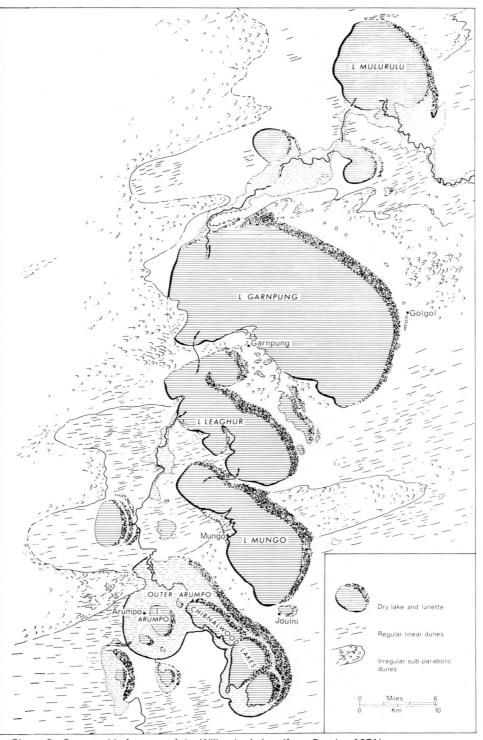

Figure 3 Geomorphic features of the Willandra Lakes (from Bowler, 1971).

The following labels appear on the map:

L MULURULU

L GARNPUNG

·Golgol

·Garnpung

L LEAGHUR

L MUNGO

Mungo·

OUTER ARUMPO

Arumpo· EL
ARUMPO

CHIBNALWOOD LAKES

Joulni

Dry lake and lunette

Regular linear dunes

Irregular sub-parabolic
dunes

0   Miles   6

0   Km   10

At Dry Creek the brownish yellow silts of the Keilor terrace are set into and disconformably overlie an older clay-rich alluvial deposit, the D Clay of Gallus (1971), sometimes erroneously referred to as the older Arundel terrace defined by Gill (1957). Within this 7 m layer of dense silty clay below the Keilor terrace (Figure 4) Gallus has established a series of occupational layers extending near or into the basal gravels of that unit. Whilst some uncertainty may attach to the typological significance of individual components within the archaeological assemblage, the origins of large quartzite flakes often bearing impact marks and percussion cones, together with their concentration along discrete horizons within the clay-rich sediments, provides indisputable evidence of Man's presence. From the base of this deposit, Gallus and his co-workers have collected faunal remains including substantial numbers of extinct giant marsupials (Marshall, 1974). Archaeologists have long anticipated the exciting possibility of Man's coexistence with the giant fauna and speculated on his role in their extinction (Jones, 1968; Merrilees, 1968). The clinching evidence to which Jones (1975) referred as 'being tantalisingly close' may indeed lie in the alluvial sediments at Keilor.

Several major questions centre on the age of the D Clay. Direct dating by radiocarbon analysis has yielded inconclusive results, a situation that is likely to persist until larger excavations provide a better opportunity for recovering suitable organic carbon. In the absence of reliable C^{14} age estimates we must rely on detailed stratigraphic and pedologic analysis of the sequence (Figure 4).

In 1971 I collected oriented samples to help evaluate the pedogenic history and age of the deposit. Several observations are pertinent.

    1.   The thick accumulation of fine textured alluvial body indicates deposition by overbank flow. By comparison with younger dated alluvial terraces in the Maribyrnong Valley a minimum of 6000 to 8000 years is required for uninterrupted accumulation.

    2.   Accumulation was slow enough to develop deep and well developed soil profile features throughout. These appear as hard carbonate cylindroids, well developed prismatic cleavage and micropedologic features (cutans) that indicate a degree of pedologic organisation consistent with soil formation extending through a long period of time.

The development of soil carbonate layers is particularly instructive. These occur in three separate and discrete horizons, suggesting oscillatory periods of soil development during alluvial deposition. Moreover, their horizontal attitude parallels the terrace surface of the D Clay, indicating that the entire period of soil formation is related to that surface; it predates the period of stream incision and the cutting of the irregular surface that led to the later deposition of the overlying silts of the Keilor terrace.

Within the D Clay, the soil evidence suggests that periods of deposition oscillated with more stable periods during which active pedogenesis more or less kept pace with accumulation. The slow and oscillatory processes allowed

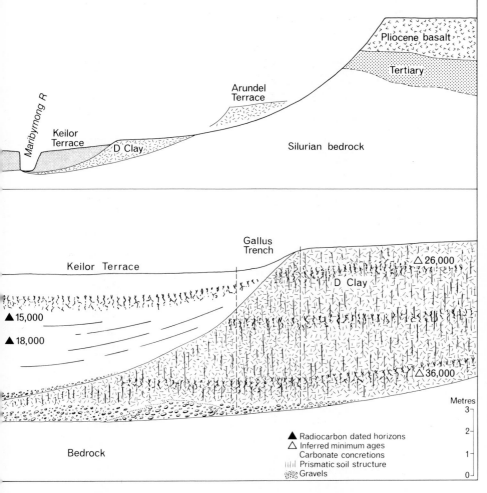

Figure 4 Cross section through the Maribyrnong River Valley near Dry Creek, Keilor. The relative position of the Arundel terrace is shown although it is not present at this locality.

carbonates to form early in the history of the deposit and permitted pedogenesis to affect the entire 7 m. By contrast, sediments of the Keilor terrace are thin (4–5 m) and despite the passage of at least 15,000 years since deposition of the main body of that terrace the resulting pedogenesis is considerably less in degree than that developed on the underlying D Clay. The combined time required to account for the events separating deposition of basal Keilor terrace silts (18–20,000 BP) from deposition of the lowermost zone of D Clay must therefore be reckoned in terms of at least 16,000 years (6000 for sediment accumulation, 10,000 for development of pedogenic features). The age of the clay may therefore be reckoned as in Table 1.

Table 1: Age estimates of the D Clay based on available C^{14} dates, rates of deposition and duration of pedogenesis.

Deposit	Event and duration	Minimum age in years BP
	Pedogenesis . . . 8000 years	8000 to present
Keilor Terrace	Top levels of terrace sediment	8000
	Mid levels of terrace sediment	15–18,000
	Channel incision into D clay	20,000
	Pedogenesis from level terraces surface . . . 6000 years min.	26,000
D Clay	Deposition and simultaneous pedogenesis through 7 m . . . 10,000 years min.	36,000

Deduced Minimum Ages for D Clay
a. Uppermost level   20,000 + 6000 = 26,000 (conservative)
                       20,000 + 10,000 = 30,000 (possible)
b. Basal levels   20,000 + 6000 + 10,000 = 36,000 (conservative)
                       20,000 + 10,000 + 15,000 = 45,000 (possible)

Thus a conservative age estimate of the lower levels of the D Clay would place it at 36,000 BP whilst an age to 45,000 BP is indeed possible.

Even if the minimal estimates are the more accurate of the two their final verification by conventional C^{14} methods presents difficulties. Firstly, the occurrence of well preserved organic carbon suitable for dating is rare. The unsatisfactory nature of C^{14} estimates from gravels near the base of this layer at the confluence of Dry Creek and the Maribyrnong River (18,300–27,300 BP, ANU–81; 30,300–32,700 BP, ANU–65) provide an example of the problems encountered. The small size of available carbon in an age range approaching the limits of the method presents considerable difficulty. Moreover, in this environment the dangers of contamination by younger humic acids, with the possible introduction of large errors making dates appear too young, impose an additional constraint. But even if our attempts to date this sequence are limited to intelligent stratigraphic speculation, the evidence already available is sufficient to establish this deposit as being as old as any example of Man's presence yet recorded in Australia; already it may be the oldest.

Limiting ages of occupation   The evidence of Man's presence on the continent in the records of both Lake Mungo and Keilor, is consistent with his having arrived and traversed to the southernmost regions by 36,000 BP and almost certainly by 40,000 BP. But how long before that time did men first set foot on this land? Jones (1975) considered the main episode of Pleistocene extinctions occurred 'a geologically short time before 25,000 to 30,000 years ago,' and that:

> if Man and the 'giant marsupials' ever lived at the same time in the same neighbourhood, they might only have done so over a short time, so brief as to seem an instantaneous event in the archaeological record.

In the light of the Lake Mungo and Keilor evidence Jones' view would support an arrival time not long before 40,000 BP.

A definitive dating of Man's first arrival is not possible. However, by analysis of evidence from habitats favourable for human occupation we may be able to establish a *prima facie* case that at certain times in the late Pleistocene he was *not* occupying potentially favourable sites. We may single out two types of sites: (a) open freshwater lakeside environments; and (b) coastal dune habitats.

A long record of dependency on these water-controlled ecological niches has been established, especially for the former which act as oases in dry inland regions. As early as 36,000 BP men were collecting shells from Lake Mungo while on the coast Lampert (1971) and Jones (1971) have established patterns of early marine exploitation.

In both these habitats, the backward extension in time of the occupational record is interrupted by changes in the physical environment which involves the absence of water nearby. Thus the oldest record of a coastal oriented economy is limited to about 8000 years at Rocky Cape in Tasmania (Jones, 1971) and to about 5000 years on the south coast of New South Wales (Lampert, 1971a and b). Older evidence of shoreline occupation relating to periods of low sea-level is now buried by waters of the continental shelf. In the semi-arid zone lakes the water-based economy extends back in time from the drying of the lakes to at least 36,000 BP. Although the lake basins were formed much earlier, beyond about 44,000 BP they were dry; therefore the record of lakeshore occupation cannot be expected to continue uninterrupted beyond that time.

Both the lacustrine and marine environments, favourable to exploitation by Man, fluctuated in response to the major global Pleistocene climatic rhythms; in so doing they preserved in their sediments the record of those changing environments and of the animals, vegetation and men that occupied them. Thus we have only to examine the next oldest lunette and coastal foredune to search for occupation of much greater antiquity than that to be found in the last depositional episodes.

In the Willandra lakes the lunette units with abundant occupational evidence disconformably overlie a much older landscape unit (*Golgol* of Bowler, 1971) in which the degree of pedogenesis permits us to make some estimate of its age. By comparison with all other soils on dated materials in southeastern Australia, the formation of the Golgol soil, with its intense rubefaction and carbonate segregation, must be reckoned in tens of thousands of years. A minimum of 30,000 years for soil formation seems consistent with present evidence of known rates of pedogenesis even allowing for substantial changes in these rates with climatic variations. Since the basal sediments of the last lake-full phase are at least 40,000 years old, a minimum age of 70,000 must be assigned to the period of lunette building that produced the Golgol unit.

The estimate may be taken one step further. Study of lunettes through a large region of southeastern Australia has established that their main period of formation ended with the close of the last glacial episode about 18,000 to 15,000 BP. The penultimate glaciation that ended with a major rise in sea-level to near its present position took place about 120,000 years ago. By analogy this may be taken as the limiting age of formation of the Golgol lunette which owes its presence to the lake-full conditions that accompanied the cold environments of that time. On this basis sediments that make up the Golgol unit are assumed to be about 120,000 years old.

Deposits of Golgol age have been closely examined but no evidence has been found to substantiate the presence of Man on the lake shores at that time. Even if Man had not yet developed adaptive techniques to exploit the lacustrine biota (as he obviously had by 36,000 BP) the presence of the fresh water bodies and their oasis effect would have been sufficient to attract men to their shores if already present in that area.

On the east coast of Australia there are two systems of coastal barriers or dune ridges; a modern one that developed since the Holocene sea-level rise and an ancient system that relates to the last time that the sea stood near its present position (Langford-Smith and Thom, 1969; Thom, 1973). Whilst occupational evidence in the form of shell middens and stone artifacts is abundant both on and within sediments of the younger (outer) barrier system (Lampert, 1971b) there is yet no evidence to associate the development of the inner system with occupation of the region (Campbell, 1972).

The age of the inner barrier is in dispute. Some C^{14} dates have suggested an interstadial age of about 30,000 years but this is not substantiated by reliably constituted sea-level curves from other parts of the world (Chappell, 1974). The last time that the sea rose to near its present position allowing construction of the inner barrier was about 120,000 years ago as outlined earlier.

Thus we now have two early and separate landscape-sedimentary systems both in environments favourable to human occupation; neither have yielded evidence of Man contemporary with their formation. Although he might have been occupying ecologic niches elsewhere in the continent, the evidence available suggests that Man's entry into these areas of southern Australia occurred some time between 120,000 and 40,000 years ago.

Even if the earliest inhabitants arrived only a short time before 40,000 BP Man's occupation of the continent over that time would still span environmental changes, the scale and magnitude of which were perhaps unequalled throughout the previous 1·8 million years of the Pleistocene period. Of the various Quaternary glacial episodes, that from which we have recently emerged within the last 20,000 years was perhaps the most severe. The remainder of this paper will explore some effects of that episode in an attempt to set the physical scene in which early Man's adaptations to the various climatic, physiographic and ecologic elements of this land found their expression.

Climate of earliest adaptive period
Man had already traversed from his point of entry and adapted to the continent-wide range of physical settings before the last major episode of climatic deterioration. Thus, as pointed out by Jones (1975), his early

presence at Lake Mungo and Keilor, attributed here to 36,000 BP, indicates he had already adapted successfully to the entire range of ecologic situations equal to those found now within the continent.

The conditions that pertained before 40,000 BP were, with minor exceptions, probably little different from those of today. Consideration of global situations deducted from marine isotope curves shows that at most times for the past 120,000 years, world ice volumes were larger than today. The growth of ice caps resulted in a gradual fall in sea-level about 80,000 BP followed by a small rise and fall at 60,000 BP. The sea then fell progressively attaining minimum levels (equivalent to maximum ice volumes) about 18,000 to 16,000 BP. Thus throughout the past 100,000 years we may assume that mean temperatures, in accord with global ice volumes, were perhaps marginally lower than those of today. However, soon after 44,000 BP both global and local evidence suggests a substantial change in temperature and hydrologic regimes.

Before 44,000 BP the large semi-arid region of northern Victoria and western New South Wales contained stable vegetated landforms much as we see there today. The first evidence of major hydrologic change is registered by the filling of the Willandra lakes about 44,000 BP. The onset of wetter conditions at this time heralded the beginning of the most severe glacial episode of late Quaternary time.

Environments 44,000 to 15,000 BP   Of the variety of geologic and geomorphic processes operating on the landscape, its flora, fauna and human occupants, those that accompanied the maximum refrigeration warrant special consideration. This period of reduced temperatures witnessed important changes in a wide range of climatic, hydrologic and vegetation patterns. It is appropriate to explore here some of the pertinent evidence paying particular attention to age, nature of the changes and their various effects on the land.

In semi-arid southern Australia before 44,000 BP lakes were dry, dunes were stable while the rivers of the Murray-Darling system provided the arterial waterways as they do today. By 44,000 BP changes were already taking place. Increased frequency and magnitude of floods brought large quantities of water to previously dry areas of the interior. Dry lake basins such as those of the Willandra system began to fill. After a short period of ephemeral activity under the influence of increased discharge, they soon became permanent water bodies. This change in the hydrology of the southeastern semi-arid zone resulted in the filling of scores of lake basins (Figure 2) producing a regional rise in water-tables with important consequences still largely unexplored for biological productivity. In the Willandra system alone more than 1000 km^2 of open water was introduced to a region where no permanent water existed previously. Murray cod, golden perch, crustacea and freshwater molluscs entered the lakes of this semi-arid region providing new sources of sustenance for the inhabitants (Allen, 1972).

To understand this hydrologic change we must look to the stream catchments, the source of the waters that flooded the plains. In the Snowy Mountains region the presence of *Nothofagus* below block streams of the Toolong Range before 35,000 BP (Caine and Jennings, 1968), suggests a wider distribution of rainforest elements at that time than exists in the area today. With the increased run-off evidenced by the rise in lake levels this suggests either a rise in precipitation or more effective precipitation due to reduced evaporation loss accompanying a substantial summer temperature lowering in the highlands.

By 32,000 BP the lakes had reached their maximum stands while in their catchments evidence of massive slope instability at that time, marking the onset of periglacial conditions (Costin, 1972), coincided with and almost certainly controlled the hydrologic changes recorded in the lakes far to the west. This period then marks the beginning of the major cold phase, a period that saw the development of small but permanent glaciers on Kosciusko and the highlands of western Tasmania. Although the areal extent of mainland permanent ice was small, the surrounding periglacial zone with its snow and seasonal ice was much more extensive. Galloway (1963) estimated the area of permanent ice in southeastern Australia at 50 km^2 compared with a conservative estimate of more than 2000 km^2 subjected to periglacial activity (Peterson, 1971).

The evidence from this region enables some estimates of absolute temperature changes to be made. Costin and Polach (1973) regard slope instability on Black Mountain and at Lake George near Canberra as providing evidence for periglacial activity down to and below 1000 m. This would require a mean temperature lowering in the Canberra region of 9°C and perhaps as much as 14°C (*op. cit.*, p. 22), in general accord with earlier estimates of a 9°C lowering in the Snowy Mountains determined by Galloway (1965).

Cold processes at this time have been invoked to explain slope instability of slopes on the Flinders Ranges in South Australia. Williams (1973) in considering the origin of the extensive alluvial fans that spread out from the foot of the ranges regards frost shattering as the effective agent in preparation of slopes for stripping by seasonally intense rains.

In Tasmania where the Central Plateau retained the largest area of permanent ice on the continent, high precipitation on the western slopes was associated with periglacial solifluction down to 600 m above sea-level (Nicholls, 1958).

In the arid zone and in tropical Australia, the effects of maximum temperature lowering are less well understood. Reduced evaporation losses associated with cool air masses would have reduced water stresses substantially in desertic regions provided precipitation remained constant. These conditions probably pertained during the early stages of the cold episode whilst sea-level was still falling.

From northern Australia, the evidence is sparse. Extensive shoreline dunes developed around Lake Woods near Newcastle Waters bear witness to a water body some 5000 km^2 in extent compared to the present lake-full area of less than 1000 km^2. Although the age of this massive expansion is not dated, evidence from the apparently cyclic development of strandlines and pedogenesis on the innermost dune suggest a correlation with recurrent periods of temperature minima through Pleistocene time. This correlation would link the extension of the lake with the maximum temperature lowering as recorded from southern Australia. However, the regional continuity of these wet conditions across northern Australia is far from generally established. In the rainforested area of the Atherton Tablelands, conditions of maximum temperature reduction were accompanied there by a reduction in precipitation (Kershaw, 1970). Dry sclerophyll forest prevailed until soon after 10,000 BP when the present rainforest vegetation entered the area.

Attempts to estimate the magnitude of temperature reductions across the continent are fraught with difficulty. In the southern highlands evidence of altitudinal variation in the treeline or orographic snowline permit independent estimates of temperature variations to be made (Galloway, 1965; Costin and Polach, 1973). Outside the area of periglacial activity, temperature dependent criteria are difficult to obtain.

In the Willandra lakes, Allen (1972) has drawn attention to the temperature limitations on the spawning of golden perch, *Plectroplites ambiguus*, for which Lake (1967) established a minimum requirement of 23·6°C. If Lake's tank experiments are applicable to field situations they indicate that summer temperatures were exceeding this range in the Lachlan system even during the coldest phases of late Quaternary time. At Mildura today mean air temperatures exceed 23·6°C only in the months of January and February. A regional drop of 6°C would be sufficient to prevent this temperature from being exceeded on all but rare occasions, thus inhibiting the spawning of *Plectroplites ambiguus* in this region during maximum refrigeration. Its presence at this time therefore presents *prima facie* evidence that the mean temperature drop over the plains was probably less than 6°C and certainly less than the 9–10°C postulated from the southeastern highlands. On theoretical grounds alone the temperature reduction of inland regions should be smaller than that registered at higher altitudes; the large temperature lowering postulated for southeastern Australia should not be extrapolated across the continental interior.

In the lakes of western New South Wales, stable high water level conditions persisted for some 6000 years from 32,000 until at least 26,000 BP. Throughout that time men returned to camp on the shoreline dune at Lake Mungo leaving a legacy of cooking hearths, unionid shells and artifacts as described by Jones and Allen (in Bowler *et al*, 1970). During this period, equivalent to the maximum extent of permanent ice in the southeast, men around the foothills and margins of the plains lived in full view of the permanently snow-capped southern highlands.

At 26,000 BP, the sequence at Lake Mungo records the first sign of instability in the lacustrine and associated dune environment that heralded the later disappearance of lakes and permanent ice from the region. During the highwater phase the lake was bordered on the east by a beach of well-sorted quartz sand which nourished a stable vegetated quartz foredune. Soon after 26,000 BP small oscillations in lake level permitted clays to be blown from the exposed floor onto the adjacent dune, a change that indicates a substantial reduction of flow through the system. This event is close to the age of the Lake Mungo cremation, dated to 25,000 BP (Bowler *et al*, 1972). The lake remained in an ephemeral rather than full condition for perhaps 3000 years. After 22,000 BP an accelerated trend towards aridity resulted in a drop in the levels of Lake Mungo and other lakes in the system. The Snowy Mountains record a parallel and perhaps controlling expression of the same event. Twynam cirque near the summit of Kosciusko had been at least partially evacuated of its ice by 20,000 BP (Costin, 1972), long before the main period of ice recession recorded from other parts of the world. Thus the evidence from both the Willandra lakes and catchment region are consistent in recording that a substantial change in the hydrologic and climatic regime had already begun before 20,000 and probably before 22,000 BP.

Following the early low level oscillation in the Willandra system, both the exposed lake floor and dune sediments were subjected to a period of soil formation, an event that relates to a dry but relatively stable period. These conditions persisted until the last and final pulsation in the lakes of the semi-arid zone (*Zanci phase* of Bowler, 1971). The onset of this brief phase can be estimated only approximately as having commenced about 18,000 BP. By 17,000 BP water deficiencies were again apparent and the entire Willandra system began to dry progressively, starting with those lakes farthest downstream. By 14,000 BP the entire system was defunct.

Lunette building   The drying of lakes in western New South Wales was accompanied by and to a large extent controlled the building of the marginal transverse dunes on their eastern shore (lunettes) (Figures 2 and 3). The development of these depositional landforms provided the most favourable locus for the burial and preservation of a wide range of faunal and archaeological evidence as apparent in the records from lakes Menindee (Tedford, 1967), Nitchie (Bowler, 1970; Macintosh *et al*, 1970) and Victoria (Gill, 1973a). The last phase of lunette construction in western New South Wales and northern Victoria was associated with events of the Zanci phase commencing about 17,500 BP and continued for some 1500 years. Radiocarbon results from lakes through a wide range of hydrologic settings including Lake Albacutya, Glen Emu and Tyson Lake, as well as those in the Willandra system, are consistent in recording that lunette formation had ceased by 13,000 BP. Similarly in western Victoria, where lunettes were formerly regarded as having developed during the 'mid-Holocene arid period', recent evidence from Lake Corangamite indicates that here too dune formation occurred about 16,000 BP (GaK–3214, Gill, 1973b).

To explain the mechanism of clay dune formation in southeastern Australia Bowler (1973) postulated the existence of seasonally oscillating high salinity conditions. These existed during the transition from the earlier high lake levels to the dry phase that followed. The final drying allowed vegetation to colonise the lake floors, thus ending the deflationary phase. Thus by 13,000 BP the landscape and hydrologic systems of northern Victoria and western New South Wales and probably the entire region of the eastern semi-arid zone had assumed its main physical characters which have persisted with little change to the present day.

Hydrologic changes and lunette building in the southeast also have their counterparts in the southwest of Western Australia. There lakes with lunettes similar to those in New South Wales had a hydrologic history in which we have dated the final phase of lunette construction as having occurred between 18,000 to 14,000 BP. We are dealing with a continent-wide and, therefore, a climatically controlled event.

Desert or longitudinal dunes   The arid continental interior with its extensive array of seif dunes is surrounded by a perimeter of vegetated and stable quartz dunes. These extend into the semi-arid zone on both the southern and northern sides of the desert. Speculation still surrounds questions pertaining to the origin and last phase of activity of these fossil systems, the legacy of past periods of increased aridity. Whilst they have been correlated with the mid-Holocene arid period (Brown, 1945) some have related them to periods of glacial low sea-level. Thus Fairbridge (1961) recorded dunes running below sea-level onto the continental shelf of north-west Western Australia while Sprigg (1965), from evidence in coastal South Australia, postulated a low sea-level origin for similar dunes on the southern desert margin. Whilst corroborative evidence for these claims is not yet available, some support for Fairbridge's contention is provided by Jennings (1976) who has established the continuity of seif dunes at least 15 m below present high water in the Fitzroy estuary.

In western New South Wales continental dunes have encroached across the strandlines of some lakes in the Willandra system (Figure 3); here dated water level oscillations permit the age of dune activity to be established with a high degree of accuracy. The main field of linear dunes is of considerable antiquity and was certainly in existence before the period of Golgol deposition some 120,000 years ago. Churchward (1963) demonstrated that reactivation of the dunefield occurred during successive phases of aridity resulting in the addition of a new sand blanket over the pre-existing dune topography. In this way, a layered succession of buried soils was formed, often with little destruction or re-organisation of the previous topography.

In the extensive dunefield between the Lachlan and Darling Rivers (Figure 1) it is significant that, with the several important exceptions noted above, the linear or sub-parabolic dunes have not transgressed across dry lake floors despite the long period (at least 13,000 years) for which these lakes have been dry; little linear dune activity has occurred here since that time. However on two lakes, Outer Arumpo and Garnpung (Figure 3), lobes of sub-parabolic dunes have transgressed from west to east across the strandlines onto the floor of the lake basins. On Outer Arumpo the dunes lie on the intermediate terrace level; they did not extend into the younger

Chibnalwood basins etched into the floor of that system during the final drying phases. Thus the dunes are younger than the contraction of the lake from Outer Arumpo to Chibnalwood strandlines, an event that took place between 22,000 and 18,000 BP.

The transgressive dunes on the Outer Arumpo surface maintain an irregular, ragged leading edge indicating that they were not trimmed by water in the system. However those on Lake Garnpung have been modified by water in the lake. Here dunes with the same sub-parabolic form as those on Outer Arumpo have their easternmost advancing edges trimmed into a smooth outline indicating the presence of ephemeral water simultaneously with dune advance. The evidence in both sites is consistent with the last phase of dune building having occurred synchronously with the Zanci depositional phase, an event that came to an end about 15,000 BP. Thus the continental dunes were activated during the Mungo drying phase, perhaps as early as 25,000 BP, but their regional activity in this area terminated simultaneously with final drying of the Willandra system about 14,000 BP.

Aridity: summary of evidence   Drying of the lakes and construction of lunettes on their margins simultaneously with expansion of the southern margin of the desert dunes, represent a major change from the earlier wet phase towards one of relatively intense aridity. The climatic elements responsible for these conditions are still not understood. Rainfall was probably low over large regions of the southern continent, wind velocities were high but the pattern of temperature variations remains unresolved. It is no coincidence that these changes were synchronous with the shrinkage and eventual disappearance of permanent ice from the mountains. Evidence from other parts of the world would suggest this period, between 22,000 and 14,000 BP, was the coldest of late Quaternary time.

To dry the lakes during conditions of lowest temperatures would require a drop in precipitation to less than one third of present values. However, this proposition does not satisfactorily explain all the available evidence. The high production of gypsum in semi-arid zone lakes at this time requires high seasonal evaporation, a condition more consistent with rising temperatures than with reduced precipitation. Moreover, the disappearance of ice from effective snow catchments before 15,000 BP (e.g. Carruthers Creek: Costin, 1972) cannot be explained by low precipitation alone. Therefore summer temperatures in this southeastern part of Australia may already have been rising as early as 20,000 BP or even earlier. The resulting effect of increased evaporation, superimposed on a regime of low precipitation resulted in the phase of extreme aridity the equivalent of which has not been witnessed in southern Australia since 15,000 BP.

Results we have obtained recently from Lake Frome, South Australia, and data of Williams (1973) from Lake Torrens confirm that the effects of this change extended into the arid zone over the southern part of the continent. This then represents a major change in the regional environment—a change which would have imposed considerable stresses on almost every element in the landscape including Man. The expansion of the desert on its eastern margins at this time indicates that over large areas vegetation was sparse or even absent. Areas such as the continental interior that may previously have possessed meagre water resources may have become uninhabitable at this time of maximum aridity. Archaeological evidence from such regions spanning the period between 20,000 to 15,000 BP may be expected to provide data bearing on the extent and impact of these changes in the occupational and cultural record.

The period 15,000 to present

A slight amelioration in climate after 15,000 BP is suggested by the fixation of previously unstable dunes in the semi-arid zone. Westerly winds, which previously increased in strength and frequency, gradually moderated until by 10,000 BP both wind and temperature regimes on the western plains, and by analogy throughout the arid interior, were essentially those of today. Tasmania and the montane regions probably remained colder than present but the episode of major cold had already long since passed.

About 10,000 BP lakes in different climatic settings across the continent registered a change towards a wetter regime. In the southern humid region Lake Keilambete in western Victoria which had been dry before 10,000 rose to a high level (Bowler and Hamada, 1971) while on the Atherton Tableland the first appearance of rainforest elements is associated with an event of similar age (Kershaw, 1970). The evidence for similar changes in lakes of other continents (Butzer et al, 1972) points to a world-wide increase in precipitation about this time, probably resulting from increased surface temperatures of ocean waters simultaneously with sea-level rising to near its present position. Assuming temperatures were close to those of today, an increase of 12–15 per cent in mean annual precipitation would be sufficient to explain the rise recorded in Lake Keilambete.

This wetter situation persisted until 5500 BP when Lake Keilambete began to fall, reaching its minimum level at 3100 BP. Subsequently the hydrologic and sedimentary records are consistent with the climate being dry and rather similar to that of today until 1900 BP when the levels again rose. Following a substantial drop since 1850 Lake Keilambete stands today near the lowest level recorded throughout the past 10,000 years.

The evidence therefore suggests climatic oscillations diminishing in magnitude since the major events of 15,000 BP and earlier. Hydrologic oscillations since that time have been too small to maintain lakes in the semi-arid zone in any but an ephemeral condition. The changes recorded throughout this period would pose little if any difficulty to Man in adjusting to the stresses involved.

Discussion

No matter which northern land mass provided the first immigrants to settle this continent, the range of climatic and ecologic environments they and their descendants encountered on arrival was much greater than differences between their points of origin and landfall. This situation would have existed at any time throughout the Pleistocene period. We have seen that Man had already traversed the continent by 36,000 BP and in doing so would have encountered and adapted to a range of physical and climatic conditions equal to those in existence today. The types of climatic changes experienced in late Quaternary time were superimposed on this wide spectrum of conditions already present on the continent. Of the two major Quaternary changes, increased aridity and the introduction of cold periglacial conditions, the former represented extension of environments already well developed while the latter records the development of a new climatic barrier.

Throughout the major cold phase, whilst the present diversity of physiographic and hydrologic regimes would have been retained though somewhat displaced from present zonal boundaries, new ones were added. Tropical savannah and woodland elements of northern Australia may have been compressed northwards to the open Sahul Shelf (Nix and Kalma, 1972) while the dry desertic zones of high insolation north of latitude 29° either remained or were extended northwards. However, new environments were introduced into those areas of high altitude and latitude. Extensive areas of the southeastern highlands and Tasmania coming under the influence of periglacial activity posed new ecologic barriers to Man. In their range, the new physical environments would be analogous to 'stretching' the southern continental margin southwards by 10° latitude. Tasmania (lat. 42–44°) would then have been in a position equivalent to Tierra del Fuego today. A drop in mean annual temperatures of 5–6° would make Hobart's Pleistocene climatic regime almost identical with that of Punta Arenas (Lat. 53°S).

Thus, in addition to the range of habitats available today, Man at 30,000 was confronted by a new problem. Having successfully adapted to the continental range of environments through the tropics and arid core to the southern wet zones, he now found himself facing a new barrier, one of intense cold. The long period of climatic deterioration with the slow, almost imperceptible but inexorable spread of cold inhospitable environments would have encouraged a drift away from the hillslopes of the southeast, to the warmer inland plains or sheltered coastal valleys. The wealth of ancient occupational evidence from the climatically more benign lowland sites at Lake Mungo and Keilor contrast markedly with the absence of such evidence from areas of even moderate relief near the foothills. Flood's evidence at Buchan (elevation 76 m) where Man's late appearance in the record about 18,000 BP (Flood, 1973, 1974) provides an important indication of his late occupation that may set a pattern to be expected throughout other sites of intermediate altitude in the southeast.

The emerging picture of late Quaternary Australia is one of a land whose environments exhibited a wide degree of plasticity in response to global climatic changes. Thus the arid continental core remained relatively arid throughout; correspondingly some high rainfall areas, although experiencing a substantial lowering of precipitation due to combined effects of low sea-level and low atmospheric moisture content, retained a water balance rather similar to that of today. The greatest mobility occurred in the climatically sensitive semi-arid zones and in those montane regions of the south where reduced temperatures introduced new periglacial processes. The range of changes introduced outside these two regions was probably well within the ability of Man to adapt to them; but within these regions the changes would probably have been sufficient to induce significant and, hopefully, detectable changes in the distribution and adaptation of human populations. In the semi-arid zone the alternation of periods of increased productivity with more desertic conditions would have imposed considerable stresses on the population. In the Darling River region, despite the probability of such stresses, the human economy survived these events relatively unchanged for more than 30,000 years (Allen, 1972). However, in areas affected by periglacial conditions and in the more arid regions migration and cultural adaptation may have been accelerated; in one case by the development of cold conditions and in the other by increased aridity. Final judgement on the impact of these changes must await further evidence from the archaeological record.

References

ALLEN, H.   1972   *Where the crow flies backwards*. Ph.D. Thesis, Australian National University, Canberra.

BARBETTI, M. and H. ALLEN   1972   Prehistoric man at Lake Mungo, Australia by 32000 years B.P. *Nature*, 240:46–48.

—— and H. POLACH   1973   Australian National University Radiocarbon Date-list V. *Radiocarbon*, 15:241–51.

BOWLER, J. M.   1970   Lake Nitchie skeleton: stratigraphy of the burial. *Archaeology and Physical Anthropology in Oceania*, 5:102–13.

——   1971   Pleistocene salinities and climatic change: evidence from lakes and lunettes in southeastern Australia. In *Aboriginal man and environment in Australia*, D. J. Mulvaney and J. Golson (eds), pp. 46–65. Australian National University Press, Canberra.

——   1973   Clay dunes, their occurrence and environmental significance. *Earth Science Review*, 9:315–38.

——, R. JONES, H. ALLEN and A. G. THORNE   1970   Pleistocene human remains from Australia: a living site and human cremation from Lake Mungo western New South Wales. *World Archaeology*, 1:39–60.

——, A. G. THORNE and H. A. POLACH   1972   Pleistocene man in Australia: age and significance of the Mungo skeleton. *Nature*, 240:48–50.

——, D. J. MULVANEY, D. A. CASEY and T. A. DARRAGH   1967   The Green Gully burial. *Nature*, 213:152–54.

—— and T. HAMADA   1971   Late Quaternary stratigraphy and radiocarbon chronology of water level fluctuations in Lake Keilambete, Victoria. *Nature*, 232:330–32.

BROWN, W. R.   1945   An attempted post-Tertiary chronology of Australia. *Proceedings of the Linnean Society New South Wales*, 70: 5–24.

BUTZER, K. W., G. L. ISAAC, J. L. RICHARDSON and C. WASHBOURN-KAMAU   1972   Radiocarbon dating of East African lake levels. *Science*, 175:1069–76.

CAINE, N. and J. N. JENNINGS   1968   Some blockstreams of the Toolong Range, Kosciusko State Park, N.S.W. *Journal of the Royal Society of New South Wales*, 101: 93–103.

CAMPBELL, V.   1972   Some radiocarbon dates for Aboriginal shell middens in the Lower Macleay river valley, New South Wales. *Mankind*, 8:283–86.

CHAPPELL, J. 1974 Geology of coral terraces, Huon Peninsula, New Guinea: a study of Quaternary tectonic movements and sea-level changes. *Geological Society of America Bulletin*, 85:553–70.

CHURCHWARD, H. M. 1963 Soil studies at Swan Hill, Victoria, Australia. IV. Ground-surface history and its expression in the array of soils. *Australian Journal of Soil Research*, 1:242–55.

COSTIN, A. B. 1972 Carbon-14 dates from the Snowy Mountains area, South-eastern Australia, and their interpretation. *Quaternary Research*, 2:579–90.

—— and H. A. POLACH 1973 Age and significance of slope deposits, Black Mountain, Canberra. *Australian Journal of Soil Research*, 111:13–25.

DODSON, J. 1974 Vegetation history and water level fluctuations at Lake Leake, south-eastern South Australia. 1. 10,000 B.P. to present. *Australian Journal of Botany*, 22:719–46.

—— and I. B. WILSON 1975 The past and present vegetation of Marshes Swamp in South-east South Australia. *Australian Journal of Botany*, 23:123–50.

DORTCH, C. E. and D. MERRILEES 1973 Human occupation of Devil's Lair during the Pleistocene. *Archaeology and Physical Anthropology in Oceania*, 8:98–115.

DURY, G. H. 1973 Paleohydrologic implications of some pluvial lakes in north western New South Wales, Australia. *Geology Society of America Bulletin*, 84:3663–76.

FAIRBRIDGE, R. W. 1961 Eustatic changes in sea level. *Physics and Chemistry of the Earth*, 4:99–185.

FLOOD, J. 1973 Pleistocene human occupation and extinct fauna in Cloggs Cave, Buchan, south-east Australia. *Nature*, 246:303.

—— 1974 Pleistocene Man at Clogg's Cave: his tool kit and environment. *Mankind*, 9:175–88.

GALLOWAY, R. W. 1963 Glaciations in the Snowy Mountains; a re-appraisal. *Linnean Society of New South Wales Proceedings*, 88:180–98.

—— 1965 Late Quaternary climates in Australia. *Journal of Geology*, 73:603–18.

—— 1971 Evidence for Late Quaternary climates. In *Aboriginal man and environment in Australia*, D. J. Mulvaney and J. Golson (eds), pp. 14–25. Australian National University Press, Canberra.

GALLUS, A. 1971 Excavations at Keilor, report No. 1. *The Artefact*, 24:1–12.

GILL, E. D. 1957 Current Quaternary studies in Victoria, Australia. *International Association of Quaternary Research*, 5th Congress, Madrid: 1–7.

—— 1966 Provenance and age of the Keilor cranium: oldest known human skeletal remains in Australia. *Current Anthropology*, 7:581–84.

—— 1971 Applications of radiocarbon dating in Victoria, Australia. *Proceedings of the Royal Society of Victoria*, 84:71–85.

—— 1973a Geology and geomorphology of the Murray River region between Mildura and Renmark, Australia. *Memoirs of the National Museum, Victoria*, 34:1–97.

—— 1973b Second list of radiocarbon dates on samples from Victoria, Australia. *Proceedings of the Royal Society of Victoria*, 86:133–36.

HOPE, J. H. 1973 Analysis of bone from Clogg's Cave, Buchan, N.E. Victoria. *Appendix XIV in Thesis by J. Flood*, Australian National University, Canberra.

JENNINGS, J. N. 1976 Desert dunes and estuarine fill in the Fitzroy estuary north-western Australia. *Catena* (in press).

JONES, R. 1968 Geographical background to the arrival of Man in Australia and Tasmania. *Archaeology and Physical Anthropology in Oceania*, 3:186–215.

—— 1971 *Rocky Cape and the problems of the Tasmanians*. Ph.D. thesis, University of Sydney (in press)

—— 1975 The Neolithic, Palaeolithic and the hunting gardeners: Man and land in the Antipodes. In *Quaternary Studies*, R. P. Suggate and M. Cresswell (eds) pp. 21–34. The Royal Society of New Zealand, Wellington.

KERSHAW, A. P. 1970 A pollen diagram from Lake Euramoo, north-east Queensland, Australia. *New Phytologist*, 69:785–805.

—— 1971 A pollen diagram from Quincan Crater, north-east Queensland, Australia. *New Phytologist*, 70:699–81.

—— 1974 A long continuous pollen sequence from north-eastern Australia. *Nature*, 251:222–23.

LAKE, J. S. 1967 Rearing experiments with five species of Australian freshwater fishes. *Australian Journal of Marine and Freshwater Research*, 18:137–53.

LAMPERT, R. J. 1971a Coastal Aborigines of southeastern Australia. In *Aboriginal man and environment in Australia*, D. J. Mulvaney and J. Golson (eds), pp. 114–32. Australian National University Press, Canberra.
—— 1971b Burril Lake and Currarong. *Terra Australis*, 1:1–86.
LANGFORD-SMITH, T. B. and B. G. THOM 1969 New South Wales coastal morphology. *Journal of the Geological Society of Australia*, 16:572–80.
LITCHFIELD, W. H. 1969 Soil surfaces and sedimentary history near the Macdonell Ranges. *Northern Territory Soil Publications, CSIRO, Australia*, No. 25.
MACINTOSH, N. W. G., K. N. SMITH and A. B. BAILEY 1970 Lake Nitchie skeleton: unique Aboriginal burial. *Archaeology and Physical Anthropology in Oceania*, 5:85–101.
MARSHALL, L. G. 1973 Fossil vertebrate faunas from the Lake Victoria region SW New South Wales, Australia. *Memoirs of the National Museum, Victoria*, 34:151–71.
—— 1974 Late Pleistocene mammals from the 'Keilor Cranium Site', southern Victoria, Australia. *Memoirs of the National Museum, Victoria*, 35:63–86.
MARTIN, H. A. 1973 Palynology and historical ecology of some cave excavations in the Australian Nullarbor. *Australian Journal of Botany*, 21:283–316.
MERRILEES, D. 1968 Man the destroyer: Late Quaternary changes in the Australian marsupial fauna. *Journal of the Proceedings of the Royal Society of W.A.*, 51:1–24
NICHOLLS, K. D. 1958 Aeolian deposits in river valleys in Tasmania. *Australian Journal of Science*, 21:56–7.
NIX, H. A. and J. D. KALMA 1972 Climate as a dominant control in the biogeography of northern Australia and New Guinea. In *Bridge and barrier: the natural and cultural history of Torres Strait*, D. Walker (ed), pp. 61–92. Australian National University Press, Canberra.
PETERSON, J. A. 1971 The equivocal extent of glaciation in the southeastern uplands of Australia. *Proceedings of the Royal Society of Victoria*, 84:207–11.
SPRIGG, R. G. 1965 The nature and origin of modern deserts. *Australian Museum Magazine*, 71:207–11.
TEDFORD, R. H. 1967 The fossil Macropodidae from Lake Menindee, New South Wales. *University of California Publications of the Geological Society*, 64:1–156.
THOM, B. G. 1973 The dilemma of high interstadial sea levels during the last glaciation. *Progress in Geography*, 5:167–246.
WAKEFIELD, N. A. 1967 Preliminary report on McEachern's Cave, S.W. Victoria. *Victorian Naturalist*, 84:363–83.
—— 1972 Palaeoecology of fossil mammal assemblages from some Australian caves. *Proceedings of the Royal Society of Victoria*, 85:1–26.
WILLIAMS, G. E. 1973 Late Quaternary piedmont sedimentation, soil formation and paleoclimates in arid South Australia. *Zeitschrift für Geomorphologie*, 17:102–25.

Early Man in Australia

Early populations in the Indonesian region

Teuku Jacob

THE EARLIEST EVIDENCE of hominines in Indonesia comes from lower Pleistocene deposits in Java. Although there are Pliocene sites which yield mammalian remains, no hominid fossils have ever been reported from that epoch.

The earliest date we have stems from the Puchangan formation near Mojokerto, east Java, from a level a few metres below the site where a juvenile pithecanthropine skull was recovered in 1936. It should be understood in this connection that the Puchangan formation in this area is about 200 m thick. The date obtained is 1·9 million years BP, determined from two available sample results from the site (Curtis, pers. comm.; Jacob, 1972).

The next oldest dates are in the range of 781,000–908,000 years ago, with an average of 830,000 years, indicating especially the antiquity of Sangiran 10 and 12 (the skull caps of 1963 and 1965). The pumice samples, dated by the potassium-argon method, were obtained from above, below and at the level of Sangiran 10, and from above the level of Sangiran 12, at Tanjung and Puchung respectively, south of the Chemoro River in the Sangiran dome area of central Java (Curtis, pers. comm.; Jacob, 1973c).

Tektites found at Sangiran, supposedly in the Kabuh formation, have an antiquity of around 710,000 years (von Koenigswald, 1964), and a date obtained from basalt from Mount Muria near Patiayam, central Java, overlying the Trinil bone beds, is about 500,000 years (von Koenigswald, 1968). The latter indicates the minimum antiquity of the Trinil fauna.

No other dates are available for the Pleistocene or early Holocene of Indonesia. The radiocarbon dates we have are for the Epipaleolithic Age and later, and are less than 4000 years.

The hominine fossils recovered from central and east Java in the last 85 years are listed in Table 1. It is evident that we have Meganthropus and *Pithecanthropus* remains from the lower and middle Pleistocene (if the boundary is placed at around one million years ago), and *Pithecanthropus* and *Homo sapiens* remains from the upper Pleistocene. If *Pithecanthropus* is divided into three groups (species or subspecies of *erectus*), namely *modjokertensis*, *erectus* and *soloensis*, then we have in the lower Pleistocene *modjokertensis* (and

Table 1: Hominine fossils from Indonesia grouped according to antiquity and sites

Site	Number	Discovered	Description of fossil
		Lower Pleistocene	
Perning	1	1936	Calvaria, juvenile
Sangiran	1	1936	Lower and upper jaw fragments
	4	1938–39	Calvaria
	5	1939	Lower jaw fragment
	6	1941	Lower jaw fragments
	7	1937–41	Teeth
	9	1960	Lower jaw fragment
		Middle Pleistocene	
Sambungmachan	1	1973	Skull cap
Sangiran	2	1937	Skull cap
	3	1938	Skull cap
	7	1937–41	Teeth
	8	1952	Lower jaw
	10	1963	Skull cap, cheekbone
	11	1963	Teeth
	12	1965	Skull cap
	13	1965	Cranial fragments
	14	1966	Cranial base fragments
	15	1968–69	Upper jaw fragments
	16	1969	Teeth
	17	1969	Calvaria
	18	1970	Cranial fragments
	19	1970	Occipital fragment
	20	1971	Cranial fragments
Kedungbrubus	1	1890	Lower jaw fragment, juvenile
Trinil	1	1890	Molars
	2	1891	Skull cap
	3	1892	Thighbone
	4	1900	Thighbone fragment
	5	1900	Thighbone fragments
	6	1900	Thighbone fragment
		Upper Pleistocene	
Ngandong	1	1931	Skull cap
	2	1931	Frontal bone, juvenile
	3	1931	Skull cap
	4	1931	Parietal fragment
	5	1932	Skull cap
	6	1932	Skull cap
	7	1932	Calvaria
	8	1932	Parietal fragment
	9	1932	Tibia
	10	1933	Tibia
	11	1933	Parietal bones
	12	1933	Skull cap
	13	1933	Skull cap
	14	1933	Calvaria
Wajak	1	1889	Cranium, neck vertebra
	2	1890	Cranial fragments, jaws, teeth, thighbone, tibia

Meganthropus), in the middle Pleistocene *erectus* and *soloensis* (and Megan-thropus), and in the upper Pleistocene *soloensis* (and *Homo sapiens*) (Jacob, 1973a).

The boundary between the Puchangan and Kabuh formations may not reflect the junction of the lower and middle Pleistocene as part of the Kabuh formation may belong to the lower Pleistocene. However, this depends on where the boundary between the lower and middle Pleistocene is placed in the geological time frame.

With regard to the meganthropines we cannot say very much at present. The only evidence we have consists of jaw fragments, three mandibular and one maxillary, with teeth. We know that they had big teeth and massive mandibles which had neither a chin nor a simian shelf. Some authors group them with the australopithecines, while others believe they are pithecan-thropines. If they belong to the latter, it should be to the robust pithecanthropines, probably to *soloensis*. But we would be more convinced, one way or the other, if meganthropine mandibles were found associated with their skulls.

In this regard, it should be remembered that no fossil mandibles have ever been discovered in association with skulls in Java. Mandibles, as we know, are very variable in shape and this fact is clearly demonstrated by the mandibular fragments found in the Puchangan and Kabuh formations of Sangiran (von Koenigswald, 1973). The first mandible (Kedungbrubus 1) is juvenile and cannot be directly compared with the other adult mandibles. Sangiran 1, 5 and 9 (see Jacob, 1973c for the code numbers), for example, show some differences, but all of them have a thick alveolar process, and a relatively thin base. In all cases the ascending ramus has not been preserved.

The body of meganthropine mandibles, on the other hand, is thick throughout, from the alveolar border to the base. As mentioned above, their cheek teeth are much larger. Wrinkling of the molar occlusal surface seems to be more pronounced in Meganthropus, which occasionally makes their molars difficult to distinguish from those of *Pongo*.

According to von Koenigswald (1973) the mandibular second deciduous molar in Meganthropus has pointed cusps and the talonid is sharply separated from the trigonid where a paraconid is still present.

Because of the scarcity of evidence I prefer to postpone the taxonomic diagnosis of meganthropine specimens until we have more of their fossils, particularly skulls. When more material becomes available we may assign them to *Australopithecus* or *Pithecanthropus*, or to a genus of their own. We know that these three groups are contemporaneous, at least for a certain period of time.

Pithecanthropine traits and variations
In the following discussion the term *Pithecanthropus* refers to the group of hominines now widely known as *Homo erectus*. They constitute a distinct group relative to modern man or Neanderthal man. Whether the differences are at the generic, specific, racial or subracial level is at the moment still a

matter of taste and convenience since we do not know very much about the total biological pattern of *Pithecanthropus* and Neanderthal man. What we know is just the 'total' morphological pattern of fragmentary skeletal parts; this is particularly true of the first-mentioned group. Of course, many of the differences are continuous and gradual, and transitional forms are always present, but these arguments are applicable throughout the range of taxonomic hierarchy and biological phenomena. Sharp boundaries never exist in nature and all classifications are artificial. Classification, however, is needed in all fields of science to facilitate analysis.

The characteristics of pithecanthropines are as follows (Jacob 1971, 1973b):

1. a broad-based skull which is low and long, with a cranial capacity of 800–1300 cc;
2. small and quadrangular parietal bones with marked sagittal angulation and parasagittal flatness or depression;
3. low and triangular temporal squama;
4. low and receding forehead with pronounced post-orbital constriction;
5. low occipital plane separated by an occipital torus from the extensive nuchal plane;
6. tegmen pori acustici (supraauricular tegmen);
7. absence of the foramen lacerum and petrooccipital fissure;
8. angulated petrotympanic axis; tympanic plate oriented in an oblique or horizontal plane;
9. absence of the vaginal crest;
10. the discrepancy between the internal and external occipital protuberances;
11. large posterior branch of the middle meningeal artery, branching off at a low level;
12. thick vault bones;
13. clivus not vertical, and sphenoid body exposed in basal view;
14. horizontal or less curved supra-orbital torus ending in a lateral wing;
15. relative posterior position of the foramen magnum;
16. large cheek teeth;
17. thick alveolar processes of the jaws;
18. strong lateral torus and symphyseal transverse tori of the mandible, but no chin;
19. absence of canine fossa;
20. broad nasal root.

These traits are found consistently in all specimens available. Variations, of course, are present in some traits, but the total pattern of the pithecanthropine skull is readily recognisable even by the naked brain. A group of traits is closely related to the relative underdevelopment of the cerebral cortex, and another with the massive development of the masticatory apparatus. Still another group of traits is related to the position of the skull on the vertebral column.

Indonesian pithecanthropine finds can be classified into two groups—the gracile and the robust. The first-mentioned include the Trinil fossils and most of the fossils from the Kabuh formation of Sangiran. The robust ones comprise the fossils from the Puchangan formation of Sangiran, from the lower beds of the Kabuh formation of Sangiran and Sambungmachan (Sragen, central Java), and from Ngandong (east Java) (Jacob, 1973b).

Gracile pithecanthropines have a smaller cranial capacity (800–1000 cc), parasagittal depressions, a continuous supra-orbital torus, small zygomatic bones, small mastoid processes, rounded occipital torus, no external occipital crest, no suprameatal spine, and the squamotympanic fissure is located on the posterior wall of the mandibular fossa.

Robust pithecanthropines have a larger cranial capacity (900–1300 cc), parasagittal flatness, supraglabellar disintegration of the supra-orbital torus, robust zygomatic bones, large mastoid processes, an occipital torus with a sharp inferior border, triangular prominence and external occipital crest, suprameatal spine, more pronounced supramastoid crests, more developed frontal region and more curved squamosal suture, and large external acoustic porus, while the squamotympanic fissure is located along the apex of the mandibular fossa.

The Mojokerto and Kedungbrubus specimens are juvenile and difficult to assign to either the gracile or the robust. It is possible that the Mojokerto skull belongs to the robust type considering its antiquity, the size of its braincase and the growth rate of the skull in recent man. The absence of the gracile type in the Puchangan formation is another reason why it should be grouped among the robust. The Kedungbrubus mandible is more difficult to assign because, as mentioned earlier, mandibles have never been associated with skulls.

It is interesting that the robust pithecanthropines are found in the lower, middle and upper Pleistocene, whereas the gracile ones, as far as evidence goes, are found only in the middle Pleistocene. However, the early robust types are slightly different from the late robust. The first group is sometimes called *Pithecanthropus modjokertensis* after the *juvenile* holotype from Kepuh-klagen, near Mojokerto. The only adult skull belonging to this group is Sangiran 4. It has a cranial capacity of about 900 cc, no triangular prominence or external occipital crest, and an elliptical, thin-walled external acoustic porus.

The late robust group, named *P. soloensis*, is characterised by a larger cranial capacity which, among other things, is reflected in a larger frontal, temporal, parietal and occipital regions, a triangular prominence and external occipital crest, slightly larger mastoid processes, a round external acoustic porus, and an oval foramen that lies in a fossa with an accessory foramen (Table 2).

Questions certainly arise as to whether the robust types are not simply male or adult specimens, and the gracile female or juvenile. One can also question whether *modjokertensis* and *soloensis* do not belong to just one group.

Table 2: Cranial dimensions of *Pithecanthropus soloensis* (in mm)*

Measurement	Sangiran 17	Sambung-machan 1	Ngandong 1	Ngandong 7
Cranial breadth	160	151	148	144
Cranial length	208	199	196	192·5
Cranial index	76·9	75·9	75·6	75·3
Cranial capacity (in cc)	1125	1035	1140	1190
Minimum frontal breadth	103	106	105	106
Transverse frontoparietal index	64·4	70·2	70·9	73·6
Biparietal breadth	120	121	116	113
Parietobasal index†	75	80·1	78·4	78·5
Interporion distance	133	119	127	120
Transverse arc	290	300		293
Transverse curvature index	45·9	39·7		40·1
Nasion-opisthion cord	150?		143	151
Nasion-opisthion arc	359		360	342
Total sagittal curvature index	41·8		39·4	44·2
Lambda-inion cord	69	59	57	59
Lambda-opisthion cord	93		81	85
Lambda-opisthion arc	142		108	111
Occipital sagittal curvature index	65·5		72·3	74·6
Ectinion-entinion distance	30	27	32	
Length of foramen magnum	37?			41
Breadth of foramen magnum	29			31·5
Basion-hormion distance	28			34·5
Breadth of basilar portion	23			24·5

* Compiled from Jacob (1967, 1973b).
† Ratio of distance between the parietal bosses and maximum cranial breadth.

The first question is answered by available evidence: we have both sexes and both the young and adult in the robust and gracile groups (Jacob, 1973a). Also, it is very curious indeed if at Ngandong only male or adult specimens are found, while in the Kabuh formation of Sangiran mostly the female or the juvenile were deposited. The second question is more difficult to deal with; what we need are more specimens of *modjokertensis* from the lower Pleistocene in order to appreciate their range of variation.

A closer affinity seems to exist between *P. modjokertensis* and *P. soloensis* relative to *P. erectus*. We could best explain this situation if we had absolute dates for Ngandong and Sambungmachan, and if mandibles were found in association with skulls to elucidate the affinities of the variable Sangiran mandibles.

The antiquity of Ngandong is still unsolved. Statistical studies of the cranial capacity of Ngandong man (Lestrel and Read, 1973) locate him around 265,000 years ago. This estimate might be correct considering his close affinity to other pithecanthropines (Jacob, 1967) and the discoveries of Sangiran 17 and Sambungmachan 1 in the Kabuh formation. These two specimens are very similar to the Ngandong skulls in many respects, such as the general size and shape of the skull, the skull contours in all views, the supra-orbital torus, the ear region, the occipital torus and the nuchal area, and the cranial base. Sambungmachan 1, for example, is very similar to Ngandong 1 or 7 (Jacob, 1973b). Details of this skull are shown in Figures 1, 2 and 3.

Figure 1   Occipital view of Sangiran 10 (left) and Sambungmachan 1. In both skulls the points of maximum breadth are located near the base. The smaller Sangiran 10 skull has parasagittal depressions lateral to the sagittal torus, and a mound-shaped occipital torus, while the larger Sambungmachan 1 skull has parasagittal flatness and a crested occipital torus with a triangular prominence.

Figure 2   Basal view of Sambungmachan 1. The triangular prominence is clearly observable. Fresh breaks are present posteriorly, on the orbital roof anteriorly and near the left (preserved) foramen spinosum.

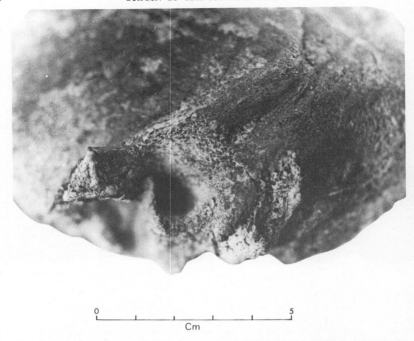

Figure 3 Detail of the left ear region of Sambungmachan 1. Note the *tegmen pori acustici*, the tympanic plate, the suprameatal spine and the (broken) mastoid process.

Figure 4 Detail of the left mandibular fossa of Sambungmachan 1. The squamotympanic fissure is located at the apex of the fossa and runs parallel to its transverse axis.

Figure 5 Right lateral view of Sambungmachan 1. The characteristic regions are the frontal, the nuchal and the ear regions.

Early *Homo* **and evolution**

For several reasons the pithecanthropines cannot be classified into the genus *Homo*. When the spirit of the time is strongly inclined toward lumping, it is very unpopular and untactful to say this. However, one cannot but notice that the cerebral cortex in *Pithecanthropus* is not well developed: the maximum breadth of the skull is still at the base, the frontal, parietal and temporal lobes are small and have few gyri and sulci, and likewise, the cerebellum is small. Of course, there is no question that they are more developed than in the australopithecines. The relatively small size of the anterior branch of the middle meningeal artery also indicates the underdevelopment of the frontal lobe (or the meninges covering it). In short, the higher functions of the brain are not developed.

Language, another important characteristic of *Homo*, is similarly not developed in *Pithecanthropus*. Not only are the three above-mentioned lobes of the brain, which are closely related to articulate speech, still small, but also the skeletal requirements to produce it are lacking (Lancaster, 1966; Lieberman and Crelin, 1971). The cranial anatomy directly linked to the vocal tract is more primitive in *Pithecanthropus* than in Neanderthal man. The clivus is not steep or vertical as in modern man, and the position of the skull on the cervical vertebrae is still primitive as revealed by the position and shape of the foramen magnum and the nuchal area (Jacob, 1967). The distance between basion and staphylion is great. Not only is the basilar portion of the occipital bone long, but also the sphenoid body. Consequently the roof of the nasopharynx is long, unlike the condition in adult modern man.

The small cortex and the limitation in communication by language would result in differences in ways of exploiting the environment relative to modern man. The nature of locomotion is not well established. According to Dubois (1932, 1934), among others, the femoral vasti muscles are very strong in *Pithecanthropus* and his 'upper limb was not quite liberated from locomotor function'. Day and Molleson (1973), on the other hand, come to the conclusion that the differences between the Trinil and modern human femora are not significant, but have some reservations about the association of the Trinil femora with *Pithecanthropus*. In addition, stone tools have never been found associated with Indonesian pithecanthropine fossils except with *P. soloensis*. To be sure, nobody denies that they used and made tools. But without articulate speech and perhaps complete freedom of the hands, progress in tool making and social organisation, two other important characteristics of *Homo*, would have been very slow.

All the points mentioned above reflect genetic differences between *Pithecanthropus* and *Homo*. Many other morphological differences presented earlier in this paper, including the discontinuous traits on the cranial base, mirrored differences in genetic constitution. As pointed out by Berry and Berry (1971), these polygenic traits characterise a large part of the genome; the accessory oval foramen in *P. soloensis*, for example, does not merely reflect genetic variation affecting the skull, but also variation affecting the vascular system. Incidentally, the location of the oval foramen with its accessory foramen in a common fossa, in Ngandong man, is unique.

Furthermore, we have no idea about the karyotype of *Pithecanthropus*, just as we are ignorant about the many other distinguishing criteria commonly used in classifying the living Primates. External characters, for example, are important in this regard. As stated previously, what we should know for a satisfactory classification is the total biological pattern, not merely some serological, biochemical, physiological, morphological, ecological or cultural data.

If, in the future, *Pithecanthropus* remains of a later period are discovered, we expect that they would look more like *Homo*, since at a certain point in geological time *Pithecanthropus* and *Homo* should appear as congeneric. At that time point there was no reproductive isolating mechanism operating between the two because the former was anagenetically evolving into the latter. In this 'twilight zone', in fact, the offspring of *Pithecanthropus* might and could be classified as *Homo*. Even two skeletal fragments of the same individual, found at different times, may be assigned to different genera. At present, however, no such fossils have been found in Indonesia.

The earliest *Homo* remains we have from South East Asia are Wajak, Niah and Tabon. It is very unfortunate that we do not have a chronometric date for Wajak. As for relative dating, we have results of fluorine, uranium and nitrogen tests. Fluorine tests of Wajak 1 by the British Museum (Natural History) gave the following results: $F = 0 \cdot 53$ per cent and $100F/P_2O_5 = 8 \cdot 28$ (T. Molleson, pers. comm.). Earlier tests done by the Technical University at Delft resulted in $F = 0 \cdot 038-0 \cdot 63$ per cent for Wajak 1 and $F = 0 \cdot 25-0 \cdot 29$ per cent for Wajak 2 (Bergman and Karsten, 1952). Other tests by the BMNH gave $eU_3O_8 = 0$ for Wajak 1 and 2 ppm for Wajak 2; N is $0 \cdot 38$ per cent for Wajak 1 and nil for Wajak 2. Dubois (1920) noted that there was very little organic material in the Wajak fossil bones.

The antiquity of Wajak would be, I think, similar to, if not more than, the antiquity of Niah or Tabon. The fossil Wajak specimens are no doubt *Homo sapiens*, but it is difficult to assign them to a group of living races. The living races as we know now have probably been present since only 10,000 years ago, at least as far as the evidence we have in South East Asia is available.

It is very interesting to note here that many skulls of early *Homo sapiens* exhibit some Australoid features, or more precisely, are described as Australoid, such as the Chou-kou-tien Upper Cave, Florisbad, Cape Flats, Saldanha, etc. This might be simply due to attempts at description (Howells, 1973), or the remains may have real affinity with the Australoids. But it is also possible that because the Australoid retains many archaic features, many upper Paleolithic skulls have some resemblance to the Australoid.

The Wajak skulls also display Australoid features: a long, almost dolichocranic skull divided by a sagittal keel, an occipital bulge, a flat nuchal area, strong superciliary arches, a heavy mandible, a large and deep palate with omega-shaped dental arch and large teeth. But on the other hand, Wajak shows many Mongoloid features like a very flat face, which is also broad due to the laterally projecting cheekbones, a broad nasal root without a nasion notch, alveolar prognathism, and a large cranial capacity (Jacob, 1967). It is also possible to argue that the archaic feature of facial flatness of Chou-kou-tien Upper Cave and Wajak is retained by the Mongoloid (Oschinsky *et al*, 1964).

Niah has a deep nasion notch, a vertical forehead, an occipital torus, a small and shallow palate, and rather large teeth. The skull is juvenile however.

In my opinion it is possible that Wajak did contribute his genes to the people of South East Asia and Australia, but he is not the direct ancestor of the living Australoids. It seems that the Australoids as we know now evolved in Australia from a common ancestor with the Melanesoids. Migration to Australia did not occur, of course, on just one occasion. The earliest one should be somewhere between the times of Ngandong and Wajak man, perhaps around 70,000 years ago. I have some reservation about pithecanthropines migrating to Melanesia or Australia. That some pithecanthropine genes were inherited by the earliest migrants is a strong possibility. These populations lived in South East Asia around 100,000 to 50,000 years ago, and their remains are waiting to be discovered.

The evolution from *Pithecanthropus* to *Homo* involves not only the supraorbital torus or the vault bone thickness, but many other morphological complexes, and hence, many gene complexes and environmental conditions played a part in the process, so that between the two groups we observe and postulate differences in size and organisation of the cerebral cortex, capacity for articulate speech, social organisation, environmental adaptation, growth characteristics, and perhaps locomotor behaviour.

Migration to Australia took place after the population had evolved into *Homo*, and most probably *H. sapiens*. This population might have inherited some genes from the pithecanthropines. Discovery of *Homo* remains, the palaeoanthropological hardware, of greater antiquity than have ever been found in South East Asia, is necessary to fill the existing gap in the fossil record between *P. soloensis* and the first *H. sapiens* in this crucial region. Before this happens we can only produce hypotheses, the palaeoanthropological software, as numerous as we want to.

Acknowledgement   This study is supported by a grant from the Directorate of Higher Education, Department of Education and Culture Jakarta.

References

BERGMAN, R. A. M. and P. KARSTEN   1952 The fluorine content of Pithecanthropus and of other specimens from the Trinil fauna. *Proceedings, Koninklijke Nederlandse Akademie van Wetenschappen*, ser. B, 55(2):150–52.
BERRY, A. C. and R. J. BERRY   1971 Epigenetic polymorphism in the primate skeleton. In *Comparative genetics in monkeys, apes and man*, A. B. Chiarelli (ed), pp. 13–41. Academic Press, London.

DAY, M. H. and T. I. MOLLESON   1973   The Trinil femora. In *Human evolution*, M. H. Day (ed), pp. 127–54. Taylor and Francis Limited, London.

DUBOIS, E.   1920   De proto-Australische fossiele mensch van Wadjak, Java, II. *Proceedings, Koninklijke Akademie van Wetenschappen*, 29:866–87.

——   1932   The distinct organisation of Pithecanthropus of which the femur bears evidence, now confirmed from other individuals of the described species. *Proceedings, Koninklijke Akademie van Wetenschappen*, 35(6):716–22.

——   1934   New evidence of the distinct organisation of Pithecanthropus. *Proceedings. Koninklijke akademie van Wetenschappen*, 37(3):139–45.

HOWELLS, W. W.   1973   *Evolution of the genus Homo*. Addison-Wesley Publishing Company, Reading, Massachusetts.

JACOB, T.   1967   *Some problems pertaining to the racial history of the Indonesian region*. Neerlandia, Utrecht.

——   1971   Diagnosis Pithecanthropus. *Gadjah Mada Journal of Medical Science*, 3(3):191–200.

——   1972   The absolute date of the Djetis beds at Modjokerto. *Antiquity*, 47: 148.

——   1973a   New finds of Lower and Middle Pleistocene hominines from Indonesia and their antiquity. Conference on the early Palaeolithic of East Asia, Montreal.

——   1973b   Morphology and paleoecology of early man in Java. 9th International Congress of Anthropological and Ethnological Sciences, Chicago.

——   1973c   Palaeoanthropologica discoveries in Indonesia with special reference to the finds of the last two decades. *Journal of Human Evolution*, 2(6):473–85.

KOENIGSWALD, G. H. R. VON   1964   Potassium–argon dates and early man: Trinil. *Report of the 6th Inqua Congress, 1961*, Warsaw, 4:325–27.

——   1968   Das absolute Alter des Pithecanthropus erectus Dubois. In *Evolution und Hominisation*, Gottfried Kurth (ed), 2nd edition, pp. 195–203. Gustav Fischer Verlag, Stuttgart.

——   1973   The oldest hominid fossils from Asia and their relation to human evolution. *Accad. Naz. Lincei*, 182:97–118.

LANCASTER, B.   1966   The biology of language. AAA Annual Meeting, Pittsburgh.

LESTREL, P. E. and D. W. READ   1973   Hominid cranial capacity versus time: A regression approach. *Journal of Human Evolution*, 2(6):405–11.

LIEBERMAN, P.   1973   On the evolution of language: A unified view. 9th International Congress of Anthropological and Ethnological Sciences, Chicago.

—— and E. S. CRELIN   1971   On the speech of Neanderthal man. *Linguistic Inquiries*, 2:203–22.

OSCHINSKY, L., P. GALL, J. MACDONALD, L. NIEMANN, M. SPENCE and S. WILSON   1964   Parallelism, homology and homoplasy in relation to hominid taxonomy and the origin of *Homo sapiens*. *Anthropologica*, n.s. 6(1):105–17.

Morphological contrasts in Pleistocene Australians

A.G. Thorne

WITH FEW EXCEPTIONS, attempts to understand something of the physical origin of the Aboriginals have been based on the examination of the living Australians and studies of museum collections of supposedly late Holocene skeletal remains. The degree of morphological and genetic variation observed in such studies has produced a variety of assessments about the numbers and physical composition of the earliest occupants of the continent, the time of their arrival and their subsequent biological histories in different parts of Australia. The exceptions concern the examination of and conclusions drawn from the small collection of prehistoric skeletal remains. Research in this area has been hampered by the rarity of such remains, the damaged and incomplete nature of those that have been discovered and the difficulties in precisely dating most of them.

The sudden increase in the number of prehistoric skeletal discoveries made in the last seven or eight years suggests that direct examination of prehistoric remains, particularly those of Pleistocene age, is becoming a more reliable basis for tracing Aboriginal morphology to its source or sources. Increasingly, it will be possible to examine skeletal form through time, regionally as well as continentally. At present however it is possible to compare only a representative Pleistocene population from one region, southeast Australia, with more recent post-Pleistocene remains from that area.

If the geographic source of the Australians can be traced to mainland southeast Asia, as seems likely, then Pleistocene and Holocene skeletal remains from that area might assist in the delineation of the physical changes that occurred before, during and since man's migration to Australia. The *Homo erectus* remains from Java, of both the gracile and robust types (Jacob, 1973, 1976), represent at least part of the morphological background of the Australians. Of their more immediate antecedents however little evidence is available—essentially the Wadjak, Niah and Tabon individuals. From New Guinea there is as yet nothing. Until additional accurately dated remains from Indonesia, New Guinea or the Philippines are recovered we will be forced to examine the post-arrival Australian evidence for clues not only to the form or forms of the migrants but the form or forms of their descendants across the continent.

The Pleistocene material examined here includes the cranial remains from Lake Mungo and Kow Swamp (Figure 1). Their form is compared with that of series of museum crania and mandibles from the same area and from other areas of eastern Australia. Cremation and burial of the Lake Mungo I individual took place 24,500–26,500 years ago (Bowler *et al*, 1972). The skeletal remains of this individual are fragmentary (Bowler *et al*, 1968; Thorne, 1971). Reconstruction of the cranium is incomplete and while the vault and base are well-preserved it is clear that most of the facial skeleton, including the right zygomatic bone and the bodies of the maxillae, is represented by small eroded pieces. The mandible is in eight non-matching sections.

An initial series of radiocarbon dates for the Kow Swamp burials and the sediments in which they were found indicated occupation of the former Lake Kow shoreline from more than 10,000 years BP until after 9000 years BP (Thorne and Macumber, 1972). Additional C^{14} analyses place the time of the earliest burials at more than 13,000 BP and the most recent at approximately 9300 years BP. Non-metrical information is available from the remains of more than 40 crania and mandibles, in varying states of preservation and reconstruction. The measurements presented here were derived from 12 crania and 6 mandibles.

The series of museum crania and mandibles used for comparative purposes are of known provenance but unknown age. For this reason a potentially serious flaw in the comparison of Pleistocene and 'near-contemporary' remains is the danger of an assumed or implied modernity for the latter. Of necessity the examination of museum collections means recording information without regard to the age of the material. The inclusion of a small percentage of prehistoric skeletal individuals in a 'modern' comparative series could result in a masking of any morphological changes that have occurred in Aboriginal cranial form in the last 10,000 years or so. It is possible also that osteological changes were occurring in late Pleistocene populations. If this was the case then the use of the Kow Swamp series as a population may itself be misleading, spanning as it does a known time range of at least 3500 years. However, for present purposes the bulk of the museum crania are assumed to be less than approximately 2000 years old, so that comparison of known Pleistocene and museum crania may provide a general or minimal indication of morphological differences.

An additional constraint on the significance of the differences observed lies in the composition of the Kow Swamp series. The specimens available at present do not constitute a large series and although most of the specimens are adult and male, adolescents and females have been included in the analysis of certain characteristics.

Non-metrical features of crania and mandibles
To examine the relationships of the non-metrical aspects of the Pleistocene

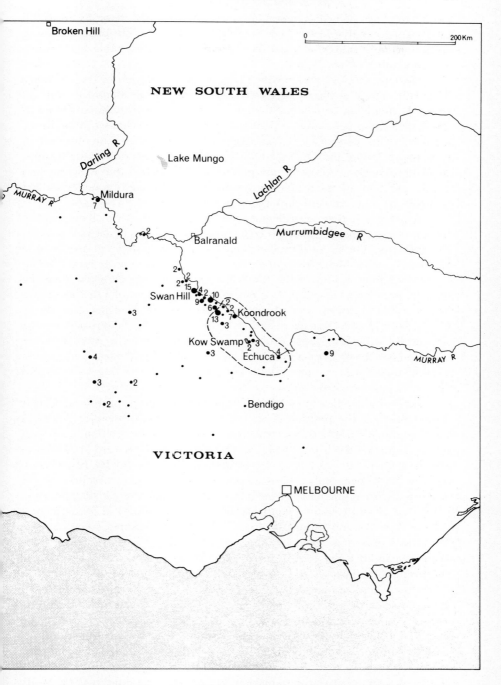

Figure 1 Distribution of northern Victorian cranial series. Numbered dots represent multiple specimens from particular localities. The dashed line defines the 'Kow Swamp area' subgroup.

crania to those of near-contemporary Aboriginals, the Kow Swamp and Lake Mungo analyses have been compared with the results of studies using collections of coastal New South Wales and Queensland crania by Larnach and Macintosh (1966, 1970).

Table 1 lists those features which demonstrate variation in the incidence of specific characteristics between the Kow Swamp groups and the museum series. It should be remembered that the thoroughly Aboriginal nature of the Kow Swamp population is demonstrated by the fact that variation in the majority of its non-metrical characteristics is similar to that observed in New South Wales and Queensland crania. Table 1 lists only those features showing variation. Also, no morphological feature of the Kow Swamp crania exhibits an incidence lying wholly outside the frequency ranges observed by other workers for eastern Australian crania.

It will be seen that several morphological features of the Kow Swamp frontal bones express a more robust form than do the eastern Australian cranial series. The supra-orbital elements, superciliary ridges and zygomatic trigones, indicate higher percentages of the 'large' grade in the Kow Swamp series. In addition, four of the seven Kow Swamp specimens retaining the glabella are classed as grade 4 or more in 48·3 per cent of 116 New South Wales crania (Larnach and Macintosh, 1966) and in 57·4 per cent of 116 Queensland crania (Larnach and Macintosh, 1970). Taken together the overall Kow Swamp supra-orbital region demonstrates a more extreme development. Forty per cent of the Kow Swamp frontal bones have pseudo-torus or torus form, compared with 20·7 per cent of New South Wales and 28·9 per cent of Queensland specimens.

An additional indication of well-developed brow ridges, or at least of their lateral parts, is the position of maximum supra-orbital breadth. During a metrical study of northern Victoria crania (see below) the position of the most lateral points on the frontal bones was noted. In 57·7 per cent (170 crania) the most lateral points lay on the frontomalar sutures (males 39 per cent, females 86·8 per cent). Thus maximum supra-orbital breadth in the Victorian series is greater than the bifrontomalar dimension in 42·3 per cent, compared to adult Kow Swamp crania (nine individuals) of 56 per cent.

Five Kow Swamp frontal bones (of 12) combine distinct supraglabellar fossae and ophryonic grooves. Medium and marked supraglabellar fossae are found in 28·2 per cent of New South Wales crania, with medium and deep ophryonic grooves in 25·6 per cent (Larnach and Macintosh, 1966). For Queensland crania the incidences are 41·2 per cent (supraglabellar fossae) and 39·5 per cent (ophryonic grooves) (Larnach and Macintosh, 1970). Although these authors state that the ophryonic groove 'is an extension laterally of the supraglabellar fossa' (1966), they do not record the various expression combinations of fossa and groove. It is clear from their tables that supraglabellar fossa development is by no means matched by a similar development of the ophryonic groove. For example, in New South Wales crania (Larnach and Macintosh, 1966) while 27·7 per cent of males display 'medium' supraglabellar fossae, only 15·4 per cent display 'medium'

Table 1: Non-metrical features of Kow Swamp and eastern Australian crania. (Percentage comparison)

Feature and grade	Kow Swamp	NSW*	Queensland†
Superciliary Ridges	N = 15	N = 117	N = 114
Small	40·0	48·8	47·4
Medium	20·0	25·6	24·1
Large	40·0	25·6	28·5
Zygomatic Trigones	N = 12	N = 116	N = 116
Slight	33·3	37·9	31·0
Medium	8·4	25·9	42·2
Large	58·3	36·2	26·8
Brow Ridge Form	N = 15	N = 116	N = 114
Cunningham's Type 1	26·7	5·2	0·9
Cunningham's Type 2	33·3	74·1	70·2
Transitional Type	20·0	19·0	22·8
Cunningham's Type 3	20·0	1·7	6·1
Prominence of Temporal Crests	N = 13	N = 117	N = 116
Slight	15·4	34·2	55·2
Medium	33·3	46·2	36·2
Marked	53·3	19·6	8·6
Prominence of Malar Tuberosity	N = 16	N = 111	N = 111
Absent	6·3	12·6	0·0
Slight	31·2	41·5	46·0
Medium	12·5	18·9	24·3
Marked	50·0	27·0	29·7
Breadth of Naso-frontal Articulation	N = 9	N = 107	N = 114
Narrow	—	17·8	37·7
Medium	55·6	37·4	40·4
Broad	44·4	44·8	21·9
Subnasal Prognathism	N = 7	N = 107	N = 109
Absent	—	2·8	0·9
Small	—	22·4	21·1
Medium	—	47·7	52·3
Large	100·0	27·1	25·7
Depth of Infraorbital Fossa	N = 7	N = 111	N = 112
Absent	—	0·9	0·9
Slight	42·8	46·9	43·7
Medium	28·6	36·9	41·1
Deep	28·6	12·6	11·6
Very Deep	—	2·7	2·7
Size of Incisive Foramina	N = 5	N = 113	N = 110
Absent	—	1·8	0·9
Small	—	9·7	24·6
Medium	—	51·3	48·2
Large	100·0	37·2	26·3
Prominence of Parietal Eminence	N = 10	N = 118	N = 116
Slight	90·0	60·2	58·6
Medium	10·0	30·5	29·3
Marked	0·0	9·3	12·1

* From Larnach and Macintosh (1966).
† From Larnach and Macintosh (1970).

ophryonic grooves. For females, 5·8 per cent display 'marked' fossae but there are no cases of 'deep' grooves. However, even if one assumes a maximum combination of distinct fossae and grooves (New South Wales 25·6 per cent, Queensland 39·5 per cent) the Kow Swamp frontal bones demonstrate a higher incidence of distinct groove and fossa (41·7 per cent).

Macintosh and Larnach (1972) record the total absence of a 'lateral supraorbital wing' in 202 Australian crania (and in 143 crania of other groups). These authors regard this feature as diagnostic of *Homo erectus*. They state that 'in ancient fossil skulls there is some variation in the persistence of *Homo erectus* traits. The lateral supraorbital wing is absent in all of them.' (*ibid*, 1972). Twelve Kow Swamp crania preserve the relevant region and three (25·0 per cent) possess the flange-like projection.

Kow Swamp IX is the only individual (of 10) to display keeling or gabling of the vault. All other Kow Swamp crania are rounded across the sagittal suture. Larnach and Macintosh record 'moderate' and 'marked' gabling in 41·7 per cent of 115 New South Wales crania (1966) and in 57·7 per cent of 116 Queensland crania (*ibid*, 1970). Fenner (1939), studying mostly South Australian crania, records gabling in 85 per cent of females and 93 per cent of males.

A transverse occipital torus is evident in the majority of Australian crania. Fenner records an incidence of 93 per cent in male crania and in 82 per cent of females (1939). Larnach and Macintosh found it present in 93·2 per cent of New South Wales crania (1966) and in 87 per cent of Queensland individuals (*ibid*, 1970). A torus is present on all Kow Swamp occipital bones but is more extensive in adults as it always reaches the occipito-mastoid suture. In New South Wales and Queensland crania the torus reaches the suture in 22·9 and 23·9 per cent of cases respectively (Larnach and Macintosh, 1966, 1970). A supratoral sulcus or fossa (as defined by Weidenreich, 1940) is recognisable in the 10 available Kow Swamp occipital bones. Fossae are present in seven individuals, sulci in three. In New South Wales crania fossae are present in 26·3 per cent and sulci in a further 22·9 per cent (Larnach and Macintosh, 1966). For Queensland crania these authors note fossae in 23·7 per cent and sulci in 34·8 per cent (*ibid*, 1970). Thus 50·8 per cent of the New South Wales crania and 41·5 per cent of Queensland specimens display neither fossa nor sulcus.

Mastoid crests are present in all 14 Kow Swamp individuals in which this area is preserved. Larnach and Macintosh note crest absence in 57·8 per cent of New South Wales crania (1966) and in 45 per cent of Queensland individuals (1970).

Although the Kow Swamp mandibles, like the crania, are decidedly Aboriginal, a number of non-metrical features distinguish them from museum collections of eastern Australian material. The following distinctions are based on a comparison of the Kow Swamp series with the eastern Australian mandibles studied by Larnach and Macintosh (1971).

All Kow Swamp rami (8 sides) display distinct eversion of their lower borders. Larnach and Macintosh (1971) note eversion in 40·9 per cent of male mandibles and 3·5 per cent of females. The four specimens preserving the anterior surface of the symphysis display negative 'chins', the condition found in 37·9 per cent of eastern Australian mandibles (*ibid*, 1971). The six Kow Swamp mandibles preserving their antero-inferior symphyseal surfaces have 'marked' digastric fossae, noted by Larnach and Macintosh (1971) in 34·1 per cent of 91 male mandibles. In the four male Kow Swamp examples there is a pronounced basal trigone, compared with an incidence of 28·3 per cent in eastern Australian males (*ibid*, 1971). A predigastric sulcus is distinct in four Kow Swamp specimens. This structure was absent in the bulk of the mandibles examined by Larnach and Macintosh (1971), being faint in 13·6 per cent and distinct in only 4·6 per cent of males.

The results of non-metrical comparisons of the Lake Mungo I cranium and mandible with museum collections can be stated quite simply: there are no differences. The Lake Mungo cranial remains are quite consistent with the forms observed in eastern Australians. Further, the cranial features of Lake Mungo, a female individual, fall within the range of variation observed in eastern Australian females.

Given this consistency it may be significant that the cranium and mandible demonstrate minimal expression of virtually all morphological characters. Even within a large series of female Aboriginal skulls it would be difficult to match the extreme gracility seen in Lake Mungo I. If the Kow Swamp morphology demonstrates an extension of the Aboriginal variability in terms of robusticity, Lake Mungo I suggests the reverse.

Metrical features of crania and mandibles

Measurements of the Kow Swamp and Lake Mungo cranial remains are set out in Table 2. The mandibular dimensions of the Kow Swamp series are listed in Table 3. (As the Lake Mungo mandible is represented by eroded fragments no measurements of this specimen are available at present.)

The measurements of the Pleistocene remains have been compared with a series of skulls from northern Victoria. The geographical distribution of the series is shown in Figure 1. The specimens were drawn from collections held by the National Museum of Victoria. The majority were recovered in the Murray Valley. Of the 170 adult crania used in the analysis 124 have associated mandibles. The specimens have been sexed, using the method of Larnach and Freedman (1964). There are 100 males, 67 females and 3 unsexed individuals.

Collective data for the Victorian and Kow Swamp series are presented in Table 4, together with the results of 't' test calculations, made to establish the significance of differences noted between the two populations. For several reasons, particularly the differences in sample size, the calculations employed the formulae described by Brownlee (1960).

It will be seen from Table 2 that many of the listed measurements cannot be taken on the Lake Mungo cranium. The available measurements can be compared with those for the Victorian comparative series. With one exception, orbit height, the dimensions of the Lake Mungo cranium lie

Table 2: Measurements of Kow Swamp and Lake Mungo crania (in mm)

	KS1	KS2	KS3	KS4	KS5	KS6	KS7	KS8	KS9	KS14	KS15	KS17	Lake Mungo
Glabella-Opisthocranion	(192)	—	—	—	192	175	(205)	194	(190)	214	—	(206)	(181)
Nasion-Opisthocranion	(190)	—	—	—	190	170	(199)	185	(185)	—	—	—	—
Glabella-Inion	(186)	—	—	—	170	155	—	—	—	—	—	—	(170)
Nasion-Inion	(179)	—	—	—	165	151	—	—	—	—	—	—	—
Glabella-Lambda	199	—	—	—	190	163	—	187	(185)	206	—	—	173
Nasion-Lambda	195	—	—	—	188	162	—	—	—	—	—	—	—
Nasion-Basion	—	—	—	—	—	95	—	—	—	—	—	—	—
Basion-Sphenobasion	—	—	—	—	—	22	—	—	—	—	—	—	18
Basion-Opisthion	—	—	—	—	—	32	—	—	—	—	—	—	36
Basion-Prosthion	—	—	—	—	—	108	—	—	—	—	—	—	—
Nasion-Bregma	122	112	—	—	118	105	124	—	—	—	—	—	—
Nasion-Bregma Projection	18	28	—	—	15	19	20	—	—	—	—	—	—
Bregma-Lambda	119	—	—	—	122	116	—	115	115	126	—	—	106
Lambda-Opisthion	102	—	—	—	(108)	95	—	—	—	—	—	—	95
Lambda-Inion	73	—	—	—	76	66	—	62	66	—	—	—	66
Lambda-Opisthocranion	63	—	—	—	28	30	—	48	58	62	—	—	47
Inion-Opisthion	39	—	—	—	(35)	35	—	—	—	—	—	—	40
Opisthion-Opisthocranion	49	—	—	—	(89)	75	—	—	—	—	—	—	64
Maximum Supraorbital Breadth	120	111	121	111	112	98	122	(110)	(124)	112	(118)	—	107
Bi-Frontotemporale	86	101	106	92	97	91	103	(100)	(108)	96	—	—	90
Bi-Frontosphenoidal Sutures	90	(90)	—	92	93	83	100	(97)	—	—	(92)	—	—
Bi-Stephanion	81	117	—	—	111	100	115	—	—	—	—	—	103
Bi-Coronale	105	—	—	—	116	106	(120)	—	—	—	—	—	110
Bi-Parietal maximum	(128)	—	—	—	139	127	(145)	—	(132)	(150)	—	(148)	130
Bi-Auriculare	—	—	—	—	115	100	—	—	—	—	—	—	—
Bi-Asterion	(122)	—	—	—	109	101	—	—	114	—	—	—	103
Bi-Mastoideale	—	—	—	—	97	78	—	—	—	—	—	—	—

Measurement	1	2	3	4	5	6	7	8	9	10	11
Bi-Infratemporal Crests	110	—	—	—	—	73	—	—	—	—	84
Basioccipital Breadth	144	—	—	—	—	21	—	—	—	—	32
Foramen Magnum Breadth	106	98	105	118	—	29	—	—	—	—	—
Bi-Ectoconchion	89	101	(140)	(155)	90	96	—	108	(135)	101	(145)
Bi-Zygion	28	—	(100)	(120)	—	132	—	(165)	—	(155)	(104)
Bi-Zygomaxillare	51	—	—	—	—	104	—	107	—	100	79
Nasion-Prosthion	51	26	25	—	60	73	—	—	45	(90)	23
Bi-Maxillofrontale	32	44	43	—	21	23	—	(43)	—	—	43
Mf-Ek (left)	31	44	(41)	—	39	39	—	43	—	—	33
Mf-Ek (right)	29	33	30	34	39	39	—	32	—	32	—
Orbit Height (left)	56	33	(30)	—	31	34	45	34	—	(32)	27
Orbit Height (right)	21	—	31	—	40	34	32	32	—	—	56
Piriform Breadth	87	11	(53)	—	(7)	29	—	(39)	—	(65)	23
Nasion-Nasospinale	110	—	—	—	71	53	88	(50)	—	98	—
Palate Height	61	101	104	114	91	14	—	(90)	76	—	64
Frontomalare Orbitale-Auriculare	74	60	—	—	53	85	—	113	—	—	71
Bi-Frontomalare Orbitale	(66·67)	64	—	—	(66)	99	—	—	(69·47)	(70·09)	97
Alveolar Length	14·75	—	—	15	75·39	63	—	(70·73)	—	—	(71·84)
Alveolar Breadth	34	25·0	19	34	18·09	73	—	16·12	(16)	16	(71·82)
Cranial Index	30	10	19	—	7	72·39	(10)	19	—	—	17
Frontal Curvature Index	23	(21)	—	—	15	12·71	(13)	22	—	(26)	—
Post-Orbital Constriction (Temp.)	45·14	5	(34)	—	(15)	15	—	28	—	28	—
Post-Orbital Constriction (F–S)	61·76	38·40	(71·42)	—	(34·98)	25	—	—	—	—	45·44
Malar Eversion	61·80	75·00	(58·49)	—	—	45·99	(76·74)	—	—	(58·06)	(54·48)
Palatal Index	51·78	—	—	—	113·68	87·18	(78·00)	—	—	—	48·21
Orbital Index (Mean L + R)	—	—	—	—	—	55·30	—	—	—	—	—
Upper Facial Index	—	—	—	—	—	54·71	—	—	—	—	—
Nasal Index	—	—	—	—	—	—	—	—	—	—	—
Gnathic Index	—	—	—	—	—	—	—	—	—	—	—

Table 3: Measurements of Kow Swamp mandibles (in mm)

	KS1	KS5	KS7	KS8	KS9	KS14
Mandibular Length	116	110	—	—	(120)	(115)
Bi-Condylar Breadth	(147)	136	—	—	—	—
Bi-Gonial Breadth	127	115	—	—	—	—
Symphyseal Height	38	38	36	—	39	39
Symphyseal Thickness	15	15	19	—	—	16
Body Thickness*	20	18	19	13	—	20
Body Height*	35	36	36	28	34	30
Ramus Height	76	73	—	—	(72)	(65)
Ramus Breadth (max.)	45	45	—	—	51	43
Ramus Breadth (min.)	36	38	—	—	35	32
Gonial Angle	109	117	—	—	121	118
Sigmoid Notch Depth	(13)	15	—	—	(14)	—

* Between M1–M2.

within the ranges for the museum series. Further, with the same exception, the dimensions lie within the ranges for females of the comparative series. Of 23 dimensions available for the Lake Mungo cranium 16 lie within one standard deviation of the mean for the comparative series females. Of the remainder, basioccipital breadth in Lake Mungo is 32 mm, at the upper limit for females in the comparative series. Orbit height (27 mm) lies just outside the ranges established for the Victorian series total (28–42 mm) and females (28–38 mm). It also lies outside the range of $29 \cdot 1$–$36 \cdot 9$ mm established by Freedman (1964) for New South Wales coastal female crania.

Although the Lake Mungo orbit height is somewhat lower than that of the museum series, and its basioccipital bone is broad by female standards, the cranium displays no essential metrical features that would exclude it from the museum population.

The statistically significant metrical differences between the Kow Swamp and Victorian comparative series involve the following dimensions and indices:

Nasion-Bregma projection	Frontal Curvature Index
Bregma-Lambda	Palatal Index
Lambda-Inion	Symphyseal Height
Lambda-Opisthocranion	Symphyseal Thickness
Maximum Frontal Breadth	Body Height
Bi-zygomaxillare	Ramus Height
Bi-maxillofrontale	

As the Kow Swamp series was recovered from an isolated locality, and the museum series, gathered from a wide area of northern Victoria, the museum series was used to test whether differences between the two series were reflected geographically. The museum series was divided into two subseries— a group of 43 specimens recovered from the Kow Swamp area (see Figure 1) and the remaining 127 specimens from outside that area. The results of 't' tests reveal several differences, significant at the 5 per cent level, between the subseries of museum crania and mandibles. I can offer no explanation of the differences at present, but none correspond to dimensions shown to differ significantly between the prehistoric Kow Swamp series and the total northern Victorian museum series.

Metrical features of dentitions

Although a large number of isolated teeth and tooth fragments were recovered at Kow Swamp the enamel crown remains associated with the numbered crania and mandibles are neither extensive nor well-preserved. Apart from postmortem erosion of the dental remains and damage sustained during earthmoving on the site, all individuals display pronounced occlusal attrition and/or varying degrees of premortem tooth loss. Several tooth fragments were recovered with the Lake Mungo remains, but only a few scraps of enamel are preserved and no measurements of the tooth crowns can be made.

Because of the small number of unworn teeth available, a detailed metrical analysis of the Kow Swamp dentitions is deferred until either more specimens and teeth are recovered or suitable techniques permit the comparison of worn and unworn Aboriginal dentitions. The ranges of mesiodistal and buccolingual dimensions of the available Kow Swamp teeth are set out in Table 5, together with the ranges for these dimensions established by Campbell (1925) in a substantial series of Australian dentitions. It will be seen that most Kow Swamp tooth dimensions lie within the ranges established by Campbell. However, for both maxillary and mandibular teeth, molars particularly, the Kow Swamp mean mesiodistal and buccolingual dimensions are generally higher than for the corresponding mean dimensions of Campbell's series. This situation appears to support, at least in part, Davies' conclusion that average tooth size in prehistoric Australians was greater than in 'modern Aboriginals' (Davies, 1968).

Discussion

The comparison of the Kow Swamp cranial remains with the various series of museum crania reveals a number of differences between the prehistoric and recent groups. As sub-adult Kow Swamp individuals are included in the comparison, I suggest the results reflect the minimum range of differences. Hopefully, additional remains and analysis will permit the separation of adults and juveniles for comparative purposes. The Kow Swamp crania are large by more recent Aboriginal standards. They indicate a greater robustness or ruggedness, although this has to be seen as a feature of the population as a whole and not of all individuals. The limited data available for the dental remains indicate that the mean size of the Kow Swamp molar teeth is greater than that observed in recent Aboriginal dentitions.

The morphological characters or measurements that distinguish the prehistoric and museum series are concentrated on the face and forehead. Of the 13 statistically significant metrical differences, nine relate to the facial and frontal areas of the cranium and the mandibular corpus. Non-metrical morphological differences demonstrate a similar concentration facially.

Table 4: Comparison of Kow Swamp and Victorian crania and mandibles (in mm)

Variable	Victorian Series				Kow Swamp Series				t
	N	Mean	S.D.	Range	N	Mean	S.D.	Range	
Glabella-Opisthocranion	167	184·28	7·10	167–202	4	193·75	15·97	175–214	
Nasion-Opisthocranion	167	179·62	6·60	161–195	2	180·00	14·14	170–190	
Glabella-Inion	166	174·67	8·50	149–193	3	170·00	15·00	155–185	
Nasion-Inion	166	167·93	8·15	144–187	2	158·00	9·89	151–165	
Glabella-Lambda	167	179·01	7·04	163–197	5	189·00	16·36	163–206	
Nasion-Lambda	167	175·90	6·40	163–192	3	181·67	17·39	162–195	
Nasion-Basion	146	100·23	4·74	88–111	1	—	—	95	
Basion-Sphenobasion	146	22·99	2·60	17–31	1	—	—	22	
Basion-Opisthion	145	34·61	2·43	30–41	1	—	—	32	
Basion-Prosthion	147	102·36	5·52	85–117	1	—	—	108	
Nasion-Bregma	169	110·63	4·90	97–124	5	116·20	7·76	105–124	·05
Nasion-Bregma Projection	167	25·79	2·45	20–35	5	20·00	4·85	15–28	·05
Bregma-Lambda	168	114·23	6·56	94–131	6	118·83	4·45	115–126	
Lambda-Opisthion	157	93·41	4·61	81–106	2	100·00	7·07	95–105	
Lambda-Inion	166	61·90	5·70	45–77	5	68·60	5·73	62–76	·05
Lambda-Opisthocranion	165	27·67	8·73	8–50	6	48·17	15·78	28–63	·05
Inion-Opisthion	157	45·07	5·73	27–61	2	37·00	2·83	35–39	
Opisthion-Opisthocranion	158	76·20	7·65	32–90	2	62·00	18·38	49–75	
Maximum Supra-orbital Breadth	169	108·04	5·24	95–120	8	113·17	7·82	98–122	·05
Bi-Frontotemporale	169	94·03	4·62	85–106	8	96·50	6·70	86–106	
Bi-Frontosphenoid Sutures	168	87·42	4·04	79–98	5	91·60	6·11	83–100	
Bi-Stephanion	165	100·78	6·51	79–116	5	104·80	14·84	81–117	
Bi-Coronale	164	108·04	4·59	97–119	3	109·00	6·08	105–116	
Bi-Parietal Maximum	162	130·08	5·96	117–183	2	133·00	8·49	127–139	
Bi-Auriculare	159	111·99	5·47	97–125	2	107·50	10·61	100–115	
Bi-Asterion	165	106·35	5·29	93–125	3	108·00	6·56	101–114	
Bi-Mastoideale	159	99·56	5·11	85–111	2	87·50	13·44	78–97	
Bi-Infratemporal Crests	156	82·68	6·83	62–92	1	—	—	73	
Basioccipital Breadth	145	26·57	2·42	20–33	1	—	—	21	
Foramen Magnum Breadth	146	29·79	2·37	25–38	1	—	—	29	
Bi-Ectoconchion	148	101·18	4·80	90–114	8	103·25	8·86	90–118	

Measurement	n	Mean	S.D.	Range	n	Mean	S.D.	Range	Sig.
Bi-Zygomaxillare	163	92·18	5·59	78–116	5	103·60	3·05	100–107	·001
Nasion-Prosthion	168	65·86	4·77	55–81	4	72·75	12·12	60–89	·01
Bi-Maxillofrontale	169	18·86	2·28	14–28	6	24·33	2·50	21–28	
Mf-Ek(left)	158	43·84	2·25	38–51	6	43·17	4·40	39–51	
Mf-Ek (right)	161	44·23	2·35	39–51	6	43·50	4·46	39–51	
Orbit Height (left)	161	32·50	2·08	28–39	7	32·39	1·25	30–34	
Orbit Height (right)	159	32·72	2·24	28–42	7	32·71	1·38	31–34	
Piriform Breadth	167	27·10	2·14	23–32	4	29·00	1·63	27–31	
Nasion-Nasospinale	167	47·66	3·24	41–55	4	51·25	7·63	40–56	
Palate Height	159	12·30	3·02	4–22	3	15·33	5·13	11–21	
Frontomalare Orbitale-Auriculare	169	75·88	3·50	68–85	5	81·40	7·50	71–88	
Bi-Frontomalare	168	100·92	4·72	90–112	8	103·75	8·07	91–114	
Alveolar Length	166	58·72	3·88	49–71	5	60·20	4·32	53–64	
Alveolar Breadth	166	65·35	4·14	57–76	4	70·50	4·51	64–74	
Cranial Index	161	70·66	3·40	64·74–98·92	2	72·49	0·12	72·40–72·57	·05
Frontal Curvature Index	167	23·30	1·87	18·18–30·17	5	17·34	4·71	12·71–25·00	
Post-Orbital Constriction (Temp.)	168	14·04	3·86	3–25	8	16·88	16·88	7–34	
Post-Orbital Constriction (F–S)	167	20·58	4·04	12–36	5	21·00	5·61	15–30	
Malar Eversion	149	12·95	4·97	0–25	5	21·80	9·63	5–28	
Palatal Index	166	38·49	4·59	29·00–52·54	4	43·74	3·58	38·40–45·99	·05
Orbital Index	148	74·41	5·27	61·70–86·42	3	74·63	12·74	61·76–87·18	
Upper Facial Index	153	50·53	3·54	41·67–60·00	2	58·56	4·60	55·30–61·81	
Nasal Index	166	86·96	4·93	45·28–73·17	3	51·56	3·26	48·21–54·72	
Gnathic Index	146	102·21	3·94	88·54–111·34	1	—	—	113·68	
Mandibles									
Mandibular Length	104	105·71	6·18	92–123	2	113·00	4·24	110–116	·001
Bi-Condylar Breadth	100	115·89	7·75	96–131	1	—	—	136	
Bi-Gonial Breadth	111	97·55	8·87	80–118	2	121·00	8·49	115–127	·05
Symphyseal Height	123	32·73	3·56	25–42	5	38·00	1·22	36–39	
Symphyseal Thickness	123	13·96	1·46	11–17	4	16·25	1·89	15–19	·05
Body Thickness	124	15·44	1·97	11–21	5	18·00	2·90	13–20	
Body Height	123	27·74	3·04	22–37	6	33·17	3·37	28–36	
Ramus Height	116	64·47	5·19	58–81	2	74·50	2·12	73–76	·01
Ramus Breadth (max.)	118	42·03	4·17	30–52	4	46·00	3·46	43–51	·05
Ramus Breadth (min.)	120	32·75	4·08	23–43	4	32·25	2·50	32–38	
Gonial Angle	117	121·00	7·40	104–138	4	116·25	5·12	109–121	
Sigmoid Notch	118	10·56	1·59	7–16	1	—	—	15	

Table 5: Crown dimensions of Kow Swamp and other Aboriginal dentitions (in mm)

Tooth	Dimension	Kow Swamp			Other Aboriginal*		
		N	Range	Mean	N	Range	Mean
I¹	MD	11	8·2– 9·9	9·55	56	8·5–10	9·37
	BL	11	7·7– 8·5	8·14	93	7–9	7·9
I²	MD	9	6·8– 8·1	7·69	78	6·5–9	7·65
	BL	9	6·7– 7·8	7·37	126	6–8·5	6·91
C	MD	9	8·0– 8·7	8·37	116	6·5–9·5	8·43
	BL	9	8·1– 9·4	8·96	159	7·5–11	9·0
P¹	MD	11	6·9– 8·0	7·63	124	7–9	7·81
	BL	11	9·6–10·6	10·17	163	8·5–12	10·3
P²	MD	9	6·6– 7·8	7·34	89	6·5–8·25	7·23†
	BL	9	7·5–10·7	9·91	168	8·5–12	10·14
M¹	MD	10	10·4–13·4	11·75	198	10–13	11·43
	BL	10	12·4–14·4	13·34	255	11·5–14·75	12·84
M²	MD	8	10·2–12·9	11·63	168	10–12·5	10·93
	BL	8	11·8–14·4	13·69	241	11–16	13·1
M³	MD	12	9·4–14·9	11·25	142	8–13	10·03
	BL	11	12·2–15·3	13·49	193	10–15	12·33
I1	MD	8	4·9– 6·7	5·81	43	5–7	6·0
	BL	7	4·7– 6·8	6·10	77	5·5–7·5	6·3
I2	MD	7	5·5– 7·7	6·64	51	6–7·5	6·7
	BL	6	6·3– 7·1	6·68	92	6–7·5	6·6
C	MD	8	6·8– 7·4	7·25	88	7–9	7·6
	BL	7	7·6– 9·1	8·37	120	7–10	8·3
P1	MD	7	6·9– 8·0	7·63	93	7–9	7·6
	BL	6	8·6– 9·8	8·95	120	7–10	8·8
P2	MD	11	6·8– 8·6	7·99	79	6·5–9	7·7
	BL	10	8·8– 9·7	9·31	109	7–10	8·9
M1	MD	9	11·7–14·1	12·62	139	11–14	12·3
	BL	8	11·2–13·2	12·06	186	10–13·5	11·9
M2	MD	7	10·7–14·1	12·56	152	10–14·25	12·5
	BL	6	10·3–12·5	11·38	184	10–13·5	11·7
M3	MD	5	12·8–14·7	13·36	136	9–14	11·9
	BL	5	11·5–13·6	12·22	152	8–13	11·1

* Campbell, 1925.
† The figure shown in Campbell (1925 :17) is 1.23 mm.

Within the facial area differences focus on the frontal bone. Compared to the Victorian comparative series metrically, and eastern Australian crania non-metrically, the Kow Swamp frontal bones are flattened and broader anteriorly (but not longer antero-posteriorly). The anterior part of the bone displays several differences, associated with a more extreme development of the supraorbital region and the areas superior and lateral to it.

An additional characteristic of the Kow Swamp crania is bone thickness. Some thickness measurements of the major vault bones in this series have been reported (Thorne and Macumber, 1972), but to date comparable measurements of other Australian crania have not been collected. During the measurement of the Victorian series it was my strong impression (but at present it is only that) that parts of the Kow Swamp crania were thicker generally than in the comparative series. The frontal and zygomatic bones and the anterior parts of the parietal bones of the Kow Swamp series seem disproportionately thicker than the posterior parts of these crania. (I thus correct here an earlier statement that *all* vault bones are 'uniformly thick'— Thorne and Macumber, 1972.) However, two mandibular dimensions involving bone thickness were recorded for the Victorian museum series. The metrical comparison indicates a significant difference in the symphyseal region of the Kow Swamp mandibles, which are thicker.

I have discussed the morphological status of the Lake Mungo individual elsewhere (Thorne, 1971). This female skeleton is lightly constructed and has weakly developed muscle insertion sites. The cranium and mandible display no features, metrical or non-metrical, that would exclude them from recent series. The cranium falls within the range of near-contemporary female form and further 'is at the morphologically modern end of the female range' (Thorne, 1971). Given the robusticity and tendency for greater cranial size in at least some of the available Pleistocene skeletal material, the general form and size of the Lake Mungo skeleton is striking.

Some implications of the Kow Swamp and Lake Mungo morphologies for Aboriginal origins have been discussed previously (Thorne, 1971; Thorne and Macumber, 1972; Bowler *et al*, 1972; Howells, 1973). I wish only to point out here that certain features, or groups of features, of the Kow Swamp crania and mandibles support general derivational concepts that have been expressed by others. Weidenreich (1946) has suggested that osteological details of some prehistoric and recent Aboriginal crania are evidence of a 'continuous line of evolution' from the Javan Solo and Pithecanthropine forms. More recently, Macintosh (1965) has noted 'the mark of ancient Java' on Australian prehistoric crania. The diagnostic features of the Kow Swamp skulls strengthen these statements. In particular, the overall form of the frontal bones of some individuals points directly to Pleistocene Indonesia— the combination of extreme recession, pronounced postorbital constriction, supraorbital torus and the lateral supraorbital wing.

Several alternative explanations of the Kow Swamp morphology have been suggested. These include pathology, artificial deformation and adaptive response to environmental pressures, particularly nutritional.

Examination of the cranial and post-cranial skeletons of the Kow Swamp individuals has not revealed any evidence of a pathology that could account for the characteristic form of the crania. Apart from alveolar conditions due to the deposition of calculus and pronounced occlusal attrition, the group is surprisingly free of evidence of disease or injury, compared with more recent Aboriginal series. No sign of abnormality or pathology is visible in those cranial bones that are thickened. The surfaces of the tabular portions appear normal, compared to other parts of these crania and to other series of crania. In section the thickening is seen to be due to a general expansion of tabular and dipoic elements (Thorne and Macumber, 1972).

It has been suggested that recession of the forehead in Kow Swamp crania, and the associated facial prognathism, may result from artificial deformation. Culturally, this would imply that such a practice was present in the Murray

Valley some 10,000 years ago and had disappeared by the time of European contact. There is no ethnographic evidence for such a practice in this or any other area of Australia and no osteological evidence in crania of recent date for this or any other area of the continent. It is not evident in the prehistoric Keilor or Green Gully individuals found to the south of Kow Swamp, or in the Lake Mungo, Mossgiel, or Lake Nitchie individuals found to the north-west. It was not practised by the ethnographic Tasmanians, a population resident on an extension of the Australian mainland at the time the Kow Swamp group was living on the shores of Lake Kow, and subsequently isolated by the formation of Bass Strait. Osteologically there are no structural characters in the Kow Swamp crania that would support deformation. Given the extreme recession anteriorly some corresponding reaction should be observable posteriorly. There is none—indeed the occipital region of the Kow Swamp cranium is fully developed and expanded.

The presence of a relatively low parietal curvature index in the Cohuna cranium is stated by Macintosh and Larnach (1976), to clear that individual of similar suspicions. Although it remains imprecisely dated the Cohuna cranium was almost certainly a member of the Kow Swamp population. It should be remembered also that the question of possible deformation applies to *all* specimens with flattened foreheads and projecting faces. Should we not ask why Solo man, for example, was not practising cranial deformation?

The notion that the Kow Swamp morphology is wholly or partially the result of local adaptation cannot be discussed in any depth, in the absence of detailed information about environmental conditions in the area during late Pleistocene times. What evidence there is suggests that conditions in the area have changed very little since then. It is clear that during the late glacial period streams in the area had much greater discharges than at present (Pels, 1966; Bowler, 1967; Thorne and Macumber, 1972). The fauna represented by remains recovered during the excavations at Kow Swamp is similar to that found at the time of initial European explorations and essentially still present today. The area supported a rich and varied fauna and flora, both aquatic and terrestrial, that was available to Aboriginals throughout the year. It is difficult to conceive of significant environmental or dietary changes that could account not only for the development of the special features of the Kow Swamp population but also their relatively sudden disappearance by mid-Holocene times. Finally, the general environmental stability of the Kow Swamp region during and since the late Pleistocene is emphasised by comparison with nearby areas over the same period. The Willandra Lakes system (Bowler, 1976), experienced a series of major climatic and resource fluctuations that undoubtedly placed considerable stress on human populations. Yet as the Lake Mungo remains demonstrate, modern Aboriginal morphology was present in that area for at least 25,000 years.

Two general conclusions bearing on Aboriginal origins can be drawn from existing prehistoric skeletal remains. Firstly, there has been significant morphological change within Australia, certainly over the last 10,000 years.

It would be surprising if this was not the case, given the size and ecological diversity of the continent, man's occupation of it for more than 30,000 years, and our knowledge of demonstrable genetic change in the recent past. Although change occurred in at least one area of southeast Australia, the evidence of the Lake Mungo cremation indicates that change was not universal, or at least was not occurring at the same rate in all areas.

The fact of change in Australian populations, however, does not in itself tell us anything about Aboriginal origins. Kow Swamp and Lake Mungo confirm and extend the contrast noted in earlier discoveries of Australian prehistoric remains, but they do not resolve the problem of two late Pleistocene morphologies, or even indicate whether they are really elements, or extremes, from within a broader range of Pleistocene skeletal form.

Nevertheless, the characteristics of the Kow Swamp population point to the general ancestry of the Aboriginals, both spatially and chronologically. The morphologically archaic aspects of the crania of these people link them with early populations in Indonesia. The extension of these characters and their maintenance on the Australian continent until relatively recently also indicates that whatever modifications were developed by the migrants or their non-Australian ancestors, basic regional skeletal characteristics were maintained within the population.

References

BOWLER, J. M.   1976   Recent developments in reconstructing late Quaternary environments in Australia. In *The origin of the Australians*, R. L. Kirk and A. G. Thorne (eds), pp. 55–77. Australian Institute of Aboriginal Studies, Canberra.

——, A. G. THORNE and H. A. POLACH   1972   Pleistocene man in Australia: Age and significance of the Mungo skeleton. *Nature*, 240:48–50.

BROWNLEE, K. A.   1960   *Statistical theory and methodology in science and engineering.* John Wiley and Sons, New York.

CAMPBELL, T. D.   1925   *Dentition and palate of the Australian Aboriginal.* Hassell Press, Adelaide.

DAVIES, P. L.   1968   An 8,000 to 12,000 years old human tooth from W.A. *Archaeology and Physical Anthropology in Oceania*, 3(1):34–40.

FENNER, F. J.   1939   The Australian Aboriginal skull; its non-metrical morphological characters. *Transactions of the Royal Society of South Australia*, 63(2):248–306.

FREEDMAN, L.   1964   Metrical features of Aboriginal crania from coastal N.S.W., Australia. *Records of the Australian Museum*, 26(12):309–25.

HOWELLS, W. W.   1973   *The Pacific Islanders.* Weidenfeld and Nicolson, London.

JACOB, T.   1973   New finds of lower and middle Pleistocene hominines from Indonesia and their antiquity. *Conference on the early palaeolithic of East Asia*, Montreal.

——   1976   Early populations in the Indonesian region. In *The origin of the Australians*, R. L. Kirk and A. G. Thorne (eds), pp. 81–93. Australian Institute of Aboriginal Studies, Canberra.

LARNACH, S. L. and L. FREEDMAN   1964   Sex determination of Aboriginal crania from coastal New South Wales, Australia. *Records of the Australian Museum*, 26: 295–305.

—— and N. W. G. MACINTOSH   1966   *The craniology of the Aborigines of coastal New South Wales.* Oceania Monograph No. 13, Sydney.

—— and ——   1970   *The craniology of the Aborigines of Queensland.* Oceania Monograph No. 15, Sydney.

—— and ——   1971   *The mandible in eastern Australian Aborigines.* Oceania Monograph No. 17, Sydney.

MACINTOSH, N. W. G.   1965   The physical aspect of man in Australia. In *Aboriginal man in Australia*, R. M. and C. H. Berndt (eds), pp. 29–70. Angus and Robertson, Sydney.

—— 1967   Recent discoveries of early Australian man. *Annals of the Australian College of Dental Surgery*, 1:104–26.

—— and S. L. LARNACH   1972   The persistence of *Homo erectus* traits in Australian Aboriginal crania. *Archaeology and Physical Anthropology in Oceania*, 7(1): 1–7.

—— and ——   1976   Aboriginal affinities looked at in world context. In *The origin of the Australians*, R. L. Kirk and A. G. Thorne (eds), pp 113–126. Australian Institute of Aboriginal Studies, Canberra.

PELS, S.   1966   Late Quaternary chronology of riverine plains of south eastern Australia. *Journal of the Geological Society of Australia*, 13:27–40.

THORNE, A. G.   1971   Mungo and Kow Swamp; morphological variation in Pleistocene Australians. *Mankind*, 8(2):85–89.

—— and P. G. MACUMBER   1972   Discoveries of late Pleistocene man at Kow Swamp, Australia. *Nature*, 238:316–19.

WEIDENREICH, F.   1940   The torus occipitalis and related structures and their transformations in the course of human evolution. *Bulletin of the Geological Society of China*, 19(4):480–559.

—— 1946   *Apes, giants and man*. Chicago University Press, Chicago.

Aboriginal affinities looked at in world context

N.W.G. Macintosh and S.L. Larnach

In 1949 MACINTOSH published 'A survey of possible sea-routes available to the Tasmanian Aborigines'. The terminal paragraph said 'This paper is a survey of what appears possible and of what does not appear possible'. He believed then, as he believes now, that he committed himself no further than that. Nevertheless some readers labelled him as espousing the 'voyagers' and opposed to the 'overlanders'; others implied that he was identifying the Tasmanians as Melanesians.

Some sixteen years later Macintosh and Barker (1965) disavowed adherence to the 'drifter' theory or to Tasmanian derivation from Melanesia; and added that with the proof of a higher antiquity for Man on the mainland and the revelation of a constant land bridge to Tasmania before 12,000 years ago, the 1949 paper became irrelevant. Tasmanian Man had to be derived from mainland Aboriginal Man.

It is a whimsical turn of events that Howells (1973a,b,c) using a most sophisticated multivariate analysis, finds that Australians, Tasmanians and Melanesians have the same basic morphological pattern, *but* that within that population Tasmanians cluster closer to Tolais than to South Australians. Further, Giles (1976) using samples from eleven regions for a multiple discriminatory analysis of linear dimensions, concluded that 'the Melanesians stick together, while a relationship—not a strong one but intriguing—emerges between the Torres Strait Islanders and the Tasmanians, and the latter move away from Swanport' (South Australia). The similarity to Howells' conclusions based on samples from three regions is striking.

Howells also finds the Australian Keilor skull closer to Tasmanians than to Australians. Macintosh (1963) had written that none of the Australian fossil skulls showed Tasmanian traits. His view has since changed and six years or more ago he agreed with Howells that the Keilor skull looks more Tasmanian than Australian. He has more recently cleared the Keilor cranium of its crusts, reassembled and dated it; but a complete morphological study of this cranium still needs much more work.

Macintosh (1952) in a small paper on analysis of stature of Djauan and Ngalbun tribesmen in Arnhem Land, found an extraordinarily regular gradient between 151·1–182·2 cms and complete continuity between the extremes. Additional observations led to a conclusion that variations are within the individual tribes rather than between tribes, and to the statement that 'The Australian Aborigines are not modern hybrids but ancient hybrids, as we all are, and in the modern sense they are a homogeneous people but possessing a gene pool with a wide range of variation'.

From then on he found that he was counted with the homogeneity school opposed to the bi-, tri- or multi-hybrid school, which was not really true of his thinking. He believes he sat on the fence until Larnach and he had completed the Queensland cranial analysis in 1970. If we had found negrito evidence in the Cairns rainforest crania it would have been shouted from the housetops.

Macintosh (1963) published a small paper and a photo of orthogonal surveys of the Cohuna, Talgai, Mossgiel crania contrasted with the Keilor cranium. The text related briefly to lateral contour comparison and in particular supported Weidenreich's (1943) opinion that special features of the *Pithecanthropus—H. soloensis* forehead have undergone very little change in the Australian. We no longer hold any such view.

In a paper by Macintosh (1965) there was further illustration using X-ray skiagrams of the contrast between the Cohuna-Talgai-Mossgiel group and the Keilor cranium. The history and controversies of previous authors and their hypotheses about these crania were analysed and for that period of time the analysis was satisfactory. The view, with supporting data, that Man must have come to Australia by water craft was put forward in as much eustatic and geographical detail as was then possible.

The splendid anatomical description by Fenner (1941) of the Aitape frontal bone was acknowledged but the relic was declared an unhelpful liability and extreme doubt was cast on its antiquity. That prediction was later confirmed.

However Macintosh was not to escape from that 1965 paper unscathed. He had put the Talgai, Mossgiel, Cohuna crania into one group and the Keilor, Tartanga, Wadjak crania into another group. This classification was based not only on subjective appearance and impression, but also on contour in the comparison of all normae although only the laterals were illustrated in the paper; but nowhere did he say (nor in his opinion did he imply) that these groups represented two races or even subraces.

It is ironic that most readers have seized on this comparison as an indication of two races, two migrations, two peoples, 'flat heads' and 'round heads', first one then the other being given precedence in antiquity and cultural associations according to what radiocarbon dates accompanied the successive excavations. The present authors do not believe one word of this. Our view is that they are equal representatives ranged *towards* (because they fall inside the extremes of the range) either end of a continuum of a single population. (As examples of difficulty arising from implication of two races see Mulvaney, 1969 p.160; Rhys Jones, 1973 pp.278, 280; Howells, 1973c p.151–2.)

We published our monograph on the craniology of the New South Wales coastal Aborigines in 1966. This population exhibited morphological homogeneity which was not to say that frequencies of all the traits used were uniformly stable. Indeed some traits showed clines running from north to south, but these clines were continuous and not random or sporadic.

Into these really objective cranial data we inserted the fossil skulls. Macintosh (1967) published what was intended to be a refutation of the two subrace idea, and said 'The subjective impression of two separate types is not confirmed by this type of analysis'. The choice of the word 'type' proved to be an unhappy one. It was at once interpreted as race.

Subsequent work by Larnach and Macintosh included a paper in 1967, monographs on Queensland craniology in 1970, eastern Australian mandibles in 1971, papers on *H. erectus* traits in 1972, Keppel Islanders in 1972, and on the contrast between Queensland and New Guinea crania, 1973. The following is a summary of these publications:

1.   A series of Aboriginal crania obtained from the narrow coastal strip of New South Wales, situated between the Pacific Ocean on the east and the Great Dividing Range on the west, was selected for intensive study.
2.   The first objective was to determine which cranial traits showed the greatest contrast (Larnach and Freedman, 1964). Seven traits showing such maximum contrast were used as the basis for the determination of the sex of Aboriginal crania and met with marked success.
3.   In the study of the New South Wales coastal crania a variable morphological pattern was discovered, based upon the incidence shown by the grades of development of twenty traits. The variability shown by this pattern is due to the varying degree of expression of the component traits making up the pattern.
4.   By the assignment of values to the expression of the individual traits a score for the pattern can be calculated for each skull. This score can be taken as a measure of the expression of the pattern as a whole. The higher the score the better is the expression of the pattern, and conversely, the lower the score the poorer is the expression of the pattern. The scores can then be plotted out for comparison with Aboriginal crania from other regions within Australia, and with crania belonging to other racial groups from outside Australia.
5.   The scores separated Aboriginal crania of coastal New South Wales from both Caucasoid and East Asian Mongoloid crania, and without any overlap.
6.   The same scores did not show such good separation of Australian from New Guinea skulls. To improve the separation twelve traits, selected only for their discriminative value, were used with greater success in the separation. Perhaps we should not be unduly surprised that the racial group most difficult to separate from Australians should be precisely that group which is geographically the nearest.
7.   An examination of the distribution of the scores within eastern Australia shows an interesting situation for there appears to be a north-south gradient or cline. The mean scores on the New South Wales coast show the greatest contrast with that of New Guinea crania, but this contrast diminishes the further north the sample is taken.

The Cape York area, geographically the nearest to New Guinea, shows the least contrast with New Guinea.

8.   The skulls from the two small Keppel Islands off the coast of central Queensland must be accepted as unquestionably Australian Aboriginals, and yet as a population, they exhibit certain traits which place them in a somewhat special position within the framework of the general Australian people. As Klaatsch said of them in 1908, 'I do not care to term such a group of individuals a race'. What, then, are they? The answer appears to be that this small group exhibits the most striking instance we have seen of micro-evolution within the Australian Aboriginals.

9.   No evidence can be detected of the presence of a Negritic component in the Cairns rainforest Aboriginals. Although this area is relatively protected from intrusion, its population does not exhibit the same degree of micro-evolution as that shown by the Keppel Islanders. If it occurs in the Cairns rainforest at all it is minimal.

10.   The mass of metrical data provided by Hrdlicka entirely from his own measurements helps to support the finding of a north-south gradient in eastern Australia. Hrdlicka's metrical data also provide a picture of the distribution, state by state and measurement by measurement, of the Australian physical type and of its geographical modifications, and there is no question that changes in some frequencies do occur. For example, crania of the Northern Territory are smaller but higher than those of South Australia and are intermediate in these characters between South and Western Australia. There is a regional mosaic distribution of some of these traits and of course there is the largeness and massiveness of the Murray Valley skulls some extremes of which were referred to by Wood Jones (1934). We believe this is relevant to the Kow Swamp crania, some of which we have seen, but not been able to study. This will be discussed in more detail later.

11.   A detailed study of pooled eastern Australian mandibles also gave a method for the good separation of the sexes. A similar method also provided good discrimination between Australian and East Asian Mongoloid mandibles.

12.   A study of the ancient fossil crania recovered from Australia disclosed a preponderance of size and ruggedness in comparison with that seen in modern Australian skulls. Despite this, the fossil crania must be classed as belonging to the Australian Aboriginal physical type. No figures are available for the mean scores of these fossil skulls but our impression is that there is a better expression of the Aboriginal morphological pattern than is usually seen in modern Australian skulls. To use a word not often used these days, the 'Australianness' is not only distinct but seems to occur in a more exaggerated form in the fossil crania than in modern skulls.

13.   The Cohuna cranium has from time to time been accused of being a victim of artificial skull deformation. The late Dr Duckworth of England (personal communication) was one who so commented, and a number of non-Australian visitors have suggested such a possibility. Dr Dale Stewart was one who discounted the possibility immediately, but the late Dr Kotchetkova, shown a cast in Moscow in 1970, was vehemently insistent that it was artificially deformed. It seemed we should check this objectively. It took some time before the problem was solved. The key lay in a comparison between the parietal curvature indices (as measured with coordinate calipers). Artificially deformed skulls showing extreme frontal recession have a very high parietal

curvature index (with a range from 25·9 to 34·5). Fossil skulls showing extreme frontal recession are definitely cleared of any suspicion of artificial deformation if their parietal curvature index is less than 25 (Cohuna reads 22·5).

It is interesting to note that the Murrabit skull—a fossil Australian skull—is almost an identical twin to Cohuna. Its frontal curvature index is very nearly identical. It has a massive mandible.

14. A comparison of Australian skulls with those of *Homo erectus* clearly shows the complete absence of the *Homo erectus* cranial pattern in the former. The marked difference between the two groups of crania (a mean score of 7·7 for Australians contrasted with a mean score of 49 for *H. erectus*) is consistent with the vast time span separating them and distinctly obviates any risk of confusing one form with that of the other.

It has since transpired that some items need clarification or elaboration.

(a) Professor T. Jacob (1976) uses twenty of what he calls characteristic traits to discriminate between *Pithecanthropus* and other groups. Apparently these features apply more to the Javanese forms of *Homo erectus* than to other examples of *H. erectus*. In *Homo erectus leakeyi* (Olduvai hominid 9) some of these traits are absent. For example, there *is* a vaginal crest; there is no suprameatal tegmen; and the tympanic plate is orientated to produce a vertical external auditory meatus. In profile the angulation of the occipital is less acute than in either the Pekin or Javanese forms. Furthermore, owing to missing portions of the cranium it is sometimes impossible to form judgments about the status of some of the traits.

(b) Professor R. Dart accepted our discriminating pattern, but thought additional ethnic groups, including Africans should be tested. We had already found mean scores of 3·33 for Mongoloids, 2·6 for European, 5·3 for Maoris, 4·5 for American Negroes, 4·7 for New Guineans. The Aboriginal Australian shows a somewhat higher persistence of individual traits of the *H. erectus* pattern than the other five ethnic groups. Stewart (1974) apparently accepts our seventeen trait pattern and adds 'Although American populations do not figure in this comparison, in my opinion they would rate close to Macintosh and Larnach's Mongoloid sample'.

We have formed the opinion that the enthusiasm with which some Australian workers have embraced *H. erectus* for Australians should be cooled, and that the most archaic appearance we can expect in Australia is a very generalised example of early *H. sapiens sapiens*. Macintosh (1973) is already on record as saying that no *Homo erectus* pattern has been found in Australia and predicting that it never will be.

(c) Colin Groves (personal communication) pointed out that we had dropped two features from our *H. erectus* pattern i.e., the vaginal crest and the suprameatal spine. Both these traits are absent from Pekin Man and Java Man, but present in *H. erectus leakeyi*. Groves apparently thinks *leakeyi* should be dropped from *H. erectus*. Such line of thought completely ignores that *leakeyi* scores 46 out of a possible 51. No other hominid skull outside the Pekin and Javanese varieties comes anywhere near this.

(d) Professor Tobias in December 1973 (personal communication) suggested that we should have stressed the horizontality of the lateral supra-orbital wing when viewed from in front. In other skulls, including Neanderthals, Rhodesian, Australians etc., the lateral border of the trigone curves downwards, but never in *H. erectus*. He also drew our attention to the angulation of the skull base relative to frontal recession, but this will need further study.

15.   The suggestion by Weidenreich that Solo Man formed an ancestral stage in the evolution towards Australians, led us to extend our study to a comparison of Solo crania with Australian crania. It was concluded that Solo crania exhibited great morphological differences from any modern crania, and that the presence in the former skulls of some unique features make it extremely unlikely that they can be ancestral to Australians.

16.   We then made critical examination of the use of discontinuous traits in taxonomic work. We doubt the assumption of workers in this field that 'there are no sex differences in the incidences of the variants' and that sex can consequently be disregarded. We also express doubt regarding the selection of some traits, and show some scepticism regarding the ease of scoring some characters. The possible correlation of some traits is discussed. Furthermore the genetic basis of these traits is not always clear, and the genetic ancestry common to mice and men is so far back in time that to extrapolate conclusions from the former to the latter may sometimes be guesses (see for example Kellock and Parsons, 1970). We conclude that the use of discontinuous traits is best applied to the study of populations *within* a major group, and its application for the comparison *between* major groups, such as Australoids and Mongoloids, may give fallacious results.

17.   An attempt is made to find the place of the Aboriginal Australian in human taxonomy. Special attention is paid to the multivariate studies of W. W. Howells in his attempt to reach a classification of modern Man. The use of genetic data appears to support Howells' results. Howells in his verbal summing up at the Conference on which this volume is based referred to that mutual support; and additionally he revised his views (expressed in Howells, 1973c) about 'two extensions out of the head form of recent Australians', accepting instead that the extensions are variations within a single population, a view which the present authors have been advancing for some years. Thorne however, taking part in the same discussion, did not appear to agree, although his claims are less than expressed in Thorne and Macumber (1972).

Quest for identification

Elliot Smith (1931) said 'The earliest members of the species *Homo sapiens* found in Europe—namely the Aurignacian Grimaldi skeletons and the Combe Capelle skull—present certain analogies to the Australian. Hence it seems possible that during the upper Palaeolithic period in Europe members of the Australian race, or perhaps it would be less questionable to call it people presenting a proto-Australian likeness, may have reached eastern Europe (and possibly as far as the Italian Riviera and Combe Capelle in southern France). Nevertheless all the undoubted members of the Australian race lie east of Mesopotamia.'

Keith (1929) said 'More than any other man, the aborigine of Australia and Tasmania seems to have conserved the qualities of the stock which gave rise to all modern breeds. We may look upon him as the best living representative of Pleistocene man.'

In 1949 Keith was a little more explicit by using the word generalised. 'Taking him all in all, the Australian Aborigine represents better than any other living form the generalised features of primitive humanity.'

Napier (1971) deduces that modern races of man are a relatively recent phenomenon; that most authorities see them as rising from a common ancestor of *H. sapiens* stock such as Cro-Magnon Man perhaps some 30,000 years ago. Warmer post-glacial conditions opened up routes for migration and dispersion of *H. sapiens* and sufficient subsequent geographic isolation for the evolution of true races. He adds that it is possible 'that the original races of mankind (whatever they were) are of an even more recent origin than we suppose—perhaps not more than 10,000 years old'.

Poulianos (1974) considers that the Petralona skull exhibits both primitive and progressive morphological features, the latter being shown by an orthognathous face, the height of the brain case, the maxilla and the malar morphology. He sees a progressive trend from Swanscombe-Steinheim-Vertesszollos to Petralona towards modern man and concludes that modern man developed locally in Greece, not necessarily coming from western Asia.

On the other hand Howells (1973a) thinks that recent work tends to place the Petralona skull more towards the middle Pleistocene period. Although it needs to be properly cleaned and fully described, he sees it as showing recognisably *Homo erectus* features. The profile of the occipital is well angled and it slopes in rather sharply from a broad base. Hemmer (quoted by Howells, 1973a) has shown that 'relations of brain size and skull length are those of other *erectus* crania, conforming to its external features . . . from its size and form (it) appears to rate as a moderately advanced specimen in the whole erectus spectrum'.

Jelinek (1972) analysed 'the so-called superstructures of the skull', i.e. the supra-orbital arc, supramastoid crest, occipital torus and external occipital protuberance in a series of populations, beginning with eight Predmost skulls. The trace then successively dealt with 38 Neolithics, 72 upper Bronze Age, 49 Hallstatt Period and finally 59 old Slavic population, all series from Moravia and analysed separately for males and females. The 'superstructures' are shown to undergo progressive reduction and while relatively common in Neolithic and early and late Bronze Age, they had become rare in the early Middle Ages. Sexual dimorphism decreased *pari passu* with the reduction of robustness. However, there is little, if any, dispute about the Predmost skulls representing true *H. sapiens*.

Coon in 1965 said 'Southern China, southeast Asia, and those Indonesian islands which were joined to the continent during the glacial periods of low sea level, constitute the homeland of the Australoid subspecies'. He sees Mongoloids as crowding peripheral Australoids out to sea and also the possibility of continuous gene flow between the two races.

Howells (1973a) says in a footnote that he regards 'all populations of modern man as descended from one original source, however hybridised with other surviving forms some of them may have become eventually'. No single hypothesis can be upheld exclusively as to where they came from. In any event Neanderthals were replaced everywhere by modern men some 37,000 years ago. 'India', he says, 'unfortunately is a blank, little being known either archaeologically or skeletally'. In eastern Asia the evidence is slight. He quotes McNeish as considering entry of Man from Asia to America at about 27,000 years ago if not earlier. The skeletal remains found (Tepexpan, Minnesota, Midlands) appear to be general Indian in form.

Yamaguchi (1967) found that the results of metric and non-metric osteological comparisons and distance analyses are generally unfavourable for assumption of any relationship between the Ainu and the Australian Aboriginals. He suggests the Australians and the Ainu were derived from a generalised upper Palaeolithic or Mesolithic common population in Asia such as represented by Wadjak skulls from Java, Choukoutien Upper Cave remains, Liu-Kiang skull from south China and Niah skull from Borneo.

Jacob (1967) also made a somewhat similar suggestion, when he said that the Palawan Tabon skull 'might similarly reflect the same stage'. Later, Jacob (personal communication) has apparently made some most exciting discoveries, including the presumed contemporaneity of Solo Man and *Pithecanthropus*, and he places Solo closer to *modjokertensis* than to *erectus*. His views on Wadjak may have altered from those he expressed earlier.

Stewart (1974) has made a valuable comparison of early Australian Man and early American Man, the factors operating on the only two available exits from south-east Asia (one to the north-east and one to the south-east), factors operating on these migration routes and on the populations after arrival in their new continents. Although Macintosh (1974) had preceded it with a brief exposition on similar lines, Stewart's paper can be regarded as the first intensive study of such a comparison. Stewart points out that the timing of Man's crossing over from Asia 'is crucial to reconstructing everything that happened to him thereafter. To some extent this applies also to the sedentes—the men who remained back in Asia'. He says the surest way of pin-pointing arrival time is by finding remains and directly dating them if possible by isotopic means. He warns this is easier said than done, because 'the invasions probably began as a mere trickle and search for the remaining evidence, either at the entrance to, or within each *cul-de-sac* takes the character of looking for a needle in a haystack'.

Quoting the 1967 geological work of Hopkins, Stewart looks at three bridge Beringia periods of 10–14 thousand, 15–25 thousand and around approximately 50 thousand years. He sees parallels for Australia and concludes that time range for Man to start moving out of Asia at the two available exits (north-east to Alaska and southeast to Australia) must be geared to a time long before the last maximum lowering of sea-level. He apparently is indicating a ceiling of appreciably more than 50,000 years ago for the beginning of migration from Asia.

Support for Stewart's thinking may lie in a very recent and exciting report by Dr Jeffrey Bada, Oceanographer of the Scripps Institute. Professor Dart on 28 November 1972 recommended one of the present authors (N.W.G.M.) to study Bada's isoleucine racemisation dating of bone (some 55,000 years) from Zululand/Swaziland sites and to seek application of that technique to Australian material (preoccupation prevented us from pursuing that advice).

Human skeletal material housed for many years in the San Diego Museum was thought (as early as 1935 or even 1920) by geographer Dr George Carter to have high antiquity; but most other observers considered it to be in the order of 7500 years, which of course suggests that its morphological appearance could not have been very different from relatively modern North Amerind skeletal remains. In this regard, it is significant that Stewart (1974) said 'so far as the evidence goes, the earliest people to reach North America were little, if any, different from modern Indians . . . By contrast the Australian Aborigines, *early and late* (italics ours) appear to have been much more primitive looking . . . Also, their culture has remained on a very simple level.'

Now it appears that Dr Bada has obtained from that San Diego stored skeletal material readings of 48,000 years for bone collected from Del Mar and of 44,000 for bone collected from La Jolla (press reports, New York, May 1974).

The various authorities whom we have quoted, provide some common denominators on the subject of the emergence of a generalised form of *H. sapiens sapiens* morphologically, the relevance of isotopic dating, the overwhelming importance of the preservation of all skeletal material for re-examination by new techniques as they become available, and the application of geographic and climatic data.

An hypothesis

As recently as the mid 1950s, it was being asserted forcefully that Man had occupied Australia for no more than 8000 years. By the mid 1960s we had objective evidence for 16,000 years. Now we have proof that 32,000 years ago Aboriginal Man was firmly established in western New South Wales, and over 20,000 years ago at the extreme north, south and east coasts. Western Australia, long blank, apparently will soon announce antiquity of a high order at Miriwun on the Ord River and Devil's Lair in the extreme south-west (Dortch, 1976).

Such established antiquity is the most important contribution made to the potential solution of the origin and derivation of the Aboriginal Australian, because it brings him into contemporaneity with early Man elsewhere. No one doubts that the Aboriginal Australian is a genuine example of *H. sapiens sapiens*. He is not a partly modified *H. neanderthalensis* or *H. soloensis* or *H. erectus*, although he does exhibit a somewhat higher frequency of traits of the *H. erectus* pattern than five other present day peoples whom we have considered in relation to that pattern.

Admittedly the Australian skeletal remains are of lesser antiquity than the sites referred to above. The Mungo female (or females) of some 25,000 years (Bowler *et al*, 1970) is (are) gracile. Of somewhat similar date, a male skeleton exposed recently at Lake Mungo (Bowler and Thorne, 1976) was demonstrated by slides, as was its mandible on 21st May at this Conference. It appeared to Macintosh to be morphologically acceptable in a modern Aboriginal series.

One mile to the south of the Lake Nitchie skeleton site, Macintosh recovered cremated bone fragments which are directly collagen dated at 15,300 BP. Enough of the inion region of the occipital bone is present to indicate massive thickness, a mound-like torus and no external occipital protuberance.

Of the earlier found relics Talgai now has a minimum antiquity of 14,000 to 16,000 years. Its maximum age will not be known unless some new dating technique is invented. Keilor is 12,900 BP. If F.N.U. content comparisons are valid, Cohuna should be older than Talgai and Keilor. Murrabit although morphologically practically identical with Cohuna is apparently much younger. Mossgiel is not collagen dated. At a guess it might be up to 11,000 BP deduced from its bone carbonate C^{14} date and from its F.N.U. content. The Kow Swamp population is apparently 9000 to 10,000 BP.

In our opinion all these items fall within the range of modern series. Anatomical variation from 25,000 years ago to the present is unchanged and so appears to give overwhelming support for a homogeneous population.

In the opinion of Macintosh the Nitchie skeleton is anatomically intermediate in Aboriginal ranges, although its stature of 1875 mm is exceptionally tall for an Aboriginal male. It also has the highest number of archaic traits recorded for an Aboriginal skull. However the skull contours are more gracile than rugged in spite of its large size. Status burial is indicated because of associated red ochre, ritual fire, tooth avulsion and a necklace of 180 pierced *Sarcophilus* teeth. (For description of the Lake Nitchie site and burials see Bowler, 1970; Macintosh *et al*, 1970; Macintosh, 1971.)

A 4000 years old west coast Tasmanian skeleton presented by Dr A. Wallace at the Anatomical Society of Australia and New Zealand meeting in early 1974, is of classical Tasmanian form, and so predictably female which accords with Howells' 1973 findings (see Wallace and Doran, 1976).

How should we interpret this mélange of gracile, intermediate and rugged items? To us, there is only one answer; a practically unchanging population over a period of 25,000 years and exhibiting a wide range of variability.

Howells (1973c) offers a different opinion. He says 'I do not like to sound paradoxical in talking about two populations which (like my Australian colleagues) I nevertheless view as members of the same major stock, but that is the situation'. Howells—dispassionate and detached as always adds a footnote 'Macintosh is less impressed with the idea of extension, considering all the fossils to fall within the range of the total modern population'.

Dispassionate and detached in turn, Macintosh directs attention back to the 12th point enumerated above, which admits that the majority of ancient Australian crania disclose a preponderance of size and ruggedness compared in frequency with that seen in moderns.

Note however that Howells (at this Conference) reversed his published opinion, as already commented upon, and accepted the view of the present authors.

We now turn our attention to Graeme Pretty's work at Roonka. In many ways this is the most important and exciting excavation that has been carried out in Australia. Assiduous, and meticulous, the work has taken some years of patient tenacious effort. Apart from the excellent recording of the rich array of grave goods, the varied postures, the status identifications, there is the enormous significance of continuity of material from 18,000 years ago to the present, although the actual skeletons disappointingly only date from c 7000 to 8000 BP.

Dr M. Prokopec has undertaken to describe this material. The completed analysis of this material should provide striking illumination on the range of morphological change which may or may not be expressed in one region continuously over a period of time. Indeed, no other collection offers such opportunity. If these skeletons indeed be gracile in the main they will provide confirmation of the mosaic regional distribution of traits produced by the founder effect, and the local results of selection on the original migrants. This would account for the contrast between this population and that of Kow Swamp, and for that matter an extension of population through the Murray Valley (referred to by Wood Jones in the 1920s and 1930s). As illustrations of the mosaic distribution of traits we may note the following contrasts in Australia: the mean height index is least in South Australia and greatest in the Northern Territory and Queensland; the maximum cranial length is greatest in South Australia and least in the Northern Territory and Western Australia; the mean orbital index is greatest in South Australia and Queensland and least in Victoria; the basion-nasion length is longest in South Australia and shortest in Western Australia and Queensland; the maximum bizygomatic breadth is greatest in Victoria and least in the Northern Territory and Queensland; the maxillo-alveolar index is greatest in Queensland and least in South Australia and the Northern Territory; and the basion-alveolar point length is longest in Victoria and shortest in Queensland. These are but a few examples. Between these contrasts other states show intermediate values.

Outside the Australian continent

The oldest known example of a skull which is indubitably an example of *Homo sapiens sapiens* was excavated from Niah Cave in Borneo and dated from adjacent charcoal as 40,000 years old. There are more than a few recorded instances where dated charcoal is not contemporary with apparently associated bones and the need for a direct radiocarbon date on the collagen content of this Niah skull itself cannot be overstated. Even if the date of 40,000 years is not precisely accurate, it is reasonably close to the known minimum antiquity for the Australians; the Niah skull anatomy certainly falls within the Australian anatomical range and has been said to resemble the Australian Lake Mungo skull, dated at about 25,000 years.

The following examples of indubitable *H. sapiens sapiens* skulls from Europe together with their estimated ages are worth noting: Combe-Capelle 34,000 years, Predmost 30,000, Cro-Magnon 20,000–30,000, Piedmont 26,000, Vestonice 26,000. In America, the Tepexpan, Minnesota and Midlands skulls are now being credited with an antiquity of about 27,000 years. In the southeast Asian region skulls in the upper Choukoutien cave near Pekin are about 10,000 years old; some authorities say 30,000 years old. The Wadjak skulls of Java anatomically similar to the Keilor skull from Australia (13,000 years old) are undated. The 23,000 years old Tabon Cave relics from Palawan in the Philippines have been identified tentatively by Macintosh as matching only the Aboriginal Australians. These skulls, together with other Asian skulls such as Sampung show some similarity of basic morphology, as though derived from a generalised upper Palaeolithic population emergent as *H. sapiens sapiens* but not yet clearly differentiated into races. Attempting to deduce some pattern from the chronology and the distribution of these relics, we are freed from the task of trying anatomically to make the Aboriginal Australian a descendant of any of them.

Now the startling possibility emerges that southern China some 70,000 years ago was a common dispersal area for the earliest generalised type of *H. sapiens sapiens* and that radiating migrations were an exploding phenomenon of the warm Interstadial of 4-Wurm I and II between 30,000 and 40,000 years ago (Kurten, 1968). Migrations hiving off to the northeast via Behring Straits which were free of glaciation 30,000 years ago would have had little difficulty in reaching Alaska but would have experienced extreme difficulty in finding an ice free corridor for entry to the American plains. Migrations hiving off to the west faced the obstacles of central Asian high altitude plateau and mountain ranges with ice sheets, thus necessitating a more southerly route through India, and the subsequent encounter with the Neanderthal peoples of western Asia and Europe.

But to the southwest via Indonesia, the Philippines and Sulawesi, the migration route had only one hazard, the sea crossing of the Wallace and Weber Deeps.

If further work in chronology and comparative anatomy should confirm this pattern, we could postulate the Aboriginal Australians as the earliest examples of evolving generalised modern *H. sapiens sapiens* to arrive in their ultimate area of migration. This hypothesis would also explain why Aboriginal Australians have retained a moderately higher frequency of *Homo erectus* traits than other modern *sapiens* groups.

References

BOWLER, J. M.   1970   Lake Nitchie skeleton—stratigraphy of the burial site. *Archaeology and Physical Anthropology in Oceania*, 5(2):102–13.
——   1976   Recent developments in reconstructing Late Quaternary environments in Australia. In *The origin of the Australians*, R. L. Kirk and A. G. Thorne (eds), pp. 55–77. Australian Institute of Aboriginal Studies, Canberra.
——, D. J. MULVANEY, D. A. CASEY and T. A. DARRAGH   1967   Green Gully burial. *Nature*, 213:152–54.
——, R. JONES, H. ALLEN and A. G. THORNE   1970   Pleistocene human remains from Australia: a living site and human cremation from Lake Mungo, western N.S.W. *World Archaeology*, 2(1):39–60.
COON, C. S.   1965   *The living races of Man*. Alfred A. Knopf, New York.
DORTCH, C.   1976   Early and late stone industrial phases in Western Australia. In *Stone tools as cultural markers*, R. V. S. Wright (ed), Australian Institute of Aboriginal Studies, Canberra. (in press).

FENNER, F. J.   1941   Fossil human skull fragments of probable Pleistocene age from Aitape, New Guinea. *Records of the South Australian Museum*, 6:335–56.
FREEDMAN, L.   1964   Metrical features of Aboriginal crania of coastal N.S.W. *Records of the Australian Museum*, 26(12):309–25.
GILES, E.   1976   Morphological variation in Australia and neighbouring areas. In *The origin of the Australians*, R. L. Kirk and A. G. Thorne (eds), pp. 161–172. Australian Institute of Aboriginal Studies, Canberra.
HOWELLS, W. W.   1973a   *Evolution of the genus Homo*. Addison-Wesley, Massachusetts.
——   1973b   *Cranial variation in man*. Papers of the Peabody Museum, 67.
——   1973c   *The Pacific Islanders*. Weidenfeld & Nicolson, London.
——   1976   Metrical analysis in the problem of Australian origin. In *The origin of the Australians*, R. L. Kirk and A. G. Thorne (eds), pp. 141–160. Australian Institute of Aboriginal Studies, Canberra.
JACOB, T.   1967   *The racial history of the Indonesian region*. Utrecht: Neerlandia.
——   1976   Early populations in the Indonesian region. In *The origin of the Australians*, R. L. Kirk and A. G. Thorne (eds), pp. 81–93. Australian Institute of Aboriginal Studies, Canberra.
JELINEK, J.   1972   Supraorbitale Morphologie, Torus Occipitalis and Geschlechts-dimorphismus in der Entwicklung der vorzeitlichen Populationem Mitteleuropas. *Homo* 1(2):89–100.
JONES, R.   1973   Emerging picture of Pleistocene Australians. *Nature*, 246:278–81.
KEITH, A.   1929   *The antiquity of man*. Vol. 2. Williams & Norgate, London.
——   1949   *A new theory of human evolution*. Watts, London.
KELLOCK, W. L. and P. A. PARSONS   1970   Variation of minor non-metrical cranial variants in Australian Aborigines. *American Journal of Physical Anthropology*, 32:409–31.
KLAATSCH, H.   1908   The skull of the Australian Aboriginal. *Report from the Pathological Laboratory of the Lunacy Department, New South Wales Government*, 1(3):43–167.
KURTEN, B.   1968   *Pleistocene mammals of Europe*. Weidenfeld & Nicolson, London.
LARNACH, S. L. and L. FREEDMAN   1964   Sex determination of Aboriginal crania from coastal N.S.W. *Records of the Australian Museum*, 26(11):295–308.
—— and N. W. G. MACINTOSH   1966   *Craniology of Aborigines of coastal N.S.W.* Oceania Monograph No. 13, University of Sydney.
—— and ——   1967   The use in forensic medicine of an anthropological method for determination of sex and race in skeletons. *Archaeology and Physical Anthropology in Oceania*, 2(2):156–61.
—— and ——   1970   *Craniology of the Aborigines of North Queensland*. Oceania Monograph No. 15, University of Sydney.
—— and ——   1971   *The mandible in eastern Australian Aborigines*. Oceania Monograph No. 17, University of Sydney.
—— and ——   1972   The Keppel Islanders. *Archaeology and Physical Anthropology in Oceania*, 7(1):8–14.
—— and ——   1974   A comparative study of Solo and Australian Aboriginal crania. In *Grafton Elliot Smith: The man and his work*, A. P. Elkin and N. W. G. Macintosh (eds), Sydney University Press, Sydney.
MACINTOSH, N. W. G.   1949   A survey of possible sea routes available to the Tasmanian Aborigines. *Record of the Queen Victoria Museum*, 2(3):123–44.
——   1952   Stature in some Aboriginal tribes in southwest Arnhem Land. *Oceania*, 22:208–15.
——   1963   Origin and physical differentiation of the Australian Aborigines. *Australian Natural History*, 14(8):248–52.
——   1965   The physical aspect of Man in Australia. In *Aboriginal man in Australia*, R. M. and C. H. Berndt (eds). Angus & Robertson, Sydney.
——   1967   Fossil man in Australia. *Australian Journal of Science*, 30(3):86–98.
——   1971   Analysis of an Aboriginal skeleton and a pierced tooth necklace from Lake Nitchie, Australia. *Anthropologie*, 9(1):49–62.
——   1972   Radiocarbon dating as a pointer in time to the arrival and history of man in Australia and Islands to the north-west. *Proceedings of the 8th International Conference on Radiocarbon Dating*, Wellington, N.Z.: XLIV–LVI.

———   1974   Early man and the dog in Australia. In *Grafton Elliot Smith: The man and his work*, A. P. Elkin and N. W. G. Macintosh (eds), pp. 83–94. Sydney University Press.

—— and B. C. W. BARKER   1965   *The Osteology of Aboriginal Man in Tasmania.* Oceania Monograph No. 12, University of Sydney.

——, K. N. SMITH and A. B. BAILEY   1970   Lake Nitchie skeleton—Unique Aboriginal burial. *Archaeology and Physical Anthropology in Oceania*, 5(2):85–101.

——, and S. L. LARNACH   1972   The persistence of *H. erectus* traits in Australian Aboriginal crania. *Archaeology and Physical Anthropology in Oceania*, 7(1):1–7.

—— and ——   1973   Cranial study of Queensland with a contrast between Australian and New Guinea crania. In *The human biology of Aborigines in Cape York*, R. L. Kirk (ed), pp. 1–12. Australian Institute of Aboriginal Studies, Canberra.

MULVANEY, D. J.   1969   *The prehistory of Australia.* Thames & Hudson, London.

NAPIER, J.   1971   *The roots of mankind.* George Allen & Unwin, London.

POULIANOS, A. N.   1974   The transitional period from the Neanderthaloid stage to *Homo sapiens*. Anthropos, Athens, 1(1):5–10.

SMITH, G. E.   1931   The Evolution of man. In *Early man: his origin, development and culture*, pp. 13–46. Ernest Benn Limited, London.

STEWART, T. D.   1974   Perspectives on some problems of early man common to America and Australia. In *Grafton Elliot Smith: The man and his work*, A. P. Elkin and N. W. G. Macintosh (eds), pp. 114–35. Sydney University Press, Sydney.

THORNE, A. G.   1976   Morphological contrasts in Pleistocene Australians. In *The origin of the Australians*, R. L. Kirk and A. G. Thorne (eds), pp. 95–112. Australian Institute of Aboriginal Studies, Canberra.

—— and P. G. MACUMBER   1972   Discoveries of late Pleistocene man at Kow Swamp, Australia. *Nature*, 238:316–19.

WALLACE, A. C.   1974   Early Tasmanian morphology—new archaeological evidence. *12th Annual Conference A.S.A.N.Z.*, Sydney, pp. 33–34.

—— and G. A. DORAN   1976   Early man in Tasmania. In *The origin of the Australians*, R. L. Kirk and A. G. Thorne (eds), pp. 173–183. Australian Institute of Aboriginal Studies, Canberra.

WEIDENREICH, F.   1943   The skull of *Sinanthropus pekinensis*. Palaeontol. Sinica N.S., D. 10:1–298.

WOOD JONES, F.   1934   Contrasting types in Australian skulls. *Journal of Anatomy*, 68:323–30.

YAMAGUCHI, B.   1967   *Comparative osteological study of the Ainu and the Australian Aborigines.* Australian Institute of Aboriginal Studies, Canberra.

Human remains from Lake Mungo

Discovery and excavation of Lake Mungo III

J.M. Bowler and A.G. Thorne

ON FEBRUARY 26, 1974, in the course of a general review of the geomorphology and stratigraphy of the Willandra lakes, Bowler was examining the southern end of the Lake Mungo lunette (Figure 1). At this locality two major stratigraphic units have been recognised—Zanci, a zone of upper grey aeolian calcareous silts and Mungo, an underlying basal sequence of beach-derived aeolian sands partly cemented by calcrete (Bowler, 1971). The lower or Mungo unit at this site was deposited during a period of high lake level between 40,000 and 25,000 BP, a period that coincided with the maximum extent of glacial conditions in the southeastern highlands. Bowler's examination was concentrated on this unit in the hope of finding new evidence bearing on the environment and occupation relating to this important period.

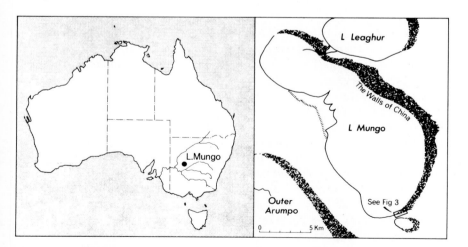

Figure 1 Map showing the location of Lake Mungo in southwestern New South Wales and the area at the southern end of the lunette where human skeletal remains have been discovered.

Prolonged and heavy rains during 1973 had swept across the eroded dune surface, uncovering a new crop of archaeologic and other prehistoric finds. At a point some 500 m east of the Lake Mungo I cremation/burial site (Bowler *et al*, 1970) the late afternoon sun was highlighting a small white object protruding through the sandy surface at a stratigraphic level deep within the Mungo unit. Closer examination revealed the object to be the exposed left side of a carbonate-encrusted human cranium. The central area of exposed bone protruded some 2–3 cm above the eroded surface. Much of the bone was coated with a thin layer of calcrete which was pinkish in colour, a feature not known from carbonate of similar age elsewhere in this horizon. Blowing away loose drift sand revealed the left orbit, several maxillary teeth of the left side and the lateral surface of the left mandibular condyle. The left zygomatic bone was missing but no evidence of it or other bone fragments could be found in the erosion products downslope from the cranium. Rather than probe further Bowler, recognising that the cranium alone was sufficient to justify detailed excavation, contacted Thorne in Canberra.

On Thursday February 28, W. F. Shawcross, S. N. Rajaguru, C. P. Groves, Anthea Carstairs and Thorne arrived at Lake Mungo to undertake with Bowler the investigation of the remains and their stratigraphic and chronologic significance.

Excavation of the remains

Several factors demanded immediate investigation and removal of the skeletal remains. Firstly, the exposed surfaces of the cranium were fragile, despite a thin carbonate encrustation, and several areas of collapsed and crumbling bone were visible. The missing left zygomatic bone appeared to have been detached from the cranium by force, rather than through erosion. Stock grazing in the paddock enclosing this area of the lunette could well have been responsible for the damage. The area on the lunette in which the bones lay consisted of loose sands in the process of relatively rapid erosion. Finally, the threat of heavy rain, with possible destruction of the site, imposed an additional urgency.

After removing loose sand from around the cranium, minor probing defined the left side of the mandible. Although slightly displaced the bone lay in a general position of articulation with the cranium, suggesting that the remains might have resulted from the burial of a fleshed or partly-fleshed cadaver. Unlike the cremated remains of Lake Mungo I there was no evidence of burning around the skeletal remains or of the bones themselves.

A 2 m by 30 cm trench was excavated in plan across an area considered likely to reveal the lower part of any thoracic skeleton present, the general orientation of any other post-cranial remains and any signs of grave margins. At a depth of approximately 5 cm the distal ends of both humeri were uncovered. The proximal ends of the radii and ulnae were located and traced distally. Subsequently, the upper parts of the left iliac crest and left femur were located and exposed. From their orientation the right femur was exposed and traced distally. At this point it was clear that at disposal the left knee had overlain its fellow but considerable deterioration of the skeleton in this region made precise identification difficult. However, the proximal ends of the tibiae and fibulae were located and the bones exposed. The bones of the ankles and feet had undergone deterioration similar to that of the knee region. Sufficient fragments of the left foot remained to establish that at the time of disposal it had been rotated laterally, so that the foot pointed upwards.

It was apparent during excavation that all bones were extremely fragile. For this reason exposure of individual bones was limited to a demonstration of the general orientation of the skeleton. The extent of excavation is seen in Figure 2.

Because of this skeletal fragility, very few individual bones were excavated so as to reveal their lower surfaces. In three of the four areas where this was done—right ulna, mid-shaft of left femur and mid-shaft of left tibia—the lower surfaces of the bones were severely eroded. This is attributed to the action of water penetrating the carbonate crust and passing beneath the bones to lie between the lower surface of the bones and their enveloping carbonate crust. The fourth area in which the lower bone surface was excavated involved the mandible; in this case the right half of the bone appeared to be well preserved.

To reduce the risk of further damage to the remains the skeleton was removed in blocks of sand. The post-cranial bones were removed with as much surrounding grave fill and carbonate crust as possible, usually in small blocks containing several bones. The cranium and mandible were removed in a single unit 50 × 50 × 30 cm.

Almost as soon as excavation began it was apparent that the pink colouration, noticed by Bowler at the time of discovery, had a wide distribution around the skeleton. We believe the pink staining to be due to the scattering of a quantity of a red ochre over the cadaver in the prepared grave. Small lumps of ochre were recovered but it is likely the bulk of the ochre was scattered over the cadaver as a powder. In the unconsolidated sands the extent of ochre colouration indicated the size, depth and shape of the grave, particularly around the upper half of the skeleton.

If the limits of pink staining can be taken to represent the grave margins a preliminary statement can be made of the disposal procedure. A shallow grave, 1·8 m by 1·3 m, was excavated in soft quartz sand on the southern flank of the lunette which, from reconstruction using sediment structure, was sloping 20° to the south, away from the lake shore. The cadaver was placed in the grave essentially on its back, but rotated slightly to the right side. As the right shoulder was rotated towards the head and the head rotated to the right side, the mandible came to lie over the right clavicle. The hands were placed together, over the lower part of the pelvis. The left knee lay over the right and the right foot lay under the left ankle. The left foot was rotated so that it projected upwards.

The vertex of the cranium lay approximately 5 cm from the cranial end of the grave. The region of the right elbow lay at or about the limit of red

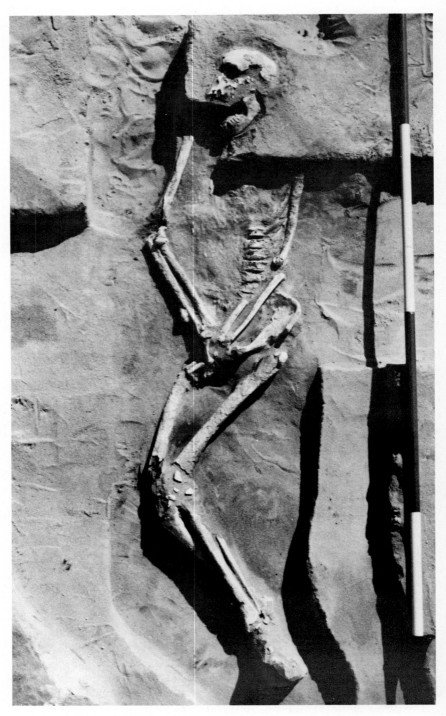

Figure 2   The Lake Mungo III burial during excavation. Scale in 50 cm units.

ochre staining, suggesting that at burial the right elbow rested against the wall of the grave on that side. The left humerus lay some 40 cm from the edge of the stained area on that side, that is, well within the limits of the prepared grave. The zone of pink staining faded in the region of the pelvis, except for a dense concentration around the bones of the hands. The grave limits on either side of this area were indistinct. Another, smaller area of staining was visible around the knees, which like the right elbow, appeared to rest against one wall of the grave, as indicated by the abrupt, vertical termination of the pink staining. The stained area faded rapidly below the knees and was not discernible beyond the area where the left tibia and fibula lay over their fellows. The grave margins in the area of the feet were not detected. However, the fact that the left foot was rotated so as to face upwards may indicate that it rested against the wall of the grave. The slight flexion of the legs supports this conclusion. The long axis of the grave, based on a line from cranium to feet, was 25° east of north.

Laboratory excavation of the sections of grave fill that surrounded the skeleton when it was removed may provide additional information about the dimensions and contents of the grave and further details of the disposal of this individual.

Skeletal morphology

Until the remains are fully prepared and reconstructed no detailed statement concerning the osteological characteristics of this individual can be made. As the remains are fragile, eroded and broken their removal from encrusting carbonate and subsequent reconstruction will be a lengthy process. However, a few general remarks can be made.

The skeleton is that of an adult individual. Parts of the sagittal and coronal sutures display advanced closure externally. Pronounced osteo-arthritic lipping is evident on the lower thoracic and lumbar vertebral bodies. Both mandibular third molars are fully erupted and occlusal abrasion has removed the bulk of their occlusal enamel surfaces. Both mandibular canine teeth and the right first and second molars had been lost premortem. The alveolar surfaces surrounding the canine sockets had undergone extensive resorption.

No evidence as to sex is available from the cranium as yet, or from post-cranial sources. However the mandible has been assessed in terms of the sexing method of Larnach and Macintosh (1971) in which mandibles with scores of 20–33 are classed as male. The Lake Mungo III mandible has a score of 24 using this method, suggesting that the individual is male. The general form of the mandible and of the presently exposed areas of the cranium show no signs of the robusticity that characterises most other prehistoric skeletal remains from Australia. This may be significant if the skeleton is indeed male, and given the 'extreme gracility' of the Lake Mungo I cranium (Thorne, 1971).

Stratigraphy of the burial

To establish the stratigraphic position of the burial and to pinpoint the level from which insertion took place we used three sources of evidence:

1.   from the burial excavation;
2.   from a shallow trench dug across the strike of the dune, 2 m west of the remains; and
3.   from a larger trench 2 m deep and 11 m long, dug with tractor and back-hoe at right-angles to the axis of the dune and some 8 m west of the skeleton (A—A[1] in Figure 3).

Data from these three closely spaced excavations enable us to reconstruct in detail the burial and subsequent depositional stratigraphy.

In this region the Mungo unit can be subdivided into a number of soil-sedimentary zones. The core zone consists of medium sized well sorted quartz sands deposited during a high water stand in the lake. During the period of high water-level corresponding to the most intense human occupation, a low foredune of well sorted quartz sand was blown from the beach nearby. When this dune had grown to moderate size it was colonised and stabilised by vegetation. On the stable surface organic matter accumulated and carbonates were leached to more than a metre below its surface; in this way a well developed soil horizon was formed. The concentration of carbonate and the persistence of alkaline environments in the lower horizons of this ancient soil provides one of the best locations for the preservation of bone and shell. It was in such a zone that the cemented bones of the Lake Mungo I cremation were preserved along with adjacent hearths and food remains (Bowler *et al*, 1970). In February 1973 low altitude vertical aerial photographs of this site had been taken in colour and black and white by Bowler. The soil-sedimentary zone was then mapped on these (Figure 3), enabling us immediately to place the remains in their correct stratigraphic context in relationship to other dated horizons in this sequence.

The skeleton was located in soft calcareous, well-sorted medium quartz sands similar to those that comprise the core of the Mungo unit at this locality. The shallow trench nearby revealed a sequence in which a zone of dark humic-stained non-calcareous sands 0·8 m thick dipped to the south in a stratigraphic position immediately above the skeleton. This zone of weak organic accumulation passed down to quartz sands, weakly cemented by diffuse soft earthy carbonate located 1·5 to 2·5 m below the uppermost level of dark sands. The association of humic rich sands leached of carbonate passing down to the carbonate rich zone defined the well developed buried soil within the lower Mungo unit. This horizon had been mapped over some 5 km of the lunette and dated elsewhere in the sequence (see Table 1).

The second task that confronted us was to establish whether the grave was dug into a pre-existing soil or whether it pre-dated the main period of pedogenesis.

Excavation revealed the presence of a grave outlined by a difference in colour between the sediment immediately adjacent to the remains and that of the surrounding sands. This was due mainly to the presence of ochre

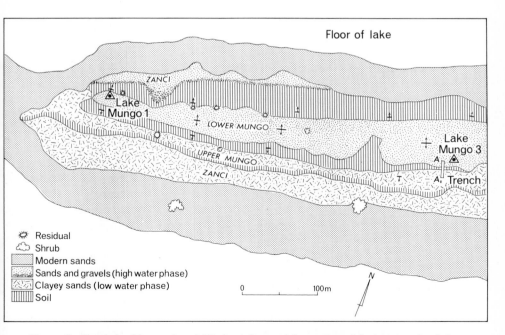

Figure 3 The Lake Mungo I and III sites shown (a) on an aerial photograph of the southern portion of the lunette and (b) on a plan of lunette stratigraphy drawn to the same scale.

Table 1: Radiocarbon dates from various localities on the Lake Mungo
dune relating to age of the Mungo unit

ANU Lab. No.	C[14] Age	Sample Description
[1]618B	24,710 ± 1270 1100	HCl insoluble residue from human remains Lake Mungo I
[2]689	25,310 ± 810	Carbon from fireplace at base of greenish grey sandy clay (Upper Mungo)
[2]686	25,570 ± 520	Carbon from fireplace at base of greenish grey sandy clay (Upper Mungo) near contact with grey-brown sand (Lower Mungo)
[1]375B	26,250 ± 1120	Carbon from hearth in horizon equivalent to Mungo I cremation within Lower Mungo unit
[2]667	26,270 ± 270	Carbon from oven at base of greenish grey clayey sand
[2]685	28,140 ± 410	Carbon from under baked clay in grey brown sand (Lower Mungo)
[2]683	28,310 ± 410	Carbon from fireplace in grey brown sand of Lower Mungo unit
[2]680	30,780 ± 520	As for 683
[3]331	32,750 ± 1250	Unionid shells on eroded surface cut across Lower Mungo unit 1·5 km east of Lake Mungo III burial
[2]687	35,300 ± 1550 1300	Carbon from burnt area on Lower Mungo soil 10 km north of burial site

[1] Bowler *et al* (1972).
[2] Barbetti and Polach (1973).
[3] Bowler (1971).

which was expressed as a faint reddish zone outlining the original position
of the body. The bones, especially the feet and lower parts of the legs which
extended south into the higher part of the soil sequence, were covered and
weakly cemented by a crust of white calcrete. This corresponded to and was
the continuation of the zone of maximum carbonate accumulation which
extends along the deflation surface remaining stratigraphically just below the
dark A-horizon. Two lines of evidence therefore provided presumptive
evidence that burial occurred before the main period of pedogenesis:

1.   The dark humic stained sands of the A-horizon were not present
      in the grave fill, as would be the case if the grave had been dug
      through and infilled by pre-existing A-horizon sands. The colour
      contrast between fill and surrounding sediment would therefore
      be considerably greater than the weak colour differentiation
      that outlined the grave.

2.   The degree of carbonate cementation of the bones was compar-
      able with that of the surrounding B-horizon sediments, suggesting
      that the main period of carbonate organisation occurred after
      burial.

One further line of field evidence remained to be established. Although
deflation had removed the cover sands down to all but a few centimetres
above the post-cranial remains, trenching alongside the burial enabled us to
reconstruct the stratigraphic section of the dune surface into which it was

inserted. Assuming that in soft sands the depth of the grave would be not more than about 1 m, this enabled us to establish the approximate maximum horizon from which burial took place. The upper level of A-horizon sands representing the stable surface during pedogenesis, when reconstructed and projected in cross-section across the burial site, lay at least 1·5 to 2 m higher than the cranium. Therefore the grave was not dug from the surface of this soil but from an earlier horizon at least 0·5 m below that surface. Some sediment accumulation occurred on the dune after burial and during the period of soil organisation. Burial took place before that final accumulation of quartz sand and before the main period of pedogenesis as represented by the accumulation of the overlying dark organic zone and associated carbonate segregation.

Age of burial soil

As indicated above, the dark soil developed above the skeleton can be traced extensively along the length of the Mungo lunette. At the site of the cremation it occurs as a truncated soil with diffuse organic staining which, mixed with carbonate, produces a distinct ashen grey appearance. It corresponds there to zone 3 of Figure 12 of Bowler et al (1970).

Further to the north, occupational hearths in which Barbetti (1972) established a palaeomagnetic excursion about 30,000 BP are located in a horizon with similar pedogenic and stratigraphic relationships to that observed at the burial (Barbetti and Polach, 1973). Similarly, at a number of other sites further north along the lunette the dark soil with its characteristic carbonate segregation occurs in an identical stratigraphic position.

Perhaps the most important aspect that enables us to identify the burial soil and to extrapolate between sites is this soil's relationship to the sediment that immediately overlies it. Between the dark A-horizon and the upper level of the Mungo unit as defined by the reddish brown A-horizon, there lies an important zone of calcareous clayey sands, finer in texture and with a higher clay content than the basal well-sorted sands of the Mungo unit. This clay-rich member contains well preserved laminae with sub-planar bedding typical of aeolian clay deposits. The presence of clay pellets observed in thin-section confirm its origin by deflation from a partly exposed lake floor during a drying phase. The oscillation it represents came after the high and stable water-level phase represented by the earlier well sorted quartz sands derived from wave nourished lake beaches.

The contact between the lower quartz sands and the upper clay-rich member is everywhere abrupt and wherever a complete sequence is preserved the dark soil always lies immediately below that contact. The base of the aeolian clay, representing as it does an oscillation in lake level, may reliably be assumed to be the same age throughout the length of the Mungo lunette. Thus from ages determined at one site, we may extrapolate reliably to others along the lunette.

Radiocarbon dates available from the organic soil and related horizons at several sites along the dune are listed in Table 1.

Age of burial

The burial was inserted before the main period of pedogenesis represented by the dark buried soil. From the general pattern of available dates pedogenesis was already active by 32,000 BP but ceased with the deposition of the overlying calcareous clayey sands about 25,000 BP. The burial is therefore considerably older than 25,000 years and in pre-dating pedogenesis it may indeed be approaching 32,000 years in age. It is worth recalling that the age limits 25,000 to 32,000 BP were those estimated for the Lake Mungo I cremation before radiocarbon dates from the actual site were available (Bowler et al, 1970). Radiocarbon dates subsequently suggested that the age of that burial was close to 26,000 BP (Bowler et al, 1972). In its stratigraphic position, the Lake Mungo III burial is almost indistinguishable from the first. However, its position relative to the early phase of pedogenesis is clearer and more diagnostic. Whereas Lake Mungo I lay in a sequence thin enough to allow it to be influenced by both the early and later phases of Mungo pedogenesis, this new burial lay some 6 to 10 m below the projected surface of the upper Mungo soil (Figure 4). It was therefore influenced only by the single, early soil forming phase that ended by 25,000 BP.

On the basis of this evidence a minimum of 3,000 years would seem necessary to account for post-burial pedogenetic modification of the remains. Since this modification was completed by 25,000 BP, the soil stratigraphic evidence suggests a minimum age of 28,000 BP for the burial with an age close to 30,000 BP seeming more realistic.

Radiocarbon samples have been selected for direct dating from sediment and other materials in close association with the burial. The materials available are those listed below:

1. Diffuse organic carbon from a small sub-circular concentration 40 cm in diameter located 1 m south of the skeleton and close to the base of the buried A-horizon;
2. Charcoal fragments associated with burnt animal bones from a small hearth in grey calcareous sediments of the aeolian phase overlying the reddish brown upper Mungo soil 3 to 4 m above the burial;
3. Soil carbonate from cemented B-horizon 0·5 m west of the remains from a horizon equivalent to that cementing the bones;
4. Carbonate encrustation surrounding the bones;
5. Fragments of the human bone for dating of carbonate and collagen components.

Unfortunately all the materials available for direct radiocarbon dating present some difficulties or other. No charcoal or shell that might be regarded as suitable for reliable dating occurred in direct association with the burial. Furthermore, since the bones were not burnt, dating by collagen in these materials known to exceed 20,000 BP cannot be expected to provide a tight age control. The use of carbonate here is designed to test the rapidity with which carbonate in soil and bone is equilibrated with younger carbon.

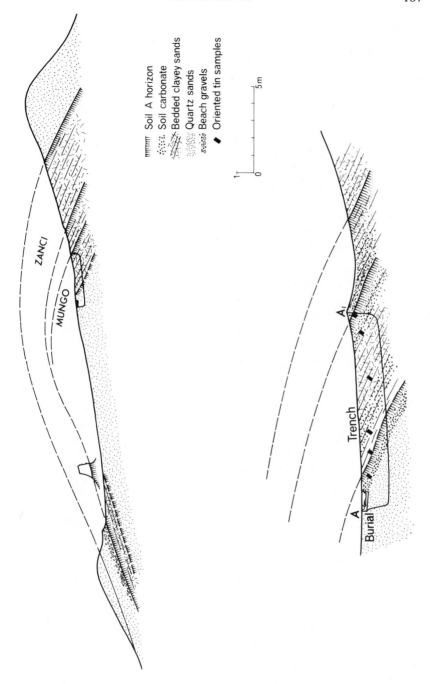

Figure 4 Sections through the eroding lunette showing the stratigraphic relationship of the Lake Mungo III remains to sedimentary features. The orientation of the trench section A-A' is indicated in Figure 3b.

However, a comparison of C^{14} activity of bone and soil carbonate will provide a means of determining if any considerable age difference exists between them. In other words, if the burial was inserted into pre-existing soil in which carbonate segregation was already well advanced the phase of carbonate cementation that affected the bones should, being younger, have a higher activity than the carbonate of the soil into which the burial was inserted. On the other hand, if the age of the burial is close to or pre-dates the earliest phase of pedogenesis its carbonate will register a level of C^{14} activity similar to that of the soil.

In summary, the materials available for radiocarbon dating, whilst providing a test for the stratigraphically based chronology, are unlikely to refine the burial age beyond those limits established here by stratigraphic correlation. With the main period of pedogenesis known to have taken place before 26,000 BP and the burial inserted during or before this event, the age estimated at between 28,000 to 32,000 BP may be as precise as both present and future circumstances will allow.

Conclusions

1. Lake Mungo III represents the first discovery of articulated human remains older than 15,000 years BP from Australia and expands the morphological and cultural information available from the earliest known period of Man's occupation of the continent.

2. The remains result from the primary burial of a fleshed cadaver, rather than from cremation followed by burial.

3. The age of the burial is at least 28,000 years BP and probably closer to 30,000 BP. Therefore this individual may stem from the same population as that represented by Lake Mungo I.

4. Preliminary anatomical analyses indicate that Lake Mungo III is morphologically consistent with Lake Mungo I and contrasts with the more recent Kow Swamp population that is robust and characterised by osteologically primitive features.

References

BARBETTI, M.   1972   Evidence of a geomagnetic excursion 30,000 yr BP. *Nature*, 239:327–30.
—— and H. POLACH   1973   A.N.U. Radiocarbon Datelist V. *Radiocarbon*, 15: 241–51.
BOWLER, J. M.   1971   Pleistocene salinities and climatic change: evidence from lakes and lunettes in south-eastern Australia. In *Aboriginal man and environment in Australia*, D. J. Mulvaney and J. Golson (eds), pp. 41–65. Australian National University Press, Canberra.
——, R. JONES, H. ALLEN and A. G. THORNE   1970   Pleistocene human remains from Australia: a living site and human cremation from Lake Mungo, western New South Wales. *World Archaeology*, 2:39–60.
——, A. G. THORNE and H. POLACH   1972   Pleistocene Man in Australia: age and significance of the Mungo skeleton. *Nature*, 240:48–50.
LARNACH, S. L. and N. W. G. MACINTOSH   1971   *The mandible in eastern Australian Aborigines*. Oceania Monographs 17, University of Sydney.
THORNE, A. G.   1971   Mungo and Kow Swamp: Morphological variation in Pleistocene Australians. *Mankind*, 8(2):85–89.

Morphological Variation

Morphological Analysis

Metrical analysis in the problem of Australian origins

author W.W. Howells

WITH THE DEMONSTRATION of early arrival in the continent, the problem of Australian Aboriginal origins has changed dramatically in the last decade. Particularly important is the discovery of skeletons of varying antiquity, and the authentication of others found earlier but until recently held in suspicion. The net effect is to remove the previously existing limitation on analysis, that of basing reconstructions of origin wholly on the study of the living Aboriginals and on skeletons presumed to be of the same populations and of generally recent date. Not that such analysis has lost importance. But, in approaching biological origins through morphology, this means that skeletal material, particularly crania, takes on new dimensions.

In applying metrical analysis we must in fact rely to a great extent on recent material in order to have the quantity and specificity of data which is needed in order to develop the kind of population parameters sought. And even this is far from sufficing to answer positively all the questions we would like to ask.

But there is no harm in asking. We may address ourselves to a series of problems, however well we may answer them, by working outward from Australia and downward in time, to a certain extent concomitantly. The following problems strike me as important.

Does variation among living populations of the continent (or among their crania), not including the Tasmanians, shed light on the past? This is not something I can answer from my data and analysis, but others (e.g., Fenner, Birdsell, Abbie, Macintosh and Larnach, and present work by Giles) have applied themselves to it. It does now seem that reconstructions based on the historic people alone, and concerned primarily with homogeneity or hybridity as the secret of Aboriginal origins, have not arrived at the answer: for example, the scenario of the past predicted by Birdsell's tri-hybrid hypothesis (1967) has not been sustained by the new prehistoric evidence.

What is the meaning of variation among the early skeletons? This is a most pressing matter now that many such are known and dates are falling into place. In this case the solution lies in more of the same. But this is another matter I cannot deal with here.

What is the nature of the differences between Australians and Melanesians? Macintosh has observed (1965) that the Australians form one pattern, the Papuo-Melanesians another. There are subsidiary questions. Are the Tasmanians essentially 'Melanesian' in any such dichotomy as this? What is the degree of the differences among all these relative to other populations near and far? What is the nature of variation among the Melanesians, skeletal or living; i.e., such things as the Australoid appearance of some (in eastern Melanesia) and the non-Australoid appearance of others? Most of these are matters for which multivariate studies have some positive answers.

Do the Australians, Tasmanians and Melanesians, regardless of the above, nevertheless form a supergroup, a major population complex or, in familiar vocabulary, a race? This involves archaeological evidence as well as biological. We may look for signs of related populations elsewhere. We may consider people like the Ainus, or the meaning of Negritos in Malaysia and the Philippines; but it is not enough now to compare and to weigh connections. It is also necessary to face problems of time and space, and relevant evidence.

I can deal with some of these questions, but some only, using multivariate analysis on cranial morphology. It is a problem for discussion how such evidence compares with that from genetic markers. There has been argument in the past as to whether genetic or morphological evidence is more stable, or best reflects the genealogy of populations. I do not see a future in such argument. The matter has not been settled either way; the only route is to inspect both kinds of evidence, to see how far they coincide, and to ask, when they do not, why they do not.

Major relationships of the Australians

Coon (1962), accepting Weidenreich's premise of local evolution through the Pleistocene, viewed the Australoids as one of five major geographical races of man, including the Melanesians and the Negritos. Birdsell, in contrast, postulated an amalgam of three distinct strains: archaic white (allied to the Ainu), Negrito (continuous genetically with the Andamanese and the Congo Pygmies), and Carpentarian from India. My own principal evidence, based on crania, certainly favours Coon's view, at least in distinguishing Australians from people elsewhere while allying them closely with Tasmanians and Melanesians.

As the point of departure I use a general study by multiple discriminant analysis recently published (1973a). Seventeen populations were included, each numbering about 50 crania for each sex in most cases, measured uniformly in a large number of diameters and angles. Every effort was made to use series representing definable local populations (not possible with Tasmanians or South African Bushmen) as distinct from the kind of conglomerate group (e.g., 'Caucasian', or 'Eskimo') which has not infrequently been used in comparative studies, whether cranial, anthropometric or serological. They were chosen on a world-wide basis, making the comparison broad rather than deep, since no major geographic region had more than four representatives. The analysis was run separately on 'males' and 'females' (as judged from the specimens by myself); the high coincidence in the two sets of results suggests that they are meaningful throughout. That is to say, while with 17 groups it is mathematically possible to derive 16 independent and uncorrelated discriminant axes, or multivariate variables, one would usually assume that only about half of these would have any biological significance. While only 9 or 10 in this case did seem to make much sense, the agreement between sexes is good through all 16, indicating that the very minor functions are not mere error fluctuation.

Even the use of only the more important of the functions, as reference axes, allows various kinds of plotting and clustering of the populations. In addition, further analysis, using correlations of the functions with original measurements, and doing a factor analysis separately from the above analysis, permits the morphological nature of the functions to be interpreted; that is, after finding the main axes of difference among populations, it can be said what these mean in terms of actual morphology.

So much for technical matters. The clear result of the two most important functions is the setting off by themselves of the three southwest Pacific peoples (hereinafter referred to collectively as Sowespac). These are the series:

South Australians of the Jarildekald and Warki-Korowalde tribes of the lower Murray River and the shores of Lakes Alexandrina and Albert. The skulls are in the South Australian Museum in Adelaide; most are from a cemetery at Swanport, and the whole selection was overseen for me by Norman Tindale. This should be a most satisfactory actual population (even though the individuals are not strictly contemporary) which had an occupation of the area lasting many centuries.

Tasmanians. This series, unlike most of the rest, does not represent a single community or locality, but only the surviving crania wherever found, which might on reasonable if not irrefutable grounds be assigned to the Tasmanian Aboriginals. The problems of such assignment are too well known for more comment here, but their pertinence lies in the possibility that the series, as made up, is too generalised: that is to say, a high variability produced by assembling skulls of different local groups might extend the range of the group, in measurements and in the multivariate variables, in such a way that other groups, or individuals, might be statistically less 'distant', less well discriminated, from the Tasmanians than from other groups, simply because the Tasmanian variation would be relatively wide. There are some signs, in the standard deviations of function scores, of such greater variance, though they are not impressive. And when it comes to classifying the individual skulls by using the functions, the hypothetical effect is not apparent.

Tolais of the Gazelle Peninsula, New Britain. These skulls were collected by R. Parkinson from villages on the southwest shore of Blanche Bay, a part of the territory occupied by the Tolai. For this study they represent Island Melanesia, whether they are actually typical of the whole region or not.

The analysis defines the Sowespac groups as being narrow in the cranial vault (Africans are very narrow in the base as well), short in the facial height, and prognathic in a general way; these features are shared with Africans, opposing them all to Mongoloids. The Sowespac groups differ from Africans (and are more like European crania) in a marked subnasal prominence in the midline profile and in a degree of prominence of the nasal saddle, as well as by a narrowness of the interorbital space. The nasal prominence is disguised by another important feature, the marked prominence of the glabellar region and supra-orbitals. Contrasting with Africans again, the frontal profile is flat, and the malars project further forward and are larger.

Such traits are perhaps less familiar and less obvious to the eye than the usual cranial or nasal indices. But the discrimination is saying that they are the high-ranking features which in fact distinguish the three populations from others and give them a mutual similarity.

Table 1 gives a few comparative figures in the direct measurements bearing out the above, as to distinctions from Africans. The simotic angle is that which measures the pitch of the nasalia across the nasal saddle: the means show that it is distinctly narrower in the Sowespac groups than in Africans. The former groups are intermediate among world values, exceeded only by Europeans and American Indians. The subspinale radius measures the projection of the subnasal profile forward of the ear axis: African populations vary but fall short of the Sowespac values. The absolute projection of glabella is shown in standardised form (the grand human mean being zero). The Africans and the Sowespac peoples are at the opposite poles of human variation.

Table 1

Africans	Male	Female	Male	Female	Sowespac
		Simotic angle			
Teita	133·73	142·00	104·19	112·04	*S. Australian*
Dogon	121·06	126·24	102·20	108·33	*Tasmanian*
Zulu	115·54	121·79	102·64	112·71	*Tolai*
Bushmen	140·93	141·55			
		Subspinale radius			
Teita	98·68	91·73	100·52	95·45	*S. Australian*
Dogon	91·40	87·92	100·18	94·48	*Tasmanian*
Zulu	96·47	91·91	102·76	96·89	*Tolai*
Bushmen	89·85	86·63			
		Glabella projection (z-scores)			
Teita	−17·17	−15·08	19·01	21·79	*S. Australian*
Dogon	−11·16	−10·67	21·35	26·01	*Tasmanian*
Zulu	−11·19	−8·72	12·99	11·77	*Tolai*
Bushmen	−9·28	−6·97			

There are, of course, cranial distinctions among the three Sowespac groups, but they are of low degree and difficult to state in terms of functions, factors or absolute measurements. Tolais are more extreme in absolute curvature of the profile of the parietals along the sagittal suture (according to the scores from the factor analysis), the other two groups being near the mean. Tasmanians are extremely low in the orbit and wide in the nasal aperture, compared to Australians, as well as being (an old observation) shorter and broader in the vault. But these measurement differences do not manifest themselves in the two kinds of multivariate analysis; they are ignored as unimportant kinds of difference, whatever our preconceptions may be.

If we turn to generalised measures of morphological distance these three populations form a group with low mutual separations (within which the Tasmanians and the Tolais are closer than either is to the Australians). Taking distances computed from all 16 of the original discriminant functions, for both sexes, the Sowespac mutual distance figures (Table 3 in Howells, 1973a) run from 2·00 to 4·00, while against all other 14 populations their several distances run from 4·00 to 11·00 (roughly), with any figures in the lower part of the range being rare. (There is *no* special likeness to Andaman Islanders.) In a different set of distance figures, computed from 10 functions, in which the distances are not reciprocal (i.e., the distance from A to B is not necessarily the same as from B to A), but are based on the centroid, or mean point, of each population, and computed using the variation of that particular population, figures are like this (citing male series only here):

	to other Sowespac groups	**to non-Sowespac groups**
Australians	·44 to ·61	·77 to 1·19
Tasmanians	·42 to ·59	·74 to 1·30
Tolais	·29 to ·59	·70 to 1·02

Tasmanians and Tolais have the lowest mutual figures. (Note that these figures should reflect any unnatural variation in the Tasmanian series, tending generally to reduce their distance figures, as discussed above; no effect of this kind is to be seen.)

The first distances referred to above can be used to cluster the populations by joining the two having the least mutual distance (two European populations, Norwegian and Hungarian), taking their mean point to compute new distances, and repeating the process until all are joined in what looks like, but is not, a family tree. Figure 1, taken from the published report (Howells, 1973a) shows the result for the series of both sexes. In each case, the three Sowespac groups form a single unit, in which the Tasmanians and Tolais join first. This group is linked to one including four African groups (Zulu of South Africa, Dogon of West Africa, Teita of East Africa, followed by Andaman Islanders and *then* by South African Bushmen). This joining is the last before an obligatory joining of all populations: these higher connections

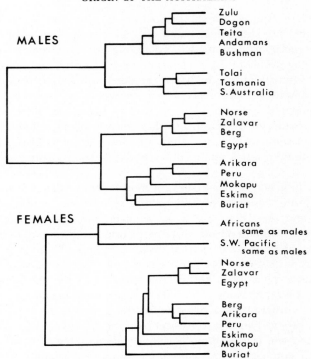

MALES

Zulu
Dogon
Teita
Andamans
Bushman

Tolai
Tasmania
S. Australia

Norse
Zalavar
Berg
Egypt

Arikara
Peru
Mokapu
Eskimo
Buriat

FEMALES

Africans
    same as males
S.W. Pacific
    same as males

Norse
Zalavar
Egypt

Berg
Arikara
Peru
Eskimo
Mokapu
Buriat

Figure 1 Worldwide cranial series: clustering by successive mergers.

are not as significant as the lower ones, since the computer program relent-lessly joins everything; and in the females, the Sowespac and African groups are seen to join, as far as mutual distance goes, *after* a group which unites Europeans and Eskimos. In other words, this kind of clustering does not actually assert a close connection of Africans and Sowespac peoples; quite the reverse.

The clustering process forces distances which are based on 16 dimensions into two, so that some distortion of actual relations occurs (three points being all whose exact mutual distances can be shown in a plane). Another way of displaying relations is shown in Figures 2 and 3, a method suggested by Andrews (1972), and already used by Stern and Oxnard (1973) for primates. This plots a function,

$$f_x(t) = x_1/\sqrt{2} + x_2 \sin t + x_3 \cos t + x_4 \sin 2t + x_5 \cos 2t + \ldots$$

which here uses the first 10 discriminant function scores simultaneously without distortion.[1] In Figures 2 and 3 the three Sowespac groups are shown as individually plotted curves, against a background of the total areas covered

---

[1] This is a trigonometric series (standard in mathematical analysis), the value of $f_x(t)$ being periodic with a period 2π. Between the values of $-3 \cdot 14$ and $+3 \cdot 14$, the values of $\sin t$ and $\cos t$ change gradually between 0 and 1, plus and minus, thus modulating the contributions of all the contributing discriminant functions simultaneously.

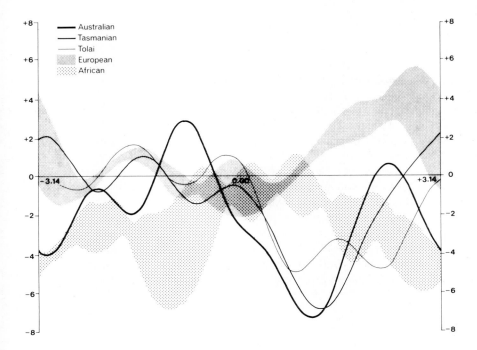

Figure 2 European, African and southwest Pacific male cranial series: multi-dimensional plot combining ten discriminant functions.

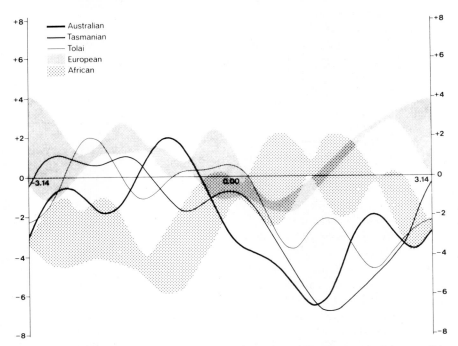

Figure 3 European, African and southwest Pacific female cranial series: multi-dimensional plot combining ten discriminant functions.

by, respectively, three European groups (Norway, Hungary, Austria) and three African groups (West, East, South). The Sowespac peoples are seen to be equally distinct in pattern from both of these, and the whole pattern is similar in the two sexes: the Sowespac peoples overlap more with Europe than with Africa on the left hand side, and are distinct from both on the right hand side. At $t = 0 \cdot 00$, all populations are fairly well bunched, this being a point at which functions 1, 3, 5, and 9, a combination in which these nine populations are either not extreme, or in which their departures from the mean cancel out. At ca. $t = +1 \cdot 25$, however, function 2 comes strongly into play, a function which does (here in combination with others) distinctly differentiate the Sowespac peoples. These are examples, not an attempt to read the plot in depth. But it may be seen that there is also a degree of differentiation among the Sowespac peoples themselves, a pattern evident in both sexes, and that the Australians may be the most extreme of the three.

A second discriminant analysis has been done, this time including a number of Far Eastern groups more recently studied and not included in the published report. Included are:

South Australians
Tasmanians
Tolais

Norwegians (mediaeval Oslo)
Buriats (Siberia)
Hawaiians (Mokapu peninsula, Oahu)
Eskimos (Inugsuk culture, Greenland)
Arikara Indians (Sully site)
Peruvian Indians (Yauyos district)

Ainus (Hokkaido)
North Japanese (Hokkaido)
South Japanese (northern Kyushu)
Shang Dynasty Chinese (An Yang tombs)
Hainan Chinese (recent)
Atayal (Taiwan aboriginals)
Philippine Islands (general)
Guam (Marianas, 'latte' period)

There is less work for the discriminant analysis, due to the close clustering of the Chinese and Japanese series throughout, and the tendency of the Formosan and Philippine groups to approximate them as well. (An Yang Chinese and Philippine Islands are not represented by female series.) Of the total possible discrimination achieved by 16 functions together, the first six account for about 82 per cent; the first function alone is responsible for 28 per cent and functions 2 to 6 for 54 per cent. Speaking very roughly, discrimination separating Americans, Europeans, Asiatics, Hawaiians, and Guamanians from one another is probably not much more than twice that separating all of them from the Sowespac groups.

Figures 4 and 5 are plots of the first two functions together, for males and females respectively. Isolation of the three Sowespac groups on the first function (horizontal axis) is clear, and in fact is the main work of this important function, although the Buriats of Siberia are somewhat removed at the other end, distinctly so in the males. This function expresses features already named in the previous analysis: prognathism and subnasal projection, facial lowness, cranial narrowness, and elevation of the nasal saddle, all these being only moderately or slightly evident in Mongoloid peoples. The second function (vertical axis) does not discriminate among the Sowespac groups; rather, it sets off the Eskimos from the herd on the clear count of forward projection of the whole facial mask (Buriats are also extreme in males but not in females, while at the opposite end Peruvian Indians are extreme in females but not in males). The Sowespac groups follow the crowd, although in fact the Australians are the group least removed from the Eskimos.

Functions 3 and 4 (in Figures 6 and 7) together act to contrast groups which are also peripheral geographically: Norwegians, Ainus, Buriats, Hawaiians, Eskimos and American Indians. Function #3 is difficult to read, but seems to express (for Hawaiians) a combination of cranial height plus generalised facial prominence, *without* midline projection but *with* some alveolar prognathism; and the opposite character for Norwegians, American Indians and Buriats. Function #4, the first on which the Sowespac groups themselves are somewhat separated, gives no clear morphological interpretation. Taken all together, the four functions do little to discriminate among the Sowespac groups, while they place the Norwegians slightly closer than the Ainus to the Australian sample.

Figure 8 shows a clustering of the populations in this second analysis, for the male cranial series, based on 10 discriminant function mean scores. The Sowespac peoples again take a markedly isolated position. The closeness of Chinese, Japanese, Formosan and Philippine groups is evident. Norwegians and Ainus are grouped, but the closeness is somewhat exaggerated here.

Turning again to distance figures, mutual distances computed by using 10 discriminant functions for both sexes vary from 2·6 to 3·3 within the Sowespac cluster and from 4·6 to 10·00 between these three and all others. (Here, in the females, is the only case where Australians rather than Tolais are closest to the Tasmanians.) The second set of distances, reckoned away from the centroid of each group, and including both sexes, gives these figures:

	to other Sowespac groups	to non-Sowespac groups
Australians	·43 to ·63	·79 to 1·84
Tasmanians	·46 to ·72	·75 to 1·43
Tolais	·31 to ·63	·71 to 1·41

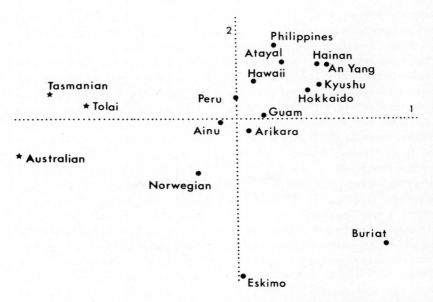

Figure 4 Circumpacific cranial series, male, plotted on discriminant functions 1 and 2.

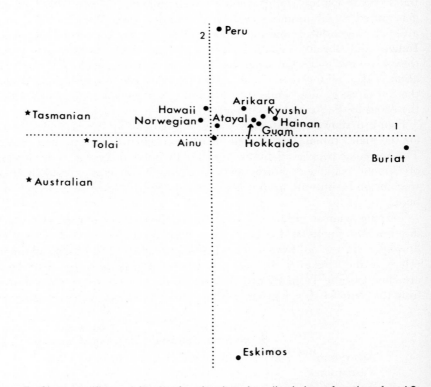

Figure 5 Circumpacific cranial series, female, plotted on discriminant functions 1 and 2.

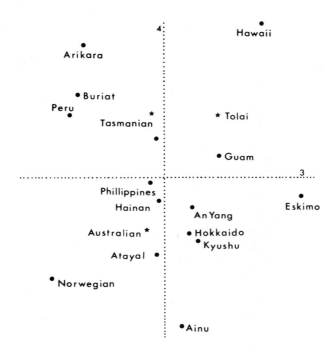

Figure 6 Circumpacific cranial series, male, plotted on discriminant functions 3 and 4.

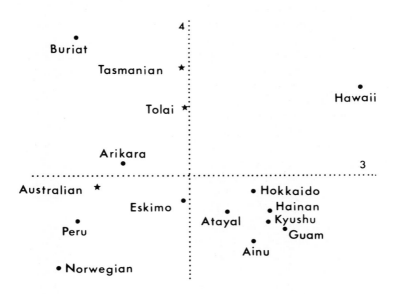

Figure 7 Circumpacific cranial series, female, plotted on discriminant functions 3 and 4.

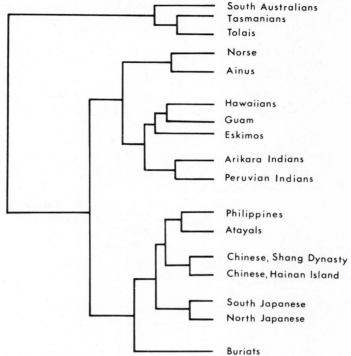

Figure 8 Circumpacific cranial series, male, clustering by successive mergers, from distances based on ten discriminant functions.

The above has been a rather tedious examination of figures generated by statistical reduction of a large number of measurements. The results have the virtue of being objective, uninfluenced by any conceptions or biases of the operator. There are at the same time one or two cautions to be observed. First, we do not know the real meaning of the kinds of cranial variation expressed between populations. Nor do we understand the apparent long-time endurance of such features in a given population, and thus their value in indicating genetic relations between populations well separated in time and space. In past generations it was often assumed that likenesses in form were indeed measures of actual kinship, whether of whole groups of people, or of individuals apparently deviating within a population toward an ancestral form. Presence of a Mongoloid element in the South African Bushmen was accepted on the basis of eye-folds and a skin more yellowish than is found in other Africans. The evidence from the first cranial study I have been citing contains no support whatever for such a connection, and simply allies the Bushmen with other sub-Saharan peoples. More broadly, the Melanesians were once normally classed as Oceanic Negroids, on the basis of skin colour and hair form, an arrangement which set them off from the Australians but did not exclude the Tasmanians, unless the latter were Negritos. Multivariate analysis of crania satisfies me that the three kinds of

Pacific peoples have a common cranial morphology which sets them off from Africans, and closer study of features of the living (Hrdy, 1973) suggests that the characters which appeared to be shared with Africans are in fact more likely to be convergent adaptations. But it must be remembered that the logic is circular: the cranial evidence makes better sense, therefore it is the best evidence.

A second caution relates to the use of most statistical distances. We must not really look on them as a measure of likeness/unlikeness: by and large they are essentially a measure of unlikeness; of distance, but not of closeness. They answer, not 'Can we join two populations', but 'Can we separate them?' That is their statistical nature. It is only when the populations concerned have some natural connection, i.e., a known genetic continuity, or geographical propinquity, that such distances among them can be used to relate them to one another in a system. In the present material, the Chinese and Japanese series are evidently a complex of populations which can be treated this way, and the Sowespac peoples are clearly a looser complex of the same kind.

Relations of other populations and individuals to Australians

The above leads into the matter of judging, from the same cranial evidence, the degree of separation of other peoples from the Australians. Tasmanians and Tolais have been discussed already: almost invariably in the figures, the Tasmanians are closer to Tolais, but of these two, they are the one less removed from the Australians.

The Ainus are a case for special consideration because of the frequent suggestion (e.g., Hooton, 1946) that they and the south Australians are basically an 'archaic white' or Caucasoid population, modified in Australia by Tasmanian 'Negrito' admixture. The discriminant analysis yields the following figures. If distance away from the *Australians* is measured by a mutual generalised distance computed from the mean discriminant scores, these run, in the male series:

Tasmanian, 3·31; Tolai, 3·92; Norwegian, 6·52; Ainu, 7·00; Peru, 7·64; Guam, 7·82; Eskimo, 7·83 . . . Buriat, 11·60.

In females: Tasmanian, 2·67; Tolai, 3·04; Norwegian, 5·06; Atayal, 5·42; Ainu, 5·58; Peru, 5·83 . . . Buriat, 9·95.

However, when distance is read away from the *Ainu*, all that need be said is that the above Ainu-Australian mutual values are exceeded, among 16 in all, only by the distance from Australians to Buriats and, in the case of females, among 14, only by that to the Tasmanians and the Buriats. In the other kind of distance, the one-way Mahalanobis distance from each population centroid, the values have a different order for many groups, but the result is much the same: from the *Australian* male centroid:

Tasmanian, 0·57; Tolai, 0·63; Norse, 0·82; Ainu, 0·86; Philippines, 0·91 . . . Guam, 1·84.

From the female centroid: Tasmanian, 0·48; Tolai, 0·61; North Japan, 0·79; Norse, 0·89; Peru, 0·98; Hainan Chinese, 1·05; Ainu, 1·11 . . .

However, in the one-way distances from the *Ainu*, the male Australians are farthest of all 16 non-Ainu groups; the female Australians are eleventh in line, out of 14 other populations. From the male Ainus, Norwegians are least distant; from the females, Japanese and Arikara.

Now there is nothing absolute about all these figures; they are relative and indicative, and in fact not much can be said as to their stability or distributions. However, the Mahalanobis distances (the second set) can be read in terms of chi square. From this, although discrimination among the specimens is actually very good, the Japanese and Chinese mean points, or centroids, are not significantly distant from one another at all, and the Atayals also join this group. Tasmanians and Tolais are not mutually different at a 5 per cent level of significance, and the Australians differ at approximately a 1 per cent level from both. But there is no chance of the Ainu series coinciding with the Sowespac group, whichever way probabilities are estimated. From the figures above one might better go the whole hog in the 'archaic white' hypothesis, and relate the south Australians directly to the Norwegians; but the probabilities of such coincidence are also extremely low. In other words, the fact that Ainus are, in a couple of lists above, among the least 'distant' from the Australians does not mean that the distance is one signifying any real cranial approximation. And, granting of course that relationship need not mean morphological identity, the Ainus are still not in any special relationship to Australians. In chi square terms they are least far from the other Far East groups, insignificantly so in most cases for the females, while they are enormously distant from the Australians; they are simply, and only in the males, rather less distant from Australians than the rest of a faraway population group.

After noting that the Philippine, Guam and Hawaiian series are all well away from Australians in the same terms – almost always further than from Tasmanians or Tolais – we are left with no other Oceanic populations represented by series of skulls. I have, however, a number of individual Pacific skulls which have been scored on the same discriminant functions for purposes of 'classification', or measurement in the same chi square terms for distance in the hyperspace of ten dimensions used in most of these tests. I shall note in summary fashion the results, in simple probability terms, relative to the three Sowespac peoples. It is to be understood that no *other* population is closer than any of these, unless so specified.

> North Australia (inc. Cairns region), 7 skulls. Three are more or less normal 'Tolais' and slightly less normal 'Tasmanians' but with little or no probability of being 'Australians'. One is a 'normal' Tasmanian, one is equidistant from Australians and Tasmanians, one has a miniscule (1/10 per cent) chance of being Tasmanian, and one rejected from all. Some kind of Delphic comment on north-south differences in Australia?
>
> New Guinea, 3 skulls. One could be any of the three at a 5 per cent or greater probability, especially Tasmanian. The other two have no chance as high as 1/10 per cent of being any of these.
>
> Baining, 2 skulls. Both could readily be either Tasmanian or Tolai, but with no possibility of being Australian.

Solomons, 11 skulls. One is excluded from all of these populations and all are excluded as being Australian except one at a chance of less than 1 per cent. Nine could be Tasmanian or Tolai, generally at comfortable odds. One has very slight chances of being Tolai or Australian; one (from the Lau Lagoon, where Micronesian mixture is possible) is acceptable as Chinese, Japanese or Guamanian.

Santa Cruz, 1 skull. Tolai at better than 5 per cent, Tasmanian or Australian at better than 1/10 per cent only (0·001).

New Hebrides, 11 skulls from different regions. Ten are acceptable Tolais (though in two cases at rather low odds), and in five cases are acceptable as Tasmanians with a probability also sometimes low. Seven are excluded from Australians on any terms while three have probabilities less than 2 per cent; one makes a fully acceptable Australian.

New Caledonia, 3: one acceptable only as Hawaiian (ca. 1 per cent); one as Tasmanian, or perhaps Tolai (greater than 1 per cent), one excludable from all populations.

Philippine Negritos, 2: one also excluded from all other populations, one readily Tolai or Tasmanian but certainly not Australian. (NB: In the earlier analysis this skull was accepted as Tolai or Tasmanian at ca. 2 per cent, Australian at lower probability, and African at a little better than 1/10 per cent. It was completely excluded as Andamanese.)

Fiji, 4 skulls, of which one looked strongly Polynesian and the other three strongly Melanesian (unsatisfactory evidence of provenience within Fiji). The first was acceptable only as 'Hawaiian'; the other three could pass as Tasmanians in every case and as Tolai (or Norwegian) in two; never as Australian.

This body of evidence, which is something like letting the three Sowespac groups look in the mirror, suggests that Tasmanians, Tolais and Island Melanesians form a single constellation of populations, from which the south Australians, at least, are somewhat removed; at the same time, on a worldwide basis, the Australians still belong in the same major complex, and are in no reasonable way to be connected instead with Africans or archaic whites. Thus, in Macintosh's terms, the Australians form one pattern, the Papuo-Melanesians another, but both fall in the same population complex.

Prehistoric relationships

We may begin considering these by graphing populations and individual skulls using the multidimensional plot already described. Here it is governed by six functions from the second discriminant analysis, so that patterns have no relation to those in Figures 2 and 3.

Figure 9 shows a plot of:
(a) the three Sowespac (male) series, all of which lie entirely in the 'minus' half of the field, each displaying a certain individuality; (b) as a dotted zone, the total limits of means of four Chinese and Japanese series. Corresponding to their close grouping in Figure 8, they form an extraordinarily narrow band, lying almost completely in the positive half of the field, and totally discrete from the Sowespac lines; (c) the Norwegians and Ainus as dotted lines, with a pattern discrete from the others included, and surprisingly

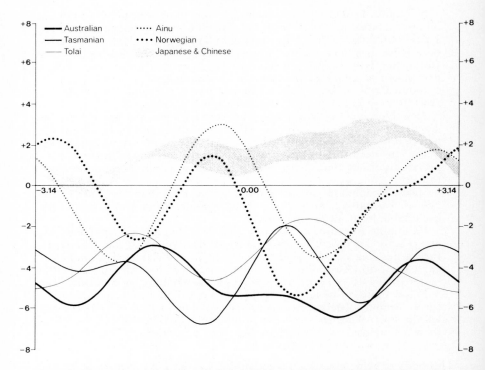

Figure 9 Multidimensional plot using ten discriminant functions (male series), showing southwest Pacific groups, also Ainu and Norwegians (dotted lines) and total range of four Japanese and Chinese groups (dotted zone).

similar, reinforcing the likeness between the two suggested by numerical values already covered. Checking the function scores at any value of *t* indicates that somewhat different emphases act to produce the coincidence statistically, but also that the pattern is generally coherent in that there are no gross distinctions between the two populations in any function, as there are in fact between both of them and the other sets shown. Therefore, although I am not persuaded of a close relation of Ainus and Europeans, from the evidence of crania a clear separation of them is unjustified, and a gathering of Ainus into a Far Eastern Mongoloid grouping is no more justified on this basis than is an approximation of them to Australians. (A plot of the two American Indian populations, Arikara and Peru, not shown, makes them very similar to one another, but on a pattern different from Ainus and Europeans.)

A quick look at another question: how do Island Melanesians appear in this context? One Baining skull, which discriminant analysis showed could be classed as either 'Tasmanian' or 'Tolai', is plotted here (Figure 10), as a dotted line. It is also given a second position, by changing its first function value to correspond with that of the Tasmanians. This is the constant

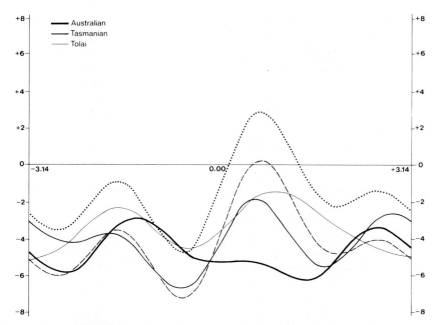

Figure 10 Multidimensional plot using ten discriminant functions (male series), showing southwest Pacific groups plus a single male Baining skull (dotted line), and same skull with first function value from Tasmanian series (dashed line).

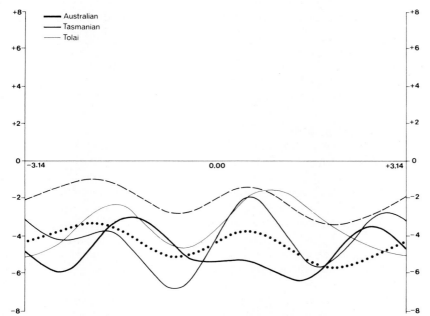

Figure 11 Multidimensional plot using ten discriminant functions (male series), showing southwest Pacific groups plus Keilor skull (dashed line), and Keilor with first function changed to correspond with mean of Tasmanians and Australians (dotted line).

quantity in the function, and should bring the line closer to that of Tasmanians without altering its general conformation. In either case, the pattern of this skull seems to correspond best with that of Tasmanians, and nearly as well with that of Tolais. It does not correspond well with that of the Australians, above all at a point corresponding to $t =$ ca. $+1 \cdot 00$. This position registers functions 2 through 5 all in some strength, and in fact Tasmanians do have opposite values, if not large ones, from Australians, in most of these functions. Tolais differ from both, but evidently not enough to separate them to the degree to which Australians are separated from the others.

The only prehistoric skull for which I have measurements[1] is Keilor. Figure 11 shows the same treatment for Keilor: a dashed line for its own position on discriminants, a starred line for Keilor modified by being given a first function value halfway between Tasmanians and Australians. For approximation to one or the other this is not very satisfying, the modulation of the plot for Keilor being relatively mild; and in fact it conforms to the Tolai curve as well as to any. In any event, its inflections seem to follow those of the Tolais and Tasmanians better than those of the Australians.

However, classification by the discriminant functions tells another story. In the first discriminant analysis, of worldwide populations, the chi square distance of Keilor from the 10-function Tasmanian centroid was $18 \cdot 4$, giving a probability of just 5 per cent; from the Tolais the value was $28 \cdot 6$, somewhat within the probability limit of $0 \cdot 001$ or $1/10$ per cent; from the Australians the value was $30 \cdot 1$, beyond the $0 \cdot 001$ limit. In the second analysis the distance of Keilor from Tasmanians was $12 \cdot 2$, at about 25 per cent probability; from Tolais $18 \cdot 8$, barely beyond a 5 per cent probability; from Norwegians, $22 \cdot 9$, between P $= \cdot 02$ and $\cdot 01$ (2 per cent and 1 per cent); from Arikara, $24 \cdot 9$, just beyond 1 per cent and from Australians, at $31 \cdot 7$, again beyond $1/10$ per cent.

Evidence from the living
In 1970 I published a clustering analysis like that on the cranial populations (e.g., Figure 1), but on a large number of Oceanic populations using few measurements, not the other way around as with the crania. The results need only be summarised. The closest groups were formed by peoples in New Guinea and Island Melanesia, to which were added groups in a less close relationship, which included both Melanesians and Micronesians. This was then joined by an essentially Polynesian sub-cluster, including Fijians. The most remote group included all the Australians (29 samples from the whole continent), as well as a few from New Britain, three from the Loyalty Islands, and one from northern New Caledonia. The main result, for present purposes, was the clear distinction of Australians, and the lack of coherent differentiation among the Australian populations.

---

[1] Made by myself in 1966 before the skull was further cleaned of encrustation by Professor Macintosh.

No populations of Indonesia or Asia were included in this analysis. I have recently done preliminary work on another set of populations from just these areas: India through Southeast Asia and Indonesia up to Japan, Korea and the Ainus. I have not had time to study the results in detail, but when the Australians are included in the cluster analysis, they are absolutely isolated at the highest level: in a total of 184 samples the 28 from Australia make up a separate branch which (as necessitated by the program) joins another single branch containing all the others, without overlap. (At the conference I reported that the Australian branch contained one sample from Bali, but this turns out to result from an undetected error in transcribing the original data, changing a nose breadth of 39 mm to 50 mm.) So this analysis provides no signs of Australian connections in Asia, and only emphasises the distinctiveness of Australians from a great conglomeration of samples which includes not only varied 'Mongoloids' but also Ainus, Andamanese, Sakais, Semangs, Veddas, Philippine Negritos, Oraons, Mundas, Kurumbas and Paniyans.

Conclusions

The indications from all these analyses are quite plain. The Australians are clearly distinguished as a major set of populations from anything in Asia, Ainus included, which has been brought to the test. Morphological variety within the Australian populations must exist, although rather primitive examination of samples, by multivariate analysis, does little to pick it out. It seems likely that other multivariate studies on crania would find such variety; here only a few specimens from North Australia have been used, but they do seem to represent something statistically outside the range of the south Australian sample. Larnach and Macintosh (1966, 1970) have done a simple kind of multivariate study using paragenetic cranial traits rather than measurements. They found no distinctions of consequence in crania of Queensland and New South Wales.

As for the Tasmanians, they find their cranial affinities with the Melanesians, on all counts. Together, Tasmanians and Melanesians (as represented by Tolais) are variants of one general population pool, as far as the evidence goes. The Australians are more distinct: there is almost a hiatus between them and Melanesians. Nonetheless the basic morphological pattern is much the same; they belong to the same population complex, not to another one. Finally, one prehistoric skull, Keilor, identifies itself with the Tasmanian-Melanesian side, not with the Australian; this, however, is only a single piece of evidence, even if an impressive one.

The major question, then, is why the Australians differ as they do from the peoples all around them. Obviously this is an historical question. No source is pointed to for this difference in the evidence above. Nor is any particular homeland for the whole population complex now known. Skeletal evidence, too meagre to be tested here, points to an earlier occupation of Indonesia by such populations, an area I have suggested may be looked on as Old Melanesia (Howells, 1973b). But nothing carries progenitors back any further than about 40,000 years. One thing multivariate analysis has contributed to the examination of such evidence is the picking out of important cranial differences which may be seen even in fragments, such as the higher nasal saddle of Australo-Melanesians. It is this trait, plus the development of glabella, which leads me to think that certain prehistoric skulls of Indonesia are of Melanesian form, while others, and especially those of Southeast Asia, are not.

Acknowledgements   The research reported on was supported by grants from the National Science Foundation GS–664 and GS–2645. The program for the multidimensional plots in the figures was written by John G. Rhoads, to whom I am much obliged.

References

ANDREWS, D. F.   1972   Plots of high-dimensional data. *Biometrics*, 28:125–36.
BIRDSELL, J. B.   1967   Preliminary data on the trihybrid origin of the Australian Aborigines. *Archaeology and Physical Anthropology in Oceania*, 2:100–55.
COON, C. S.   1962   *The origin of races.* Knopf, New York.
HOOTON, E. A.   1946   *Up from the ape.* Rev. ed. Macmillan and Co., New York.
HOWELLS, W. W.   1970   Mount Carmel man: morphological relationships. Proceedings, 8th International Congress of Anthropological and Ethnological Sciences. Tokyo and Kyoto, 1968. Vol. 1, pp. 269–72.
——   1973a   *Cranial variation in man. A study by multivariate analysis.* Peabody Museum Papers, vol. 67.
——   1973b   *The Pacific Islanders.* Weidenfeld & Nicolson, London.
HRDY, D. B.   1973   Quantitative hair form variation in seven populations. *American Journal of Physical Anthropology*, 39(1):7–17.
LARNACH, S. L. and N. W. G. MACINTOSH   1966   *The craniology of the Aborigines of coastal New South Wales.* Oceania Monographs, no. 13, University of Sydney.
—— and ——   1970   *The craniology of the Aborigines of Queensland.* Oceania Monographs, no. 15, University of Sydney.
MACINTOSH, N. W. G.   1965   The physical aspect of man in Australia. In *Aboriginal Man in Australia*, R. M. and C. H. Berndt (eds), pp. 29–70. Angus and Robertson, Sydney.
STERN, JACK T. Jr. and C. E. OXNARD   1973   Primate locomotion: some links with evolution and morphology. *Primatologia*, 4(11).

Cranial variation in Australia and neighbouring areas

Eugene Giles

La question peut donc être réservée. Nous ignorons encore si la race australienne actuelle a pris naissance sur place avec les caractères que nous lui connaissons; si, au contraire, elle est venue toute constituée de l'Asie; ou bien si c'est une race croisée, et, dans ce cas, de quels éléments elle se compose.

Paul Topinard (1876)

THE CALLING IN 1974 of a Conference on the Biological Origin of the Australians bears witness to the persistence of Paul Topinard's question for now almost a century. Much has changed in the way the question is framed, and much more would be expected of an answer. In particular, the question has slipped into a quantitative mode. What is the relative position of the Australians' origin vis-à-vis Melanesians (which Melanesians?), Southeast Asians (which Southeast Asians?) or other identifiable populations? Does time play a significant role in varying these relationships, or, put another way, were there migrations either from several places at the same time, or from the same place over a time frame encompassing autochthonous biological change, or both? What has been the role, if any, of biological adaptation within the Australian continent? These questions are not simply answered; positions advocating monophyletic origins (Abbie, 1968), diphyletic origins (Morrison, 1967) or triphyletic origins (Birdsell, 1967) continue to be maintained.

In searching for solutions to these broad questions, several basic attributes of the Australian population must be kept in mind. One is the burgeoning radiometric evidence for a very substantial time depth to the occupation of Australia by Man (e.g., Bowler *et al*, 1970). Acknowledgement of an antiquity of 30,000 years or more is now difficult to avoid. Such dates, encroaching on Neanderthal times in Europe and much earlier than confirmed New World evidence, allow time not only for successive migrations but also for considerable *in situ* microevolution. Determining what the evidence says regarding these possibilities separately or in combination will take well-honed techniques.

Sadly enough, the disruptive effect of European contact on indigenous Australians during the period of colonisation is reflected today in an extant population so eclectic and nonrandom in terms of genetic sampling of the precontact continental population as to bring into serious question biological data drawn from it and used for historical reconstruction. I would be the last to disregard the evidence of single-gene marker traits – I believe them to be extremely important – but the severe effects of culture contact in Australia suggest no little caution in their use.

For these and many other reasons a prudent course in the investigation of such complex problems as the biological origins of the Australians would be one in which as many lines of evidence as possible are examined in the process of drawing conclusions. In this perspective I offer here preliminary results from research begun in 1967 during the tenure of a Visiting Fellowship at the Australian National University. My intention is to outline as candidly as possible why the particular approach chosen was utilised, the merits I see in the research program, and I welcome in return frank evaluations of the data employed, the methodologies, and the conclusions tentatively arrived at. Since this research is definitely ongoing – particularly in its analytic phase – revision is not only possible but a virtual certainty.

The examination of crania

Human crania formed the first objects of attention by museum anthropologists; indeed, that 'museums became veritable cities of skulls, and the reputation of a scientific traveller almost stood or fell with the number of crania which he brought back with him' (Haddon, 1910 : 40, quoting Hagen) ultimately resulted in both the availability of very large cranial samples and the wide dispersion of exemplars of different populations among the world's museums.

Australian crania, as well as those of other populations, have been subjected to statistical analyses, with and without the aid of computers, with increasing tempo over the years (e.g., Larnach and Macintosh, 1966, 1970, 1971; Kellock and Parsons, 1970; Yamaguchi, 1967; Howells, 1973; Brown, 1973). An aim often found in such studies is to assess biological relationships among groups or populations within Australia and between Australian populations and external ones. The assumption is that morphological similarity, whether metrical or in discrete characters, indicates genetic relationship proportional to the similarity. It is 'highly likely', as Howells (1973) says, that important aspects of cranial form persist through time by virtue of functional adaptation, though this is hardly proved. It would also seem to be probable that traits based in the expression of many genes (polygenic) are less likely to be subjected to the effects of random genetic drift than are single-gene traits (Cavalli-Sforza and Bodmer, 1971) – not an inconsiderable factor when dealing with the sort of small populations that typify Australian Aboriginals. In any event, if the evaluation of phylogenetic relationships waited upon the elucidation of genetic causality in any trait-by-trait sense, it would never get done. If genetic structure of a population is at question, no doubt single-gene traits provide the neatest key. When it comes to examining interrelated populations from an historical perspective, it is by no means obvious that they provide superior definition to polygenic features.

Two desiderata are immediately obvious when the purpose of the investigation is to assess the extent and direction of population variation among Australians and their relationship to their nearest neighbours, the New Guineans. One is the most comprehensive possible methodology for determining similarities and differences in cranial morphology, and the other is to garner the most representative possible population samples. Both of these ideals were consciously aimed at; how far short of the mark the actuality is is important in gauging the significance of the results. Delineating the attempt is best covered in three phases.

The nature of the mensuration   Each cranium examined provided three sorts of data. The first and simplest was an estimate of sex based upon visual appreciation. I am less than sanguine about achieving high levels of accuracy in such attempts for reasons stated elsewhere (Giles and Elliot, 1963; Giles, 1966) and feel that mensurational methods will yield similar results (Larnach and Freedman, 1964). However that may be, the present analysis is based on visual sexing in which degree of doubt was recorded but not considered in the analysis.[1]

Sixteen measurements were taken on each skull and used in the study. These measurements were:

Glabello-occipital length	Palate-external breadth
Maximum width	Opisthion-forehead length
Basion-bregma height	Mastoid length
Maximum diameter bi-zygomatic	Maximum frontal breadth
Prosthion-nasion height	Bijugal breadth
Basion-nasion	Nasal height
Basion-prosthion	Orbit height, left
Nasal breadth	Orbit breadth, left

These are rather standard cranial measurements whose designation suggests their nature. A full description of the first eleven is found in Giles and Elliot (1963), the remaining five followed the recommendations given in Howells (1973) (these were available in manuscript form before publication). In some cases estimates were made where this could reasonably be done with accuracy; a skull for which one or more measurements would have to be omitted was rejected.

For each cranium black-and-white 35 mm photographs were made of the left side, the front and the back. These photographs were standardised in terms of lighting, camera distance, positioning of the skull, and marking with

[1] An exception to my providing the sex estimate was the New South Wales coastal population. Here the sex estimates arrived at by Professor N. W. G. Macintosh and Mr S. L. Larnach were entered from the records they kindly provided.

pins of the bregma and lambda. A 200 mm lens allowed distortion to be reduced to the point advocated by Gavan *et al* (1952) by permitting the camera to be 233 cm away from the skull whose maximum diameter did not exceed 233 mm. The analysis of the morphological data contained in these photographs is not yet completed. It involves first digitising some 128 coordinate points on an optical scanner and then a trend-surface analysis of the resulting patterns. The time involved in completing this with accuracy and repeatability for some 1300 crania has turned out to be far greater than initially expected. When finished, however, the approach (which to my knowledge has not previously been applied to a serious phylogenetic problem in anthropology) will not only provide its own resolution of interpopulational variation 'space' based upon a particularly comprehensive denotation of morphology, but also permit a comparison with and an evaluation of morphology extracted as linear measurements between points. But it is this latter approach that specifically concerns this paper.

The populations   Ideally cranial samples should represent biological populations in time and space. In practice, museum collections usually do nothing of the sort. There is an enormous number of Australian crania resident in museums around the world. Unfortunately many of these have little locational identification other than Australia. The difficulties with museum collections of crania in terms of populations in time ought not to be present in material excavated from a single site in which archaeological control indicates a restricted time period. Such a collection that provides a satisfactory sample size of reasonably complete skulls has not come to my attention, and such a sample is not included among those used here.[2]

In terms of geography at least some of the museum collections appear to provide reasonable approximations to a population (ignoring possible disparities in time). The Swanport sample from the South Australian Museum comes from a very limited area and probably time. So it would seem does the Murray River material in the collections of the Australian Institute of Anatomy, to mention two of the better examples. Others cannot be put in quite such a favourable light, but the difficulties are best described on a sample-by-sample basis.

Eleven populations have been designated to represent the material. The initial and continuing aim of the research was to consider the closest available approximations to biological populations; therefore rarely were all the specimens in a given museum included – only those which fitted into a population. In the following listing of populations the museums from which the data were gathered – twenty-two in all – is given in brackets, the sample size of males, females and total is given in parentheses in that order.

---

[2] In 1971 through the courtesy of Dr W. Wood in Port Moresby I examined photographs of the cranial material excavated from Broadbeach, Queensland. The material appeared to be largely fragmentary, largely juvenile, and largely male. Relatively few skulls appeared complete enough for a proper application of the techniques used in this paper.

1. *Swanport, S.A.* (44, 31, 75) These specimens were all collected by F. R. Zietz from a site about five miles southeast of Murray Bridge, S.A. (Stirling, 1911). They probably represent the best approximation to a real population in this study. One specimen appears to have been traded to Dr Ales Hrdlicka during his visit to Australia in 1925; it is now to be found in the Smithsonian Institution. [SAM, USNM[3]]

2. *Murray River Basin.* (126, 99, 225) All of this population was collected by Mr G. Murray Black in the period 1929 to 1940 from, according to his written recollection, the 'Tocumwall district, Diniliquin, Barham, Lake Victoria, Menindie and the Lachlan River (Lake Cargelligo) and Neds Corner'. The provenence of individual skulls is poor; the whole very large sample is taken to be one population. [AIA]

3. *New South Wales Coastal Area.* (64, 47, 111) To some extent this is a rather heterogeneous sample, but it is from a relatively restricted area and the same sample has been the subject of previous investigation (Larnach and Macintosh, 1966). [AMS, DASU, MMSU]

4. *Queensland.* (129, 95, 224) This 'population' may well be farthest from any semblance to a biological population. The criterion for admission was merely being a cranium attributable to the State of Queensland excluding the Torres Straits Islands. Obviously the relatively large sample can be subdivided, but for the present it represents people from that sector of the continent. [AMNH, AMS, BMNH, DAEU, DASU, DLCU, MMSU, QMB, SAM]

5. *Port Darwin. N.T.* (52, 41, 93) The bulk of the Port Darwin material comes from the W. Ramsay Smith collection now divided about equally between Canberra and Edinburgh. Ramsay Smith specimens not specifically attributable to Port Darwin have been omitted; a few each from several other collections have been added. [AIA, AMNH, AMS, BMNH, DAEU, MMSU, NMM, PMHU, QMB, SAM]

---

[3] The museums whose collections have been utilised for this study are abbreviated in the text as follows: *AIA* Australian Institute of Anatomy, Canberra; *AMNH* American Museum of Natural History, New York; *AMS* The Australian Museum, Sydney; *BMNH* British Museum (Natural History), London; *DACU* Department of Anatomy, Cambridge University; *DAEU* Department of Anatomy, Edinburgh University; *DAMU* Department of Anatomy, Melbourne University; *DAOU* Department of Anatomy, Oxford University; *DASU* Department of Anatomy, University of Sydney; *DLCU* Duckworth Laboratory, Cambridge University; *FMNH* Field Museum of Natural History, Chicago; *IRSN* Institut royal des Sciences naturelles, Brussels; *MHP* Musée de l'Homme, Paris; *MMSU* Macleay Museum, University of Sydney; *NMM* The National Museum, Melbourne; *PMHU* Peabody Museum, Harvard University; *QMB* Queensland Museum, Brisbane; *QVM* Queen Victoria Museum, Launceston; *RSM* Royal Scottish Museum, Edinburgh; *SAM* The South Australian Museum, Adelaide; *TMH* Tasmanian Museum, Hobart; *USNM* United States National Museum, Washington, D.C.

6. *Arnhem Land, N.T.* (24, 11, 35) This population is a residual one, including all designated Arnhem Land specimens except those included in the more restricted Port Darwin and Anson Bay samples. [NMM, QMB, USNM]

7. *Anson Bay, N.T.* (17, 10, 27) This sample, though small, was singled out from the Northern Territory material because of some indication of its unity at least in terms of collector and provenance. [SAM]

8. *Tasmania.* (54, 57, 111) The interest in this population seems always to outweigh the problematic status of so many presumed specimens (N. J. B. Plomley, personal communication). Listings of most of the material have been made and debated (Wunderly, 1939; Plomley, 1966), no purpose would be served in this paper by arguing individual cases. Generally a wide net has been cast, eliminating only truly patent interlopers (e.g., one of the two specimens in Brussels); presumed morphological criteria distinguishing Australians from Tasmanians (e.g., Wunderly, 1939) have not been employed to avoid the self-fulfilling categorisation that would undoubtedly ensue. Further analysis of the Tasmanians is warranted with a more restricted sample, or several alternative samples, but for the present an encompassing position has been taken. [AIA, AMNH, AMS, BMNH, DACU, DAEU, DAMU, DAOU, FMNH, IRSN, MHP, NMM, QVM, RSM, SAM, TMH]

9. *Torres Straits Islands.* (60, 25, 85) Most of the Torres Straits material comes from the British Museum (Natural History). It is quite possible that grouping these islands together violates natural population structure, but there may have been considerable gene flow among the islands. No specific island provided an adequate sample, so these people must be considered here as one population, one of course of great interest. [AMNH, AMS, BMNH, DLCU, MHP, MMSU, PMHU, SAM, USNM]

10. *New Guinea.* (50, 43, 93) The New Guinea sample comes entirely from the Field Museum in Chicago and is, in effect, those specimens designated the Sepik group and the Purari Delta group by Hambly (1940). No doubt a better sample could be obtained from New Guinea (e.g., Pietrusewsky, 1973). The purpose of a New Guinea sample at this point is mainly as a foil for the Australian material. [FMNH]

11. *New Britain.* (141, 92, 233) This large sample is composed of the collection of Richard Parkinson, now divided between New York and Chicago. All evidence (Howells, 1973) suggests that these crania were from a relatively small set of villages in the Gazelle Peninsula, and thus are a more satisfactory, if more distant, Melanesian population than the New Guinea proper sample. [AMNH, FMNH]

There is no question but that these eight Australian and three outlier populations are constituted in a fashion which can easily be attacked. The principal justification for their use is that there appear not to be better ones (contrary information would be appreciated) for the sort of multivariate analyses that have demonstrated value in taxonomic work (e.g., Howells, 1973). With the paucity of available data sources for the biological history of the Australians, the information value that may lie in the large if somewhat quaint collections of skulls around the world ought not to be left unprobed.

Discriminant function analysis   The real demonstration of the worth of the cranial data will come with the completion of the analysis of cranial form involving the patterning of the coordinate points on the cranial photographs. As a preliminary step a multiple discriminant function analysis utilising the sixteen linear measurements on the eleven populations has been carried out to see if the cranial series does in fact offer some promise of providing useful information. The multiple discriminant function technique in cranial analysis has recently been so elegantly and thoroughly presented by Howells (1973) that the barest summary will be made here. As will be apparent *seriatim*, Howells' monograph has provided a guide in this preliminary venture, including the form of the figures.

Discriminant function analysis is seen at its simplest in dealing with such problems as the sexing of skulls (Giles, 1970). If one has a series of measurements (variables) on male and female crania (populations), discriminant function analysis crafts a series of weights which serve to maximise the differences between the two populations, in this case the sexes. In that example there will be one discriminant function. When the measurements for each male are multiplied by the appropriate weight, the resulting set of points (which will fall along a line) will maximally distinguish itself from a similar set of points constructed from the females. Though no longer easily depictable, multiple discriminant function analysis extends this method to many populations, putting them as point clusters maximally separated in a multi-dimensional space. The relationship among the clusters of points representing the populations is the focus of interest.

Discriminant function analysis can be called distortive (Hursh n.d.) in that it is a computationally complex way of rearranging the variables in order to identify and display differences. It creates super-variables (functions) to do this and their ability is great. Thus a potential problem in multiple discriminant function analysis is that it, in effect, may discriminate on the basis of sample variance rather than populational variance. Adequate sample size helps, of course, but it is wise to retain some perspective when evaluating the results of such a powerful statistical technique. It does, however, provide a cognitively comfortable way of viewing complex morphological variation extracted as linear quantities, certainly more so than any univariate statistical procedure.

Results of the analysis

A multiple discriminant function analysis tends to overwhelm rather than edify if presented as raw computational output. In this paper two visualisation methods of Howells (1973) have been adapted to present the results

Table 1: Percentage of variance accounted for by successive functions

	Males	Males+Females	Females
Function 1	37·7	37·2	42·8
Function 2	26·4	26·3	22·5
Function 3	11·8	11·8	12·8
Function 4	8·7	9·1	8·4
Function 5	5·4	6·9	5·7
Function 6	4·9	4·7	3·8
First two functions	64·1	63·5	65·3
First three functions	75·9	75·3	78·1
First six functions	94·9	96·0	96·0

as clearly as possible. One way of viewing the discriminated populations is to look at the relative position of group means of variables on the functions. Figure 1 shows these, rescaled for uniformity of presentation and calculated separately for males, males and females, and females. (Small sample size negated the use of females alone for Arnhem Land and Anson Bay.) Each function accounts for a decreasing percentage of the variance explained. Although ten functions are calculated (there are eleven populations), only six of these have been illustrated, since the remaining four account for only 5 per cent of the variation. Table 1 indicates the amount of variance accounted for function by function.

If we look at the male population on the first discriminant function (Figure 1) it appears that this function, which accounts for the largest percentage of variance of any (37·7) places the two Melanesian populations together (10 and 11) and close to the Torres Straits Islanders. The three populations from Arnhem Land (5, 6 and 7) also form a group, as do the eastern Australian populations and Tasmania, with the Murray River group most separate. The eastern Australian group is dispersed in the combined male and female population, and the Arnhem Land groups are pushed down into affinity with the Melanesians and Torres Straits Islanders.

A more satisfactory overall view of the male results is diagrammed in Figure 2. It is of course not possible to represent completely a three-dimensional diagram on a sheet of paper, but Figure 2 attempts to do so with the placement of the group means simultaneously on functions 1 and 2 (the dots on the plane surface) and on functions 1, 2 and 3 (the apparent positions of the balloons). The points on the plane surface formed by functions 1 and 2 account for 64 per cent of the variance. They show a clear grouping of the three Arnhem Land populations (5, 6 and 7) and the Melanesians (10 and 11). It is manifest that the Tasmanians, Torres Straits Islanders, and the Swanport sample are rather distinct from each other and from the rest.

Conclusions

Tantalising suggestions of biological relationship are evinced in Figure 2, particularly when viewed in the three-function, three-dimensional aspect – the position of the balloons. When the third function is added, the Arnhem Land set becomes clearly distinguished from the eastern set of Murray River,

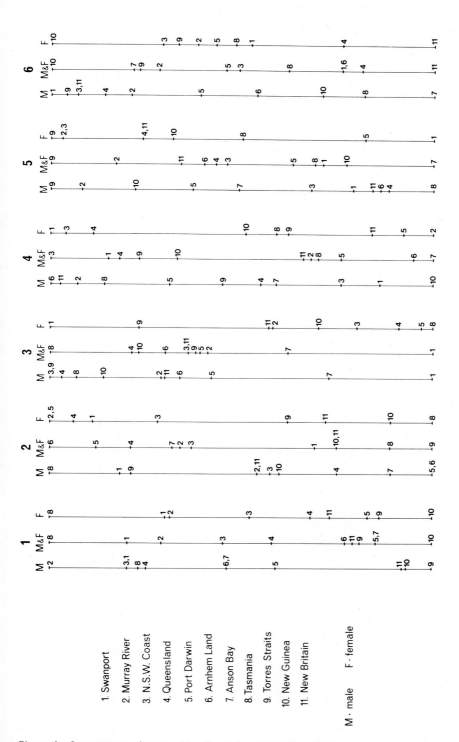

1. Swanport
2. Murray River
3. N.S.W. Coast
4. Queensland
5. Port Darwin
6. Arnhem Land
7. Anson Bay
8. Tasmania
9. Torres Straits
10. New Guinea
11. New Britain

M · male   F · female

Figure 1   Group mean placement by discriminant functions 1–6.

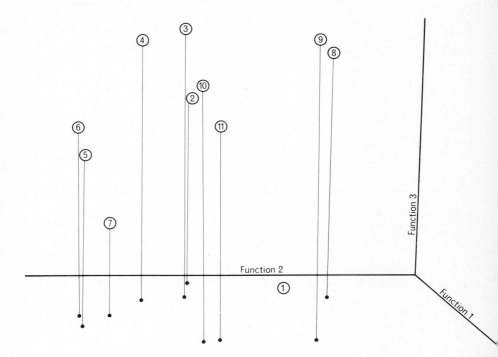

Figure 2 A pseudo-three-dimensional diagram of male group mean placement simultaneously by functions 1 and 2 (dots) and by functions 1. 2 and 3 (balloons). 1 = Swanport; 2 = Murray River; 3 = New South Wales coast; 4 = Queensland; 5 = Port Darwin; 6 = Arnhem Land; 7 = Anson Bay; 8 = Tasmania; 9 = Torres Straits; 10 = New Guinea; 11 = New Britain.

New South Wales coast, and Queensland. The Queensland population shows no particular affinity to either Melanesia or the Torres Straits Islands. The distinctiveness of Swanport is curious; it is rather far from any other group, more so than might be expected. The Melanesians stick together, while a relationship – not a strong one but intriguing – emerges between the Torres Straits Islanders and the Tasmanians, and the latter move away from Swanport.

These preliminary results from a multiple discriminatory analysis of linear dimensions are stimulating in themselves, and offer enough promise, in my view, of elucidating relationships among the Australians to warrant easily the further examination of the cranial photographs. It is unquestionable that meaningful variation is present in the skulls examined – the results in Figure 2 are hardly happenstance. Howells (1973 : 154), in his scrutiny of crania on a world-wide basis, concluded that 'in the Southwest Pacific, *Tolais* [the New Britain population of this paper], *Tasmanians*, and *South Australians* [Swanport] form a well-defined, isolated group morphologically, in which Australians and Melanesians seem to show little essential cranial difference'.

The results of this investigation suggest that multivariate statistical procedures are sufficiently powerful to extract relationships of phylogenetic significance from cranial morphology even within this relatively homogeneous regional grouping.

Acknowledgements   I wish to express my appreciation for various kindnesses and help not only to the museums and departments of anatomy mentioned in footnote 3, but also to the following persons in alphabetical order: Prof. A. A. Abbie, Dr J. L. Angel, Mr A. Bartholomai, Dr W. Bryden, Dr A. S. Clarke, Dr G. Cole, Dr D. Collier, Miss E. Crosby, Mr W. F. Ellis, Miss V. M. Friel, Mr E. D. Gill, Dr G. A. Harrison, Prof. R. J. Harrison, Dr J. -L. Heim, Dr E. H. Hipsley, Prof. W. W. Howells, Mrs K. Hursh, Mr S. L. Larnach, Prof. N. W. G. Macintosh, Mr J. McNally, Mr D. R. Moore, Prof. and Mrs R. M. Moriarty, Dr N. J. B. Plomley, Miss R. Powers, Mr G. Pretty, Mr M. C. Quinnell, Prof. L. J. Ray, Miss A. M. Roberts, Prof. G. J. Romanes, Prof. H. L. Shapiro, Dr P. J. Stanbury, Dr T. D. Stewart, Mr R. P. Stone, Dr F. H. Talbot, Dr A. G. Thorne, Dr F. Twiesselmann, Dr G. Walker, Dr M. Walker, Mr A. L. West, Dr W. Wood and my wife Inga. This research was supported in part by NSF grant GS-2585 and grants from the University of Illinois Research Board and indirectly by an NSF Postdoctoral Fellowship and USPHS grant GM-15457.

References

ABBIE, A. A.   1968   The homogeneity of Australian Aborigines. *Archaeology and Physical Anthropology in Oceania*, 3:223–31.

BIRDSELL, J. B.   1967   Preliminary data on the trihybrid origin of the Australian Aborigines. *Archaeology and Physical Anthropology in Oceania*, 2:100–55.

BOWLER, J. M., R. JONES, H. ALLEN and A. G. THORNE   1970   Pleistocene human remains from Australia: a living site and human cremation from Lake Mungo, western New South Wales. *World Archaeology*, 2:39–60.

BROWN, T.   1973   *Morphology of the Australian skull studied by multivariate analysis.* Australian Institute of Aboriginal Studies, Canberra.

CAVALLI-SFORZA, L. L. and W. F. BODMER   1971   *The genetics of human populations.* Freeman, San Francisco.

GAVAN, J. A., S. L. WASHBURN and P. H. LEWIS   1952   Photography: an anthropometric tool. *American Journal of Physical Anthropology*, 10:331–53.

GILES, E.   1966   Statistical techniques for sex and race determination: some comments in defense. *American Journal of Physical Anthropology*, 25:85–86.

――   1970   Discriminant function sexing of the human skeleton. In *Personal identification in mass disasters*, T. D. Stewart (ed), pp. 99–109. Smithsonian Institution, Washington, D.C.

―― and O. ELLIOT   1963   Sex determination by discriminant function analysis of crania. *American Journal of Physical Anthropology*, 21:53–68.

HADDON, A. C.   1910   *History of Anthropology.* Watts, London.

HAMBLY, W. D.   1940   Craniometry of New Guinea. *Field Museum of Natural History, Anthropology series*, 25:81–290.

HOWELLS, W. W.   1973   *Cranial variation in Man: a study by multivariate analysis of patterns of difference among recent human populations.* Peabody Museum of Archaeology and Ethnology, Harvard University, Papers, 67. Cambridge, Mass.

HURSH, T. M.   n.d.   *The study of cranial form: measurement techniques and analytic methods.* Ms.

172   ORIGIN OF THE AUSTRALIANS

KELLOCK, W. L. and P. A. PARSONS   1970   A comparison of the incidence of minor nonmetrical cranial variants in Australian Aborigines with those of Melanesia and Polynesia. *American Journal of Physical Anthropology*, 33:235–40.

LARNACH, S. L. and L. FREEDMAN   1964   Sex determination of Aboriginal crania from coastal New South Wales, Australia. *Records of the Australian museum*, 26: 295–308.

—— and N. W. G. MACINTOSH   1966   *The craniology of the Aborigines of coastal New South Wales.* Oceania Monographs, 13. Sydney.

—— and ——   1970   *The craniology of the Aborigines of Queensland.* Oceania Monographs, 15. Sydney.

—— and ——   1971   *The mandible in eastern Australian Aborigines.* Oceania Monographs, 17. Sydney.

MORRISON, J.   1967   The biracial origin of the Australian Aborigines. *Medical Journal of Australia*, 2:1054–56.

PIETRUSEWSKY, M.   1973   A multivariate analysis of craniometric data from the Territory of Papua and New Guinea. *Archaeology and Physical Anthropology in Oceania*, 8:12–23.

PLOMLEY, N. J. B.   1966   *A summary of published work on the physical anthropology of the Tasmanian Aborigines.* Queen Victoria Museum, Records, 24. Launceston.

STIRLING, E. C.   1911   Preliminary report on the discovery of native remains at Swanport, River Murray; with an inquiry into the alleged occurrence of a pandemic among the Australian aboriginals. *Transactions of the Royal Society of South Australia*, 35:4–46.

TOPINARD, P.   1876   *L'Anthropologie.* Reinwald, Paris.

WUNDERLY, J.   1939   The cranial and other skeletal remains of Tasmanians in collections in the Commonwealth of Australia. *Biometrika*, 30:305–37.

YAMAGUCHI, B.   1967   *A comparative osteological study of the Ainu and the Australian Aborigines.* Australian Institute of Aboriginal Studies, Canberra.

Early Man in Tasmania
New skeletal evidence

A.G. Wallace and G.A. Doran

THE PRECISE RACIAL affinities of the Tasmanian Aboriginals are still uncertain. The surprisingly wide variation in fossil skulls discovered on the Australian mainland predicates the need for knowledge of early Tasmanian morphology.

Description of the typical Tasmanian skull and its range of variation has often suffered from doubts concerning the authenticity of some of the material labelled as Tasmanian in museums. In the nineteenth century, when a Tasmanian skull was a collector's item, it is possible that certain material was erroneously labelled in private collections and the error later perpetuated.

Another problem was the early acceptance of Tasmanian features from small samples (e.g. Topinard, 1872) and a subsequent tendency to reject as unauthentic specimens which failed to comply with these criteria. Such circular reasoning naturally tended to narrow the apparent range of variation.

Skeletal material derived from a time before European contact is therefore of great importance in constructing an unimpeachable record of Tasmanian morphology. Furthermore the Tasmanian situation may offer a unique opportunity in the study of human evolution. The island had been occupied by a people, averaging perhaps 5000 in number (Jones, 1971), over at least 9 millenia of isolation following the last post-glacial sea-level rise. Such circumstances are without parallel elsewhere in the world and dated skeletal material throughout such a time-span would be of great scientific interest.

Macintosh and Barker (1965), in their monograph, review the extensive literature on Tasmanian morphology. Whatever the range of variation eventually proves to be, they point out that there is general agreement in the description of typical features. Thus they state that in comparison with Australian Aboriginals the Tasmanians tended to have a higher cranial breadth-length index, a lower cranial height-length index, a lower face, lower orbits, broader nasal aperture, shorter palate and higher nasal index. Parietal bossing, para-sagittal grooving and depression of the sagittal suture within a groove have also been stressed.

Figure 1   The Mt Cameron West skeletal remains during excavation.

The Tasmanian custom of cremation has lessened the likelihood of finding skeletal remnants but from time to time bones are likely to be discovered, particularly following wind erosion in sand dunes that have become unstable. This paper describes one such discovery. The only skeletal remains excavated in context prior to this have been fragments of charred skull bones and a molar tooth taken from a midden at West Point by Rhys Jones in 1966, and dated to around 1500 years BP.

In early 1973, following unusual, strong easterly winds, part of a skull was exposed in sand dunes in northwest Tasmania. The site was 600 m inland from highwater mark at the Mount Cameron West petroglyphs. Aboriginal shell middens (mostly of *Haliotis*) abounded in the locality. The site occurs within a blown-out sand dune of Holocene age. The long axis of the blow-out depression trends from w.s.w. to e.n.e. It is unlikely that these dune sands are greater than 6000 years in age as they can only have been deposited in their present position after the maximum stage of the Holocene marine transgression (see Fairbridge, 1961).

Excavation showed that the skull, of which the vertex had been exposed, was set in an upright position facing towards the northeast. In front were crossed the shafts of a femur and a humerus (Figure 1). To the right of the skull lay parts of the mandible. A few other bone fragments lay within 15 cms of the skull near the level of its base. No other bone appeared to lie beneath the skull – an observation subsequently confirmed in the laboratory.

The surface sand was soft and dry to a depth of 3–4 cms below which the sandy matrix was damp and firm. As it dried it became clear that the bones were fragile, in particular the facial skeleton. Removal of the skull *en bloc*, as advised by Macintosh (1968), was therefore undertaken by undercutting the whole block and transferring it into a sand box for transport. This operation may have obscured the stratigraphy but there was no clear evidence of any burial pit.

Associated charcoal had been collected during the excavation – partly in the form of flecks within the sand but also as two small discrete pieces from the level of the base of the skull. When the walls of the excavated pit were examined and further sand was removed working outwards in a vertical plane a new feature was noted. There were within the sand carbon-stained structures, having the form of sticks, about 2 cms in diameter and extending vertically downwards from the sand surface to a level about 15 cms below the base of the skull. Any attempt at removal of these formations resulted in their disintegration. These structures, which may have been the remnants of poles, were distributed in the general form of an arc to the west side of the skull and within 1 m of the skull. They were plotted as in Figure 3. Several areas further away were examined but no similar structures were found.

It is of interest to speculate on the nature of these carbonised remnants. Two possibilities were considered. First, that they were mineralised root systems. Such are not infrequent in sandy areas but tend to be more irregular and dendritic. Second, that they were relics of some structure associated with the bones – in which case Peron's (1907) observations are relevant. He described wooden and bark teepees which he found in 1803 on Maria Island erected over burial pits.

The flecks of carbon, the discrete lumps and the remnants of possible sticks were bagged separately and despatched for dating to the A.N.U. Radiocarbon Dating Laboratory, Canberra. When the carbon was separated for analysis it was found necessary to pool the specimens to gain an adequate quantity. A radiocarbon date of 4260 ± 360 years BP has been given (ANU–1136). Until the bones themselves are dated the age of the skull remains uncertain. The bones appear to have been arranged and this, together with the intact nature of the associated structural remnants, suggests that we are dealing with remains which have not been previously disturbed and that the bones are contemporary with the associated carbon.

General description of the skull

The skull has been acceded to the Tasmanian Museum and Art Gallery, Hobart, as L319.

Parts of the facial skeleton (Figure 2) have been blackened as if by fire but there is no extensive charring of the bone. The vault and the base of the skull are largely intact but fragile. The facial skeleton is fragmented and has been crushed post-mortem. The upper incisors and right upper canines are

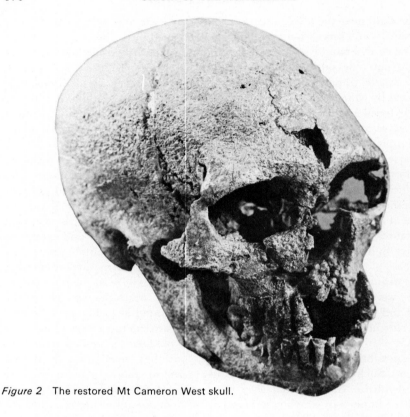

Figure 2   The restored Mt Cameron West skull.

missing, together with associated alveolar bone. The palate has split in the
median plane with the two halves gaping 3 mm. The face and mandible have
now been largely re-constructed. Measurements of the skull are given in
Table 1.

The skull is dolichocephalic, pentagonoid, phenozygous and shows marked
post-orbital constriction. There is definite parietal bossing with a little
para-sagittal grooving. The glabella is grade IV(Broca); the superciliary
ridges are of medium prominence; there is no supra-orbital torus. The
forehead is sloping (frontal curvature index 20). The occiput is prominent
and rounded in profile; there is neither external occipital protruberance nor
external occipital crest. The mastoid processes are very small indeed;
juxtamastoid ridges are present. Very prominent auditory exostoses or tori
are present on the left side. The squamous suture is low and exhibits practically no arch. The courses of the squamotympanic fissures are transverse.
The sagittal suture, in its posterior third, lies in a well-marked obelion
depression.

The sagittal, coronal, lambdoidal and parieto-temporal sutures are all
unfused but ossification has occurred at the spheno-occipital synchron-
drosis.

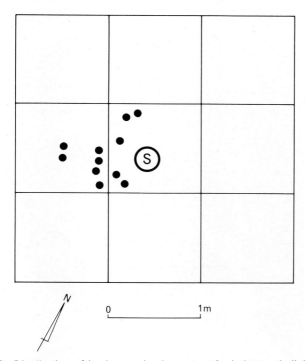

Figure 3 Distribution of 'carbon-stained structures' relative to skull (S).

Table 1: Cranial (L319) measurements and indices

Measurement	Biometric Symbol	Value in mm
Maximum cranial length	L	186
Maximum cranial breadth	B	139
Basi-bregmatic height	H^1	124
Basi-nasal length	LB	96
Basi-alveolar length*	GL	102
Upper facial height*	G^1H	59
Supra-orbital breadth		111
Minimum frontal breadth**		86
Frontal subtense		22
Bimaxillary breadth	GB	97
Bizygomatic breadth	J	134
Nasal height	NH^1	47
Orbital breadth	O^1, (R)	42
Orbital height	O_2 (R)	28
Post-orbital constriction		25

Cranial Capacity (Von Bonin) $404 \cdot 9 + 26 \cdot 3 \times 10^{-6}(L \times B \times H^1)$ = 1248cc.
Cranial Index $74 \cdot 7$ (Dolichocranial)

Superior Facial Index* $100 \dfrac{G^1H}{J}$ = 44 (Hypereuryene)

Orbital index (R) $100 \dfrac{O_2}{O^1_1}$ = 67 (Chamaeconch)

* = estimated   ** at fronto-sphenoidal suture.

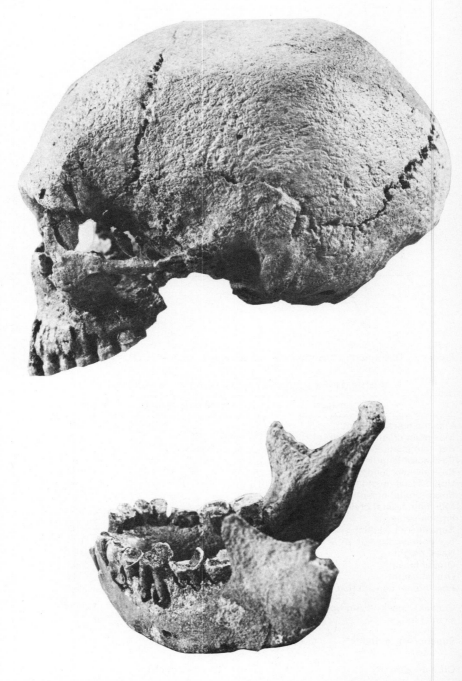

Figure 4 The Mt Cameron West cranium shown in left lateral view and mandible shown in left postero-lateral view.

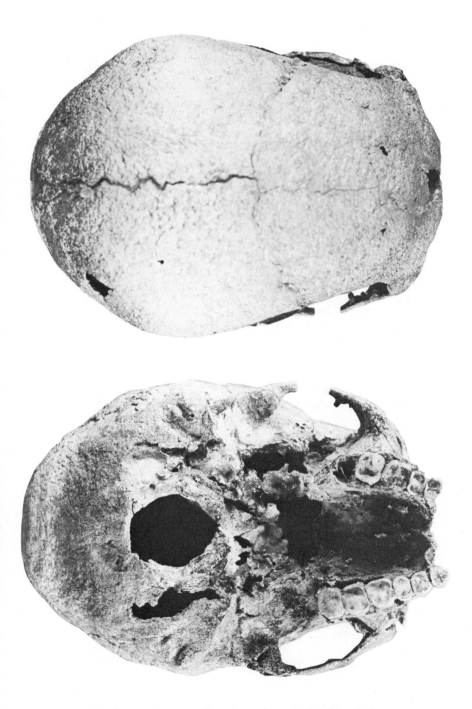

Figure 5 The Mt Cameron West cranium shown in vertical and basal views.

Table 2: Dental measurements (mm)

		crown length	cement/ enamel length	crown breadth	cement/ enamel breadth
R	M^1	11·3	10·4	12·4	7·7
	M^2	11·2	9·0	12·7	6·8
	M^1	10·8	9·0	12·7	6·7
L	M^2	11·1	8·9	13·3	7·7
	M^3	11·5	9·1	13·2	7·0
	M$_1$	—	9·5	—	10·1
R	M$_2$	12·5	10·0	12·0	9·7
	M$_3$	13·7	10·0	11·5	9·5
	M$_1$	—	9·5	—	9·7
L	M$_2$	11·7	9·9	12·4	9·7
	M$_3$	11·8	10·0	11·8	9·8

Palate and Arches				
	Length	Breadth	Height	Index
Max. arch	≃58·5	71·0	—	121·0
Mand. arch	≃61·0	65·0	—	106·0
Palate	≃53	43	19·0	81

Teeth and alveolar arches

With the exception of the right upper third molar, a complete set of maxillary and mandibular posterior teeth is present. The missing third molar, together with the upper incisors, upper right canine and lower central and left lateral incisors, appear to have been lost post-mortem.

All teeth, excepting the lower left canine, show marked occlusal wear, particularly the lower first molars which are worn in a steep inclined plane from lingual to buccal. Mandibular occlusal wear, according to Broca's (1879) classification, progresses posteriorly from grade II on the left canine to grade IV on the first molars, then back to grade III on the second and third molars. Maxillary occlusal wear is grade III on all teeth. There is moderate approximal attrition on all teeth, and evidence of chronic periodontal disease, but not of dental caries. The teeth are megadont and lie in the upper part of the range for Australian Aboriginals. Measurements of the molar teeth and alveolar arches are shown in Table 2 and of the mandible in Table 3. Tooth dimensions stated are approximate maximum length and breadth of the crown and maximum length and breadth of the roots immediately below the cemento-enamel junction as advocated by Macintosh and Barker (1965).

Table 3: Mandible and palate measurements and indices (mm)

Mandibular total length	= 110
Bicondylar width	= 125
Mandibular index	= 88 (Mesognathic)

$$\text{Index of mandibular robustness} = 100 \times \frac{\text{Thickness at mental foramen}}{\text{Body height (premolar height)}}$$

$$= 100 \times \frac{14 \cdot 5}{32 \cdot 5}$$

$$= 44 \cdot 6$$

The palate and superior alveolar arch are broad, mesostaphyline and brachyuranic respectively, as indicated by the breadth/length indices. The maxillary alveolar arch may be classified as parabolic, the mandibular as hyperbolic.

Sex and other comparisons

The skull was scored using Larnach and Freedman's (1964) system for sexing Aboriginals from coastal New South Wales by seven characteristics. Values are as follows:

Feature	Points
Glabella	2
Superciliary ridges	2
Zygomatic trigone	1
Malar tuberosity	1
Mastoid process	1
Occipital markings	1
Palate size	3
	11

The total of 11 points designates a female. This, of course, is based on the assumption that sexual dimorphism in coastal New South Wales can be equated with that in Tasmania.

The skull was then scored using the 20 characters employed by Larnach and Macintosh in their study of the cranial of male Aboriginals of coastal New South Wales (1966) differentiating them from Mongoloids and Europeans and later used by them on female Aboriginals from Queensland (1970). Three of the characters could not be scored but the other 17 gave a total score of 34 and thus the true score would be in the range 37–43, falling into the normal distribution for Australian female Aboriginals.

Scoring was also performed for the 17 characteristics used by Macintosh and Larnach (1972) in their study of the persistences of *Homo erectus* traits in Australian Aboriginal crania. Here a total of 18 points placed the skull near the upper limit (20) of their range but outside their range for Mongoloid, European, Maori, Negro or New Guinea material.

A comparison was also made with the values for the Lake Mungo, Kow Swamp and recent Aboriginal crania given by Thorne (1971). Results are shown in Table 4.

Table 4: Comparative cranial measurements (mm)

	Lake Mungo	Kow Swamp	Recent Australian Aboriginal	Tasmanian L319
Max. cranial length	181	193–216	166–200	186
Max. cranial breadth	119	126–140	121–142	139
Supra-orbital breadth	107	110–138	96–126	111
Post-orbital constriction	15	22– 35	8– 30	25
Frontal curvature index	23·3	12·5– 19	17·3–31·7	20
Bizygomatic breadth	—	130–155	116–151	134

Conclusion

The skull, which may be over 4000 years old and unquestionably Tasmanian, thus displays many of those features which most authors would consider typically but not exclusively Tasmanian. No single feature, however, appears to fall outside the Australian Aboriginal range and this new material lends support to the concept of the essential kinship of the Tasmanian and Australian Aboriginals.

References

FAIRBRIDGE, W.   1961   Eustatic changes in sea level. *Physics and chemistry of the earth*, 4:99–185.

JONES, R.   1971   *Rocky Cape and the problem of the Tasmanians*. Ph.D. Thesis. University of Sydney.

LARNACH, S. L. and L. FREEDMAN   1964   Sex determinations of Aboriginal crania from coastal New South Wales, Australia. *Records of the Australian Museum*, 26(11): 295–308.

—— and N. W. G. MACINTOSH   1966   *The craniology of the Aborigines of coastal New South Wales*. Oceania Monographs 13, Sydney.

——   1970   *The craniology of the Aborigines of Queensland*. Oceania Monographs 15, Sydney.

MACINTOSH, N. W. G.   1968   The recovery and treatment of bone. In *Australian archaeology and a guide to field and laboratory techniques*, D. J. Mulvaney (ed), pp. 83–89. Australian Institute of Aboriginal Studies, Canberra.

—— and B. C. W. BARKER   1965   *The osteology of Aboriginal Man in Tasmania*. Oceania Monographs 12, Sydney.

—— and S. L. LARNACH   1972   The persistence of *Homo erectus* traits in Australian Aboriginal crania. *Archaeology and Physical Anthropology in Oceania*, 7(1):1–7. No. 1. 1–7.

PERON, F.   1807   *Voyage de Decouvertes aux Terres Australes*.

THORNE, A. G.   1971   Mungo and Kow Swamp: morphological variation in pleistocene Australians. *Mankind*, 8(2):85–89.

TOPINARD, P.   1872   Etude sur les Tasmaniens. *Memoirs de la Société d'Anthropologie de Paris*, 1(3):307–29.

Aboriginal palaeophysiology

W.V. Macfarlane

HOMINID SKELETAL CHANGES have been followed for over 3 million years, but only inferences can be made on the associated functions. Simpson (1953) has pointed out that a morphological change of generic proportions usually required 3 to 10 million years to evolve. The genus *Homo* may have evolved rather more rapidly, with special brain increments at an average rate of 1 g in about 3000 years. Some functions are singularly stable. It is possible, for instance, to time the persistence of water turnover rate and sodium pump Na K ATPase activity in the oval red cells of camelids. Three million years ago remnants of the genus *Camelus* walked from the Dakotas in North America to the deserts of Asia and Africa, while the genus *Lama* moved to South American forests, hills and Patagonian savannahs. Camelids became extinct in North America. In spite of the lapse of time and diversity of habitats to which the two genera have been distributed, there is still physiological identity after 3 million years in the low water turnover rate and very high Na K ATPase activity in the red cells of the two genera measured in Adelaide (Table 1). This physiological stability in the face of diverse ecosystems, gives a measure of the inertia of some major functions. There are not many

Table 1: Water turnover and red cell Na K ATPase concentration of camel, llama and guanaco, together in the same environment

	Weight kg	Water turnover ml/kg$^{0.82}$/24 hr	Na K ATPase μM P/mg/hr
Camels	350–400	91–102	53
Llamas	95–133	43–76	48
Guanacos	45–51	68–72	43

Although the genus *Camelus* separated geographically 3 million years ago from *Lama*, when the camels moved to Asia and Africa, the water turnover of the llama-guanaco group is lower than that of camels. Llamas have lived in wetter and colder climates than the camels over most of the 3 million years. The unusually high concentration of salt pumping Na K ATPase of red cells is maintained in *Lama*, which often lived in low-salt environments, as it is in *Camelus* which tolerates 5 per cent sodium chloride in drinking water.

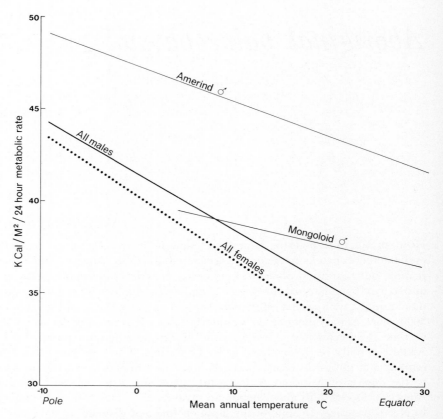

Figure 1 The basal metabolic rates of ethnic groups distributed from equator to pole. Groups related to mean temperature (based on Roberts, 1952). Mongoloid peoples have the lowest rates, and Amerinds the highest. Eskimos have higher rates than tropical Maya, but these are some 30 per cent above Europeans in the same latitudes. All Amerinds appear to derive from Siberians with high rates of metabolism, who moved to the Americas some 20–30,000 years ago.

examples in which such timing is possible. Yet there is analogy in some respects between the Camelids and the Hominids. Over 20,000 years ago Mongoloid groups from Siberia with high metabolic rates and high incidences of group A mucoproteins on the red blood cells, moved across Bering Strait into Alaska thence to South America. Eskimos and other Amerinds have maintained a high rate of metabolism in all environments (Figure 1). The rate is highest in the cold northern and southern areas and somewhat lower in the meso-american and tropical zones (Roberts, 1952). So the Maya living in a hot wet environment, have higher metabolic rates than Europeans living in the same area and lower rates than Athabascans or Eskimos. The basic genetic level of metabolic function evolved in northern Asia, although somewhat modulated by American environments, appears to have persisted over more than 20,000 years.

These analogues may be applied speculatively to the problems of Aboriginal physiology. Since there is speculation on Aboriginal origins, and since information on the functions of human groups is sparse, an attempt has been made here to look broadly at the biological history of the Aboriginals, in the hope that some day it may be understood.

The general premise that Australopithecines, *H. erectus* and *H. sapiens* originated in the tropical zone of Africa is well supported archaeologically. Australoid explorers moving south from Asia in the last 30,000 to 50,000 years, are likely to have come from hot wet environments (Golson, 1972). A second major wave that may have come to Western Australia 8000 to 9000 years ago at about the time the Indian dingo arrived, could also have been tropical in origin. Certainly the microliths and kinship systems of Veddoid people in south India would fit the cultural pattern of Aboriginal ancestors. Abbie (1969) has maintained that there is little evidence of a diversity of Australoid peoples in Australia, now that negrito groups of Queensland cannot easily be identified, and both early and later invasions may have been by groups of similar wet tropical people.

Tropical characteristics of *H. sapiens*
In general, the physiological components that suggest evolution of Man in a hot wet region are:

1.   Pigmented skin. This protection against ultra-violet radiation is found in other sparsely-haired tropical animals like chimpanzee, elephant, buffalo, banteng or pig.

2.   Lack of seasonal breeding pattern. Again this parallels elephant, pig and cattle, which breed throughout the year, but conception frequency is influenced by food supply and temperature (Macfarlane, 1970). In Arnhem Land the maximum Aboriginal conception rate occurs in winter; the low is in summer.

3.   High water turnover and high sweating rates. Mammals evolved in the tropics use more water than desert types. Man has a greater rate of sweating than any other animal (Macfarlane, 1957, 1971). Other primates sweat less than man, while cattle achieve rates of sweating about one third the human rate (though they have greater sweat production than other ruminants). Pigs, curiously, have sweat glands but they are not active in the heat. Wallowing appears to have replaced sweating in pig thermoregulation. Kuno (1934, 1956) pointed out that more sweat glands were active in people inhabiting the tropics, than in temperate climate populations.

4.   Relatively low concentrating power of the kidney. Man and pig are nearly equally low in renal osmotic competence, reaching only 1200–1400 m osmol/l (compared with the desert mouse *Notomys* which concentrates to 9000 m osmol/l). Animals evolved in the wet tropics lack a tubular loop of Henle in the kidney, or only a short loop is found, since presumably there was adequate water in the region of origin, and water reabsorption with urinary concentration was not specially developed.

5.   Low basal metabolic rate. Tropical people of any racial origin appear to use less energy per unit of mass than those of the same race in cool or cold regions (Roberts, 1952; Macfarlane, 1963). This seems to have evolved in relation to the climate but it is also related to activity patterns. Amerinds have high metabolic rates, but Asiatics have relatively low rates.

6.   Low arterial blood pressure is found in most tropical peoples who have had minimal contact with European life-patterns, but non-tropical groups such as the Eskimo, also have low blood pressures.

The physiology of Aboriginal non-urban people studied over the past 50 years (Moodie and Pederson, 1971) indicates that Aboriginals fit well into the equatorial group of *H. sapiens*.

Although there are differences in functions between Aboriginals and Europeans in the same environment, these differences may arise from genetic-evolutionary processes, from habituation to difficult environments, or from adaptations (in the sense of functional adjustments to non-optimal conditions). A tentative classification of the source of Aboriginal physiological variables would be:

Intrinsic (genetic, evolutionary in origin):
  a. High rates of water turnover and of sweating, with suppression of sweat by saturated air.
  b. Low metabolic rate.

Habituation (acquired by the nervous system):
  a. Ability of desert peoples to sleep in the cold, without shivering.
  b. Ability to sleep in the heat, on hard surfaces, and while pestered by ants or flies.
  c. Rapid ingestion of water.

Environmentally or nutritionally determined adjustments of function:
  a. Low sodium content of sweat.
  b. Low arterial pressure.
  c. Low glucose tolerance and glucosuria on European diets.
  d. High body water and extracellular fluid spaces.

Functional differentials

Metabolic rate measurements made by Wardlaw, Davies and Joseph (1934), Hicks, Moore and Eldridge (1934) and Hicks (1964) indicate that desert tribesmen in winter use less oxygen than Europeans.

No systematic measurements of metabolism amongst tribal Aboriginals have been made for 40 years. If the essential finding of a relatively low metabolic rate is correct this would be in agreement with the generally low metabolic rate in tropical peoples. There appears to be no information on this function among Australoid people in Malaya, the Philippines or southern India. Determination of the hierarchy of metabolic rates amongst these groups of the region would be valuable because of the apparently enduring inertia of this physiological rate (Roberts, 1952). The Mongoloid peoples show uniformly lower metabolic rates on any latitude than other

Table 2: Hierarchy of water turnover among grazing ungulates

Breed species or genus		Body weight kg	Body solids % wt	Water turnover/24 hr		Environment
				ml/kg	ml/kg$^{0.82}$ ± SD	
Boran cattle	(6)	417	28	76	224 ± 14	Dry
Eland	(5)	247	20	78	213 ± 43	grasslands
Wildebeest	(1)	175	27	53	137	Kenya
Kongoni	(2)	88	15	52	116	lat. 1°S
Oryx	(1)	136	30	29	70	
Shorthorn cattle	(2)	447	36	149	415	Spring
Leicester sheep	(2)	62	39	166	362	pasture
Donkey	(1)	375	38	75	217	Temperate
Goats	(2)	36	40	89	170	lat. 35°S
Camel	(1)	716	46	39	126	

Water turnover rates appear to have been evolved appropriately to environment – high rates in wet tropics and low rates in deserts. When mammals move to other environments the rank order of water use remains unchanged. So tropically evolved cattle on arid grassland retain high water turnover, relative to the desert oryx or camel.

racial groups, and it would be expected that the Chinese have lower rates than Australoids on the same latitude.

Water turnover is a function which persists as a specific rate in spite of changes of habitat. The turnover of water is an integral function. Tracer water (D_2O or TOH)[1] is ingested and when it equilibrates with all body water spaces after 2 hours, a sample of blood will provide a measure of the ratio of D_2O or TOH to H_2O, and thus the degree of dilution of the marker. This gives the total body water volume. From that time water taken either as part of food, derived from the oxidation of hydrogen in foodstuff, or ingested as such, dilutes the marker further. There is an exponential dilution, which yields the turnover rate, as a fraction of the initial fluid volume. This function is a singularly stable characteristic of an individual's race or species. Water turnover is, of course, adjusted to the type of food, to work, to heat balance and lactation. But different mammals in the same environmental conditions maintain a rank order or hierarchy (Table 2) that runs parallel with and is more easily measurable than metabolic rate (Macfarlane *et al*, 1971). Identical twin cattle have identical turnover (to 2 per cent) when the pairs graze together (Macfarlane and Howard, 1966). In the same environment human innate differences of water handling appear.

Animals showing high rates of water use in the tropics continue to use water at the same relative rate in the arid centre of Australia (cattle: Macfarlane and Howard, 1971). In the desert people – Njadadjara, Pintubi and Pitjantjatjara – as well as in the Arnhem Land semi-jungle groups like the Dalabon, there are three linked water functions. The first is the turnover of water at about twice the rate of Europeans in the same environment and

---

[1] Deuterium oxide or tritium hydroxide.

of the same age group (Table 3). There is little difference in the relative rates of water use between the Western Desert and the tropical savannah of Arnhem Land (Macfarlane 1969, 1973). Secondly, as part of the high rate of water turnover comes a high rate of sweating of Aboriginal children and adults. The whole-body sweat rate is nearly twice that of Europeans in the same environment; but the water turnover is not dependent only on sweating. During cool periods when sweating is not necessary there is still greater Aboriginal intake and urinary output of water than amongst Europeans. Wardlaw, Davies and Joseph (1934) made tentative observations in this direction and these have been quantitated (Macfarlane, 1973). The third point is that with the high rate of water turnover goes skill in rapid water ingestion. The ability to drink 2 l in 30 sec is common amongst desert men, and Dalabon people in Arnhem Land are not much slower at drinking.

Presumably if a higher rate of water use were physiologically intrinsic to the Aboriginals, a behavioural pattern would develop in which large quantities of water would be taken when available (Macfarlane 1969, 1973). Small children can drink as much as a European finds comfortable, in a shorter time. This could be the result of practice in a social pattern that has developed around water. Women bring water to the camp in dishes often

Table 3: Mean water content and turnover of Melanesian, Aboriginal, and European adult males, during summer

		Body water ml/kg	Body solids† %	Water turnover* ml/1./24 hr
New Guinea Lat. 6°S				
Tropical island (hot)				
Melanesians	(17)	645	35·5	114
Europeans	(2)	600	40·0	70
Mountains (cool)				
Melanesians	(27)	731	26·9	66
Europeans	(2)	620	38·0	68
Arnhem Land Lat. 12°S				
Wet tropics				
Aboriginals	(16)	695	30·5	173
Europeans	(3)	618	38·2	130
Central Desert Lat. 25°S				
Aboriginals	(13)	660	34·0	143
Europeans	(4)	617	38·3	86

* Expressed as amount per litre of body water turned over daily, because of differing body solids content in the groups.
† The body solids are proportional to the amount of fat stored.

In each environment the Aboriginals or the Melanesians used more water than Europeans. The greatest differential was in the desert, but in hot wet environments both Melanesians and Aboriginals turned over more water than Europeans with them.

In the cool Highlands of New Guinea there is little sweating, and the Melanesians, water turnover rates are close to those of Europeans in the region.

from a distant waterhole. Men drink the water rapidly and if there is no exercise to reduce urinary flow, it passes out with equal speed (as it does in cattle). Desert animals such as the camel when watered show a much delayed output through all channels, and the turnover rate is one third that of cattle in the same environment. In this respect Europeans in the desert behave and function rather more like camels than cattle.

On the same analogy, since cattle originated in the tropics and have retained high rates of water turnover, even in the Aboriginal country of central Australia, it is not unlikely that evolution in a wet tropical area for Aboriginals would have resulted in persistence of high water turnover functions through the relatively short time course of *H. sapiens* differentiation and distribution. Coastal Melanesians turn over more than Europeans in the same environment (Table 3). Measurements on the Veddas of southern India and Ceylon or on Malayan Australoids would be of value in the context of Aboriginal origins, but they appear not to be available (Seligman and Seligman, 1911).

Sweat suppression One curious finding about Aboriginal water handling is that sweating is very rapidly suppressed by the humid environment of an arm-bag, which provides a local saturated atmosphere. In all Aboriginal peoples studied, from the central desert to Arnhem Land, as well as urbanised Aboriginals, the rate of reduction in sweat flow was five to more than ten times faster than amongst Europeans (Table 4). Little is known

Table 4: Suppression of sweat by an arm bag (saturated air). Central Arnhem Land, adult male subjects

			Left arm continuously in arm bag for 90 min			*Right arm*, two sessions of 30 min in arm bag		
			0–30	31–60	61–90	0–30	31–60	61–90
Arm sweat rate	E	(3)	0·67	0·37	0·31	0·60	–	0·69
	ratio		1·0	0·55	0·46	1·0		1·15
ml/min	A	(9)	0·38	0·13	0·03	0·41	–	0·29
	ratio		1·0	0·34	0·08	1·0	–	0·71
Sodium	E		44·5	39·2	43·0	44·6	–	60·2
m equiv/	A		33·6	29·5	30·8	33·3	–	37·2
Potassium	E		9·5	7·1	7·8	9·9	–	9·5
m equiv/l	A		9·7	8·0	8·9	8·4	–	8·9

While walking in the sun (dry bulb 36°, wet bulb 27°C) suppression of sweating was more rapid and complete in adult Dalabon than in Europeans, during 90 min continuous wearing of an arm bag (left arm). With 30 min respite from the saturated air of the arm bag (right arm) there was recovery of sweating in that arm but still some reduction of sweat rate by the Dalabon. The left arm output of sweat fell progressively through this period. The differing rates of flow did not affect salt concentration in either group, though the sodium level was lower in Dalabon than in Europeans. On the other hand Dalabon sweat sodium was more concentrated than that of desert Njadadjaras and Pitjantjatjaras.

A – Aboriginal   E – European

about the dynamics of sweat suppression and even less is available on the ethnic distribution of rates of suppression. Since it takes place in Aboriginals from both hot wet and hot dry regions it could be a function which derives from the common ancestor of these tribes. It could be expected that Australoids in the equatorial zone might show the same feature if they were ancestral to the Australians. Sweat suppression in coastal New Guinea Melanesians is greater and faster than among Europeans also, but not as rapid as in Aboriginals. Mountain men suppress sweating less than those on the coast. The New Guinea Highlands have been inhabited for at least 15,000 years, and they could represent a physiological isolate.

The use of sweating rate as a measure of heat acclimatisation has difficulties in the context of sweat suppression. An assessment of Aboriginal people in Cape York as less acclimatised to heat than Europeans, was derived from one hour's exposure to saturated air at 32°C as the test environment, in which the Aboriginals sweated less than Europeans (Wyndham, McPherson and Munro, 1964). The saturated air in the test tent would suppress sweating in Aboriginals much more rapidly than in Europeans and sweat rate would not be a good criterion of heat adaptation for non-saturated environments. Ladell (1950) reported a somewhat similar view of low acclimatisation status of west African tropical people relative to Europeans. It may be that the tropical Australoid mechanism for reducing the amount of sweat produced in saturated air would conserve water in an equatorial situation where sweating would not produce cooling. In saturated air, sweating is of no thermo-regulatory use and reduction of sweat would be a valid adaptation to jungle conditions. Persistence of this function would offer no selection differential since saturated air is unlikely to occur in the desert. Overall the high rate of sweat suppression amongst all the Aboriginal groups studied, including the urban subjects, suggests a persistent function which probably had its origin in wet tropical conditions.

Habituation

A century ago Ernest Giles (1889) was impressed by the ability of his Aboriginal assistants to sleep on hard ground, in the heat of the night, while ants crawled over them. Giles paced miserably up and down without sleep. This turning off of neuronal information on pressure, heat and touch is what happens in habituation (Glaser, 1966). It is the same process that allows people to become accustomed to winter bathing in ice water. The nerve cells of the spinal cord (Macfarlane, 1964) and some at higher levels, change their responses to powerful intermittent stimulation. Inter-neurones cease to transmit to reflex outputs or to consciousness, information on states of per-ipheral heat, cold or pressure. No conscious effort is required and presynaptic inhibition probably occurs. Habituation is induced most readily in the young. States of habituation, once achieved, persist during the life of the individual with only slow decrement.

The University of Adelaide expeditions (Hicks, 1964) in the 1930s observed that Aboriginals slept naked near fires in August cold without shivering. This was investigated further by Scholander *et al* (1958) and Hamel *et al* (1959). Scholander *et al* found that skin temperatures of 15–17°C on the feet did not interfere with sleep, nor was metabolic rate raised, in desert Aboriginals. Further investigation by Hamel and his colleagues confirmed these findings, but in Arnhem Land the Aboriginals were much less habituated to cold and did not readily sleep at temperatures tolerated by the desert people.

These observations fit the hypothesis of habituation, where the tropically-reared people were not able to adjust to cold, but those born to desert winters were like Darwin's Patagonians, who were undisturbed though naked in a snow storm.

These habituation processes occur in all peoples, so that no clear deductions on the ecophysiological significance of Giles' or Hicks' observations are possible – other than that the Aboriginals did habituate. There could be some metabolic component, also, in these responses but it is not readily applicable to the problem of tropical origins.

Acquired adaptive changes

Body fluid spaces are expanded in desert Aboriginals. There were 20 per cent larger extracellular and total body water spaces in the least acculturated Njadadjaras than in those who had greater contact with Europeans. The European relative water content was lower still (Macfarlane, 1969).

Although a large extracellular volume is valuable in the desert as a water reserve, this expansion is common to all mammals in hot regions (Macfarlane, 1964a). The progressive reduction of fluid spaces as acculturation occurs probably reflects mainly nutritional changes among Aboriginals, particularly fattening under the influence of additional carbohydrate.

Glucos tolerance is reduced in Aboriginals who move from the primarily carnivorous food pattern of the desert to a wheaten flour diet on missions or stations. It is clear that the high incidence (over 40 per cent) of glucose in urine of Aboriginals on European regimes is associated with obesity. This in turn is linked with insulin resistance and poor cellular deposition of glucose, which accordingly appears in the urine. In general there is no lack of insulin (Wise, 1970). Glucosuria is not found significantly in nomadic Aboriginals. But in settlements the high carbohydrate intake results in obesity and appears to disturb the use of insulin by tissues, which fail properly to adapt. There is no evidence that this is a racial characteristic, since obese Europeans may show the same responses. The incidence of this glucose problem could, of course, be similar among other possible relatives of Aboriginals.

In New Guinea there is a similar disturbance associated with dietary change. Pig bel is a *Clostridium welchii* enterotoxaemia which follows massive ingestion of meat. The highland Melanesians are essentially herbivorous living on taro and sweet potato. A sudden change from high carbohydrate to high protein dietary, results in growth of the *Clostridium* in the intestine, and there is poor resistance to its protein toxin.

Arterial blood pressure is normally low in unacculturated peoples, and it rises in the context of European food and living. As Nye (1937), Caseley-Smith (1959), Abbie (1969) and others (see Moodie and Pederson, 1971) observed, the desert peoples have low pressures, below 100 Torr systolic, but with European contact the pressures rise. In New Guinea the same sequence has been observed among highland Melanesians, and it is associated with increments in the amount of salt available (Macfarlane, 1971). This seems a less likely association among Aboriginals who usually have salt in adequate amount from the extracellular fluid of the kangaroos or wallabies eaten. But the combination of increased calorie and salt intake probably would account for the rise of pressure that has occurred.

Neither the low initial pressures nor the rise with acculturation is peculiar to Aboriginals. It is common to many groups from Yemenite Jews to Eskimos.

Concentration of sodium in arm sweat: Sodium ion concentration was very low (21 m equiv/l) in Njadadjaras of the Rawlinson Ranges, and it rose in other groups proportionally to the amount of European contact. Arnhem Land Dalabon people living in houses reached 35–50 m equiv/l sodium, not much less than European sweat in the same environment. In spite of the similar sodium concentrations, there was 10 times faster suppression of sweating by these Aboriginals than among Europeans.

Presumably the increase of sweat sodium arose from greater salt supplies and the eating of saltier food as money and stores became part of the pattern of living. This could be expected to occur to all Aboriginal groups before long.

Renal concentration: Desert Aboriginals rarely reached 1000 m osmol/l compared with working Europeans at 1300 m osmol/l.

Seasonality of conception: Equatorial animals mate and conceive at any time of the year and this is true of human responses. In the tropics, however, where there are hot-dry and warm-wet seasons, conception in man is seasonal (Macfarlane, 1970). In the hot season there are fewer conceptions by 30–50 per cent in India than during the cooler season. In the Northern Territory, Aboriginal conceptions are fewer by 20–25 per cent in the summer, than in winter. This response is most likely due to temperatures above the thermoneutral point (about 28°C for naked humans). It is not known what conception patterns occur among southern Aboriginals. Probably in Tasmania they followed the Europeans and conceived more in winter than in summer. So if there were an equatorial origin for Aboriginals it is not likely to have influenced the season of maximum conception, which is environmentally determined, and changes with latitude.

Conclusions

It may reasonably be postulated that the rates of use of energy and water evolved in the progenitors of Aboriginals have remained relatively unchanged over the past 40,000 years, as in other species. This would hold for low (tropical) metabolic rates. Water turnover and the rate of whole-body sweating remain relatively high in both tropical and desert Aboriginal groups. The persistence of high rates of water use in the desert, suggests a wet tropical origin for these people. Cattle, which evolved in the jungle, are analogous with high rates of water turnover even when they live on the desert fringe.

Suppression of sweating in a saturated environment is rapid and nearly complete in all Aboriginals. This could be an adaptive function since sweat production in the humid tropics without evaporation of sweat is not of use in thermoregulation. Suppression appears to remain in the desert (where hot saturated air is not found) as an evolutionary relic.

Other functional differences among Aboriginals could be due to habituation (heat, cold, discomfort tolerances) or to nutritional background (low and rising blood pressures, low and rising sweat-sodium concentration, insulin resistant glucose intolerance in acculturated people). These functions appear to change in all racial groups.

References

ABBIE, A. A.   1969   *The original Australians*. Muller, London.

CASELEY-SMITH, J. R.   1959   Blood pressures in Australian Aborigines. *Medical Journal of Australia*, 1:627–33.

GILES, E.   1889   *Australia twice traversed*. Low, Maston, Searle and Rivington, London.

GLASER, E. M.   1966   *The physiological basis of habitation*. Oxford University Press, London.

GOLSON, J.   1972   The remarkable history of Indo Pacific man: missing chapters from every world prehistory. *Search*, 3:13–21.

HAMMEL, H. T., R. W. ELSNER, D. H. LeMESSURIER, H. T. ANDERSON and F. A. MILAN   1959   Thermal and metabolic responses of the Australian Aborigines exposed to moderate cold in summer. *Journal of Applied Physiology*, 14:605–15.

HICKS, C. S.   1964   Terrestrial animals in cold: exploratory studies on primitive man. *American Handbook of Physiology, Environment*, 4:405–12.

——, H. O. MOORE and E. ELDRIDGE   1934   The respiratory exchange of the Australian Aborigine. *Australian Journal of experimental and Medical Science*, 12:79–89.

KUNO, Y.   1934   *The physiology of human perspiration*. Churchill, London.

——   1956   *Human perspiration*. Thomas, Springfield.

LADELL, W. S. S.   1950   Inherent acclimatisation of indigenous West Africans. *Journal of Physiology, London*, 112:15–16P.

MACFARLANE, W. V.   1957   Water and salt turnover in canecutters working on the coastal subtropics of Australia. *Medical Journal of Australia*, 2:229–32.

——   1963   Endocrine functions in hot environments. In *Physiology and psychology in arid environment*. Reviews of Research, pp. 153–222. UNESCO, Paris.

——   1964   Habituation to heat and cold at the spinal cord level. In *Physiology and psychology in arid environments*. Proceedings of the Lucknow Symposium, pp. 351–54. UNESCO, Paris.

——   1964a   Terrestrial animals in dry heat: ungulates. *Handbook of Physiology. Environment*. 4:509–39. American Physiological Society, Washington, D.C.

——   1969   The water economy of desert Aboriginals. *Journal of Physiology. London*, 205:13P.

——   1970   The seasonality of human conception. *Biometeorology*, 4:167–82.

——   1971   Ecophysiology of water: mammalian functions in arid areas. In *Research in physiology*, F. F. Kao, K. Koizumi and M. Vassalle (eds), pp. 637–46.

——   1973   Functions of Aboriginal nomads during summer. In *The human biology of Aborigines in Cape York*, R. L. Kirk (ed), pp. 49–65. Australian Institute of Aboriginal Studies, Canberra.

—— and B. HOWARD   1966   Water content and turnover of identical twin *Bos indicus* and *B. taurus* in Kenya. *Journal of Agricultural Science*, 66:297–302.

—— and ——   1971   Water in the physiological ecology of ruminants. In *Physiology of digestion and nutrition in ruminants*, A. T. Phillipson (ed). Oriel Press, Newcastle.

MOODIE, P. M. and E. B. PEDERSON   1971   *The health of Australian Aborigines: an annotated bibliography*. Australian Government Publishing Service, Canberra.

NYE, L. J. J.   1937   Blood pressures in the Australian Aboriginal, with a consideration of possible aetiological factors in hyperpiesia and its relation to civilisation. *Medical Journal of Australia*, 2:1000–01.

ROBERTS, D. F.   1952   Basal metabolism, race and climate. *Journal of the Royal Anthropological Institute*, 82:169–83.

SCHOLANDER, P. F., H. T. HAMMEL, D. H. LEMESSURIER and Y. LYNING   1958   Cold adaptation of Australian Aborigines. *Journal of Applied Physiology*, 13:211–18.

SELIGMAN, C. G. and B. Z. SELIGMAN   1911   *The Veddas*. Cambridge University Press, Cambridge.

SIMPSON, G. G.   1953   *The major features of evolution*. Clarion; Simon and Schuster, New York.

WARDLAW, H. S. H., H. W. DAVIES and M. R. JOSEPH   1934   Energy metabolism and insensible perspiration of Australian Aborigines. *Australian Journal of Experimental and Biological Medical Science*, 12:63–74.

WYNDHAM, C. H., R. K. McPHERSON and A. MUNRO   1964   Reactions to heat of Aborigines and Caucasians. *Journal of Applied Physiology*, 19:1055–88.

WEINER, J. S. and K. HELLMANN   1960   The sweat glands. *Biological Review*, 35:141–86.

WISE, P. H., S. M. EDWARDS, B. H. THOMAS, R. B. ELLIOT, L. HATCHER and R. CRAIG   1970   Hyperglycaemia in the urban Aboriginal: the Davenport survey. *Medical Journal of Australia*, 2:1001–06.

Head size increases in Australian Aboriginals

An example of skeletal plasticity

T. Brown

DURING MAN'S PAST the interplay of genetic and environmental influences has resulted in the progressive modification of many physical traits commonly used to characterise populations. These long-term determinants of morphological variation have always been important in the study of human origins and affinities.

However, variables acting over a much shorter time span can also lead to morphological change, either temporary or permanent, in individuals and in populations. A striking example of rapid response to changing conditions is provided by the well-documented increases in average heights that have been recorded over the last century for many groups. Skeletal tissues are particularly responsive to environmental stimuli, an attribute sometimes termed skeletal plasticity.

At any age, the size and shape of a bone and its spatial relationships with neighbouring bones are regulated by the interaction of many determinants, all exerting a special influence at different times and with different intensities during the processes of growth and remodelling. Apart from genetic determination, environmental agencies such as maternal health, illness, nutrition and functional activity are among those known to affect the growth patterns and morphology of skeletal tissues. The consequences may be favourable or adverse. It has also been shown that the ability to recover from environmental shock such as illness or undernutrition depends to a great extent upon the health and developmental status at the time of the insult (Widdowson, 1970).

These considerations are important in the study of human origins and affinities, particularly in the interpretation of measurement data obtained from skeletal material. Hughes (1968) has drawn attention to skeletal plasticity and its relevance to studies of morphological variability and its determinants in earlier human populations.

The study of morphological variation, then, must be focused on more than the tabulation and comparison of parameters for body size and shape. It must also take into account the biological determinants of human variability and the changes in body dimensions that are known to occur in response to environmental stimuli. Little is known of the interplay of heredity and environment on the growth patterns of earlier peoples and it would appear worthwhile to study these factors in present populations as opportunities present. Information accrued in this way will assist in the interpretation of data obtained from earlier groups.

This paper is concerned with skeletal plasticity in general and as a particular example it draws from studies of Australian Aboriginals and other populations to demonstrate the magnitude of changes in head size that have occurred in recent times. The continuing study of Birdsell (1974) will elucidate further the nature of body size changes in successive generations of Aboriginals, particularly as it utilises measurement data from parent-offspring dyads.

Secular changes in body size

The comparison of body measurements obtained from present and past generations has provided evidence of progressive increases in the average heights and weights of many populations. Both cross-sectional and family studies have confirmed these changes which are often referred to as secular trends (Tanner, 1962; Damon, 1965; Falkner, 1966; Garn, 1966; Kimura, 1967; Sinclair, 1969; Moore, 1970; Malina, 1972). Increases in body size have been found to be accompanied by earlier physical maturation and are usually more marked in juveniles and adolescents than in young adults. The secular changes are commonly attributed to improved nutrition and living conditions together with better health although it has been suggested that heterosis, the break-up of small isolated groups, may be partly responsible (Damon, 1965; Strouhal, 1971). Accelerated growth rates and secular trends observed in some populations have also been linked with increased sugar consumption (Ziegler, 1966; Schaefer, 1970). In Canadian Eskimos, reported by Schaefer, increases in average height were accompanied by weight losses, lowered protein intake but increased sucrose consumption. He suggested that blood sugar homeostasis was disturbed resulting eventually in hypoglycaemia which stimulated the secretion of growth hormone.

Rather less is known of secular changes in dimensions of the head and face despite a long-standing interest by anthropologists in the cephalic index and its determinants in different populations. Abbie (1947) has referred to the earlier work of Boas who derived evidence that a change in environment could influence the headform of new generations; Abbie also collated the views of other anthropologists on this question. Hughes (1968) has also discussed the determinants of head size and shape, referring to anthropometric surveys of human populations and experimental studies using laboratory animals. The present review is limited to more recent studies of secular changes in dimensions of the head. Evidence available so far indicates that, like stature and weight, the average values of some head dimensions have also increased in recent generations.

Changes in head dimensions have been studied on Western Apache fathers and sons measured in 1940 and 1967 (Miller, 1970), immigrant and two generations of Japanese-Americans from Hawaii measured in 1967 (Froehlich, 1970), adult Skolt Lapps measured in 1934 and 1968 (Lewin and Hedegård, 1971), London school children aged 8 to 12 years measured in 1932 and 1971 (Lavelle, 1972), and three groups of young adult Japanese males measured in the 1910s, 1940s and 1965 (Morita and Ohtsuki, 1973). The findings of these studies indicate that uniform changes in head size and shape have not occurred in all groups nor in males and females of any one group. Discussing the nature of observed changes in the Skolt Lapps, Lewin and Hedegård observed that secular increases in craniofacial dimensions may appear in genetically isolated populations as a result of improved nutrition and not genetic drift. These authors also summarised previous reports of changes in head size, particularly those related to Norwegian groups.

This study is concerned with changes in a limited number of craniofacial dimensions recorded on a relatively isolated group of adult Australian Aboriginals. Evidence of increases in average stature and weight for the same people has been reported previously (Barrett and Brown, 1971; Brown and Barrett, 1973a). Average values of five head dimensions measured on young adult Aboriginals by the present author in the 1960s are compared with values obtained from young adults living in the same geographical region by Campbell, Gray and Hackett (1936).

The comparison is extended by the inclusion of the cephalic index and two body measurements – stature and radius length. Additional information is provided by using the data of Campbell *et al* (1936) and Abbie (1957) to compare the average values of head dimensions in older Aboriginals from the same region.

The study population and methods
Measurements of the head and body were recorded as associate observations in the longitudinal growth study of the dentofacial structures of Aboriginals living at Yuendumu, a Commonwealth Government settlement situated about 285 km north-west of Alice Springs in the Northern Territory of Australia. The settlement was established in 1946 as a ration depot for Aboriginal people whose previous way of life, centred around hunting and food-gathering, has been replaced almost entirely by a settlement existence providing European foods and other amenities. Most of the 1000 people now living at Yuendumu belong to the Wailbri group of Aboriginals. The methods used in the longitudinal study and information about Yuendumu and its people have been given previously (Barrett, Brown and Fanning, 1965; Brown and Barrett, 1971, 1973b).

Records for the growth study were accumulated during ten visits to the settlement between 1961 and 1971. The present comparison is limited to measurements of 75 young adults – 32 men and 43 women. Young adult status was decided by the emergence of all third molar teeth and, in some instances, by reference to growth curves constructed for individual subjects to show the rate of increase in stature. For some, particularly those born after the establishment of Yuendumu, records of birth dates were available; for others, however, ages were estimated on the basis of dental and physical examination. All of the 75 subjects but five were estimated to be aged between about 15 and 25 years at the time of measurement. Two males and one female were aged between 25 and 35 years, and one male and one female younger than 15 years were included because all third molars had emerged and it appeared that little further growth in the head could be expected. The average age was about 19 years both for males and females.

Although the growth study data include many measurements of the head obtained indirectly from standardised roentgenograms, the present comparison is limited to a few direct measurements included in the earlier studies referred to. Comparative data were insufficient to allow an analysis of changes in the head size of juvenile or adolescent Aboriginals. Techniques employed for the measurements made in the 1930s, the 1950s, and the 1960s may have varied slightly; however, the extent of bias, if any, introduced by this source could not be determined.

The measurements available for comparison were: head length, head breadth, bizygomatic diameter, bigonial diameter, morphological face height (measured from nasion to gnathion with the teeth in occlusion), stature and radius length. The cephalic index, that is the ratio of head breadth to head length, was calculated for each subject. The most recently obtained measurements were made at Yuendumu between 1961 and 1971 using standard instruments and techniques. Recordings were made by the same observer on seven of the ten visits.

Campbell *et al* (1936) reported an anthropometric survey carried out between 1927 and 1933 on several groups of Aboriginals living in the same geographical region as Yuendumu. The measurements were analysed to provide mean values of head and body dimensions for each Aboriginal group separately, and for the subjects combined according to sex and estimated age. The values used for comparison with the young adults of Yuendumu are those reported for 87 men and 35 women estimated to be aged from 17 to 25 years. Campbell *et al* also reported average values of the same measurements for an older group of Aboriginals from the same locality, 95 men and 67 women aged between about 26 and 45 years. These data are compared with those reported by Abbie (1957) for 22 men aged from about 23 to over 65 years, and 20 women aged from about 16 to over 60 years. All of Abbie's subjects were Wailbri people measured at Yuendumu in 1951.

Results

Table 1 compares the average values of the variables measured on young adults in the 1930s and 1960s. The averages for all dimensions were greater in the 1960s group, both for males and females. Differences were significant at $p < 0.05$ for bizygomatic diameter, morphological face height and in females radius length; the other dimensions differed in average values between groups at $p < 0.01$. The cephalic index was lower in males and

Table 1: Differences between average values for head dimensions, cephalic index, stature and radius length in young adult Australian Aboriginals

Variable		Subjects Measured[1] in 1930s			Subjects Measured in 1960s			Differences in Average Values Percentage change shown in brackets
		N	Average (cm)	Standard Deviation	N	Average (cm)	Standard Deviation	
Head Length	M	85	19·3	0·6	32	20·3	0·9	1·0* (5)
	F	35	18·2	0·6	43	19·0	0·5	0·8* (4)
Head Breadth	M	87	14·0	0·5	32	14·2	0·3	0·3* (2)
	F	35	13·4	0·5	43	13·7	0·5	0·3* (2)
Bizygomatic	M	87	13·8	0·5	32	14·0	0·5	0·2† (2)
Diameter	F	35	12·8	0·5	43	13·0	0·4	0·2† (2)
Bigonial	M	87	9·9	0·6	32	10·3	0·5	0·4* (4)
Diameter	F	35	9·2	0·3	43	9·8	0·4	0·6* (7)
Morphological	M	87	11·2	0·7	32	11·5	0·6	0·3† (2)
Face Height	F	35	10·4	0·6	43	10·7	0·6	0·3† (3)
Cephalic	M	—	72·2	—	32	70·0	3·2	−2·2
Index	F	—	73·6	—	43	72·0	2·4	−1·5
Stature	M	87	167·5	6·2	32	173·3	6·1	5·9* (4)
	F	35	157·0	6·2	43	163·0	5·0	6·0* (4)
Radius	M	87	25·9	1·6	32	27·2	0·9	1·3* (5)
Length	F	34	24·2	1·6	43	25·0	1·3	0·7† (3)

[1] Campbell et al (1936). Cephalic index computed from average values of head breadth and length.
* Difference in average values significant at $p < 0.01$.
† Difference in average values significant at $p < 0.05$.

females of the 1960s compared with those of the 1930s. The groups differed in average stature by 5·9 cm in males and 6·0 cm in females, these values slightly exceeding previously reported estimates of increases in average height of Australian Aboriginals between the 1930s and 1960s (Barrett and Brown, 1971). The present sample of young adults was larger, by 6 males and 4 females than that used to derive the previous estimates and, furthermore, the measurements were obtained up to 1971, two years later than the values reported before.

The increases, expressed as percentages of the 1930s averages, ranged from about 2 to 5 per cent for the head dimensions although in females a slightly higher increase of 7 per cent was recorded for bigonial diameter. For stature and radius length, the increases were between 3 and 5 per cent. In general, it would seem that the percentage increases in most head dimensions were somewhat similar in magnitude to those recorded for the two body measurements. Moreover, the percentage increases were similar in males and females.

Table 2: Differences between average values for head dimensions, cephalic index, stature and radius length in older adult Australian Aboriginals

Variable		Subjects Measured[1] in 1930s			Subjects Measured[2] in 1950s			Differences in Average Values — Percentage change shown in brackets
		N	Average (cm)	Standard Deviation	N	Average (cm)	Standard Deviation	
Head Length	M	95	19·6	0·6	22	19·1	0·8	−0·4† (−2)
	F	67	18·6	0·6	20	18·4	1·0	−0·2 (−1)
Head Breadth	M	90	14·0	0·6	22	14·0	0·5	0·0 (0)
	F	67	13·5	0·4	20	13·5	0·5	0·1 (1)
Bizygomatic	M	95	13·9	0·5	22	13·8	0·6	−0·2 (−1)
Diameter	F	67	12·8	0·4	20	12·9	0·5	0·1 (0)
Bigonial	M	95	10·3	0·6	22	9·9	0·9	−0·4† (−4)
Diameter	F	67	9·3	0·5	20	8·8	0·5	−0·5* (−6)
Cephalic	M	—	71·6	—	22	73·3	3·6	1·7
Index	F	—	72·6	—	20	73·9	4·5	1·3
Stature	M	94	168·7	5·4	22	168·8	5·5	1·1 (1)
	F	67	156·1	5·0	20	157·1	4·8	1·1 (1)
Radius	M	95	26·0	1·8	22	26·5	1·6	0·4 (2)
Length	F	67	23·7	1·8	20	24·1	1·2	0·4 (2)

[1] Campbell *et al* (1936). Cephalic index computed from average values of head breadth and length.
[2] Abbie (1957).
* Difference in average values significant at $p < 0·01$.
† Difference in average values significant at $p < 0·05$.

In Table 2, the mean values for the same variables, excluding morphological face height, are compared in the two groups of older Aboriginals measured in the 1930s by Campbell *et al* and in the 1950s by Abbie. The differences in mean values, both absolute and percentage, were low and apart from bigonial diameter did not exceed 2 per cent. Except for two variables in males and one in females there were no significant differences between the average values of the 1930s and the 1950s. Furthermore, the almost equal distribution of positive and negative differences indicated no consistent tendency for a general increase or a decrease in average values between the 1930s and 1950s. This comparison provided no convincing evidence of marked changes in the head dimensions of older Aboriginals between the 1930s and the 1950s.

The increases in five dimensions of the head recorded for the young adult Aboriginals are compared in Table 3 with increases reported in two other populations, Skolt Lapps (Lewin and Hedegård, 1971) and Western Apaches (Miller, 1970). In each instance the period of observation spanned about three decades. This comparison is interesting because all three

Table 3: Secular changes in head dimensions and cephalic index recorded in adults of three populations[1]

Variable		Australian Aboriginals 1960s–1930s	Skolt Lapps[2] 1968–1934	Western Apaches[3] 1967–1940
Head Length	M	10·1	4·3	6·5
	F	8·1	1·1	
Head Breadth	M	2·7	2·3	0·5
	F	3·0	2·7	
Bizygomatic	M	2·2	1·9	1·9
Diameter	F	2·1	0·8	
Bigonial	M	4·4	2·1	3·1
Diameter	F	6·0	1·8	
Morphological	M	2·7	6·2	5·2
Face Height	F	3·3	4·3	
Cephalic Index	M	−2·2	−0·5	−1·2
	F	−1·5	1·0	

[1] Differences in average values between the years shown are in mm.
[2] Data from Lewin and Hedegård (1971), sample size ranges from 23 to 41.
[3] Data from Miller (1970), measured on 143 fathers and sons.

groups have, in recent decades, experienced similar changes in living conditions and food habits. Increases in average head dimensions were recorded for each variable in the three groups, the changes being more marked in the Aboriginals. Of particular interest was the observation that bigonial diameter increased in average value more than bizygomatic diameter in males and females of all three groups. This tendency towards a reduction in the excess of middle facial breadth over lower appears to have been a general concomitant of the head size changes in these three populations.

Discussion

The comparison of head measurements between the Aboriginal groups is complicated by uncertainty of the tribal affinity and age distribution of the subjects included in the samples. Differences in measuring techniques may have also biased the results to some extent. However, so far as we can determine, there are no other readily available sources of metric data gathered on separate occasions over a 30 year period and relating to Aboriginal groups living in a restricted geographical region of Australia.

Average values reported by Campbell *et al* were derived from the pooled measurements of nomadic Aboriginals from several tribes living within the same geographical region as Yuendumu but long before its establishment as a settlement. His subjects were grouped according to estimated age. Abbie's sample, measured at Yuendumu in the 1950s a few years after the settlement was established, was drawn from Wailbri people with estimated ages extending from early adulthood to advanced old age. The young adults measured at Yuendumu in the 1960s, 15 to 25 years after its establishment, were mainly Wailbri but a few Pintubi people were included; ages were known for many of these subjects.

The findings provide evidence of an increase in the average values of head dimensions measured on young adult Australian Aboriginals in the 1930s and the 1960s. In contrast, there was no consistent pattern in the differences between the same dimensions measured on older Aboriginals in the 1930s and 1950s. Almost every young adult measured in the 1960s grew to maturity while living under settlement conditions and it is likely that the increases in head size date from about the time Yuendumu was established in 1946.

It is difficult to designate a common basis for the comparison of the secular changes in head size reported for different ethnic groups. The samples vary greatly in number and age constitution and the subjects were measured at different times during this century. Furthermore there are obvious problems arising from differences in the degree of genetic admixture, environment, levels of health and general living conditions. Changing patterns of food consumption have probably been more pronounced in people living under settlement or reservation conditions.

Kaplan (1954) elaborated on these difficulties in her extensive comparison of twenty-five studies concerned with environmental correlates of human plasticity. Many studies referred to by Kaplan produced evidence of increases in length and breadth dimensions, including those of the head, as a result of changing environment. However few attempts were made to quantify the nature of changes in living conditions, diet, general health and other factors important in the comparison of body size in successive generations. The impetus for human plasticity, according to Kaplan's comparisons, appears to be varied in nature and also little understood.

Although quantitative data relating to changing environmental conditions are not detailed, the recent studies of head size changes referred to above warrant additional comment. Froehlich (1970) found that the pattern of changes in average head size differed in males and females selected from immigrant and first generation Japanese-Americans of Hawaii. In the males, head breadth, head length, bizygomatic diameter, and facial height all increased in mean value as did the cephalic and facial indices. Females, however, displayed a decrease in average facial height and head length accompanied by a rise in cephalic index and a fall in facial index. In adult Japanese males studied by Morita and Ohtsuki (1973), brachycephaly increased on average between the 1910s and 1965 by over three units. This change was consequent upon an increase in average head breadth of $6 \cdot 8$ mm which exceeded by far the $0 \cdot 8$ mm increase in head length. In Japanese males measured in the 1940s and 1965, however, little change in the cephalic index was observed with average head length and breadth increasing by $3 \cdot 6$ mm and $3 \cdot 1$ mm respectively over the twenty-year period.

In adult Skolt Lapps measured in 1934 and 1968 secular increases were recorded for all craniofacial dimensions in males and females studied

either on a population basis or on a family level using data from two generations (Lewin and Hedegård, 1971). Changes in the neurocranium appeared
to consist predominantly of increased head breadth in females and increased
head length in males. On a population basis, increased dolichocephaly
occurred in the males and increased brachycephaly in females. However,
when two generations of females were compared on a family basis, the
daughters displayed slightly increased dolichocephaly. Changes in the facial
skeleton were characterised by an increase in the facial index arising from a
greater increase in facial height than in bizygomatic diameter, both in males
and females. Likewise in the Western Apache males studied by Miller (1970),
the secular changes in one generation included a reduction in the cephalic
index and an increase in facial index.

The findings of the Skolt Lapp study in particular are relevant to the
present investigation of Australian Aboriginals. In both populations,
measurements were obtained from adults on two occasions, once in the 1930s
and once in the 1960s. Both populations have also maintained relative
genetic isolation while being subjected to changes in food habits and living
conditions dating from about the mid-1940s.

It appears that Aboriginals, Skolt Lapps and Western Apaches have
displayed similar patterns of secular change in the craniofacial dimensions,
at least in recent decades. Lewin and Hedegård (1971) have summarised
these changes: 'the facial index is increasing, facial height having increased
more than bizygomatic breadth, and in the neuro-cranium there is a
tendency towards dolichocephalization'.

The comparison shown in Table 3 brings to light a further consequence of
the increases in facial dimensions common to the three populations. On the
average, bigonial diameter increased more than bizygomatic diameter both
in males and females. As a result, the marked excess of middle facial breadth
compared with lower facial breadth, a morphological characteristic of each
group, appears to have become less pronounced. However the difference in
facial breadths still ranged from about 32 mm in Lapps to almost 40 mm in
the Apaches and Aboriginals. In contrast, the difference measured in a group
of modern Swedish men was only 22 mm (Lewin and Hedegård, 1970).

The present study also throws light on some of the questions raised by
Abbie (1947) in his discussion of head form in Australian Aboriginals. Abbie
suggested that 'within a homogeneous group under stable conditions the
cephalic index remains constant for a long time, and this must be due
mainly to hereditary transmission'. He also proposed that 'a change in
environment – a change usually for the better – may be sufficient to jolt the
hereditary mechanism out of its accustomed groove'. In the two groups of
young adult males compared in our study the average cephalic index fell from
72·2 in the 1930s to 70·0 in the 1960s; for the young adult females the
reduction over the same period was from 73·6 to 72·0.

Abbie also drew attention to a generalisation of earlier anthropologists
postulating a negative correlation between stature and cephalic index, that
is, the greater the stature the lower the index and the longer the skull. To

test this generalisation, Abbie computed correlation coefficients between stature, head length, head breadth and cephalic index using measurements of 50 male and 50 female Australian Aboriginals published by previous workers. Significant coefficients were found only for the variable pairs stature-head length in males ($r = 0 \cdot 46$) and stature-cephalic index in males ($r = -0 \cdot 37$). In the young adults from Yuendumu the correlations between stature and head length were $0 \cdot 33$ in males and $0 \cdot 53$ in females; for stature and head breadth the associations were weaker, $0 \cdot 29$ in males and $0 \cdot 32$ in females.

The finding of secular increases in both stature and head length and a reduction in cephalic index for Australian Aboriginals, Skolt Lapps and Western Apaches is in keeping with the generalisation referred to above. However, according to Abbie the generalisation probably has significance only within single homogeneous groups of people. Comparisons between groups and the interpretation of evolutionary trends in head form are more difficult.

The cephalic index has been accepted as a useful measure by anthropologists who have shown longstanding interest in the determinants of human head form. However, in spite of considerable research, the interpretation of variations in the cephalic index remains a controversial topic. Abbie (1947) reviewed the opinions of earlier anthropologists in his discussion of evolutionary trends in head form. He suggested that the cephalic index of different populations tended to converge upon a common mean within a restricted range of 80 to 82, that is, with the passage of time high indices were downgraded and low indices upgraded.

More recently Strouhal (1971) studied the effects of inbreeding in an anthropometric survey of Nubian people. Although much of the recorded variation could be ascribed as regional, he considered that a high rate of endogamy could lead to 'inbreeding depression' of some body dimensions and functional measures such as hand-grip strength. Strouhal referred to earlier studies of the cephalic index and proposed that 'increase of homozygosity seems to promote an increase of the index, i.e. formation of isolates contributes to brachycephalization, while increase of heterozygosity is followed by a fall in the index – the modern trend'.

On the other hand Morita and Ohtsuki (1973) reported that brachycephalisation appeared to have been progressing in Japan for the last 50 years and considered that 'progressive brachycephalisation seems to have been worldwide'. Beals (1972) also supports the view of a general evolutionary trend towards brachycephalisation but attributes this to the result of adaptation to cold environments.

Accumulated evidence from studies carried out this century indicates that body size changes have occurred in many populations. Dimensions of the head also have changed in recent generations although the pattern of these changes is by no means uniform in the populations studied. The different interpretations placed on recent changes in head size and shape can often be explained by a failure to distinguish clearly between long-term evolutionary trends and the short-term plastic changes observed in many skeletal dimensions.

Hulse (1960) commented on this confusion and distinguished between adaptation in populations and plasticity in individuals. Adaptation was considered to be the possession by a population of a genetic system resulting in phenotypic expressions favourable to survival and reproduction. On the other hand, Hulse regarded plasticity to be the possession by individuals of genetic systems capable of varied expression in response to environmental stimuli. Viewed in this light, it could be misleading to interpret the responses of individuals and populations to changing environmental conditions as indications of general evolutionary trends, particularly where there is no marked evidence of changing genotype.

The effects of improved nutrition and living conditions on growth and maturation are now well documented in many populations and most investigators would, with justification, attribute secular increases in body size to these causes. In Aboriginals from the region of Yuendumu there is some evidence of increases in average values for stature, weight, radius length and head dimensions over the last few decades. However, Aboriginal children today still lag behind Caucasoid children in growth when this is assessed by the comparison of curves for weight and height attained (Kettle, 1966; Kirke, 1969; Maxwell and Elliott, 1969; Lickiss, 1970; Brown and Barrett, 1971, 1972). Morbidity and mortality levels in Aboriginal infants and children are high and evidence of growth retardation associated with protein-calorie malnutrition has been presented by Jose and Welch (1970) and Moodie (1973) among others.

It is obvious that the interaction of numerous factors is responsible for the secular increases in body size reported for many populations. Nutrition is only one determinant although it is probably of great importance. In the Yuendumu Aboriginals we are presented with what appears to be a paradoxical situation – secular increases appearing to date from about the time of continual European contact and yet the evidence of protein-calorie malnutrition and growth retardation in settlement Aboriginals is very strong.

In view of the high rate of infant mortality in Australian Aboriginals (Moodie, 1973), it could be expected that a selective effect might lead to survival of children with the greatest growth potential. However, comparison with past generations is made difficult by the lack of quantitative information on food habits, food values and patterns of health, disease and mortality in Aboriginal groups prior to contact with Europeans.

Food habits at Yuendumu have changed drastically since its establishment. In the 1950s, little money circulated in the community and the people relied on the issue of dry rations and a daily meal provided by the settlement staff. Nursing mothers, infants and school children were favoured with food supplements. Traditional food gathering and hunting were more common then than later. A communal dining hall was established in the 1960s and for some years the people of Yuendumu were provided with three meals a day on the payment of a small charge. However, with the introduction of higher wages in 1969, the money income of the community from all sources increased substantially. As a consequence, most Aboriginals now prefer to prepare their own meals from supplies purchased at the canteen. Unfortunately, this trend has been accompanied by a marked increase in the consumption of low-protein foods – flour, bread, canned foods and biscuits, for example. It is quite likely that the young adults reported in this study grew to maturity in the 1950s and early 1960s under more favourable dietary conditions than the children of later years. Future studies should clarify these matters further.

A further concept of growth stimulation has been suggested which bears closer study, particularly in relation to Aboriginal nutrition. Ziegler (1966) demonstrated a relationship between high sugar intake and growth trends in a sample of recruits from Switzerland and suggested that sugar 'has a direct influence on the endocrine system and stimulates the anterior lobe of the hypophysis'. This work was given further credence by the study of Schaefer (1970) who investigated growth acceleration in Canadian Eskimos in whom sugar consumption rose from 26 lbs per capita in 1959 to 104·2 lbs in 1967. Schaefer provided experimental evidence that rapidly absorbable carbohydrates disturbed blood sugar homeostasis in this group leading to fluctuations in insulin and growth hormone levels. After consuming loads of rapidly absorbable carbohydrates, unpreceded by meat, Eskimos displayed peaks in blood glucose levels suggestive of a diabetic glucose tolerance curve. These peaks were followed, after about three hours, by hypoglycaemic reactions. However, if meat was taken one hour before the glucose, the glucose tolerance curve reverted from a 'diabetic' type to normal. These experiments led Schaefer to suggest that high intake of readily absorbable carbohydrates, particularly refined sucrose, unaccompanied by adequate proteins could result in states of hypoglycaemia which is known to be a stimulant for the production of growth hormone (Roth, Glick, Yalow and Berson, 1963). Schaefer summarised his views thus: 'One must, therefore, challenge the currently prevailing view that the phenomenon of secular growth acceleration is in all populations the consequence of improved nutrition and health. This, I submit, is not the case for Eskimos, and I doubt if this is true for large parts of our affluent societies who have experienced parallel development of curves of growth acceleration and incidence of diabetes mellitus'.

Is there any evidence that the above explanation may account, in part at least, for the secular increases observed in the Aboriginal population at Yuendumu? Ziegler (1972) believes so! Sugar consumption has steadily increased at Yuendumu and no doubt at other settlements; by 1972 sugar turnover at Yuendumu had reached about 6400 lbs per month for a population of about 950. Sales of refined and prepared foods, flour and canned drinks have also increased. To date there have been few investigations of disturbances in carbohydrate metabolism in Aboriginals. Elliott, Maxwell, Kneebone and Kirke (1969) investigated Aboriginal infants and mothers attending the Alice Springs hospital and found strong evidence of lactose maldigestion which could not be attributed to lack of lactose in their diet. These authors suggested that the maldigestion may be evoked by an enzymic deficiency which, in Aboriginals, could be genetic in origin.

Maxwell and Elliott (1969), concerned with the nutritional state of growth retarded children living on a central Australian settlement, assayed plasma growth hormone levels in 15 children after four hour fasting. No insufficiency was found compared with levels in Caucasoid children; in fact, examination of the charts indicated a tendency for excessive hormone levels in children up to one year of age. The sample was small, however, and further clinical tests are required before any generalisations can be made.

The prevalence of diabetes mellitus was found to be 19 per cent in urbanised Aboriginals aged 21 years and over from Davenport in South Australia (Wise et al, 1970). This compared with a prevalence of only 2·3 per cent in a community of white Australians. The diabetic and border-line diabetics were diagnosed by glucose tolerance tests, the criteria being plasma glucose levels of 225 mg/100 ml at one hour and 150 mg/100 ml at two hours after a glucose load of 50 gm. The authors referred to studies associating a high incidence of diabetes in other communities, particularly North American Indians, with the rapid transition from primitive to more sophisticated living conditions. They suggest that 'it appears possible that the Aboriginal has evolved without the ability to cope with the high carbohydrate loads inherent in Western civilization'.

At the present time there is insufficient evidence to associate growth trends in recent generations of Aboriginals with increased sugar consumption, but this aspect of nutrition deserves closer study particularly in view of accumulating reports of dysfunctions in carbohydrate metabolism and high prevalences of diabetes mellitus in this ethnic group and in others whose traditional ways of life have changed.

The studies referred to above illustrate the varied nature of human plasticity. There appears to be little doubt that a changing environment can be the stimulus that evokes a plastic response in individuals and also in population groups. However, the biological mechanisms underlying these varied responses are still imperfectly understood. In the words of Hulse (1960), 'One might anticipate then that plasticity would continue to operate in the future, as it has in the past, to maintain the genetic unity of the human species'.

Acknowledgements

Acknowledgement is made of the assistance given by the Director of Social Welfare of the Northern Territory Administration and his officers, and by the Reverend T. J. Fleming and his wife, of Yuendumu Settlement. The research was supported by a grant from the University of Adelaide, by U.S.P.H.S. research grant DE 02034 from the National Institute of Dental Research, National Institute of Health, Bethesda, Maryland, and by the Australian Institute of Aboriginal Studies, Canberra.

References

ABBIE, A. A.   1947   Headform and human evolution. *Journal of Anatomy*, 81: 233–58.

——   1957   Metrical characters of a Central Australian tribe. *Oceania*, 27: 220–43.

BARRETT, M. J. and T. BROWN   1971   Increase in average height of Australian Aborigines. *Medical Journal of Australia*, 2:1169–72.

——, —— and E. A. FANNING   1965   A long-term study of the dental and cranio-facial characteristics of a tribe of Central Australian Aborigines. *Australian Dental Journal*, 10:63–68.

BEALS, K. L.   1972   Head form and climatic stress. *American Journal of Physical Anthropology*, 37:85–92.

BIRDSELL, J. B.   1974   Summary report on fieldwork. *Newsletter New Series*, 1:17. Australian Institute of Aboriginal Studies, Canberra.

BROWN, T. and M. J. BARRETT   1971   Growth in Central Australian Aborigines: Stature. *Medical Journal of Australia*, 2:29–33.

—— and ——   1972   Growth in Central Australian Aborigines: Weight. *Medical Journal of Australia*, 2:999–1002.

—— and ——   1973a   Increase in average weight of Australian Aborigines. *Medical Journal of Australia*, 2:25–28.

—— and ——   1973b   Dental and craniofacial growth studies of Australian Aborigines. In *The human biology of Aborigines in Cape York*, R. L. Kirk (ed), pp. 69–80. Australian Institute of Aboriginal Studies, Canberra.

CAMPBELL, T. D., J. H. GRAY and C. J. HACKETT   1936   Physical anthropology of the Aborigines of Central Australia. Part 1. Anthropometry. *Oceania*, 7:106–39.

DAMON, A.   1965   Stature increase among Italian-Americans: Environmental, genetic or both? *American Journal of Physical Anthropology*, 23:401–08.

ELLIOT, R. B., G. M. MAXWELL, G. M. KNEEBONE and D. K. KIRKE   1969   Lactose digestion and breast feeding: a nutritional survey in Australian Aboriginal infants. *Australian Paediatric Journal*, 5:109–13.

FALKNER, F.   1966   General considerations in human development. In *Human development*, F. Falkner (ed), pp. 10–39. Saunders, Philadelphia.

FROEHLICH, J. W.   1970   Migration and the plasticity of physique in the Japanese-Americans of Hawaii. *American Journal of Physical Anthropology*, 32:429–42.

GARN, S. M.   1966   Nutrition in physical anthropology. *American Journal of Physical Anthropology*, 24:289–92.

HUGHES, D. R.   1968   Skeletal plasticity and its relevance in the study of earlier populations. In *The skeletal biology of earlier human populations*, D. R. Brothwell (ed), pp. 31–55. Pergamon, London.

HULSE, F. S.   1960   Adaptation, selection, and plasticity in ongoing human evolution. *Human Biology*, 32:63–79.

JOSE, D. G. and J. S. WELCH   1970   Growth retardation, anaemia and infection, with malabsorption and infestation of the bowel. The syndrome of protein-calorie malnutrition in Australian Aboriginal children. *Medical Journal of Australia*, 1:349–56.

KAPLAN, B. A.   1954   Environment and human plasticity. *American Anthropology*, 56:780–800.

KETTLE, E. S.   1966   Weight and height curves for Australian Aboriginal infants and children. *Medical Journal of Australia*, 1:972–77.

KIMURA, K.   1967   A consideration of the secular trend in Japanese for height and weight by a graphic method. *American Journal of Physical Anthropology*, 27: 89–94.

KIRKE, D. K.   1969   Growth rates of Aboriginal children in Central Australia. *Medical Journal of Australia*, 2:1005–09.

LAVELLE, C. L. B.   1972   Secular changes in the face and stature. *Angle Orthodontist* 42:221–26.

LEWIN, T. and B. HEDEGÅRD   1970   An anthropometric study of head and face of mature adults in Sweden. *Acta odontologica scandinavica*, 28:935–45.

—— and ——   1971   Secular changes in craniofacial dimensions of adult Skolt Lapps: studies on population and family levels within a genetic isolate group. *Suomen hammaslaakariseuran toimituksia*, 67:171–83.

LICKISS, J. N.   1970   Health problems of Sydney Aboriginal children. *Medical Journal of Australia*, 2:995–1000.
MALINA, R. M.   1972   Comparison of the increase in body size between 1899 and 1970 in a specially selected group with that in the general population. *American Journal of Physical Anthropology*, 37:135–41.
MAXWELL, G. M. and R. B. ELLIOTT   1969   Nutritional state of Australian Aboriginal children. *American Journal of Clinical Nutrition*, 22:716–25.
MILLER, P. S.   1970   Secular changes among the Western Apache. *American Journal of Physical Anthropology*, 33:197–206.
MOODIE, P. M.   1973   *Aboriginal health*, pp 48–96. Australian National University Press, Canberra.
MOORE, W. M.   1970   The secular trend in physical growth of urban North American Negro schoolchildren. *Monographs of the Society for Research in Child Development*, 35(7):62–73.
MORITA, S. and F. OHTSUKI   1973   Secular changes of the main head dimensions in Japanese. *Human Biology*, 45:151–65.
ROTH, J., S. M. GLICK, R. S. YALOW and S. A. BERSON   1963   Hypoglycemia: a potent stimulus to secretion of growth hormone. *Science*, 140:987–88.
SCHAEFER, O.   1970   Pre- and post-natal growth acceleration and increased sugar consumption in Canadian Eskimos. *Canadian Medical Association Journal*, 103:1059–68.
SINCLAIR, D.   1969   *Human growth after birth*, pp 116–119. Oxford University Press, London.
STROUHAL, E.   1971   Anthropometric and functional evidence of heterosis from Egyptian Nubia. *Human Biology*, 43:271–87.
TANNER, J. M.   1962   *Growth at adolescence*. Blackwell, Oxford.
WIDDOWSON, E. M.   1970   Harmony of growth. *Lancet*, 1:901–05.
WISE, P. H., F. M. EDWARDS, D. W. THOMAS, R. B. ELLIOT, L. HATCHER and R. CRAIG   1970   Hyperglycaemia in the urbanized Aboriginal: the Davenport survey. *Medical Journal of Australia*, 2:1001–06.
ZIEGLER, E.   1966   Die Ursache der Akzeleration: Ernahrungsphysiologische und medizinhistorische Betrachtungen Uber den Zuckerkonsum des modernen Menschen. *Helvetica paediatrica acta*, 21 (Supplement 15):1.
——   1972   Increase in average height of Australian Aborigines. *Medical Journal of Australia*, 1:1220.

Morphological variation in the adult Australian Aboriginal

A.A. Abbie*

PROPERLY SPEAKING, I suppose, 'morphology' comprehends all aspects of form, non-metrical as well as metrical but here I propose to treat metrical characters only; and I shall simplify the subject further by restricting myself to males for it is the more fully differentiated male who most clearly displays the physical characteristics of any people.

The subject could be simplified yet further by examining only bodily ratios, indices and proportions (see Abbie, 1968) but it is useful to look at the measurements as well.

The material comprises some 38 measurements made on 205 adult male Aboriginals (20 years of age and over), still mostly nomadic and widely distributed over the continent (Table 1). The measurements afford the source from which some 29 ratios etc. were subsequently extracted.

The methods and equipment employed were those long since standardised for field anthropometry (e.g. Martin, 1928; Ashley Montagu, 1945; Comas, 1966; Olivier, 1969 and others). Since, as I have shown (Abbie, 1968), the various Aboriginal groups betray no significant tribal or regional differences the data were pooled and put through the computer as a single cross-sectional sample.

However, not all measurements, ratios, etc. are equally informative and this paper presents only a selection that seem to be most representative; the complete series (now in preparation) will be published later.

Table 1: Number of adult males measured for various localities by age group

Age	Yuendumu	Haast's Bluff	Yalata	Maningrida	Beswick	Kalumburu	Total
21–24	2	4	3	1	6		16
25–29	3	9	5	7	4	2	30
30–39	5	16	10	6	4	5	46
40–49	2	13	8	11	7	2	43
50–59	4	4	4	6	6	4	28
60+	8	10	4	3	2	15	42
Total	24	56	34	34	29	28	205

* Dr Abbie died in July, 1976.

Stature   This ranged from 146·0 to 190·6 cm with an overall mean of 168·4 cm.

Weight   The male range was 37·2 kg to 96·2 kg to give a mean of 57·8 kg.

Weight/Stature ratio   This ranged from 233·8 to 557·7 (an exceptional case) gm/cm to give a mean of 343·1 gm/cm.

Trunk

Sitting height   In males this dimension ranged from 65·0 to 89·6 cm with a mean of 80·3 cm.

Relative sitting height   The percentage of total stature occupied by the trunk, head and neck ranged from 40·8 to 53·4 to average out at 47·7.

Shoulder breadth   The range was 26·5 to 40·8 cm with a mean of 34·5 cm.

Relative shoulder breadth   Ranged from 15·4 to 23·9 with a mean of 20·5.

Hip breadth   Ranged from 21·0 to 37·0 cm to give a mean of 26·0 cm.

Relative hip breadth   Ranged from 12·6 to 22·7 with a mean of 15·5.

Extremities

Humerus   Humeral length ranged from 25·0 to 39·0 cm to average 31·9 cm. This gave a *relative humeral length* of 15·7 to 22·7 with a mean of 19·0.

Radius   Radial length ranged from 22·5 to 35·8 cm and averaged 27·4 cm. The range of *relative radial length* was 13·7 to 22·6 with a mean of 16·2. The *radio-humeral index* ran from 70·8 to 113·2 with a mean of 85·8.

Hand length   Ranged from 14·0 to 21·8 cm and averaged 18·2 cm. The mean *relative hand length* was 10·8 and the mean *hand index* 43·1.

Femur   This bone measured from 37·0 to 53·0 cm for a mean of 44·5 cm to give a mean *relative femoral length* of 26·5.

Tibia   Tibial length ranged from 34·6 to 48·0 cm for a mean of 40·8 cm. Mean *relative tibial length* came out at 24·2 and the mean *tibio-femoral index* at 91·8. The mean *inter-membral index* was 69·7.

Foot   Foot length ranged from 19·5 to 34·6 cm with a mean of 25·0 cm. Mean *relative foot length* was 14·9 and the mean *foot index* 37·5.

Head

Length   Head length ranged from 16·7 to 21·4 cm with a mean of 19·1 cm.

Breadth   Ran from 12·3 to 15·2 cm with a mean of 13·8 cm.

Cephalic index   This proportion gave a range of 63·6 to 84·3 for a mean of 72·1.

Morphological face height (nasion-gnathion)   From 9·9 to 13·5 cm with a mean of 11·9 cm.

Bizygomatic breadth   From 10·7 to 15·0 cm to a mean of 13·3 cm.

Morphological facial index   From 75·0 to 108·2 to average 88·0.

Nose

    Height: 3·2 to 6·2 cm to average 4·7 cm.

    Breadth: 2·8 to 5·7 cm to average 4·8 cm.

    Index: 66·7 to 137·5 with a mean of 101·8.

Ear

    Height: 5·1 to 7·7 cm to average 6·4 cm.

    Breadth: 2·4 to 4·0 cm to a mean of 3·3 cm.

    Index: 38·0 to 63·5 and a mean of 50·9.

Discussion

The limited number of observations presented here brings out very well the salient features of Aboriginal physique. They emphasise the long narrow head and face, the lean linearity of the total habitus, the narrow shoulders and hips, the relatively short neck and trunk and the relatively great length of the extremities, especially in such distal segments as the forearm and hand and the leg and foot. The broad flat nose and the small neat ear are equally well defined.

These observations differ in no essentials from those presented in earlier works: e.g. Stirling (1896), Spencer and Gillen (1899, 1904), Jones and Campbell (1924), Campbell and Lewis (1926), Campbell and Hackett (1927), Campbell, Gray and Hackett (1936), Fenner (1936), Abbie (1957, 1966) for South and central Australia, and those of Burston (1913) and Howells (1937) for northern Arnhem Land. Our own observations have drawn samples from right across the continent, with an extension into the Kimberley, and comparison of the findings on the groups has shown them all to be physically the same people. So we may justly claim that, with the possible exception of Cape York Peninsula which has been exposed to much Melanesian infiltration, the Aboriginals – initially, at least – were a singularly homogeneous people.

This homogeneity has not passed unnoticed by former observers: Smythe (1878), Woods (1879), Curr (1886) and others all comment upon it, and it is evident, too, in old skeletal remains. Howells (1970), for example, found 'no significant internal differentiation' in the Aboriginal material he examined. Basedow (1925) seems less definite on this point but he made no specific tribal or group comparisons. He records that the shortest male Aboriginal he encountered was a central Australian of 4 feet 6 inches (137·16 cm) but is careful to add that other males in that tribe were over 6 feet tall. We have encountered similar groups and I feel that had the means for that group been calculated the findings would have been much the same as our own. Incidentally, the greatest stature reported by Basedow was 7 feet 4 inches (223·5 cm) in a man near Cairns. Our extremes were not so dramatic.

Other evidence for Aboriginal homogeneity may be adduced from the finding that male and female ratios, indices, etc. are extraordinarily close (Abbie, in preparation) and that many of these are determined before birth or within a few years afterwards (Abbie, 1975). Indeed, the evidence now available points strongly to the probability that all the Aboriginals in Australia are basically derived from a common genetic pool.

References

ABBIE, A. A. 1957 The metrical characters of a central Australian tribe. *Oceania*, 27:220–43.
—— 1966 Physical characteristics. In *Aboriginal man in south and central Australia*, B. C. Cotton (ed). Adelaide Government Press.
—— 1968 The homogeneity of Australian Aborigines. *Archaeology and Physical Anthropology in Oceania*, 3:221–31.
—— 1975 *Studies in physical anthropology II*. Australian Institute of Aboriginal Studies, Canberra.

214   ORIGIN OF THE AUSTRALIANS

BASEDOW, H.   1925   *The Australian Aboriginal*. Preece, Adelaide.
BURSTON, R. S.   1913   Records of the anthropometric measurements of 102 Australian Aboriginals. *Bulletin of Northern Territory of Australia*, 7A.
CAMPBELL, T. D., H. J. GRAY and C. J. HACKETT   1936   Physical anthropology of the Aborigines of central Australia. *Oceania*, 7:106–39, 246–61.
—— and C. J. HACKETT   1927   Adelaide University field anthropology: central Australia. No. 1—Introduction, descriptive and anthropometric observation. *Transactions of the Royal Society of South Australia*, 51:65–75.
—— and A. J. LEWIS   1926   The Aborigines of South Australia: anthropometric, descriptive and other observations recorded at Ooldea. *Transactions of the Royal Society of South Australia*, 50:183–91.
COMAS, J.   1966   *Manual de anthropologia física*, 2nd Spanish edition. Universidad Nacional Autónuma de México, Mexico.
CURR, E. M.   1876-7   *The Australian race*, 2 volumes. Ferres, Melbourne.
FENNER, F. J.   1936   Adelaide University field anthropology: central Australia. No. 13—Anthropometric observations on South Australian Aborigines of the Diamantina and Cooper Creek regions. *Transactions of the Royal Society of South Australia*, 60:46–54.
HOWELLS, W. W.   1937   Anthropometry of the natives of Arnhem Land and the Australian race problem. *Papers of Peabody Museum, Harvard University*, 16:1–97.
——   1970   Anthropometric grouping analysis of Pacific peoples. *Archaeology and Physical Anthropology, Oceania*, 5:192–217.
JONES, F. W. and T. D. CAMPBELL   1924   Anthropometric and descriptive observations on some South Australian Aboriginals with a summary of previously recorded anthropometric data. *Transactions of the Royal Society of South Australia*, 48:303–12.
MARTIN, R.   1928   *Lehrbuch der Anthropologie*, 2nd edition, 3 volumes. Fischer, Jena.
MONTAGU, M. F. A.   1945   *An introduction to physical anthropology*. Thomas, Springfield.
OLIVIER, G.   1969   *Practical anthropology*, trans. M. A. MacConaill, Thomas, Springfield.
SMYTHE, R. B.   1878   *The Aborigines of Victoria*, 2 volumes. Ferres, Melbourne.
SPENCER, B. and F. J. GILLEN   1899   *The native tribes of central Australia*. Macmillan, London.
—— and ——   1904   *The northern tribes of central Australia*. Macmillan, London.
STIRLING, E. C.   1896   *Report on the work of the Horn scientific expedition to central Australia. Part IV—Anthropology*. Mullen & Slade, Melbourne.
WOODS, J. D.   1879   *The native tribes of South Australia*. Wigg, Adelaide.

Australian Aboriginals and the outer world

Dermatoglyphical evidence

Miroslav Prokopec and Vladimír Šedivý

DERMATOGLYPHIC PATTERNS on fingers and palms, once laid down in the course of embryonic development, remain unchanged in a given individual during his life from birth to death. This stability in pattern is valuable when studying small populations, subdivided into many different age groups. Dermatoglyphics may also contribute to the discovery of relationships among populations, and this is important particularly for populations whose descent is in doubt.

A number of authors have paid attention to the dermatoglyphics of Australian Aboriginals: Cummins and Setzler (1951, 1960); Macintosh (1952); Mader et al (1965); Rao (1964a & b, 1965); Singh (1968) and others.

The study population and methods

During field research conducted by the Czechoslovak Scientific Expedition of the Moravian Museum in the Arnhem Land Aboriginal Reserve from July to October, 1969, finger and palm prints were taken from more than five hundred Aboriginals of various age groups. Some of the prints were found to be unsuitable (due to sweating, traumatisation, pathological mutilation, etc.) so that only 487 prints were analysed. They belonged to 116 male and 93 female members of the Rembarranga tribe including 30 individuals with one parent from some other tribe, and to 160 males and 118 females from 33 other Northern Territory tribal groups encountered at the time in the Reserve and in some of the stations bordering its southern boundary as well as in Darwin (Bagot and Kormilda College). The Rembarranga material was treated separately from that of other tribes. The Rembarranga tribe was originally settled at the Bulman waterhole, then around the Mainoru station homestead and now (since the death of the station owner Mr Jack MacKay) members are located on about ten different cattle stations, government settlements and missions in the Northern Territory. They total about 250–300 individuals.

The methods and nomenclature set out in Penrose (1968) were adopted for processing the prints both qualitatively and quantitatively. Genotypes V, R and U were calculated after Bonnevie (1924). Total and Absolute Ridge

Counts and the mainline index was calculated after Cummins and Midlo (1961) as well as after Penrose (1968). Three other indices were calculated:

(1) Furuhata Index $\dfrac{\text{whorls} \times 100}{\text{loops}}$

(2) Pattern Intensity Index $\dfrac{2 \times \text{whorls} + \text{loops}}{N}$

(3) Dankmeijer Index $\dfrac{\text{arches} \times 100}{\text{whorls}}$

The -atd- angles on the palms were classified after Penrose and Loesch (1970) as well as after Mavalwala (1963a). The main line index was calculated according to Cummins and Midlo (1961). Only true patterns and Bettmann's vestiges (Quer Muster) on 5 palmar areas were considered. Manifestation of four-finger creases was classified according to Weninger and Navratil (1957).

Results

Values for the main dermatoglyphic indices are given in Table 1. On the fingers a high number of whorls and a low number of arches was found in both sexes (whorls 55, loops 43 and arches 2 per cent in the Rembarranga and 58, 40 and 2 per cent in the non-Rembarranga).

Because of the high percentage of whorls the *Furuhata index* generally is high in Australian Aboriginals, and this is true also in the present instance for both the Rembarranga and other tribes. In the Rembarranga higher values were found for the right hands of males and the left hands of females.

Ranges for the *pattern intensity index* in Australian Aboriginals based on the authors listed in the introductory paragraph are $14 \cdot 6$–$17 \cdot 8$ in males and $14 \cdot 2$–$17 \cdot 8$ in females. It should be noted that a high frequency of whorls will influence this index also. The present results as shown in Table 1 fit within these ranges. In contrast to the two indices given above, the *Dankmeijer index* will be low in populations with a low frequency of arches and high frequency of whorls, and this is borne out by the present results. Table 1 lists also the total and absolute ridge counts, the mean number of triradii and the various 'thickening factors' as given by Bonnevie (1924).

The palm prints were subjected to similar detailed analysis. The four-finger palm crease of all types (Weninger and Navratil, 1957) are more frequent on the right hands than on the left hands of both males and females in the Rembarranga and non-Rembarranga. If we take type 1a and 1b together (Weninger and Navratil state '1a and 1b kann mann sichem als echte Vierfingerfuche auffassen') this would give a four-finger crease of $4 \cdot 3$ and $3 \cdot 2$ per cent in Rembarranga males and females and $3 \cdot 8$ and $2 \cdot 6$ per cent in non-Rembarranga males and females respectively. This trait has not been studied previously in Australian Aboriginals. Smaller -atd- angles were found in males than in females. The angle changes with age. This should be kept in mind when considering the results presented in Table 1 as there were more younger individuals in the female group than in the male group.

Table 1: Summary of dermatoglyphic traits in the Rembarranga and other tribes or Arnhem Land

Trait	Rembarranga		Non-Rembarranga	
	Males (116)	Females (93)	Males (160)	Females (118)
Finger Patterns				
Furuhata Index	129·5	119·6	146·9	140·0
Pattern Intensity Index	15·4	15·1	15·7	15·5
Dankmeijer Index	2·5	4·6	2·4	3·9
Total Ridge Count	160·8	143·8	159·0	151·4
Absolute Ridge Count	232·3	209·4	236·1	225·6
Mean No. of Triradii				
Rt Hand	7·1	7·6	7·9	7·8
Lt Hand	7·5	7·6		
Percent Frequency of Gene v			72·4	63·0
V			27·6	37·0
r			16·5	21·8
R			83·5	78·2
u			25·5	26·6
U			74·5	73·4
Palm Patterns				
4-finger palm crease per cent (Type 1)	3·9	1·0	3·7	2·6
(All types)	25·9	16·7		
Percent-atd-angles less than 45°	75·4	53·2	65·4	67·5
Mean-atd-angle Rt	42·5°	43·5°		
Left	43·5°	45·6°		
Pattern Intensity	5·3	5·5	5·5	5·5

The sum of all the triradii in the palm (pattern intensity) fails in some cases to exceed the value 4. This could be due either to an absence of an axial triradius or to the absence of triradius c. The most frequent value is 5. The mean pattern intensity is given in Table 1 also.

Fourteen different patterns were found on the hypothenar area in Rembarranga and 13 in non-Rembarranga palm prints. In both sexes the most frequent type was A^u, L^u and A^c. Only the 'true' patterns with marked triradius and the incidence of Bettman's vestiges (Quer Muster) on the thenar and on the 1st interdigital area were considered.

Higher frequency scores for patterns and vestiges were found on the left hands than on right hands in Rembarranga of both sexes. Patterns were found more often on the second and fourth interdigital areas in males than in females, whereas patterns were more frequently found in females in the third interdigital area. Two or three patterns at the same time on interdigital areas were more often found in males than in females and in the non-Rembarranga more often on the left hands than on the right hands in both sexes.

The low frequency of patterns in the second inter-digital areas corresponds with the results of other authors who have dealt with Australian Aboriginals. Greater numbers of patterns for both samples studied were found in the fourth interdigital area (in Rembarranga males in 68·1 and in females in

58·6 per cent, in non-Rembarranga males in 61·4 and in females in 54·3 per cent).

The *a–b* ridge count was calculated in the non-Rembarranga group only. The mean *a–b* ridge count gave the same value 74·0 in both sexes and the distribution is nearly normal.

Fifty-seven different types of the main line formulae (25 were common in both sexes) were found in the Rembarranga group and 58 in the non-Rembarranga group (34 were common for both sexes). The higher portion of the transversal main lines and a lower portion of C-line reduction were found in both sexes and in both groups in the right hands. The three main line formulae 11, 9, 7, —, 9, 7, 5, —, were evenly distributed in the Rembarranga males (20·4, 20·4 and 22·6). In females the formulae pointing to the greater transversality of the main lines were more frequent (28·0, 23·7 and 14·1). The non-Rembarranga group gave the following results: males 24·6, 23·9 and 17·7; females 30·8, 21·4 and 10·3.

Modal types of the D-line (after Cummins and Midlo, 1961) 11, 9 and 7 were found in Rembarranga males in 42·7, 28·9 and 28·4 per cent, in females in 46·3, 35·6 and 18·1 per cent. In non-Rembarranga males in 46·3, 32·4 and 21·3 per cent and in females in 54·3, 33·3 and 12·4 per cent.

Bimanual difference between left and right hands in the *main line index* according to Cummins and Midlo (1961) and also to Penrose (1967) were found in both sexes. The mean values of the main line index (MLI) after Cummins and Midlo (1961) are given in Table 2. Ranges for the main line index (both hands together) given by other authors for Australian Aboriginals are 8·2–9·2 for males and 8·1–9·3 for females. Our Rembarranga and non-Rembarranga groups fit well within these ranges.

Comparison with other population samples

Working from our own data and on that of other authors an attempt has been made to show the position of Australian Aboriginals within a range of dermatoglyphic characters derived from other populations. As shown in Figure 1 the *pattern intensity index* (PII) puts African Pygmies and Black Africans completely and Europeans partly outside the ranges of Australian Aboriginals. PII of the Aboriginals overlaps partly with Eskimos, American Indians and Asians and coincides with Asian Pygmies (negrito) and Micronesians (Cummins, 1955; Popham, 1953; Newman, 1960; Weninger, 1953; Šedivý, 1973). The *V-factor* discriminates African Pygmies and Black Africans from Australian Aboriginals. There is, however, a complete overlap with Europeans and in part with Mongoloids (Pons, 1953). The *four finger crease* (Vierfingerfurche – VFF) differentiates Australian Aboriginals from African Pygmies, Black Africans, Europeans, Mongoloids and Melanesians, placing them within the broad range of Asian Pygmies. For this character much depends upon the method used (Walter, 1957).

Relative percentages of whorls   From the results of Cummins and Setzler (1951), Macintosh (1952), Mader *et al* (1965), Rao (1965), Singh (1968) and others,

Table 2: Percentage frequencies of Main-Line-Index in the Rembarranga and other tribes of Arnhem Land

| | | Rembarranga | | | | | | Non-Rembarranga | | | | | |
| | | Males (n = 116) | | | Females (n = 93) | | | Males (n = 136) | | | Females (n = 118) | | |
Index		R	L	R+L	R	L	R+L	R	L	R+L	R	L	R+L
Cummins	Mean	9·0	8·3	8·7	9·4	8·4	8·9	9·5	8·5	9·0	9·5	9·0	9·2
	S.D.	2·4	2·6	2·5	2·1	2·7	2·4	2·2	2·6	2·5	2·0	2·4	2·2
Penrose	Mean	14·2	13·2	13·7	14·2	13·4	13·8	14·4	13·4	13·9	14·4	13·8	14·1
	S.D.	2·6	2·7	2·6	2·0	2·7	2·4	2·2	2·5	2·4	1·9	2·2	2·1

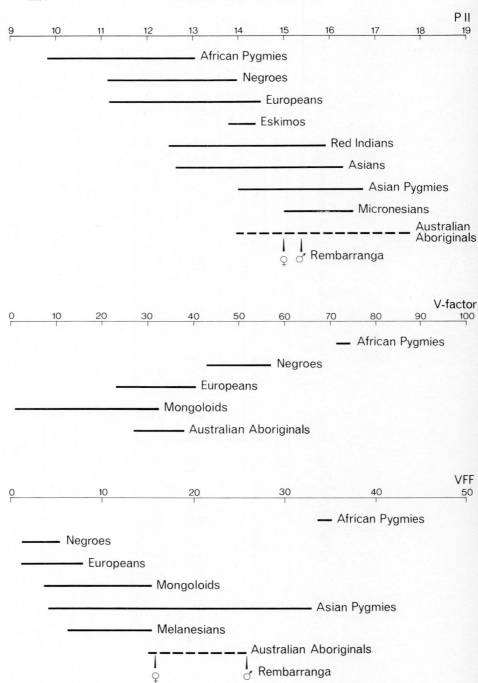

Figure 1 Pattern intensity index showing relationship between African Pygmies, Black Africans, Europeans and Australian Aboriginals.

we have drawn up ranges of relative percentages of whorls for Australian Aboriginals (Figure 2 – thick lines). The broken line represents the Rembarranga and the dots the non-Rembarranga. Many population samples from Europe, Africa, Asia and America fall between the ranges enclosed in the cross-hatched area. The maximum difference is in the relative frequency of whorls on the 2nd, 3rd and 4th fingers. The 3rd finger is particularly useful for distinguishing the samples from each other.

   Australian Aboriginals belong to populations with a very high frequency of whorls on their finger tips. Admixture with other populations may result in a reduction in the frequency of this trait. As we can see in Figure 2 Aboriginals from the remote parts of Arnhem Land investigated by Cummins and Setzler (1951) (Yirkalla, Goulburn Island etc.) show the highest frequency of whorls on the 2nd, 3rd and the 5th fingers. Aboriginals invest-igated by the present authors and by Rao (1964b, 1965) are from parts of Arnhem Land and other parts of the Northern Territory, which being more close to post contact transcontinental communication, may exhibit ad-mixture with Chinese and European elements and a resultant lowering of the incidence of whorls on finger tips.

Relative percentages of arches   The main drawback of this method is the very low frequency of arches in the Australian Aboriginal finger prints. Averages of arches on individual fingers, calculated from ours and other authors'

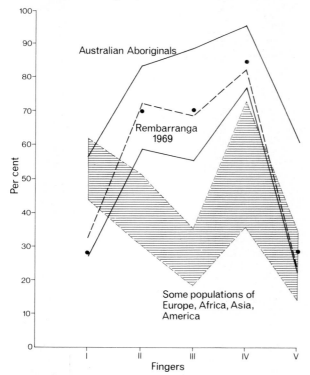

Figure 2   Relative percentage of whorls.

results are represented in Figure 3 by a broken line running from the upper left corner to the right bottom and slightly up again. The ranges of many African samples are set out on the graph by enclosed cross-hatching for comparison. It shows that the 1st and 3rd and 4th fingers with arches are good discriminating factors in distinguishing these populations from each other.

Relative percentage of arches (non-African populations) is shown in Figure 4. The dotted line represents the relative percentages of arches on individual fingers of Australian Aboriginals (non-Rembarranga). A series of non-African population samples fall within the enclosed area showing that arches on the 1st, 3rd and 4th finger can also separate African and Australian Aboriginal populations.

Total ridge count as shown in Figures 5 and 6 is higher in Australian Aboriginals (males and females) when compared with the British population (Holt, 1955).

Relative percentage of whorls in Australian Aboriginal samples according to Cummins and Setzler (1951), Macintosh (1952), Rao (1965) and the present authors is shown in Figure 7.

In conclusion, as a result of our detailed study of the finger and palm prints of 487 Australian Aboriginals from the Arnhem Land area and the comparison with similar analyses for other populations it appears that the Asian Pygmies (Negritos) and Pacific Islanders are closest in many of the traits. This is true particularly for the pattern intensity index which shows the closest relationship between Australian Aboriginal series and populations from South East Asia and the Pacific Islands.

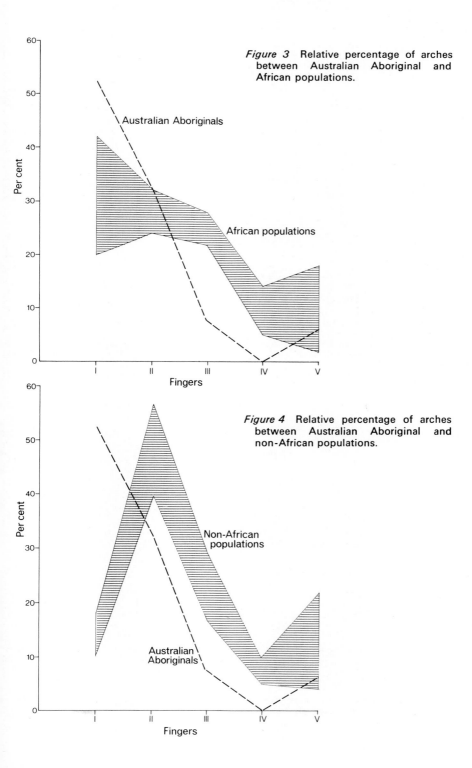

Figure 3 Relative percentage of arches between Australian Aboriginal and African populations.

Figure 4 Relative percentage of arches between Australian Aboriginal and non-African populations.

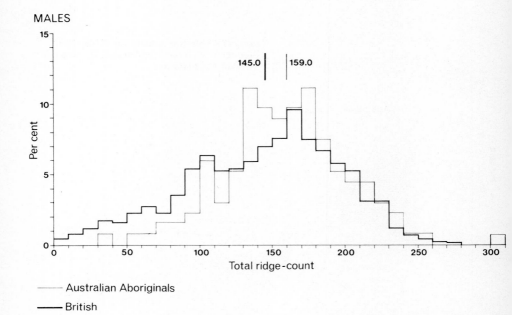

Figure 5 Total ridge count for Australian Aboriginals (males) compared with the British population (after Holt, 1955).

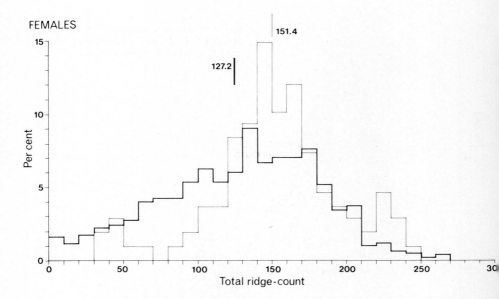

Figure 6 Total ridge count for Australian Aboriginals (females) compared with the British population (after Holt, 1955).

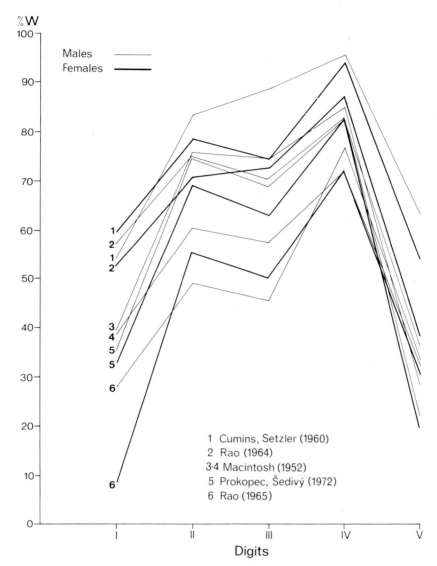

Figure 7 Comparison between the relative percentage of whorls according to present authors and various other writers.

Acknowledgements   The authors are indebted to the Institute of Hygiene and Epidemiology, Prague, for the granting of leave of absence to M.P. while with the Czechoslovak Scientific Expedition of the Moravian Museum in Brno to Australia; to Dr J. Brinke for his help and company to M.P. in the field; to the Welfare Branch of the Northern Territory Administration and to the Australian Institute of Aboriginal Studies and their officers for their support and help; to the Director and staff of the Kormilda

College, Darwin and to its pupils for their understanding for the research and to many good people in Darwin and on the stations and settlements visited for their help and support, and to all the men, women and children whose hands were investigated for their patient collaboration in the study.

References

BONNEVIE, K.   1924   Studies on papillary patterns of human fingers. *Journal of Genetics*, 15:1–111.
CUMMINS, H.   1955   Dermatoglyphics of Bushmen. South Africa. *American Journal of Physical Anthropology*, 13:699–710.
—— and C. MIDLO   1961   *Fingerprints, palms and soles. An introduction to dermatoglyphics.* Dover Publications, New York.
—— and F. M. SETZLER   1951   Dermatoglyphics in Australian Aborigines. *American Journal of Physical Anthropology*, 9:455–60.
—— and ——   1960   Dermatoglyphics of Australian Aborigines. In *Records of the American–Australian Expedition to Arnhem Land*, C. P. Mountford (ed), pp. 203–14. Melbourne University Press, Melbourne.
HOLT, S. B.   1955   Genetics of dermal ridges. Frequency distribution of total ridge count. *Annals of Human Genetics*, 20:159–70.
MACINTOSH, N. W. G.   1952   Fingerprints of Australian Aborigines of West Arnhem Land and Western Australia. *Oceania*, 35:299–306.
MADER, M. K., P. PARSONS, M. A. CONNER and D. HATT   1965   Differences between four Australian Aboriginal tribes as revealed by fingerprints. *Acta Geneticae Basel*, 15:145–53.
MAVALWALA, J. D.   1963   The utility of angle -atd- in dermatoglyphics. *American Journal of Physical Anthropology*, 21:77.
NEWMAN M. T.   1960   Populational analysis of finger and palm prints in highland and lowland Maya Indians. *American Journal of Physical Anthropology*, 18:45–58.
PENROSE, L. S.   1967   Finger-print pattern and the sex chromosomes. *Lancet*, 1:298–300.
——   1968   Memorandum on dermatoglyphic nomenclature. In *Birth defects*, Bergsma (ed). Original Article Series, 4(3):1–13.
—— and D. LOESCH   1970   Topological classification of palmar dermatoglyphics. *Journal of Mental Deficiency Research*, 14:111–28.
PONS, J.   1953   Differentialdiagnose verschiedener Rassengruppen nach der Hautleistenanalyse. *Homo*, 4:131–34.
POPHAM, R. E.   1953   A comparative analysis of the digital patterns of Eskimo from Southhampton Island. *American Journal of Physical Anthropology*, 11:203–14.
RAO, P. P. D.   1964a   Fingerprints of Aborigines at Kalumburu Mission in Western Australia. *Oceania*, 34:225–33.
——   1964b   The main-line index and transversality in the palms of Australian Aborigines. *Oceania*, 34:211–24.
——   1965   Finger and palm prints of the Aboriginal children at Yuendumu Settlement in Central Australia. *Oceania*, 35:305–16.
ŠEDIVÝ, V.   1973   *Dermatoglyfika prstu a dlani domorodcu Severniho teritoria Australie.* Rigorosni prace, Faculty of Science, Charles University, Prague.
SINGH, S.   1968   Dermatoglyphics of Australian Aborigines. *Oceania*, 38:41–48.
WALTER, H.   1957   Zur inter- und intra- rassischen Häufigkeit der Vierfingerfurche. *Homo*, 8:26–34.
WENINGER, M.   1953   Finger- und Handabdrücke von Eingeborenen der Philippinen und der Malayschen Halbinsel. *Mitteilungen der Anthropologischen Gesellschaft in Wien*, 82:92–120.
—— and L. NAVRATIL   1957   Die Vierfingerfurche in ätiologischen Betrachtung. *Mitteilungen der Anthropologischen Gesellschaft in Wien*, 87:1–21.

Variability of anthropometric traits in Australian Aboriginals and adjacent populations

Its bearing on the biological origin of the Australians

P.A. Parsons and N.G. White

IN CONSIDERING the origin of the Aboriginals we must take the anthropological information of today, and attempt to use this to ascertain what might have occurred in the past. Such information comes from two sources; the living individual and skeletal remains, both within Australia and in neighbouring regions. Two contrasting theories on the origin and racial composition of the Aboriginals have been put forward. One theory which is favoured by Abbie (1968) argues that the Aboriginals are a homogeneous population with no significant regional variations over the continent, that is they constitute one race. The other theory argues that the Aboriginals are a product of hybridisation between two or more races, probably three, migrating separately to Australia (Birdsell, 1950, 1967). Because the traditionally oriented Aboriginal is now largely extinct, it is difficult or impossible to confirm either hypothesis. A semantic problem is the issue of the amount of divergence between two human populations that constitute a race. The term race is unfortunately arbitrary, since there are no biological isolating mechanisms between human populations, as characterise different species. The multiplicity of racial classifications in the literature is therefore not surprising. It could be said that populations differing by a certain arbitrary amount measured in terms of standardised genetic distances represent distinct races. But even the calculation of genetic distances themselves is arbitrary, depending on the loci and/or the anthropometric measures used (Parsons, 1972). Therefore even if heterogeneity exists between different Aboriginal groups it does not, in itself, without historical evidence of separate waves of migration of different races from outside Australia, argue for either of the above hypotheses.

Before looking beyond Australia, it is instructive to examine biological variation in such traditionally oriented populations of Aboriginals that can still be studied. Our object here is to discover the ways in which observed patterns of variation can be interpreted in terms of the interaction of genetic, historical, linguistic, ecological and geographical parameters. This requires a knowledge of the physical and biological environments of tribes as well as their social structure and cultural environments.

Genetic and cultural differentiation

In Figure 1b is a map of Arnhem Land giving the localities of four tribes studied for dermatoglyphics (White and Parsons, 1973). Here the term tribe refers to a group of people speaking the same language, although this is not strictly so for the 'Murngin' (see footnote Figure 1). In the western region of Arnhem Land including Oenpelli, Melville and Bathurst Islands, are the Tiwi and Gunwinggu tribes. They have a number of cultural similarities, differing in many respects from north-east Arnhem Land Aboriginals, including Elcho Island, the present location of a number of groups (mainly from the Arnhem Bay region), which belong to the 'matha' linguistic cluster referred to collectively as the 'Murngin', 'Wulamba' or 'Malag'. Linguistically, the western Arnhem Land tribes have prefixing languages and the 'Murngin' suffixing. The Andilyaugwa tribe on Groote Eylandt has a prefixing language type which is substantially different from the mainland prefixing languages of the other tribes studied. Differences between the two Arnhem Land regions occur in social organisation, since basically the western moiety system is matrilineal and the eastern patrilineal (Berndt and Berndt, 1968). Furthermore, circumcision, probably the most important of the male initiation rites (Berndt and Berndt, 1968), is not practised over most of the western region, but it is performed in eastern Arnhem Land. Therefore, there are considerable linguistic and sociocultural differences between the four Arnhem Land tribes under study.

Pattern intensity indices were obtained from rolled fingerprints from individuals of each of the four tribes, and the results are presented diagrammatically in Figure 2. Clearly the western groups (Tiwi and Gunwinggu) cluster as do the eastern groups ('Murngin' and Andilyaugwa), which is not unexpected from the comments made on sociocultural and linguistic differences. The values of the 'Murngin'-Andilyaugwa cluster are particularly high, considering that the normal maximum possible pattern intensity index is 20, or 2 per each of 10 digits. Combining pattern intensity indices with total ridge-counts confirms the two clusters, using the approach of generalised distances (Mahalanobis, 1936). Data on allele frequency traits (i.e. blood groups, serum proteins and enzyme systems) have confirmed this situation (Kirk et al, 1972). Therefore there is indeed an association between sociocultural, linguistic and genetic divergence as shown by Parsons and White (1973) in more detailed analyses.

In Table 1 is presented other pattern intensity index data for Australian Aboriginals, as well as Melanesians and Micronesians. Considering first the central Australian data, high indices were obtained for the Pintubi and Pitjantjatjara tribes, and rather lower indices for the Aranda and Wailbri, as is confirmed by generalised distances taking into account ridge counts and also allele frequency trait data (Nicholls et al, 1965; Parsons and White, 1973). Therefore both sets of four tribes, the Arnhem Land and the central Australian, show heterogeneity for genetically determined traits. This indicates that each tribe has to varying degrees, gene pools discrete from the others, on a quantitative but not a qualitative basis.

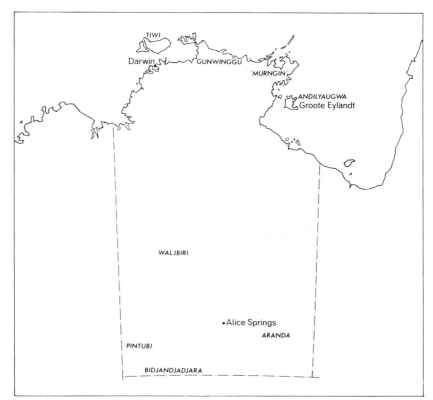

Figure 1a Map showing the approximate localities of tribes discussed in the text.

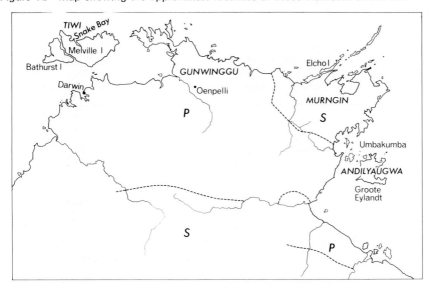

Figure 1b Map of Arnhem Land and environs showing the location of the four tribes discussed in the text, with some localities included (from White and Parsons, 1973). The dotted line indicates the approximate boundaries between the prefixing (P) and suffixing (S) language types (after Capell, 1942).

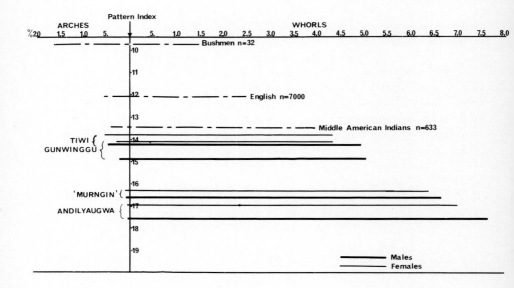

Figure 2 Frequencies of whorls and arches in males and females of the four Arnhem Land tribes in relation to pattern intensity indices. The approximate positions of Middle American Indians, English, and Bushmen are indicated (from White and Parsons, 1973).

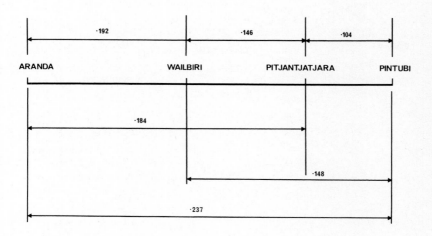

Figure 3 Genetic distances using various blood group and serum protein systems calculated from data of Nicholls *et al*, 1965, and modified from Parsons and White (1973) by omitting the Kell blood group for reasons given therein.

Language has been referred to as a possible isolating mechanism in Arnhem Land. This seems also likely in central Australia. On all criteria the Pintubi and Pitjantjatjara are biologically very close to each other. Linguistic data are in agreement since they speak different languages of the same subgroup with high common cognate frequencies (Wurm, 1970). The Wailbiri and Aranda are both genetically somewhat different from the Pintubi and Pitjantjatjara and are in fact rather divergent from each other. This agrees with linguistic data where the Aranda is in a different language group from the other three tribes, and the Wailbiri in a different language subgroup from the Pintubi and Pitjantjatjara. Although not shown by dermatoglyphic data, allele frequency data (Figure 3) show that the Wailbiri are between the Aranda on the one hand and the Pintubi-Pitjantjatjara group on the other (Parsons and White, 1973). All of these central Australian tribes belong to the same linguistic family, the Pama-Nyungan. In Arnhem Land the 'Murngin' belong to this linguistic family, while the other three tribes already discussed do not. The 'Murngin' pattern intensity indices fall well into the range of the central Australian tribes (Table 1) whereas the Tiwi and Gunwinggu at least, do not. Birdsell (1950) hypothesised that the Aranda came from a relatively recent migration of individuals southwards from the north. If so, the 'Murngin' and Aranda might be expected to show greater biological affinities than for other Arnhem Land-central Australian comparisons as indeed is shown for genetic distances based on allele-frequency traits (Table 2). Even so, the Aranda differ biologically and linguistically from the remaining three central Australian tribes as already shown.

The conclusion that biological differentiation is associated with linguistic differentiation is warranted from these considerations, as indeed would be expected if it is assumed that language is an effective isolating mechanism associated with sociocultural barriers. It is difficult to know the cause and effect relationship. Linguistic drift leading to divergence may take place in an initially homogeneous population which subsequently leads to the isolation and linguistic differentiation of the respective speakers. Especially if for some reason such as terrain, populations speaking the same language were rather isolated, this could easily occur. Once having developed, a linguistic difference could discourage social contact and act as a barrier to gene flow so that genetic divergence could occur. This implies that the proportion of intertribal marriages is low; in agreement are estimates of 10–15 per cent intertribal marriages for central Australian tribes (Tindale, 1953), but what the figure was further in the past must be a matter of conjecture.

Birdsell (1973 and earlier papers) with the help of Tindale's field data has found that the mean tribal size of the Australian Aboriginal is in the region of 500. Two points need to be made here however. First, it is more meaning-ful to consider the distribution of tribal size, i.e. note the variance about this mean, in discussing the interrelationships between demographic and environmental factors. Second, it should be stressed that the meaning of the

Table 1: Pattern intensity indices of various Australian Aboriginal populations, and for regions neighbouring Australia in Melanesia and
Micronesia. (The data with references are given in Mader (1965)
and Parsons and White (1973))

Population		Males		Females	
		n	Index	n	Index
Australian Aboriginals					
	Tiwi	105	14·2	93	13·9
Arnhem Land tribes	Gunwinggu	83	14·9	89	14·0
	'Murngin'	97	16·6	99	16·3
	Andilyaugwa	78	17·6	78	17·0
	Pintubi	64	16·8	57	16·5
Central Australian	Pitjantjatjara	139	16·3	148	15·5
tribes	Aranda	86	15·9	102	15·1
	Wailbri	73	15·6	109	14·1
Mornington Island	Lardiil	55	15·4	65	16·3
tribes	Kaiadilt	19	14·6	19	14·7
Arnhem Land	Yirrkala	41	17·8	51	17·8
localities	Groote Eylandt	43	17·6	38	16·4
	Old Beswick	74	16·0		
Western	General	53	15·1		
Australian	Kalumburu Mission	44	16·2	40	16·2
localities	Wiluna	22	15·9	31	14·2
Melanesia					
Tongariki		44	13·7	51	13·6
New Britain		257	15·0	64	14·2
Kotu Island		204	14·7		
New Guinea					
(a)		49	14·3		
(b)		159	14·0		
		($\male + \female$)			
Timor		1355	15·0		
Micronesia					
Palau					
(a)		170	14·7		
(b)		144	15·2		
Yap landlords		233	16·5		
Truk		173	16·2		
Ponape		145	15·4		
Jaluit		145	14·5		
Chamorro		127	14·2		
Kanaka		644	15·4		

term 'tribe' clearly depends on the context in which it is used. In the
biological context the tribe most logically should be defined in terms of the
breeding unit, i.e. the gene pool. For example a tribe could be defined as a
population which is, say, 85 per cent endogamous. The tribe in this sense
will often be synonymous with the language unit and/or social and political
unit. Thus the Tiwi of Melville and Bathurst Islands can be considered a
single unit biologically, linguistically and culturally. This is not always the
case though. Endogamy can cut across language groups. The Garawa and
Janjula, for instance, are classified linguistically as two tribes belonging to

separate language *Families*, but data collected by the present authors show that there has been a considerable degree of intermarriage between these two 'tribes' for the last 50 years at least. The 'Murngin' provide a further example. This broad linguistic group consists of a number of dialect units called matha, which are exogamous. Present work being undertaken suggests that within the Murngin 'tribe' there were quite discrete and largely endogamous units, although the composition of these probably was not stable (White and Parsons, 1976).

It has been suggested that the Aranda, which are said to have numbered about 1500 individuals at the time of historical contact, was in the process of differentiating into smaller dialectal units averaging about 500 each (Birdsell, 1973). This hypothesis was based on the recognition of three subdivisions within the Aranda 'tribe'. Strehlow (1947, 1973), however, lists five such units (or 'sub-groups') which he considered to be clearly defined on the basis of 'customs and speech'. A recent linguistic survey of Australia (Oates and Oates, 1970) defines two *linguistic* sub-groups within the Arandic language group: one containing a single language, the other with seven dialects including Western, Eastern and Southern Aranda. Members of these subdivisions or dialect units recognised themselves as belonging to the same language community yet they were also aware of regional differences in speech that developed. Regardless of the number of subdivisions that are in fact recognised within the Aranda 'the tendency for oversized dialectical tribes to fail to maintain homogeneous speech throughout their bands is not unexpected, and may be explained in terms of the concept of density of communication' (Birdsell *ibid*). This division into new tribes must then be assumed to be associated with sociocultural, linguistic and genetic differentiation, and furthermore the evidence obtained so far argues for positive correlations between all three factors.

The structure of the Australian Aboriginal at historical contact can therefore be regarded as made up of a number of separate breeding units, so that across 'tribes' a mosaic of gene frequencies may be expected, but even so, broad clines in allele frequencies are also apparent on an Australia wide basis (Birdsell, 1950; Kirk, 1971). The expected level of heterogeneity can be assumed to be lower than in territorial rodents such as wild mice for example, where demes or effective breeding units are made up of extremely

Table 2: Genetic distances between four Arnhem Land tribes and two central Australian tribes, based on data for the loci ABO, Rh, MN, Fy and P.T.C. (after Parsons and White, 1973)

Arnhem Land tribes	Central Australian tribes	
	Aranda	Wailbri
'Murngin'	0·141	0·202
Andilyaugwa	0·178	0·212
Gunwinggu	0·182	0·192
Tiwi	0·222	0·286

small population sizes certainly less than 100 and often considerably smaller (Petras, 1967). This would normally give total population sizes much lower than 500; the relation of the size of the effective breeding unit and total population size depending on the demography of the unit in question. Petras found that migration rates between demes in mice are very low perhaps no more than 5 per cent; the separate demes being established by territoriality of a behavioural nature. Genetic work on allelic variations at various genetic loci for haemoglobin and esterase variants show marked heterogeneity (Selander, 1970) but with the clustering of similar genotypes within demes. However, overall, between regions of Texas, variation was found to be clinal. At the local level then, the small population sizes are due to social behaviour of a territorial nature leading to a mosaic of gene frequencies.

Taking account of Aboriginal population structure, it is not easy to interpret variations in pattern intensity indices, especially as in some cases population sizes may have been very small on occasions leading to the theoretical possibility of heterogeneity due to founder effects. For example famine and ecological disasters may reduce tribal sizes periodically as would fighting. This is further complicated by polygynous marriage systems, which in tribes such as the Tiwi, Andilyaugwa and 'Murngin', are extreme. The two dermatoglyphic samples from Mornington Island (Table 1), for example, are very small because both the Lardil and Kaiadilt tribes had few representatives at the time of sampling. The Kaiadilt were moved from Bentinck Island to Mornington Island just after they suffered a population crash amounting to about 40 per cent of their total numbers in 1947 due principally to drought, leaving an effective breeding size of about 20 (Simmons et al, 1962), which is certainly a size where random founder effects are likely. Genetically they are extreme amongst Australian Aboriginals in having blood group B and no A, and the highest R^0 allele frequency found in the Australian Aboriginals. However, in spite of the dermatoglyphic heterogeneity observed, the main overall feature of the Aboriginal is a very high pattern intensity index, considering that the maximum possible is 20. The male index of 17·60 for the Andilyaugwa is as high as has been recorded anywhere.

Melanesian and Micronesian indices on average are rather lower than Aboriginal indices being mainly in the 14 to 15 range, but are certainly greater than white Caucasoids. Furthermore Melanesian and Micronesian figures are rather similar, and so provide little specific evidence on the biological origin of the Aboriginal Australians. Going further afield to Asia the range is similar, with a few values rather lower (Cummins and Midlo, 1961). In other words many tribes of the Australian Aboriginal are unique for pattern index intensity; there being no comparable figures elsewhere. Either, the high indices evolved in Australia, or were derived from a migrant group now extinct or untested. If evolved, then it would be difficult to distinguish between selection for the high indices, genetic drift due to small population sizes, or a combination of both.

Another difficulty is that discrete tribes are characteristic of the islands to the north of Australia so that heterogeneity between them would be expected. In Bougainville, Howells (1966) studied 18 ethnic groups covering most of the island's territory and found quite high correlations between linguistic 'distance' and various measures of biological distance. Furthermore Friedlaender *et al*, (1971) in a consideration of 18 villages in Bougainville found intermarriage to be largely confined to the same linguistic group, in other words there was little migration between linguistic groups. Therefore a mosaic of genetic differentiation would be expected associated with linguistic differentiation as was found, and the same seems true of New Guinea (Livingstone, 1963). Unfortunately, dermatoglyphic studies in regions to the north of Australia have not generally considered the tribe as the basic unit so that detailed comparisons are not useful.

Skeletal material

Another approach to the biological origin of Aboriginal Australians comes from the analysis of skeletal material of which a considerable abundance has been found especially in south-eastern Australia. Minor discontinuous or non-metrical traits are being increasingly used in human population genetic

Figure 4 Map of Australia showing areas 1, 2 and 3 (see text). Boundaries between areas are shown by lines. The rationale behind the location of the areas is given in Kellock and Parsons (1970a).

studies especially as evidence indicates that the degree of genetic determination of such traits may be quite high (Kellock and Parsons, 1970a for
discussion). They have advantages over some metrical traits for anthropometric work in being easily and rapidly scored, and have a virtual absence of
sex or age effects. The virtual absence of inter-trait correlations makes the
calculation of statistics relatively simple, and there is some evidence that
distance statistics based on non-metrical variants provide a better estimate of
the genetical separation of populations than those based on metrical traits
(Berry and Berry, 1967). Kellock and Parsons (1970a, b) classified crania of
Australian Aboriginals from three areas (Figure 4), and from various
Melanesian and Polynesian localities (Table 3) for 30 non-metrical variants
(Table 4).

The procedure of analysis is to obtain the percentage incidence p of each
variant in each population, then transform it into an angular value
$\phi = \sin^{-1}(1 - 2p)$ measured in radians. The variance of ϕ in a population
of size N is approximately $\frac{1}{N}$, irrespective of the value of ϕ. A measure of
difference or divergence, X, between two populations 1 and 2 with incidences
for a single variant p_1 and p_2 respectively, is given by

$$X = (\phi_1 - \phi_2)^2 - \left(\frac{1}{N_1} + \frac{1}{N_2}\right),$$

where ϕ_1 and ϕ_2 are the angular values for the two populations. In practice,
however, because some crania were partly damaged, N was taken as the
number of individuals classified for a median variant, or as half the number
of sides of individuals classified for a bilateral variant (the method, which
was devised by C. A. B. Smith, giving tests of significance is set out in Berry,
1963).

Mean measures of difference combining the 25 traits are given in Figure 5
with 5 per cent significance levels. Considering the three areas of Australia
first, areas 1 and 3 differ most followed by 2 and 3 while that between 1 and
2 is quite small. There is therefore a gradient in cranial morphology going
from the north-west to the south-east of the Australian continent (Kellock
and Parsons, 1970a). Of the three areas, the south-eastern population is the
most distinctive. In view of the fact that the mean measures of difference
between localities 1 and 3, and 2 and 3 differ significantly, then the Australian material must be regarded as genetically heterogeneous – a result in
agreement with earlier and now classic cranial studies of Fenner (1939) on
non-metrical morphological variants. Clearly this cannot be related to
tribes but the existence of clines across the continent is a pattern occurring
for a number of allele-frequency traits as already mentioned. The dilemma
is that the living Aboriginals live in regions where few skeletal remains have
been found, and conversely most of the skeletal remains occur in regions
where few Aboriginals remain.

The skeletal data do provide a basis for comparing Australian Aboriginal
cranial data with those from neighbouring regions. Overall, it is clear from
Figure 5 that the differences between Australia and the Pacific Islands listed

Table 3: Number of crania examined from each region and locality (from the summary in Kellock and Parsons, 1970b)

Region	Locality	Number of crania from each locality	Number of crania from each region
Australia	Area 1	172	
	Area 2	127	1184
	Area 3	885	
Melanesia	New Guinea	21	
	Bismarck Archipelago	10	
	Louisiade Archipelago	1	
	Solomon Islands	35	117
	Santa Cruz Islands	3	
	New Hebrides	27	
	Fiji	11	
	New Caledonia	9	
Polynesia	New Zealand and Chatham Is.	15	
	Samoa	1	
	Hawaiian Islands	1	35
	Marquesas Islands	1	
	Easter Island	17	

Table 4: A list of 30 non-metrical cranial variants used in the study of crania of the Australian Aboriginals, Melanesians and Polynesians (after Kellock and Parsons, 1970a)

Number	Variant
1	Accessory infra-orbital foramen present
2	Zygomatico-facial foramen absent
3	Supra-orbital foramen complete
4	Frontal notch or foramen present
5	Metopism
6	Ossicle at the lambda
7	Lambdoid ossicle present
8	Parietal foramen present
9	Bregmatic bone present
10	Coronal ossicle present
11	Ossicle at the asterion
12	Highest nuchal line present
13	Mastoid foramen absent
14	Mastoid foramen exsutural
15	Anterior condylar canal double
16	Posterior condylar canal patent
17	Condylar facet double
18	Precondylar tubercle present
19	Foramen of Huschke present
20	Foramen spinosum open
21	Foramen ovale incomplete
22	Accessory lesser palatine foramen present
23	Palatine torus present
24	Maxillary torus present
25	Anterior ethmoid foramen exsutural
26	Posterior ethmoid foramen absent
27	Epipteric bone present
28	Fronto-temporal articulation
29	Auditory torus present
30	Parietal notch bone present

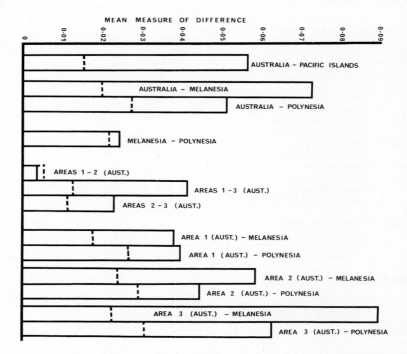

Figure 5 Mean measures of difference between crania from areas of Australia and the Pacific. The vertical dotted lines represent the values which the measures must attain before the paired comparisons are significantly different at the 5 per cent level (after Kellock and Parsons, 1970b).

in Table 3 exceed the differences within Australia. The Australia-Melanesia difference exceeds the Australia-Polynesia difference to about the degree that Melanesia and Polynesia differ, and furthermore, the Australia-Melanesia difference exceeds the Australia-Polynesia difference for areas 2 and 3 of Australia but not for area 1 (which mainly comprises the Northern Territory and northern Western Australia). In other words, area 1 has more association with Melanesia than with Polynesia. This seems reasonable because of the proximity of area 1 with Melanesia, and the evidence for relatively recent migrations from Melanesia to area 1 of Australia (Birdsell, 1950). The observation that in the southern regions of Australia, Polynesian rather than Melanesian cranial features are closer to the Aboriginals leads to many speculations on the origin of the Aboriginals and indeed on the origin of the Melanesians and Polynesians, but because of the small Polynesian sample size, any conclusions are in need of verification.

Most authors speak of an Asiatic origin for the Australian Aboriginals (Kellock and Parsons, 1970a; Birdsell 1967), as indeed is suggested by the evolutionary tree approach (Cavalli-Sforza and Edwards, 1963). This might imply that there should be a general correspondence between the traits of the

Melanesians and the Aboriginals which except for the various northern regions of Australia does not occur since the more southern Aboriginals have closer affinities with the Polynesians. The naive interpretation is that the Polynesians and southern Australian Aboriginals have some affinities perhaps by migrations from Asia. This was followed by the current inhabitants of Melanesia to their lands, and their subsequent occupancy of part or whole of area 1 of Australia. To prove this is difficult because the southern Australian Aboriginals are now essentially extinct. In any case this does not preclude influence from the American Indians in Polynesia.

Skin colour

Genetic heterogeneity among Australian Aboriginals has been further demonstrated in a study of skin pigmentary variation among five tribes recently undertaken by the present authors. Marked regional differences were observed with the 'Murngin', Burera, and Andilyaugwa of coastal Arnhem Land each being significantly darker than the Wailbiri and Aranda of central Australia (see Figure 1a for tribal localities). In all instances, differences between the two regional groups were far greater than among tribes of the same geographic region (see Table 5). An association was suggested between age and skin reflectances and males were found to be consistently darker than females. For this reason only data compiled from subjects twenty years old or less were used in the tribal comparisons shown in Table 5, males and females being treated separately. These results are therefore in agreement with heterogeneity within Australia, but more studies are needed before any comments on the origins of Australians can be made. (A more intensive analysis of the skin reflectance data together with the results described above is given, and discussed more fully, in a paper currently in preparation).

Discussion

It is of interest to look at Howells' (1970) analysis of data on the anthropometric traits; stature, head length and breadth, face width and height, and nose height and breadth in the Pacific peoples. He suggests that there are three major populations of Oceania:

1.   Australian with no significant internal differentiation as Abbie (1968) argued from similar traits but which is at variance with the heterogeneity obtained from dermatoglyphics and allele-frequency traits. Even so as shown in Figure 5, the Aboriginals form a group discrete from the Melanesians and Polynesians.

2.   A Polynesian group influencing Micronesia.

3.   A varied Melanesian group distinguishable from the Australian group but with effects or connections in Australian populations and also Polynesians.

There is therefore some agreement between Howells' (1970) conclusions and ours so far as broad comparisons are concerned, since he did not find heterogeneity within the Australian Aboriginal for anthropometric traits but nor did Abbie using traits of a similar type. Furthermore, birth weight and

Table 5: a. Skin reflectance data based on subjects ≤20 years of age. Measurements were made on the medial aspect of the upper arm using an EEL instrument and filter No. 609 (685 mμ).

Tribe	Arnhem Land						Central Australia			
	'Murngin'		Andilyaugwa		Burera		Wailbri		Aranda	
	♂♂	♀♀	♂♂	♀♀	♂♂	♀♀	♂♂	♀♀	♂♂	♀♀
Mean	22·45	25·82	24·52	24·75	22·74	24·95	31·29	31·42	29·93	31·35
Sample size	90	71	41	12	40	41	52	65	30	43
Standard deviation	2·53	3·77	2·82	3·79	2·36	2·64	3·83	3·09	4·88	4·41
Average age	12·42	12·84	9·22	12·92	12·13	10·71	12·60	13·45	10·60	13·07

b. Comparison of means – t values. (Number of degrees of freedom is in brackets)

	'Murngin'	Andilyaugwa	Burera	Wailbri
Andilyaugwa	(81) 0·901^n.s. / (129) 4·169***	—		
Burera	(110) 1·299^n.s. / (128) 0·605^n.s.	(51) 0·205^n.s. / (79) 3·053**	—	
Wailbri	(134) 9·380*** / (140) 16·419***	(75) 6·539*** / (91) 9·376***	(104) 11·021*** / (90) 12·288***	—
Aranda	(112) 7·060*** / (118) 10·740***	(53) 4·640*** / (69) 5·806***	(82) 7·941*** / (68) 8·032***	(106) 0·102^n.s. / (80) 1·377^n.s.

n.s. not significant   ** P < 0·01   *** P < 0·001.

growth rates up to one year show little variation between Aboriginal groups from Mornington Island in the Gulf of Carpentaria, Maningrida in Arnhem Land, Santa Teresa near Alice Springs, Ernabella in northern South Australia, and various localities in Western Australia, in spite of the likely environmental differences between these localities (Propert *et al*, 1968). (These data were derived from infants born early in the 1960s – it will be of interest to see the stability of the traits more recently as affected by alterations in nutrition and living-styles as was pointed out.) Therefore, in general, the living Aboriginals are homogeneous for the classical morphological metrical traits studied by anthropologists. On the other hand, they are heterogeneous for dermatoglyphics and allele-frequency traits which are much less affected by environment. Even so, both types of traits show the uniqueness of the Australian Aboriginal compared with neighbouring populations. (We have no evidence on this point for skin colour for which the Aboriginals are also heterogeneous.) Discrete skeletal variants of Aboriginal crania give similar conclusions, since heterogeneity is found but also the Aboriginals form a relatively isolated group, with some relationships to Melanesia depending to some extent on the part of Australia selected. (Metrical data on crania presented by Giles (1976) and Howells (1976) are in agreement.)

The population structure of the Australian Aboriginals is obviously of critical importance at the microevolutionary level. So far we can only be fairly sure of macroevolutionary trends as shown by evolutionary tree approaches (Cavalli-Sforza and Edwards, 1963). In many populations, e.g. the Parma Valley in Italy (see Cavalli-Sforza and Bodmer, 1971), the solution of problems of population structure is well advanced because of a wealth of demographic data, but even so, real situations show a mass of complicating factors to be taken into account. A central problem is the determination of the effective population size. For example, estimates of the mean kinship coefficient (a measure of inbreeding) and the variation of gene frequencies depend on this parameter. Cavalli-Sforza and Bodmer (1971) consider that 'the decrease in effective population size resulting from the internal subdivision of a population is sufficiently small, that, in general, it can be neglected'. This is undoubtedly true in a community organised into villages and towns as is the Parma Valley. But the Australian Aboriginal is not so organised. The population size of a tribe is often readily determinable, although, as mentioned previously, it depends in many cases on how the tribe is defined. However, the microstructure at the band or local group level and its effects on various population parameters has not been fully investigated, either theoretically or in practice.

Both theoretical work and population data are needed for a full understanding of tribal microstructure. This is a problem far more difficult than delimiting tribes, because obvious linguistic and socio-cultural differences do not exist between hordes. In the Aboriginal too, as shown by the Kaiadilt, population crashes may well have been frequent leading to founder effects, as would be reasonable for a population existing purely by hunting and collecting. Such population crashes, which are also characteristic of animals living by hunting and collecting, if common in the past, could well have lead to founder effects making it difficult to relate with any certainty the Aboriginals of today with other peoples outside Australia. In conclusion, it would seem that part of the dilemma of the origin of the Australians concerns genetic changes after arrival in Australia due both to selection (at the macroenvironmental level) and genetic drift including founder effects at the microenvironmental level. Furthermore, we have no information as to the population sizes at the time of settlement, which if small could lead to further founder effects. Compared with most populations, it is difficult to avoid the conclusion that microenvironmental variation may be of considerable significance in the evolution of the Australian Aboriginal both during and after their arrival in Australia.

Acknowledgements   We are grateful to the Australian Institute of Aboriginal Studies for financial support, without which our own field work would have been impossible. Specific acknowledgements to persons in the field and the Northern Territory Administration who helped us in data collection are given in various of the listed publications.

References

ABBIE, A. A.   1968   The homogeneity of Australian Aborigines. *Archaeology and Physical Anthropology in Oceania*, 3:223–31.

BERNDT, R. M. and C. H. BERNDT   1968   *The world of the first Australians*. Ure Smith, Sydney.

BERRY, A. C. and R. J. BERRY   1967   Epigenetic variation in the human cranium. *Journal of Anatomy*, 101:361–79.

BERRY, R. J.   1963   Epigenetic polymorphism in wild populations of *Mus musculus*. *Genetic Research*, 4:193–220.

BIRDSELL, J. B.   1950   Some implications of the genetic concept of race in terms of spatial analysis. *Cold Spring Harbor Symposium on Quantitative Biology*, 15:259–314.

——   1967   Preliminary data on the trihybrid origin of the Australian Aborigines. *Archaeology and Physical Anthropology in Oceania*, 2:100–55.

——   1973   A basic demographic unit. *Current Anthropology*, 14:337–56.

CAPELL, A.   1942   Languages of Arnhem Land, North Australia. *Oceania*, 12:364–92; 13:24–50.

CAVALLI-SFORZA, L. L. and W. F. BODMER   1971   *The genetics of human populations*. W. H. Freeman, San Francisco.

—— and A. W. F. EDWARDS   1963   Analysis of human evolution. In *Genetics Today*. Proceedings of the Eleventh International Congress of Genetics. vol. 3: 923–33.

CUMMINS, H. and C. MIDLO   1961   *Fingerprints, palms and soles: An introduction to dermatoglyphics*. Dover Publications, New York.

FENNER, F. J.   1939   The Australian Aboriginal skull: its non-metrical morphological characters. *Transactions of the Royal Society of South Australia*, 63(2): 248–306.

FRIEDLAENDER, J. S., L. A. SGARAMELLA-ZONTA, K. K. KIDD, L. Y. C. LAI, P. CLARK and R. J. WALSH   1971   Biological divergences in south-central Bougainville. An analysis of blood polymorphism gene frequencies and anthropometric measurements utilizing tree models, and a comparison of these variables with linguistic, geographic, and migrational 'distances'. *American Journal of Human Genetics*, 23: 253–70.

GILES, E.   1976   Cranial variation in Australia and neighbouring areas. In *The origin of the Australians*, R. L. Kirk and A. G. Thorne (eds), pp. 161–172. Australian Institute of Aboriginal Studies, Canberra.

ANTHROPOMETRIC TRAITS 243

ANTHROPOMETRIC TRAITS 243

ANTHROPOMETRIC TRAITS 243

HOWELLS, W. W. 1966 Population distances: Biological, linguistic, geographical and environmental. *Current Anthropology*, 7:531–40.

—— 1970 Anthropometric grouping analysis of Pacific peoples. *Archaeology and Physical Anthropology in Oceania*, 5:192–217.

—— 1976 Metrical analysis in the problem of Australian origins. In *The origin of the Australians*, R. L. Kirk and A. G. Thorne (eds), pp. 141–160. Australian Institute of Aboriginal Studies, Canberra.

KELLOCK, W. L. and P. A. PARSONS 1970a Variation of minor non-metrical cranial variants in Australian Aborigines. *American Journal of Physical Anthropology*, 32:409–22.

—— and —— 1970b A comparison of the incidence of minor non-metrical cranial variants in Australian Aborigines with those of Melanesia and Polynesia. *American Journal of Physical Anthropology*, 33:235–40.

KIRK, R. L. 1971 Genetic evidence and its implications for Aboriginal prehistory. In *Aboriginal man and environment in Australia*, D. J. Mulvaney and J. Golson (eds), pp. 326–43. Australian National University Press, Canberra.

——, L. D. SANGHVI and V. BALAKRISHNAN 1972 A further study of genetic distance among Australian Aborigines: Nine tribes in the Northern Territory. *Humangenetik*, 14:95–102.

LIVINGSTONE, F. B. 1963 Blood groups and ancestry: A test case from the New Guinea Highlands. *Current Anthropology*, 4:95–102.

MADER, M. K. 1965 A sample of fingerprints from Tongariki in the New Hebrides. *Oceania*, 35:317–20.

MAHALANOBIS, P. C. 1936 On the generalized distance in statistics. *Proceedings of the National Institute of Science, India*, 2:49–55.

NICHOLLS, E. M., H. B. M. LEWIS, D. W. COOPER and J. H. BENNETT 1965 Blood group and serum protein differences in some central Australian Aborigines. *American Journal of Human Genetics*, 17:293–307.

OATES, W. J. and L. F. OATES (eds) 1970 *A revised linguistic survey of Australia*. Australian Institute of Aboriginal Studies, Canberra.

PARSONS, P. A. 1972 Genetic determination of behavior (Mice and men). In *Genetics, environment and behavior: Implications for educational policy*, L. Ehrman, G. Omenn and E. Caspari (eds), pp. 75–98. Academic Press, New York.

—— and N. G. WHITE 1973 Genetic differentiation among Australian Aborigines with special reference to dermatoglyphics and other anthropometric traits. In *The human biology of Aborigines of Cape York*, R. L. Kirk (ed), pp. 81–94. Australian Institute of Aboriginal Studies, Canberra.

PROPERT, D. N., R. EDMONDS and P. A. PARSONS 1968 Birth weights and growth rates up to one year for full-blood and mixed-blood Australian Aboriginal children. *Australian Paediatric Journal*, 4:134–43.

PETRAS, M. L. 1967 Studies on natural populations of Mus. I. Biochemical polymorphisms and their bearing on breeding structure. *Evolution*, 21:259–74.

SELANDER, R. K. 1970 Behavior and genetic variation in natural populations. *American Zoologist*, 10:53–66.

SIMMONS, R. T., N. B. TINDALE and J. B. BIRDSELL 1962 A blood group genetical survey in Australian Aborigines of Bentinck, Mornington and Forsyth Islands, Gulf of Carpentaria. *American Journal of Physical Anthropology*, 20:303–20.

STREHLOW, T. G. H. 1947 *Aranda Traditions*. Melbourne University Press, Melbourne.

—— 1973 *Songs of Central Australia*. Angus and Robertson, Sydney.

TINDALE, N. B. 1953 Intertribal marriage among Aboriginal tribes. *Human Biology*, 25:169–90.

WHITE, N. G. and P. A. PARSONS 1973 Genetic and socio-cultural differentiation in the Aborigines of Arnhem Land, Australia. *American Journal of Physical Anthropology*, 38:5–14.

—— and —— 1976 Population genetics, social, linguistic and topographical relationships in north eastern Arnhem Land, Australia. *Nature* (in press)

WURM, S. A. 1970 *Linguistic trends in Australia*. Australian Institute of Aboriginal Studies, Canberra.

Ossification variation in two populations from Papua New Guinea

W.B. Wood

RADIOGRAPHIC EXAMINATION of the appendicular skeleton of the growing child provides unique opportunities for the acquisition of additional quantitative and qualitative growth data not generally ascertainable by other investigative techniques. Ossification timing and sequence, bone growth and maturation, mineralisation and variation can all be revealed by the radiograph.

The close association between skeletal development and the general physiological and reproductive status of the individual has been well documented and described (Tanner, 1962). Because of this association, the skeletal age as determined from radiographs of the hand and wrist, provides a useful means of comparing maturation rates between different population groups. The radiographs also provide a method of assessing the possible influence of genetic and environmental factors in the production of population differences.

In the past eight years a number of reports describing marked delays in the growth rates of several New Guinea Highland populations have appeared in the literature (Malcolm, 1966, 1968, 1969, 1970). During the same period the author has been conducting a mixed longitudinal and cross-sectional growth survey of coastal Papuan children from several Motuan villages in the immediate vicinity of Port Moresby. In a preliminary report (Wood, 1970) the author indicated that the growth rate of the coastal Papuan sample, as determined from hand and wrist radiographs, was closely comparable with published European norms (Gruelich and Pyle, 1959), but differed quite markedly from that of an Eastern Highland sample from the Bundi Region (Figure 1).

The present paper confirms and expands these earlier observations, and is based on cross-sectional radiographic data collected during the period 1968–73. The total number of individuals represented, together with their age and sex distribution, is presented in Table 1. Only those children of known chronological age have been included.

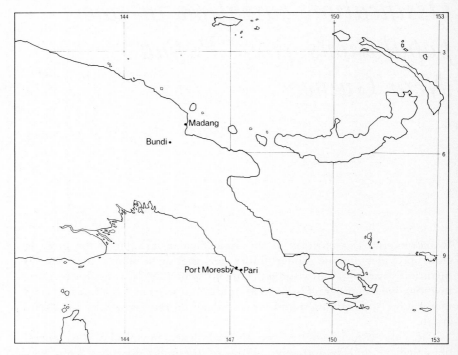

Figure 1   Papua New Guinea showing location of the study areas.

Table 1: Age and sex distribution of children examined

Age Group	Bundi		Coastal Papuan	
	No. boys	No. girls	No. boys	No. girls
0–0·49	13	4	10	12
1	24	24	39	29
2	20	17	22	22
3	19	20	21	17
4	20	21	25	25
5	13	17	13	14
6	8	14	15	12
7	18	15	38	41
8	35	13	53	64
9	42	17	45	32
10	27	16	41	44
11	22	21	51	47
12	21	11	74	46
13	21	11	61	57
14	7	3	69	59
15	10	6	30	30
16	9	2	43	29
17	6	1	34	15
18	4	9	6	6
19	—	8	2	—
20	—	5	1	—
21	2	2	—	—
	341	257	693	601

The appearance of hand and wrist ossification centres

Until the age at which all primary and secondary post-natal ossification centres of the hand and wrist have appeared, the presence or absence of these centres has been used as a measure of skeletal maturity (Francis and Werle, 1939; Pyle and Sontag, 1943), and a number of tables and charts summarising such data are available in the literature (Flory, 1936; Francis and Werle, 1939; Girdany and Golden, 1952).

In this study, the frequency of certain specified carpal and epiphyseal ossification centres of the left hand and wrist in the various age and sex groupings from coastal Papua and the Bundi region, have been recorded and tabulated in Tables 2 and 3. To facilitate presentation and comparison only the calculated percentage, and not the actual numbers of centres present, has been recorded for each age group.

Examination of Table 2 reveals the approximate order of appearance of the various wrist ossification centres in the coastal population, and the period of time during which each centre may make its appearance (up to the stage where it is universally present in all subsequent age-groups). Sex differences are readily apparent, both in the earlier onset of ossification in the female and in the shorter ossification range. These differences tend to be slight in the younger age groups, but become more marked with increasing age.

Table 3 shows the ossification timing in the Bundi population. Although the order of appearance of the various centres appears closely similar to the coastal Papuan sample, the range of ossification for any one centre is greatly exter.ded. The earliest time for onset of ossification also becomes increasingly delayed as one passes down the series; this applies to both sexes. This later onset and the greater time range required before universal ossification, indicates that the Bundi children take much longer to reach skeletal maturity in the hand than coastal Papuan children.

Comparison of Tables 2 and 3 with a similar set of figures published by Flory (1936) on American white children (Table 4) shows that the coastal Papuan child matures at closely comparable rates with the pre-war American child.

Considerable evidence has also accumulated to demonstrate a close correlation between the onset of ossification in the adductor sesamoid of the thumb and menarcheal age (Frisancho et al, 1969; Buehl and Pyle, 1942; Flory, 1936) The percentage of children at different age levels, in whom the adductor sesamoid of the thumb was present is indicated in Table 5 and compared with similar data for Japanese (Sutow, 1953), East African (Mackay, 1952) and American white (Garn and Rohmann, 1962). The much later timing in the age at appearance of the adductor sesamoid in the Bundi sample correlates well with the marked delay in menarcheal age observed by Malcolm (1966).

Unfortunately, no comparable data has been published for any Australian Aboriginal group, and the only publications dealing with ossification are those of Abbie and Adey (1953) and Grave (1971). Abbie and Adey (1953)

Table 2: Wrist ossification centres present at various ages in coastal Papuan children expressed in percentage present

Ossification Centre	Sex	Chronological age (in years)																
		0·25	1	2	3	4	5	6	7	8	9	10	11	12	13	14	15	16
Capitate	F	92	100															
	M	70	95															
Hamate	F	92	100	100														
	M	60	92	100														
Distal radius	F	—	66	100														
	M	—	49	100														
Triquetral	F		17	68	76	100	93	100										
	M		26	41	57	80	100	93	100									
Lunate	F		3	27	47	92	86	100	100	98								
	M		13	23	29	56	92	80	100	98	98	100						
Trapezium	F				12	60	71	92	100	98	93	100						
	M					20	23	40	82	79	93	100						
Trapezoid	F					36	64	83	100	92	98	100						
	M					4	8	47	87	92	98	100						
Scaphoid	F					40	64	92	100	92	91	100						
	M					4	8	33	74	81	91	100						
Distal ulna	F						14	42	41	91	100							
	M							13	11	38	64	88	98	100				
Pisiform	F								2	19	50	89	96	100				
	M									2	0	12	45	59	75	100		

Table 3: Wrist ossification centres present at various ages in Bundi children – expressed in percentage present

	Sex	Chronological age in years																		
		0·25	1	2	3	4	5	6	7	8	9	10	11	12	13	14	15	16	17	18
Capitate	F	50	96	100																
	M	69	96	100																
Hamate	F	25	96	100																
	M	54	96	100																
Distal radius	F	15	46	100	100	95	100													
	M		58	90	100	95	100													
Triquetral	F		4	53	75	81	88	88	100											
	M		4	15	37	45	69	100	94	94										
Lunate	F			18	40	62	53	93	93	100										
	M			10	16	25	54	50	72	83	93	96	95	100						
Trapezium	F				25	29	35	93	93	85	100	100	95	100						
	M				11	5	23	38	50	80	95	100	95	100						
Trapezoid	F			6	10	24	35	86	93	92	100	100	95	100						
	M					5	23	50	56	89	95	100	95	100						
Scaphoid	F					10	12	93	93	85	88	100	95	100						
	M						15	13	33	69	86	85	95	100	95	100				
Distal ulna	F							14	13	38	59	88	81	100	100	66	100			
	M									11	21	52	73	86	81	100				
Pisiform	F											13	14	45	73	67	83	100		
	M														10	29	20	78	83	100

Table 4: The appearance of carpal bones for boys and girls expressed in percentage present according to Flory on University of Chicago Laboratory School Children

Bone	Sex	B	*Chronological age in years*															
			1	2	3	4	5	6	7	8	9	10	11	12	13	14	15	16
Capitatum	F	8	96	100														
	M	2	98	100														
Hamatum	F	8	96	100														
	M	2	98	100														
Radial epiphysis	F		78	100														
	M		34	98	100													
Triquetrum	F		20	52	79	100												
	M		22	50	57	84	92	93	100									
Lunatum	F			32	50	80	91	99	100									
	M		8	18	36	64	64	87	98	99								
Scaphoid	F				12	30	61	95	99	100								
	M				4	17	34	51	75	92	99	100						
Trapezium	F			4	18	53	74	94	99	100								
	M				4	14	33	51	72	88	96	97	100					
Trapezoid	F				15	40	65	95	100									
	M				4	9	22	48	81	95	100							
Ulnar epiphysis	F						16	60	90	100								
	M						7	27	59	82	98	100						
Pisiform	F								1	19	50	79	96	100				
	M									2	6	22	28	66	95	99	99	100

Table 5: Ossification of the adductor sesamoid of the thumb at various ages expressed in percentage present

Study	Sex	8	9	10	11	12	13	14	15	16	17	18
								Chronological age in years				
Coastal Papuan	F		3	14	28	65	96	100	97	100		
	M					8	74	72				
Bundi	F						27		67	100	86	100
	M							0		11	50	50
Sutow	F			6	27	57	85	99	100			
	M					3	19	51	83	98	100	
Mackay	F		3	5	37	46	90	92	97	100	90	
	M				8	5	17	30	66	82		
Garn and Rohmann	F	2·2	7·6	31·5	69·6	91·3	100	93·1	98·8	100		
	M			1·1	4·6	27·6	67·8					

assessed the ossification status of 58 central Australian Aboriginals aged from three weeks to nineteen years. They comment that the ossification rate fell within the time range assigned to Europeans, but usually towards the earlier rather than the later limit, and that no ethnic peculiarities were disclosed.

Grave's study included serial observations on the ossification of the pisiform and adductor sesamoid in 52 male and 36 female Aboriginal children. He concluded that ossification of these two centres occurs slightly later in Aboriginal children than in Europeans. Comparison of his data with the coastal Papuan series indicates that Australian Aboriginals are slightly delayed in ossification of the pisiform relative to the Papuan group, but that ossification of the adductor sesamoid is closely comparable within the two groups.

The two major factors responsible for observed differences in growth rate between different populations appear to be genetical and nutritional. In geographical and socioeconomic situations where nutritional deficiency is prominent, delayed growth rate and timing of adolescence is a common phenomenon (Mills, 1937; Dreizen et al, 1954, 1957, 1958; Scrimshaw and Behar, 1965; Tanner, 1962). Data on the effect of a differing nutritional environment on the growth rates of children from the same ethnic stock in natural and experimental situations is also available (Greulich, 1957; Lasker, 1946).

This data emphasises the major role played by nutrition in the control of growth rate. Tanner (1962) states that where nutritional deficiencies are prominent, neither climate nor race appear to influence the rate of growth and timing of adolescence to the same extent as does nutrition.

The possible causative factors responsible for the delayed growth rates in Bundi children have been discussed at length by Malcolm (1970c). The growth response produced by the supplemental feeding of a group of Bundi school children (Malcolm, 1970a) seems to indicate that nutritional deficiency may be a major factor. However, the long term effects of a consistently improved nutritional environment have not yet been observed. Whether the increased growth on supplemental feeding is only a short term 'catch-up' effect, whether it is also accompanied by an increase in maturation rate (and hence earlier adolescence), and whether it will result in dramatic differences to final adult height have yet to be determined.

Additional evidence that environmental factors may be playing a role in the retarded growth rate is provided by the high incidence of transverse lines and bands in the distal radius which are visible radiographically (see later). Garn et al (1964) have also shown that in protein calorie malnutrition there is a marked decrease in bone mineralisation. This shows up radiographically in the form of poor bone texture and thin cortical tissue in the long bones. The quantitative measurement of cortical thickness of metacarpal 2 has been shown to be a sensitive indicator of general nutritional status. Unfortunately the overall quality of the Bundi plates did not allow accurate measurements to be taken, but subjectively, many of the plates displayed cortical thicknesses considerably less than the general thickness in the coastal series, and bone texture was of a greatly reduced quality.

Malcolm puts a strong case for a possible important genetic component in the delayed growth rate. He argues that if the Bundi population had been exposed to a deprived nutritional environment for a considerable length of time, then almost certainly strong selective pressures would have been acting on the various phenotypes, so as to favour those with a genotype for reduced growth rate and reduced final adult stature. Such individuals would have a permanently lower protein-calorie requirement for normal growth and repair, and a considerable advantage over those with a higher requirement, especially in situations of added environmental stress (e.g. infectious disease). In support of this theory he cites the differing infant and toddler mortality rates between males and females in a comparable highland population of New Guinea (1970b). The higher mortality rates in males appears to accompany the increased growth rate normally displayed by males over females.

Much has still to be learnt concerning the varying roles of environment and genetics in the production of delayed growth in Papua New Guinea. It is hoped that further radiographic studies of the Bundi and other population groups will assist in clarifying the situation.

Ossification sequence in the wrist

A number of publications in recent years have clearly demonstrated that, contrary to earlier reports and beliefs, the sequence of ossification of the various postnatal centres of the hand and wrist in healthy children is not constant, but varies considerably from one individual to another, and indeed that significant sex and population differences also exist (Garn et al, 1960, 1966, 1972). The sequence variations that had been observed and reported in earlier publications, were thought at the time to be due largely to adverse environmental influences (e.g. acute or chronic illness, malnutrition etc.) acting at the time of ossification of a particular centre, delaying its appearance and upsetting the ossification sequence that it would normally have followed.

Garn et al (1960) argue strongly that although malnutrition and stormy health histories can affect ossification timing and the rate of maturation, such factors do not play a major role in the production of divergent ossification sequences. Hertzog et al (1969) also support this theory; in a longitudinal study of sequence variation in 81 pairs of monozygotic and dizygotic like-sex twins, they produced convincing evidence that the major part of variation in ossification sequence is genetically determined.

The number of dichotomous (i.e. present/absent) ossification sequences, involving the eight carpal bones and the distal radial and ulnar epiphyses of the wrist region, were determined for the two Papuan New Guinean populations under consideration. This was done by inspecting the relevant radiographs visually, and plotting on a 9 by 9 matrix (Tables 6 and 7) the number and percentage of cases displaying each of two possible sequences for any given pair of bones. The minimum number of possible sequences is 36 (to the right of the diagonal). The maximum possible is 72. The number and frequency of the alternate sequences which actually occurred can be readily

Table 6: Frequency of dichotomous ossification sequences in coastal Papuan children

										Centre Absent								
Centre Present	Sex	Capitate %	n	Hamate %	n	Distal radius %	n	Triquetral %	n	Lunate %	n	Trapezium %	n	Trapezoid %	n	Scaphoid %	n	Distal ulna %	n
Capitate	M	—	—	100	2	100	25	100	62	100	88	100	150	100	141	100	157	100	225
	F	—	—	0	0	100	21	100	47	100	68	100	92	100	102	100	100	100	154
Hamate	M	0	0	—	—	100	23	100	60	100	86	100	148	100	139	100	155	100	223
	F	0	0	—	—	100	21	100	47	100	68	100	92	100	102	100	100	100	154
Distal radius	M	0	0	0	0	—	—	100	37	100	63	100	122	100	116	100	132	100	200
	F	0	0	0	0	—	—	96·4	27	98	48	100	71	100	81	100	73	100	133
Triquetral	M	0	0	0	0	0	0	—	—	90·6	29	100	85	100	79	100	95	100	171
	F	0	0	0	0	3·6	1	—	—	95·7	22	100	45	100	55	100	53	100	107
Lunate	M	0	0	0	0	0	0	9·4	3	—	—	100	59	96·4	54	98·6	71	100	145
	F	0	0	0	0	2·0	1	4·3	1	—	—	96·2	25	100	33	96·7	29	100	86
Trapezium	M	0	0	0	0	0	0	0	0	0	0	—	—	38·5	10	66·7	20	98·8	82
	F	0	0	0	0	0	0	0	0	3·8	1	—	—	81·3	13	75·0	12	100	62
Trapezoid	M	0	0	0	0	0	0	0	0	3·6	2	61·5	16	—	—	80·0	20	100	86
	F	0	0	0	0	0	0	0	0	0	0	18·7	3	—	—	40·0	4	100	52
Scaphoid	M	0	0	0	0	0	0	0	0	1·4	1	33·3	10	20·0	5	—	—	98·6	71
	F	0	0	0	0	0	0	0	0	3·3	1	25·0	4	60·0	6	—	—	100	54
Distal ulna	M	0	0	0	0	0	0	0	0	0	0	1·2	1	0	0	1·4	1	—	—
	F	0	0	0	0	0	0	0	0	0	0	0	0	0	0	0	0	—	—

Table 7: Frequency of dichotomous ossification sequences in Bundi children

Centre Present	Sex	Capitate %	n	Hamate %	n	Distal radius %	n	Triquetral %	n	Lunate %	n	Trapezium %	n	Trapezoid %	n	Scaphoid %	n	Distal ulna %	n
Capitate	M	–	–	100	2	100	19	100	79	100	107	100	121	100	118	100	145	100	221
	F	–	–	100	1	100	14	100	44	100	70	100	88	100	91	100	104	100	147
Hamate	M	0	0	–	–	100	17	100	77	100	105	100	119	100	116	100	143	100	219
	F	0	0	–	–	100	13	100	43	100	69	100	87	100	90	100	103	100	146
Dista lradius	M	0	0	0	0	–	–	100	60	100	88	100	102	100	99	100	126	100	202
	F	0	0	0	0	–	–	100	30	100	56	100	74	100	77	100	90	100	133
Triquetral	M	0	0	0	0	0	0	–	–	88·9	32	100	43	97·6	40	100	65	100	141
	F	0	0	0	0	0	0	–	–	93·3	28	100	45	100	47	100	60	100	103
Lunate	M	0	0	0	0	0	0	11·1	4	–	–	71·9	23	63·6	21	89·4	42	100	113
	F	0	0	0	0	0	0	6·7	2	–	–	90·9	20	95·5	21	100	34	100	77
Trapezium	M	0	0	0	0	0	0	0	0	28·1	9	–	–	41·2	7	96·2	25	100	99
	F	0	0	0	0	0	0	0	0	9·1	2	–	–	63·6	7	86·4	19	100	59
Trapezoid	M	0	0	0	0	0	0	2·4	1	36·4	12	58·8	10	–	–	93·3	28	100	102
	F	0	0	0	0	0	0	0	0	4·5	1	36·4	4	–	–	78·3	18	100	56
Scaphoid	M	0	0	0	0	0	0	0	0	10·6	5	3·8	1	6·7	2	–	–	96·3	79
	F	0	0	0	0	0	0	0	0	0	0	13·6	3	21·7	5	–	–	97·8	44
Distal ulna	M	0	0	0	0	0	0	0	0	0	0	0	0	0	0	3·7	3	–	–
	F	0	0	0	0	0	0	0	0	0	0	0	0	0	0	2·2	1	–	–

Centre Absent

Table 8: Tabulated frequency of alternate dichotomous ossification sequences in the wrist of coastal Papuan and Bundi children

Observed Alternate Sequences	Number of Observed Cases			
	Coastal Papuan		Bundi	
	M	F	M	F
Distal radius/Triquetral	37	27	60	30
Triquetral/Distal radius	0	1	0	0
Distal radius/Lunate	63	48	88	56
Lunate/Distal radius	0	1	0	0
Triquetral/Lunate	29	22	32	28
Lunate/Triquetral	3	1	4	2
Lunate/Trapezium	59	25	23	20
Trapezium/Lunate	0	1	9	2
Lunate/Trapezoid	54	33	21	21
Trapezoid/Lunate	** 2	0	*12	1
Trapezoid/Trapezium	*16	3	10	4
Trapezium/Trapezoid	10	13	7	7
Triquetral/Trapezoid	79	55	40	47
Trapezoid/Triquetral	0	0	1	0
Lunate/Scaphoid	71	29	42	34
Scaphoid/Lunate	1	1	5	0
Trapezium/Scaphoid	20	12	25	19
Scaphoid/Trapezium	**10	4	1	3
Trapezoid/Scaphoid	20	4	28	18
Scaphoid/Trapezoid	5	6	2	5
Trapezium/Distal Ulna	82	62	99	59
Distal ulna/Trapezium	1	0	0	0
Scaphoid/Distal ulna	71	54	79	44
Distal ulna/Scaphoid	1	0	3	1

* significant sex difference
** significant population difference (boys only)

ascertained by the number shown to the left of the diagonal. The tables show a total of 44 sequences each for coastal Papuan boys and girls, (but not necessarily the same sequences), 45 for Bundi boys and 43 for Bundi girls. A list of the alternate sequences to the left of the diagonal is presented in Table 8 for easier examination. While the actual number of observations of certain dichotomous sequences is necessarily small in view of their derivation from cross-sectional data, certain trends become immediately apparent and some of the results allow for the testing of significance using chi-square.

Significant sex differences (χ^2, p less than $0 \cdot 05$) were shown to exist for the trapezium/trapezoid sequences among coastal Papuan children and for the trapezoid/lunate sequences in Bundi children. Significant inter-population differences were found for the trapezoid/lunate and trapezium/scaphoid sequences, but these applied only to males. No significant inter-population differences in sequences could be demonstrated for females. However, this appears due mainly to the paucity in the number of observations of the various sequences, and with a larger sample, such trends (as suggested by the differences in the observations of the scaphoid/trapezoid sequences among females from the two populations), might become significant.

Of interest is the persistent evidence of delayed ossification of the lunate relative to the trapezium, trapezoid, and scaphoid in Bundi males. Such evidence suggests a syndrome of 'delayed lunate ossification' among Bundi boys. The presence of a similar syndrome has recently been observed in a group of Iranian boys (Garn et al, 1972).

Brachymesophalangy-5 (5-bmp)

Brachymesophalangy-5 is a not uncommon skeletal variant of the hand, and consists of an abnormal shortening of the middle phalanx of the little finger. The high correlation of relative bone dimensions in the same row compared with those in the same digit (Hewitt, 1963) has led to the ratio of the length of middle-5 to the length of middle-4 being used as the criterion for its diagnosis. Unfortunately some authors have used a ratio of less than 50 per cent as the separation point (e.g. Hertzog, 1967) while others have used the 60 per cent mark as the dividing line between normal and abnormal (O'Brien, Bagby and Burch, n.d.). Still others (e.g. Abbie, 1970; Roche, 1961), neglect to define the exact criteria used in determining the incidence of the condition in their population groups.

The frequency of the variant has been shown to range from less than 1 per cent up to about 10 per cent, and according to Hertzog (1967) is lowest in Europeans and African Negroes and highest in Asiatics. In several Central and South American populations the incidence seems to fall within the intermediate ranges (Garn et al, 1966). Among Australian aboriginals, Abbie (1970) quotes an incidence of 13·6 per cent for males (42 in 308) and 20·7 per cent in females (62 in 299) which is among the highest on record. However, as previously noted, he does not define the criteria used in determining the condition and hence inter-population comparisons using his data are limited.

From sibling observations, Garn et al (1972b) concluded that simple dominance could be ruled out as the usual method of inheritance of the variant. They felt that either recessive inheritance or more complicated forms of transmission were involved. The data of O'Brien, Bagby and Burch (n.d.) also best fitted an autosomal recessive hypothesis. However, examples of parent-child transmission have been reported in the literature (Garn et al, 1967), and Abbie (1970) seems to favour a dominant type of inheritance in the Australian Aboriginal.

In 1972 Garn *et al* reported a significant association between the presence of 5-bmp and an overall reduction in total body size relative to normal unaffected individuals. It was postulated that this might confer an adaptive advantage upon affected individuals in situations where reduced availability of calories and protein favoured small stature and reduced growth rates. Such an environmental situation has been shown to exist in the New Guinea highlands region, and hence, if the theory of Garn *et al* (1972) is generally applicable one might expect that a higher incidence of 5-bmp would be found in the Bundi population relative to the coastal Papuan population.

Table 9 gives the incidence of 5-bmp in the two New Guinea populations studied. To allow for comparison with other studies using different criteria for diagnosis, two different cut-off points have been included (<50 per cent and <60 per cent). Only children in whom the epiphysis of the middle phalanx of the fifth digit had already ossified were included in the analysis. The results are unexpected in that instead of an increase in the incidence of 5-bmp within the Bundi population, the reverse was found to apply, with the incidence in both males and females falling below that of the coastal sample. χ^2 testing of the <50 groups showed non-significant sex and inter-population differences. However the <60 groups displayed a significant sex difference for the coastal population (χ^2, $p < 0.01$), and significant population differences for both sexes ($p < 0.05$). A higher incidence in females over males is also obvious and this trend has been reported for most other population groups studied. Comparing the incidence of 5-bmp in both the New Guinea groups with the figures published for other population groups by Hertzog (1967), Papua New Guineans fall towards the bottom level of the scale and appear to equate more with Negroes and Europeans than with American Indian and Asiatic stocks. Comparisons for significance with the Micronesian and Polynesian populations listed in Table 9 are impossible because of the lack of sufficient numbers and of the diagnostic criteria used.

Radiopaque lines and bands in the distal radius

The occurrence of transverse lines or bands of increased radiopacity near the extremities of the limb long bones, has been reported since the turn of the century (Ludloff, 1903; Stettner, 1921; Harris, 1926, 1931; Sontag, 1938). Frequently referred to as Harris lines or growth arrest lines, the latest belief is that they arise more from a relative imbalance in chondrogenesis and osteoblastic activity during the recovery stage following a period of relative growth inactivity, rather than during the temporary 'growth arrest' stage itself (Follis and Park, 1952; Park and Richter, 1953; Park, 1964).

Lines have occasionally been observed in the neonate (Sontag, 1938) and thereafter the appearance of new lines follows a definite pattern rising to a peak during the first few years and then gradually falling in incidence until early puberty, after which time the appearance of new lines is relatively rare (Schwager, 1968). Sex differences also have been noted to occur (Garn *et al*, 1968) in that relatively more new lines appear in boys than in girls. However the lines are also more transient in boys and this is thought to be due to the

Table 9: Incidence of Brachymesophalangy-5

Population	Sex	Criterion	Number	%
Coastal Papuan	M	< 50	5 out of 576	0·87
—this study	F	< 50	12 out of 522	2·30
—this study	M	< 60	27 out of 576	4·68
	F	< 60	50 out of 522	9·58
Bundi				
(New Guinea Highlands)	M	< 50	0 out of 294	0·0
—this study	F	< 50	2 out of 224	0·89
—this study	M	< 60	5 out of 294	1·7
	F	< 60	5 out of 224	2·23
Micronesia	M	< 60	3 out of 48	6·25
(O'Brien, Bagby and Burch, 1964)	F	< 60	8 out of 56	14·29
Polynesia	mixed	not stated	2 out of 164	1·2
(Fry, 1960)				
American Negro	not stated	< 50	0 out of 200	0·0
(Hertzog, 1967)				
Australian Aboriginal	M	not stated	42 out of 308	13·64
(Abbie, 1970)	F	not stated	62 out of 299	20·74
American Indian	M	< 50	3 out of 51	5·88
(Philadelphia)	F	< 50	9 out of 45	20·00
(Hertzog, 1967)				
European	?	< 60	10 out of 1000	1·0
(O'Brien, Bagby and Burch, n.d.)				

more extensive remodelling that takes place in the male during growth. Persistence of lines in the adult is not uncommon, and longitudinal studies clearly demonstrate that most, if not all of these lines, are laid down in early infancy or childhood. The greater prevalence of lines in adult women compared to men again reflects the more extensive remodelling that takes place in male bones during adolescence.

Some dissension exists as to the relationship of preceding illness, malnutrition, emotional stress etc. to the production of lines and bands in the growing bones. A number of authors claim a significant association (Hewitt *et al*, 1955; Acheson and MacIntyre, 1958; Acheson, 1959; Marshall, 1966; Schwager, 1968; Sontag and Comstock, 1938). However Dreizen *et al* (1956) refute this claim, and state that the two commonest features of transverse lines are nonspecificity of cause and individuality of response. They do however admit that the rate of resorption of lines appears to be influenced by the general nutritional status of the individual.

Garn *et al* (1968) review the whole subject of lines and bands, and provide further statistical data supporting a significant disease-line association. Where most previous studies were retrospective in type, the data used in the latter analysis, was derived from an extensive longitudinal study in which sequential radiographs were accompanied by regular medical examinations and interval health histories. However Garn *et al* (1968) together with

Hewitt (1955), Dreizen *et al* (1956) and Schwager (1968), also cite instances where an illness has occurred without the subsequent production of lines, and where lines have appeared without obvious preceding illness or upset.

That nutritional deprivation plays a part in the production of lines and bands receives considerable support from several sources. Jones and Dean (1956 and 1959) reported a much higher incidence of lines in children suffering with kwashiorkor than in a control group of normal healthy children. Harris (1933), Park and Richter (1953), Platt and Stewart (1962) and Park (1964), all conducted experiments in which lines were produced in an assortment of laboratory animals fed on starvation or nutritionally deficient diets.

During the assessment of the radiographs used in the present study, the almost universal presence of well-marked transverse lines in the distal radius of the Bundi children compared with an obviously much lower incidence in the coastal Papuan series induced me to make some assessment of their relative incidence. No attempt has been made at this stage to quantify the number, size or density of lines in each individual. Instead, lines have been recorded simply as being present or absent. Each film was processed twice by the author and any film receiving a positive assessment on one round and a negative assessment on the other (due to the faintness of the lines) was delegated to the negative series. Because of the previously noted change in incidence of lines with age (Dreizen *et al*, 1956; Garn *et al*, 1968) the radiographs were also separated into a pre-fusion group, and a post-fusion group (in whom fusion was occurring or had occurred in one or more epiphyses). As there were only two Bundi males that had reached the post-fusion stage (both aged 21 years, and with transverse lines) no general observations could be made on this group. The results of my observations are listed in Table 10. The only group displaying significant intra-group sex differences were the post-fusion Papuan series. This accords well with the observations of other authors where lines were observed to be more frequent in adolescent and adult females, than in males. All inter-group comparisons displayed highly significant differences in frequency (p < 0.01). Exactly what these differences signify is still uncertain.

It is tempting to postulate that due to the known deficiency in protein intake in the Bundi child (Malcolm, 1970c) the increased incidence of lines

Table 10: Incidence of transverse lines in the distal radius

Series	Total no.	No. with lines	%
Pre-fusion—Papuan males	459	232	50·5
—Papuan females	289	161	55·7
—Bundi males	198	198	100
—Bundi females	83	80	96·4
Post-fusion—Papuan males	104	7	6·7
—Papuan females	184	34	18·5
—Bundi females	24	15	62·5

is due to the decreased rate of resorption noted to occur in association with malnutrition (Dreizen *et al*, 1956). However it may also relate to a heavier or more severe infection load in the young Bundi child compared with the coastal series, or even to the better health care that is more freely available to the coastal children, and which, if sought and applied in the early stages of an illness, might reduce the extent and duration of the 'imprint' effected by the illness on the skeleton. The part that differences in genetic endowment might play in possibly 'sensitising' the skeleton of the Bundi child to adverse influences in the environment is also unknown. It is intended that further studies will be carried out to try to elucidate these problems.

Acknowledgements   The research reported on in this paper was supported by grants from the University of Queensland and the National Health and Medical Research Council.

I gratefully acknowledge the assistance rendered to me by the following: Medical Faculty of the University of Papua New Guinea; Department of Public Health, and the Department of Education in Port Moresby; Dr Lawrence Malcolm, and the teachers, parents and pupils from Pari, Badihagwa, Hagara and Bundi Schools.

References

ABBIE, A. A.   1970   Brachymesophalangy V in Australian Aborigines. *Medical Journal of Australia*, 2:736–37.
—— and W. R. ADEY   1953   Ossification in a central Australian tribe. *Human Biology*, 25:265–78.
ACHESON, R. M.   1959   Effects of starvation, septicaemia, and chronic illness on the growth cartilage plate and metaphysis of the immature rat. *Journal of Anatomy*, 93:123–30.
—— and M. N. MACINTYRE   1958   The effects of acute infection and acute starvation on skeletal development: a study of young rats. *British Journal of Experimental Pathology*, 39:37–45.
BUEHL, C. C. and S. I. PYLE   1942   The use of age at first appearance of three ossification centers in determining the skeletal status of children. *Journal of Pediatrics*, 21:335–42.
DREIZEN, S., R. M. SNODGRASSE, G. S. PARKER, C. CURRIE and T. D. SPIES   1954   Maturation of bone centers in the hand and wrist of children with chronic nutritive failure. *A.M.A. American Journal of Diseases of Children*, 87:429–39.
——, C. CURRIE, E. J. GILLEY and T. D. SPIES   1956   Observations on the association between nutritive failure, skeletal maturation rate and radiopaque transverse lines in the distal end of the radius in children. *American Journal of Roentgenology, Radium Therapy and Nuclear Medicine*, 76:482–87.
——, R. M. SNODGRASSE, H. WEBB-PEPLOE and T. D. SPIES   1957   The effect of prolonged nutritive failure on epiphyseal fusion in the human hand skeleton. *American Journal of Roentgenology, Radium Therapy and Nuclear Medicine*, 78:461–70.
——, ——, ——, ——   1958   The retarding effect of protracted undernutrition on the appearance of the postnatal ossification centers in the hand and wrist. *Human Biology*, 30:253–64.
FLORY, C. D.   1936   Osseous development in the hand as an index of skeletal development. *Monographs of the Society for Research in Child Development*, 1:111–41.
FOLLIS, R. H. and E. A. PARK   1952   Some observations on bone growth with particular respect to zones and transverse lines of increased density in the metaphysis. *American Journal of Roentgenology, Radium Therapy and Nuclear Medicine*, 68:709–24.
FRANCIS, C. C. and P. P. WERLE   1939   The appearance of centers of ossification from birth to 5 years. *American Journal of Physical Anthropology*, 24:273–99.

FRISANCHO, A. R., S. M. GARN and C. G. ROHMANN 1969 Age at Menarche: a new method of prediction and retrospective assessment based on hand X-rays. *Human Biology*, 41:42–50.

FRY, E. I. 1960 Health survey of children from Rarotonga, Cook Islands. III. Skeletal age and skeletal observations. *Journal of Tropical Paediatrics*, 6:75–79.

GARN, S. M. and C. G. ROHMANN 1960 Variability in the order of ossification of the bony centers of the hand and wrist. *American Journal of Physical Anthropology*, 18:219–30.

—— and —— 1962 The adductor sesamoid of the thumb. *American Journal of Physical Anthropology*, 20:297–302.

——, ——, M. BEHAR, F. VITERI and M. A. GUZMAN 1964 Compact bone deficiency in protein-calorie malnutrition. *Science*, 145:1444–45.

——, —— and T. BLUMENTHAL 1966 Ossification sequence polymorphism and sexual dimorphism in skeletal development. *American Journal of Physical Anthropology*, 24:101–15.

——, S. L. FELS and H. ISRAEL 1967 Brachymesophalangia of digit five in ten populations. *American Journal of Physical Anthropology*, 27:205–10.

——, F. M. SILVERMAN, K. P. HERTZOG and C. G. ROHMANN 1968 Lines and bands of increased density—their implication to growth and development. *Medical Radiography and Photography*, 44:58–89.

——, J. M. NAGY, A. K. POZNANSKI and M. B. McCANN 1972 Size reduction associated with brachymesophalangia-5: a possible selective advantage. *American Journal of Physical Anthropology*, 37:267–70.

——, S. T. SANDUSKY, R. L. MILLER and J. M. NAGY 1972 Developmental implications of dichotomous ossification sequences in the wrist region. *American Journal of Physical Anthropology*, 37:111–15.

GIRDANY, B. R. and R. GOLDEN 1952 Centers of ossification of the skeleton. *American Journal of Roentgenology, Radium Therapy and Nuclear Medicine*, 68:922.

GRAVE, K. C. 1971 *Timing of facial growth in Australian Aborigines*. Thesis for Degree of Master of Dental Surgery, School of Dentistry, University of Adelaide.

GREULICH, W. W. 1952 The growth and developmental status of Guamanian school children in 1947. *American Journal of Physical Anthropology* 9:55–70.

—— 1957 A comparison of the physical growth and development of American-born and native Japanese children. *American Journal of Physical Anthropology*, n.s. 15:489–515.

—— and S. I. PYLE 1959 *Radiographic atlas of skeletal development of the hand and wrist*. 2nd edition. Stanford University Press.

HARRIS, H. A. 1926 The growth of the long bones in childhood, with special reference to certain bony striations of the metaphysis and to the role of vitamins. *Archives of Internal Medicine*, 38:785–806.

—— 1931 Lines of arrested growth in the long bones in childhood: correlation of histological and radiographic appearances in clinical and experimental conditions. *British Journal of Radiology*, 4:561–88.

—— 1933 *Bone growth in health and disease*. Oxford University Press.

HERTZOG, K. P. 1967 Shortened fifth medial phalanges. *American Journal of Physical Anthropology*, 27:113–18.

——, F. FALKNER and S. M. GARN 1969 The genetic-determination of ossification sequence polymorphism. *American Journal of Physical Anthropology*, 30:141–44.

HEWITT, D., C. K. WESTROPP and R. M. ACHESON 1955 Effect of childish ailments on skeletal development. *British Journal of Preventative and Social Medicine*, 9:179–86.

—— 1963 Pattern of correlations in the skeleton on the growing hand. *Annals of Human Genetics*, 27:157–68.

JONES, P. R. M. and R. F. A. DEAN 1956 The effects of Kwashiorkor on the development of the bones of the hand. *Journal of Tropical Pediatrics*, 2:51–68.

—— and —— 1959 The effects of Kwashiorkor on the development of the bones of the knee. *Journal of Pediatrics*, 54:176–84.

LASKER, G. W. 1946 Migration and physical differentiation—a comparison of immigrant with American-born Chinese. *American Journal of Physical Anthropology*, n.s. 4:273–300.

LUDLOFF, K. 1903 Ueber Wachstum und Architektur der unteren Femur-epiphyse und oberen Tibiaepiphyse. Ein Beitrag zur Rontgendiagnostik. *Bruns Beitrage zur klinischen Chirurgie,* 38:64–75.

MACKAY, D. H. 1952 Skeletal maturation in the hand: a study of development in East African children. *Transactions of the Royal Society of Tropical Medicine and Hygiene,* 46:135.

MALCOLM, L. A. 1966 The age of puberty in the Bundi people. *Papua New Guinea Medical Journal,* 9:16–20.

—— 1968 *Genesis and variation: a study in the growth and development of the Bundi people of the New Guinea Highlands.* M.D. Thesis, University of Otago, New Zealand.

—— 1969 Growth and development of the Kaiapit children of the Markham Valley, New Guinea. *American Journal of Physical Anthropology,* 31:39–52.

—— 1970a Growth retardation in a New Guinea boarding school and its response to supplementary feeding. *British Journal of Nutrition,* 24:297–305.

—— 1970b Growth, malnutrition, and mortality of the infant and toddler in the Asai Valley of the New Guinea Highlands. *American Journal of Clinical Nutrition,* 23:1090–95.

—— 1970c *Growth and development in New Guinea: a study of the Bundi people of the Madang District.* Institute of Human Biology Monograph Series No. 1.

—— 1970d Growth of the Asai people of the Madang District of New Guinea. *Journal of Biosocial Science,* 2:213.

MARSHALL, W. A. 1966 Problems in relating radiopaque transverse lines in the radius to the occurrence of disease. *Symposium of Social and Human Biology,* 8:245–61.

MILLS, C. A. 1937 Geographic and time variations in body growth and age at Menarche. *Human Biology,* 9:43–56.

O'BRIEN, W. M., G. F. BAGBY and T. A. BURCH n.d. A genetic study of brachy-mesophalangia of the fifth fingers in 1083 Pima Indians. (Unpublished manuscript written in 1964.)

PARK, E. A. 1964 The imprinting of nutritional disturbances on the growing bone. *Pediatrics 33* (Supplement):815–62.

—— and C. P. RICHTER 1953 Transverse lines in bone: the mechanism of their development. *Bulletin of the Johns Hopkins Hospital,* 93:234.

PLATT, B. S. and R. J. C. STEWART 1962 Transverse trabeculae and osteo-porosis in bones in experimental protein-calorie deficiency. *British Journal of Nutrition,* 16:483–95.

PYLE, I. and L. SONTAG 1943 Variability in onset of ossification in epiphyses and short bones of the extremities. *American Journal of Roentgenology, Radium Therapy and Nuclear Medicine,* 49:795.

ROCHE, A. F. 1961 Clinodactyly and brachymesophalangia of the fifth finger. *Acta paediatrica,* 50:387–91.

SCHWAGER, P. M. 1968 The frequency of appearance of transverse lines in the tibia in relation to childhood illnesses. Abstracted in *American Journal of Physical Anthropology.* 29:130.

SCRIMSHAW, N. S. and M. BEHAR 1965 Malnutrition in underdeveloped countries. *New England Journal of Medicine,* 272:137–44.

SONTAG, L. W. 1938 Evidences of disturbed prenatal and neonatal growth in bones of infants aged one month. *American Journal of Diseases of Children,* 55:1248–56.

—— and G. COMSTOCK 1938 Striae in the bones of a set of monozygotic triplets. *American Journal of Diseases of Children,* 56:301–08.

STETTNER, E. 1921 Uber die Beziehungen der Ossifickation des Handskeletts zu Alter- und Langenwachstum bei gesunden und Kranken Kindern von der Geburt bis zur Pubertät. *Archaeologie Kinderheilk,* 68:342–68, 439–66.

SUTOW, W. W. 1953 Skeletal maturation in healthy Japanese children 6 to 19 years of age. Comparison with skeletal maturation in American children. *Hiroshima Journal of Medical Science,* 2:181.

TANNER, J. M. 1962 *Growth at adolescence.* 2nd edition. Blackwell Scientific Publications, Oxford.

WOOD, W. B. 1970 Skeletal maturation in New Guinea. Paper read at the 42nd Congress of the Australian and New Zealand Association for the Advancement of Science.

Evolutionary process and semantics

Australian prehistoric tooth size as a local adjustment

R.V.S. Wright

IN THIS ESSAY I deal first with some general evolutionary assumptions in the use of the word *primitive*; then I look at some problems in the application of the idea to Australian crania; thirdly I argue with the assumption that large palates and teeth in Australian crania are primitive *sensu strictu*.

The argument in the third part is presented without much empirical support, and at the moment I have neither the expertise nor the inclination to gather this. Naturally I invite criticism of my assumptions – some of which I have attempted to delineate and none of which I think is irresponsible. Because the theory makes implicit predictions about the nature of future fossil discoveries it has the virtue of being refutable. I definitely do not cherish it.

I have used the word essay designedly, not pretending that this is a data paper. I gave a version of it as a seminar paper in the Department of Anthropology, University of Sydney in July 1972. Since then a detailed survey of literature on tooth wear and culture has been published (Molnar, 1972). However the central evolutionary problem of my argument remains undiscussed but is relevant to the question of the physical origins of early Man in Australia.

Ghiselin's provocative book (1969) helped me to clear away several trees which had obstructed my view of the evolutionary wood. My theoretical emphases owe much to his expositions. I have, however, preferred the utility of Dobzhansky's distinction between the ideas of adaptedness and fitness (1967).

'Primitive' – the word and the idea

Macintosh and Larnach have written, 'There is thus little or no doubt that the *Homo erectus* traits show greater persistence in Australian Aboriginal crania than in any other racial group we have been able to examine.' (1972 : 2). This can be understood as a sort of palaeoanthropological prophesy about an imaginary family tree of fossils; it is the equivalent of saying that (if we were archaeologically omniscient) these traits would be found continuously along the chain of mankind which links living men with those of the middle Pleistocene. There would be no period when one of these cranial traits was not to be found somewhere in the world, though the frequency with which the various traits occurred in different human groups could well vary. Had there been a world-wide break in the occurrence of any one of these traits its reappearance in later populations would of course be due to *new* genetic events – there being no ancestral connection and therefore no legitimate meaning in such a word as 'persistence'.

In comparative evolutionary studies it is common to label as *primitive* those forms of an inherited structure which are thought to have persisted through time; primitive attributes contrast with subsequently modified forms of the structure in other related organisms. A classic example is found by comparing the ancestry of the human hand and the horse's hoof. Because it has five fingers the human hand can be called primitive; it is close in its shape to the hand of the remote common ancestor of the man and the horse. By contrast the horse's hoof has been extensively modified *away* from the common ancestral form – in evolutionary interpretation it is an advanced homology of the primitive human hand.

That the hand is primitive in form has not been a cause of grief to the species *Homo sapiens*. There is no reason why I should object to my hand being described as primitive; nor could I reasonably envy the horse its advanced anatomy. I should not assume that when my hand is described as primitive it is being judged as a functional failure. There is no necessary relationship between a character's evolutionary primitiveness and its usefulness. The teeth of a shark are primitive but devastating.

My comments are harmless truisms in the philosophy of general biology. However for reasons of social sensitivity the same ideas and words tend to get evaded in studies of the recent evolution of mankind. In the political arena the words become loaded. If in comparative racial studies I describe a character as primitive I may not be understood as making solely a detached phylogenetic interpretation. The word primitive is taken at best as a derogatory functional value judgment and at worst as an epithet of mere racist abuse.

Therefore I emphasise that in general evolutionary studies the words primitive (and its close synonym) *archaic* are used (or should be used) only for making interpretations of relative closeness to presumed ancestral forms. As an act of good faith I affirm that my hairy Caucasoid body and thin lips can be interpreted as phylogenetically primitive. I am closer in these characters to gorillas and chimpanzees than are African Negroids. In these attributes I may well be closer to the common human ancestral form.

In summarising my attitude I emphasise that where an interpretation is made that heritable characters have persisted then the words primitive or archaic can be used to label them. In studies of human evolution our vocabulary may start irritation in other spheres where words feed human prejudice. This does not persuade me that we should try too much to alter evolutionary vocabulary. If we create neologisms these in their turn will become loaded. It is the ideas behind which are troublesome. In the war against prejudice the history of verbal euphemisms is a sorry one.

There is a further introductory point I want to draw out. The words primitive and archaic can be used in a non-evolutionary sense and purely as morphologically descriptive labels to give an impression of the form of a structure – in this loose sense no persistence from the ancestral form is necessarily implied. This usage is dangerously ambiguous, tends to circularity of argument and may divert us towards wrestling with adversaries conjured up solely by the words themselves.

The words primitive and archaic should, I suggest, be used only where the interpretation of persistence is implicit and intentional. I am not so naive as to suggest we should avoid the terms unless certain of a trait's pedigree. Rather I am merely urging a phylogenetic awareness which will avoid the begging of questions.

Some Australian usages

In this section I want to illustrate my point with some eclectic examples from the literature of Australian physical anthropology.

One of the first comparative accounts of fossil and modern Man, which was designed to isolate primitive traits, was Huxley's 1863 essay in *Man's place in nature*. He found that in the traits of curvature of the frontal bone and form of the supra-orbital ridges the Neanderthal calotte was close to one extreme of the variations to be found in Australian Aboriginal skulls and certain skulls from the Danish kitchen middens of recent European pre-history.

More importantly (from the point of view of this essay) Huxley also discussed the evolutionary significance of extended facial prognathism – a functional correlate of large palate and thus of large teeth. After surveying general mammalian anatomy he concluded that the large palate of Australian Aboriginals is closer to the presumed ancestral form of Man than is a small one. Thus already by 1863 (and in one of the most influential evolutionary books) we see the form of the Australian Aboriginal palate and teeth being interpreted as primitive in the strict sense I have outlined above. This I believe is still the prevailing opinion.

The next publication I want to mention is the thoughtful, if eccentric, evolutionary monograph by Klaatsch (1908). Like Huxley, Klaatsch emphasises that high variability is *itself* characteristic of Australian crania (e.g. 1908 : 63). This observation permeates his comparative generalisations; he is critical of earlier accounts which sought to typify Australian crania by characters which are by no means characteristic (1908 : 119). Moreover Klaatsch also demands justification for the identification of traits as primitive (from fossil man or comparative hominoid anatomy).

This perspicacious theoretical position leads Klaatsch to seek advanced (i.e. non-primitive) characters in Aboriginal crania. For example he identifies the combination of supra-orbital ridge and depressed nasion as 'absolutely not a primitive characteristic' (1908 : 153). On the evidence available to him he sees the combination as special to Aboriginal crania and *not* found in other living races, Neanderthal man or in the apes. The logic of

Klaatsch's position is often missed. Thus Gregory in a generally perceptive book on human evolution assumes that a depressed nasion is a primitive trait (1922 : 479) – because (it seems) it is found in Australian Aboriginals.

Klaatsch adopts the static attitude of evolutionary comparative anatomy – the mapping of anatomical change and retention without considering evolutionary causes. However Brace (1967 : 105), though he has the conventional attitude to Australian Aboriginal large teeth as primitive, does add an historical explanation for the retention of this character. He attributes it to a material culture which he says is closer to the Mousterian of Europe than to the upper Palaeolithic.

I deny the validity of his cultural comparison – merely asserting here that the converse holds; so Brace's *particular* use of material culture to explain the retention of large teeth lapses. But his general point of the importance of considering bio-cultural interactions remains. This style of functional explanation is a rare injection into a literature that is anaemic in evolutionary process.

As I said, Brace argues that large teeth have been retained. This means that by the criteria I have outlined above they are a primitive trait. But once we allow the idea of evolutionary process to enter the debate we can poke at intriguing problems lurking in such assumptions.

Firstly why should we assume retention? A brief and partial answer (but not I submit an unfair one) is that we unconsciously lean to teleological explanation for trends of change in human evolution – for example inevitable brain size increase and inevitable reduction in tooth size. In the case of both we may soften crude teleology by an appeal to the parallel evolution of material culture producing an increased need for brain and a reduced need for teeth. This, on the face of it, puts us in the Lamarckian camp out of which we may try to escape into the orthodox Darwinian wide-world by using passwords such as 'selection pressure' or 'selection forces'. The trouble is that these can be illegitimate translations of the theory of natural selection from a description of process to the idea of the force creating the effects (the phrase 'selection pressure' is often the Trojan horse out of which emerge Lamarckian notions).

Whatever our theoretical position, we feel that the arresting of a trend demands an explanation of the sort Brace provides. It is at this stage of the argument worth exploring whether the overt use of a strict Darwinian variation/selection model helps us to circumvent the problems produced by unconscious teleology. I shall argue that it does. And it does so, I believe, because it forces us to think critically about the mechanisms of cause and effect – the processes which retain trends, halt them and reverse them.

I want to focus now on some particular data in order to illustrate the discussion so far. Thorne (1971) and Thorne and Macumber (1972) have given preliminary accounts of precisely dated human remains from Lake Mungo (c. 26,000 years old) and Kow Swamp (c. 10,000 years old). The apparently primitive or archaic morphology is to be found in the *later* Kow Swamp remains some 16,000 years younger than the Lake Mungo skeleton. Here is a problem, though with a shrunken chronology, akin to the pre-Neanderthal debate of Europe.

On the assumption that the Kow Swamp remains are not only *descriptively* primitive but also primitive in an evolutionary sense (that is closest to the ancestral form) one *has* to invoke gaps in the fossil record and/or migrations to explain the apparent negative correlation of time with morphology.

I do not subscribe to current archaeological dogma which forbids classifying migration as explanation. Nevertheless if, for the present exercise, we *do* discount migrations and take the anatomy and dates of these fossils at face value we must conclude that, in the western rivers of the south eastern part of Australia, Lake Mungo is closer to the ancestral form; consequently, in the evolutionary sense, it has the primitive/archaic characters of smooth rounded frontal bone and small palate.

According to Thorne (Thorne and Macumber, 1972: 319, also Thorne, 1971: 86) two special features characterise Kow Swamp remains – a flatness of the frontal bone (associated with developed supra-orbital ridges) and large palates. I take only palates for examination and I assume that there is useful positive correlation between palate/mandible size and tooth size. Therefore I shall refer to tooth size because, in the evolutionary model I propose, it is the effective variable.

To summarise so far, it seems that a preliminary case can be made for there having been, in one region of Australia, an increase of tooth size over time. I am quite aware that the case needs quantification and more fossil support. My anticipatory explanations below can be screwed up if the empirical data gathered in the future does not support the present best estimate of anatomy plotted against time – that is if Mungo is atypical of its own population.

I am also aware that I am ignoring differences in the structure of the frontal bone. There is not much I can do about this with the variation/selection explanation I am offering here. I would plead, if pressed, that the rugged architecture of the front part of the cranium is a function of large dental apparatus; quite why I do not know (to appeal to pleiotropic effects is a tempting explanatory bluff when in such a corner!).

Darwinian explanation

The question to answer by a Darwinian variation/selection model is this – by what process might an increase of tooth size have taken place over time?

The answer has to satisfy three conditions which the model sets. Fundamentally these are:

(a)   that there are variations
(b)   that the variations are inherited
(c)   that the variants differ in adaptedness.

I take it as self-evident that there are variations in tooth size in all human populations. Details for living Australian Aboriginals have been published frequently (see for instance Barrett *et al*, 1964).

I assume also that tooth size has high heritability in the human species – indeed in mammals in general. Support for this proposition emerges from simple observations that gross changes of diet between different generations do not drastically change tooth size. In a cursory examination of the literature I have found somewhat more specific support in Bowden and Goose (1969). Their study of incisor and canine teeth in English families showed parent/ offspring correlations of around $+0\cdot5$, which together with other evidence was 'compatible with a hypothesis of multifactorial inheritance with genes of small and additive effect but without dominance.' (1969 : 57).

I would argue, therefore, that by analogical extension of these findings to the premolars and molars I can take the condition of heritability of tooth size as having been met.

It remains, therefore, to decide if these inherited variations in tooth size could have differed in adaptedness – and if they did how they differed.

I think that the most likely area of different adaptedness is in the effects of attrition – the mechanical abrasion of first the enamel, then the dentine (and secondarily deposited dentine) ending up with the exposure of the pulp cavity (Klatsky and Fisher, 1953: 46).

These lesions are caused by the inclusion of quartz grains in food which has to be chewed. The sand on roots is an obvious source; but silt in the guts of molluscs (though it may not be felt as intrusive grit during chewing) has insidious abrasive effects in the long-term (Dahlberg, 1963 : 173).

Today's processed foods virtually eliminate attrition or, at any rate, reduce it from the level of a pathology. A recent dental book of papers devoted to oral disease and environment makes no mention of it (Kreshover and McClure, 1966).

Once the pulp cavity is exposed by attrition there is great danger of apical abscess. Thorne (Thorne and Macumber, 1972:319) has mentioned the pre- valence of this condition in the Kow Swamp population. For another riverine population in Texas, Goldstein (1948:67–68) has observed 'Loss of teeth . . . may be as much, or more, the consequence of excessive attrition and concomitant alveolar abscess as that of caries.'

Exposure of pulp and nerve tissue with ensuing abscess obviously caused discomfort. Dahlberg (1963 : 173) has put it suggestively, 'Major events in . . . [their] . . . lives . . . not only included birth, puberty, marriage and death, but also, no doubt, long periods of distress and disability during the time that it took for an alveolar abscess to resolve.'

It seems that we have already got suggestions of the evidences we seek for differential adaptedness between individuals in a single population. In an admittedly shadowy way one feels that such discomfort would, at times of dangerous stress, affect states of adaptation – would make the discomforted individuals relatively poorer life-insurance risks than those of the same age whose larger teeth, though subjected to the same attritional load, had not yet been abraded to expose the pulp cavity. Somewhat less vague, it seems to me are the disadvantages of merely trying to gain nourishment by chewing food on an unresolved apical abscess.

But there are additional indirect pathological ways in which attrition, followed by chronic infection, might create differential adaptedness. Though I have not been able to find any population mortality statistics the qualitative assertions of pathologists predict unambiguously what the statistics on differential mortality would show were they available. Thus Thoma and Goldman (1960 : 491) say, 'All experienced clinicians today can cite numerous cases which will demonstrate the relationship of oral infections to infection of adjacent regions and to secondary disease in remote parts of the body'. The secondary diseases suggested are variable and numerous, including ulcer of the cornea, infection of the middle ear, rheumatoid arthritis and forms of heart disease (1960 : 498). Maybe this is all medical hocus-pocus; if it is not then the third fundamental condition of the model is met because it is hard to escape the conclusion that such infections would have shown a statistical tendency to lower life expectancy.

For the argument to be rounded off it is necessary to show that the tendency to differential mortality arising from oral infection overlaps with reproductive age. If there is this overlap we may be able to relate adaptedness to 'fitness' (in the Darwinian sense). Unfortunately I know of no statistics, but Thorne's preliminary comment on Kow Swamp suggests that the precondition may be met. He says, 'Although only one individual is of advanced age, the teeth of most specimens show pronounced attrition . . . The exposed roots of the mandibular first molars are commonly worn halfway to their apices . . . All adults exhibit extensive alveolar pathologies'. (Thorne and Macumber, 1972 : 316).

I would comment here that this appalling state of dental adaptedness is in a population whose mandibles are, 'by any standards . . . very large indeed' (Thorne and Macumber, 1972 : 316) and whose grinding surfaces of the second and third molars may exceed the mean for a contemporary Aboriginal population which itself exceeds other human populations with few tooth classes excepted; I make these suppositions by comparing Thorne (Thorne and Macumber, 1972:316) with Barrett et al (1964 : 283).

I contend therefore that a reasonable case can be made out that conditions for a Darwinian evolutionary explanation are met. Thus it may have been that, in part of prehistoric Australia, individuals with inherited variations for *larger* grinding surfaces tended to get exposed pulp cavities later in their reproductive life, therefore tended to die later and therefore tended to leave more children. With the maintenance of these conditions subsequent generations would have been made up of people tending to have larger premolar and molar teeth. The repetition of 'tend' is of course necessary because of the statistical nature of natural selection arguments.

Implications

Let us suppose that this is the evolutionary explanation for large palates and teeth of the Kow Swamp people and that the population is derived over some 16,000 years from a group with small palates typified by Mungo. If we assume a monogenetic origin for Man in Australia, with an original landfall some 50,000 years ago, Mungo is of course chronologically closer to the ancestral form than are the Kow Swamp remains. Therefore its small palate and teeth may be closer in form to the ancestral type of South-East Asia. Relative smallness may be the *primitive* form of dentition in the context of the origins of Man in Australia.

Does this make environmental sense? We have no direct answer from archaeologically discovered occupation sites and diets of a relevant age in South-East Asia. Nevertheless I would be prepared to guess that forests rich in rain-washed fruits (to borrow a phrase from Dahlberg, 1963 : 173) would put a lighter attritional load on the teeth of hunters and gatherers than would the late Pleistocene blowing sands and silts around rivers and lakes in the area of Australia we have been considering. The ancestral Asian population may not have required such large teeth.

But what are the implications for dental prehistory closer to home, that is in the western rivers of eastern Australia? What palaeontological predictions emerge from the discussion so far?

It would I think be useful now to recapitulate the argument in more general terms than those I have used in the dental hypothesis. In this more abstract model which follows I have excluded the uncertainties inherent in the actual dental data.

Let us consider, in the palaeontological context of a single species, a given character which can be shown to have steadily increased in mean size from time X to time Y.

We assume that this increase in size took place by the selection of larger variants of the character. We can further assume certain relationships between this character and the adaptedness of individuals. For instance in early life the chances of death were not affected by variability in the size of the character; therefore in the first part of the life of all individuals the character was selectively neutral. In later life, however, selective agents were suddenly introduced when environmental forces had reduced the size of the character – a deleterious threshold being crossed. The palaeontological record shows that this threshold was crossed *during* the reproductive lives of most individuals, both at time X, time Y and points in between.

Let us suppose that for individuals in any particular population the environmental processes were constant (those environmental processes, that is, which reduced the size of the character in individuals and triggered the selective agents). Ignoring other causes of death, we can conclude that differential mortality in the population was related to variability in the size of the character in question. This is because with a greater size of the character in an individual the threshold was crossed later in life; greater size conferred greater adaptedness – lengthening the reproductive lives of these individuals. With a smaller size of the character the threshold was crossed earlier in life; thus smaller size conferred lesser adaptedness – shortening the reproductive lives of these individuals.

If we go on to consider changes in the size of the character through time (and assume that all other relevant environmental variables remained constant between times X and Y) we can see why there was a progressive increase in the size of the character through succeeding generations.

Two specific predictions can be made about palaeontological collections:

1. In a synchronous population age at death will be positively correlated with the size of the character.

2. The mean age at death at the earlier time X will be less than the mean age at death at the later time Y.

It is important to realise that this model, by itself, does not predict that the crossing of the deleterious threshold will necessarily become less frequent in later populations. It merely predicts that as time goes on the threshold will tend to be crossed later in life. Nevertheless, if we introduce into the model additional causes of death, we can see that if the threshold is due to be crossed when individuals are older it has less chance of being crossed at all. Therefore we can make a third prediction:

3. The incidence of threshold crossing will be lower in more recent populations.

If we now narrow this discussion to our Australian study area (and remember the logical limits of the model, with the unknown effects of variables deliberately left out) we may make the following parametrical predictions which may become open to statistical examination in the future:

1. At any period in the prehistoric past, age at death will be positively correlated with tooth size.

2. The mean age at death of the Mungo population was less than the mean age at death of the Kow Swamp population.

3. The incidence of exposure of pulp cavity will be greater in the Mungo population than in the Kow Swamp population.

The variation/selection model I proposed sought originally to explain empirical data. However prediction is the reciprocal of such explanation; thus certain events *should have happened* in the prehistoric past – namely increasing size of grinding teeth. Of course the prediction is provided correctly only if the conditions of the theory have been met. Therefore if the discovery of further fossil material makes my theory unacceptable it would be interesting to investigate which of the conditions of the model has not been met. An important complicating variable is obviously material culture – fluctuating in effect through time and interfering with biological processes. To take one example – it requires little speculation to understand how the invention of the mechanical grinding of grass seeds would release great amounts of immediately swallowable energy, reduce the need for chewing and thus mitigate one of the causes of lowered adaptedness in those with exposed pulp cavities. Consider also what the invention of fishing nets would do – giving access to a greater variety and quantity of fish and thereby to yet more soft protein and calories.

My conclusion is that in the evolutionary palaeoanthropology of Australia it may not be a sophism to call small teeth primitive and large teeth advanced.

References
BARRETT, M. J., T. BROWN, G. ARATO and I. V. OZOLS   1964   Dental observation on Australian Aborigines: buccolingual crown diameters of .deciduous and permanent teeth. *Australian Dental Journal*, 9:280–85.

BRACE, C. L.   1967   *The stages of human evolution*. Prentice Hall, Englewood-Cliffs.

BOWDEN, D. E. J. and D. H. GOOSE   1969   Inheritance of tooth size in Liverpool families. *Journal of Medical Genetics*, 6:55–58.

DAHLBERG, A. A.   1963   Analysis of the American Indian dentition. In *Dental anthropology*, D. R. Brothwell (ed), pp. 149–77. Pergamon, Oxford.

DOBZHANSKY, T.   1967   On some fundamental concepts of Darwinian biology. *Evolutionary Biology*, 1:1–34.

GHISELIN, M. T.   1969   *The triumph of the Darwinian method*. University of California Press, Berkeley and Los Angeles.

GOLDSTEIN, M. S.   1948   Dentition of Indian crania from Texas. *American Journal of Physical Anthropology*, 6:63–84.

GREGORY, W. K.   1922   *The origin and evolution of the human dentition*. Williams & Wilkins, Baltimore.

HUXLEY, T. H.   1863   *Evidence as to man's place in nature*. Williams & Norgate, London and Edinburgh.

KLAATSCH, H.   1908   *The skull of the Australian Aboriginal*. New South Wales Government, Sydney.

KLATSKY, M. and R. L. FISHER   1953   *The human masticatory apparatus*. Dental Items of Interest Publishing Company, Brooklyn.

KRESHOVER, S. J. and F. J. McCLURE (eds)   1966   *Environmental variables in oral disease*. American Association for the Advancement of Science, Washington.

MACINTOSH, N. W. G. and S. L. LARNACH   1972   The persistence of *Homo erectus* traits in Australian Aboriginal crania. *Archaeology and Physical Anthropology in Oceania*, 8:1–7.

MOLNAR, S.   1972   Tooth wear and culture; a survey of tooth functions among some prehistoric populations. *Current Anthropology*, 13:511–26.

THOMA, K. H. and H. M. GOLDMAN   1960   *Oral pathology*. Mosby, St. Louis.

THORNE, A. G.   1971   Mungo and Kow Swamp; morphological variation in Pleistocene Australia. *Mankind*, 8:85–89.

—— and P. G. MACUMBER   1972   Discoveries of late Pleistocene man at Kow Swamp, Australia. *Nature*, 238:316–19.

Genetic Patterns

Genetic relationships of several aboriginal groups in South East Asia

Lie-Injo Luan Eng

THE GENETIC RELATIONSHIPS of populations in South East Asia are most complex. Until recently judgments of their ethnic affinities were mainly based on external physical characteristics and on cultural and linguistic similarities. However, external physical characteristics are greatly influenced by environment, and cultural and linguistic affinities depend more upon social contacts than upon biological similarity. Much of what has been reported is contradictory, and classification according to language has often led to confusion due to lack of agreement among observers.

Studies of blood groups have helped provide a more genetic and biological basis for analysing racial relationships, and studies of inherited biochemical traits now promise an even more exact scientific foundation for the study of population affinity and diversity.

In South East Asia, blood group studies have been carried out for more than four decades, but studies of biochemical genetic traits are relatively recent. There is some urgency to carry out such studies, especially among the numerous groups of aborigines (discussed by Dunn, 1967), because results for these groups may yield important information regarding the oldest living populations in the area, and because these groups may shrink in size, or their gene pools may become more diluted with genes from nearby populations. Except for haemoglobin abnormalities and G6PD deficiency, biochemical genetic characteristics have not been widely examined among the aboriginal populations; furthermore, available data for different groups are often lumped together, making interpretation difficult.

In Malaysia we have made special efforts therefore to carry out biochemical genetic studies in the aboriginal groups, and the following discussion will focus on Malayan aborigines in Malaysia and relate the findings to data available from nearby countries. This paper is intended not as a complete review of everything published regarding South East Asia (meaning Burma, Cambodia, Thailand, Vietnam, Malaysia, Indonesia and the Philippines), but as a consideration of those available data thought to be useful for the study of population relationships.

Relationships based on physical, linguistic, social and cultural characteristics

Ethnographic groupings of aborigines on the mainland of South East Asia were recently discussed by LeBar *et al* (1964), and those in the whole of South East Asia were summarised by Dunn (1967). More than five hundred ethnic groups of aborigines are thought to exist in South East Asia. Very few quantitative physical studies have been carried out among them and many of the ethnic classifications are based on linguistic, social and cultural characteristics. Recently, however, Kurisu (1970) statistically analysed physical measurements to try to determine the relationships of seven different aboriginal groups in Sarawak, Malaysia.

Regarding the Malay Peninsula (the area south of the Isthmus of Kra), most anthropologists agree that the Malayan aborigines can be divided into three main groups, the Negrito (Semang), Senoi (Sakai), and aboriginal Malay (Jakun) (Skeat and Blagden, 1906; Williams-Hunt, 1952). Each group is further subdivided.

The Negritos live in the northern part of the Malay Peninsula. They are thought to belong to a group also occurring in the Andaman Islands, southern Thailand, the Philippines and New Guinea. All are believed to be of the same stock (Sullivan, 1918, 1921). Although they do not have a common language, they resemble each other in physical appearance, have many similar customs and beliefs, and are the most primitive peoples in the areas where they live. The Asian Negritos are believed to be related to the African Pygmies, who are thought to be related to the Negroes.

The largest Senoi subgroups are the Temiar and Semai. The Ple, another subgroup, have mixed considerably with the Negritos in the north, as have the Temiar to a lesser extent. The affinities of the Senoi with other races are still much disputed. Cole (1945) thought them to be related to the Veddas of Ceylon and the Australian Aboriginals, while Green (1949) suggested that they were related to the Mongoloids.

The aboriginal Malays live in the southern part of the Malay Peninsula, and comprise many subgroups; the Temuan, the Jakun proper, and the Semelai are three of the largest ones. They are very similar to the Malays and are clearly related to them, both groups showing Mongoloid characteristics.

Relationships based on genetic markers in the blood

Blood group antigens   Relationships of different populations, including those from South East Asia, based on blood group findings were reviewed and discussed by Mourant (1954), Mourant *et al* (1958), and Boyd (1950). Numerous workers have reported on blood group findings in South East Asia: findings for Australia and Indonesia, including various tribal groups in Borneo, were discussed by Simmons and Graydon (1951), who were responsible for most of the work in those countries; findings for the South East Asian mainland and Indonesia were reviewed by Farinaud (1941), who carried out a considerable amount of work on the populations of mainland

South East Asia, including many tribal groups; and blood groups and relationships of aboriginal groups in the Malay Peninsula and elsewhere were discussed by Polunin and Sneath (1956). I shall not repeat these discussions on relationships based on blood group findings; however, I would like to mention several important findings, as a background for discussing population relationships based on genetic biochemical characteristics.

Blood group findings substantiate much of what has been postulated from ethnographic studies, but some of the findings throw doubt on certain assumed affinities.

In general, the South East Asian blood groups (Table 1) are characterised by a high gene frequency of B, a Mongoloid characteristic (Mourant et al, 1958), unlike the high A and absent or very low B of the Australian Aboriginals (Simmons and Graydon, 1971). Other features, also characteristic of Mongoloids, are a high frequency of R_1 (CDe), absence of A_2 and r (cde), and low N and S. This pattern also occurs among the Senoi and aboriginal Malays in the Malay Peninsula, but there are marked differences in the gene frequencies for different settlements of the same ethnic groups, which we have been able to confirm recently in the Semai (Fix and Lie-Injo, 1975). The blood group findings therefore point to a relationship of the Senoi and the aboriginal Malays to the Mongoloids. However, the gene for the Diego (Di^a) blood group, thought to be characteristic of the Mongoloids, was not found in 270 Senoi and aboriginal Malays examined by Chin (1964). In contrast, Chin found 2 of 27 Chinese to have the Diego blood group, approximately the frequency expected for Chinese. The Diego blood group was also found in Burma in 1 of 10, and Colbourne et al (1958) concluded that the Burmese are on the western fringe of the distribution of Diego antigen.

The Negritos have high R_0 and low B. Their ABO blood group findings are similar to those for the Negritos of the Andamans and the Philippines (low B, and A higher than B), supporting the idea that the Asian Negritos are related. However, further studies of the blood groups of the Onges in the Andamans by Lehmann and Ikin showed a very high A_1 frequency but no R_0 (Mourant, 1954). The very high frequency of R_0 is not found elsewhere outside Africa except in Australian Aboriginals of Bathurst Island (Sanger et al, 1951), and it was postulated by Polunin and Sneath (1956) that the Bathurst Islanders might have Negrito ancestry, especially because it is believed that Negritos were once widespread in Australia. However, the high N frequency in the Bathurst Islanders is entirely different from the low frequency of blood group N in the Negritos. In the Senoi and aboriginal Malays the R_0 frequency is low. Higher frequencies are found in Thais, Vietnamese, Malays and Javanese although they are by far not as high as those found in the Negritos.

It is interesting that Kurisu's (1970) conclusion, based on the genetic distance analysis of physical characteristics mentioned earlier, that the Land Dayak are different from other tribes in Sarawak agrees with Polunin and Sneath's (1956) conclusion, based on their ABO blood group findings, that the Dayak are of different origin than the other tribes because of their high gene frequencies of A and B.

Table 1: Frequencies of alleles of blood group systems

System	Negrito	Senoi	Aboriginal Malay	Malay (in Malaysia)	Chinese (in Malaysia)	Indians	Burmese	Thai	Vietnamese	Javanese	Filipino	Aranda	Nunggubuyu	Tiwi
ABO														
p^1	0·160	0·050	0·120	0·162	0·165	0·150	0·167	0·150	0·166	0·180	0·152	0·256	0·174	0·075
p^2	0·000	0·000	0·000	0·000	0·000	0·020	0·013			0·000		0·000	0·000	0·000
q	0·100	0·240	0·200	0·170	0·139	0·250	0·266	0·250	0·197	0·180	0·181	0·000	0·000	0·000
r	0·740	0·710	0·680	0·668	0·681	0·600	0·554	0·600	0·637	0·600	0·671	0·744	0·826	0·925
MN														
M	0·730	0·720	0·800	0·619	0·630	0·600	0·753	0·662	0·793	0·632	0·510	0·257	0·277	0·264
N	0·270	0·280	0·210	0·381	0·370	0·400	0·247	0·338	0·207	0·368	0·490	0·743	0·723	0·736
Rh														
CDE (R_z)	0·000	0·000	0·010	0·009	0·010	0·000	0·014	0·020	0·007	0·010	0·010	0·052	0·094	0·000
CDe (R_1)	0·630	0·930	0·940	0·762	0·760	0·570	0·667	0·760	0·768	0·840	0·880	0·627	0·600	0·639
cDE (R_2)	0·100	0·070	0·040	0·145	0·200	0·100	0·161	0·110	0·145	0·090	0·080	0·296	0·306	0·082
cDe (R_0)	0·270	0·010	0·010	0·080	0·040	0·040	0·000	0·110	0·080	0·070	0·030	0·025	0·000	0·279
cde (r)	0·000	0·000	0·000	0·003	0·000	0·250	0·159	0·000	0·000	0·000	0·000	0·000	0·000	0·000

NOTE: Data were obtained from the following sources: for Malayan aborigines, from Polunin and Sneath (1956); for Malays in Malaysia from Duraisamy and Amarasingham (1971) and from Lopez and Case (pers. comm.); for Indians from Prasad et al (1949) and from Wiener et al (1945) as recorded by Polunin and Sneath (1956); for Chinese in Malaysia, from Simmons and Graydon (1951); for Burmese, from Ikin et al (1969); for Thais, from Phansomboon et al (1949); for Vietnamese, ABO and Rh blood group frequencies from Fourquet (1957), MN frequencies from Nguyen Van Hung (1967a); for Javanese and Filipinos from Simmons and Graydon (1951).

An example in which blood group study throws doubt upon assumed affinities is the case of the Inthas on Inle Lake in Burma and the Tavoyan in Tavoy in southern Burma (Mya-Tu *et al*, 1968). Because of cultural and linguistic similarity, the Inthas were thought to be Tavoyans who had moved to the north. Blood group studies showed that although the ABO and MN blood groups are similar, the distribution of the Rh blood group genes is different: the Tavoyans had a high frequency of the blood group *cde* (*r*), which was not found in the Inthas (Mya-Tu *et al*, 1968). Mya-Tu *et al* therefore thought that the Inthas were not Tavoyans but a branch of the original Burmese stock that had separated before the introduction of the *cde* blood group gene from other sources. Among the many ethnic groups examined in Burma, the present day Burmese population of Mandalay and the Mons of Moulmein have a high *cde* frequency like the Tavoyans (Mya-Tu *et al*, 1971). The high frequency of *cde* in the Burmese was also reported by Ikin *et al* (1969). Mya-Tu *et al* postulated that the *cde* gene had been introduced by the Indians, because there is ample historical evidence that migrations from India into Burma occurred from early times (Hall, 1966). The affinity of the Burmese to the Indians is also shown by the presence of blood group A_2 in different population groups in Burma (Mya-Tu *et al*, 1971; Ikin *et al*, 1969).

Other blood group findings have not been as helpful in the study of affinities of the aborigines as have the ABO, MN, and Rh blood groups, and many recently discovered blood group antigens have not been studied in the aboriginal populations.

Other genetic markers in the blood   In the last two decades significant advances have been made in the study of biochemical genetics and genetic polymorphisms. However, except for abnormal haemoglobins and glucose-6-phosphate dehydrogenase (G6PD) deficiency, very few of the inherited biochemical characteristics have been studied in the aboriginal populations of South East Asia. And for most of the aboriginal groups no data is available at all.

Gene frequencies for systems that have been studied in Malayan aborigines and found to be polymorphic are listed in Table 2 (haemoglobin, hereditary ovalocytosis, and red cell enzymes) and Table 3 (serum proteins).* Many of the listed data come from earlier publications on population genetics by our group (see bibliography). However, several of the population groups that were quite small have been enlarged to make the gene frequencies obtained more meaningful. Some of the listed results were not reported earlier: those for the Temuan and Jakun groups, obtained in collaboration with Dr A. Baer and Dr Q. Welch; and those for Semai in Pahang, obtained in collaboration with Dr A. Fix. These unreported data are contained in several papers that are now in press or are being submitted for publication.

---

*Other systems, not listed in Tables 2 and 3, were examined and found not to be polymorphic.

Table 2: Frequencies of alleles of haemoglobin, hereditary ovalocytosis, and erythrocyte enzyme systems

| | | Malaysia | | | | | | | | | | | Indonesia | |
| | | Senoi | | | | Aboriginal Malay | | | | | | | | |
System	Negrito	Temiar	Semai (in Perak)	Semai (in Pahang)	Total	Temuan	Jakun	Semelai	Total	Malay (in Selangor)	Chinese	Indian	Batak (in North Sumatra)	Minangkabau
Hemoglobin														
E(βE)	0·024	0·320	0·254	0·217	0·244	0·013	0·018	0·167	0·039	0·017	0·001	0·002	0·005	0·015
A(βA)	0·976	0·680	0·746	0·783	0·756	0·987	0·982	0·833	0·961	0·983	0·999	0·998	0·995	0·985
A$_2$Ind(δInd)	0·006	0·000	0·000	0·000	0·000	0·001	0·000		0·001	0·004	0·000	0·002	0·004	0·023
A$_2$ (δA$_2$)	0·994	1·000	1·000	1·000	1·000	0·999	1·000		0·999	0·996	1·000	0·998	0·996	0·977
CoSp(αCoSp)	0·000	0·000	0·000	0·000	0·000	0·016	0·013		0·015	0·011	0·003	0·001	0·012	
A (αA)	1·000	1·000	1·000	1·000	1·000	0·984	0·987		0·985	0·989	0·997	0·999	0·988	
Hereditary ovalocytosis														
Pos	0·012	0·034	0·033	0·105	0·075	0·195	0·095		0·155	0·003	0·002	0·000	0·006	
Neg	0·988	0·966	0·967	0·895	0·925	0·805	0·905		0·845	0·997	0·998	1·000	0·994	

Glucose-6-phosphate dehydrogenase														
G6PD Normal	0·984	0·782	0·784	0·909	0·825	0·876	0·915	0·911	0·901	0·974	0·962	0·997	0·994	0·978
G6PD Deficient	0·016	0·218	0·219	0·091	0·175	0·124	0·085	0·089	0·099	0·026	0·038	0·006	0·006	0·022
6-Phosphogluconate dehydrogenase														
6PGD A	0·950	0·936	0·962	0·962	0·957	0·951	0·948		0·949	0·968	0·961	0·986	0·951	0·984
6PGD C	0·050	0·064	0·038	0·038	0·043	0·049	0·052		0·051	0·032	0·039	0·014	0·049	0·016
6PGD Elcho	0·000	0·000	0·000	0·000	0·000	0·000	0·000		0·000	0·000	0·000	0·000	0·000	0·000
Phosphoglucomutase														
PGM$_1^1$	0·779	0·627	0·779	0·508	0·605	0·899	0·780		0·884	0·808	0·761	0·682	0·761	0·769
PGM$_1^2$	0·221	0·356	0·208	0·476	0·380	0·101	0·196		0·113	0·189	0·236	0·318	0·239	0·231
PGM$_1^6$	0·000	0·000	0·000	0·000	0·000	0·000	0·000		0·000	0·000	0·003	0·000	0·000	0·000
PGM$_1^7$	0·000	0·017	0·013	0·016	0·015	0·000	0·024		0·003	0·003	0·000	0·000	0·000	0·000
Adenylate kinase														
AK^1					0·986	0·996	0·996		0·996	0·985	1·000	0·914	0·998	1·000
AK^2					0·012	0·004	0·004		0·004	0·015	0·000	0·086	0·002	0·000
AK^3					0·002	0·000	0·000		0·000	0·000	0·000	0·000	0·000	0·000
Peptidase B														
Pep B^1	0·993	0·993	0·986	0·995	1·000	0·996	0·997		1·000					
Pep B^2	0·007	0·007	0·012	0·000	0·000	0·000	0·000		0·000					
Pep B^6	0·000	0·000	0·002	0·005	0·000	0·004	0·003		0·000					

Table 2—*continued*

System	Thailand			Burma	Vietnam							Australia		
	Thai	Khmer (in Surin)	Miao	Burmese	Vietnamese	Khmer (Cambodians)	Cham	Rhade	Sedang	Stieng	Aranda	Nunggubuyu	Tiwi
Haemoglobin													
E(βE)	0·045	0·312	0·000	0·128	0·025	0·209	0·164	0·212	0·029	0·365	0·000	0·000	0·000
A(βA)	0·955	0·688	1·000	0·872	0·975	0·791	0·836	0·788	0·971	0·635	1·000	1·000	1·000
A₂Ind(δInd)													
A₂ (δA₂)													
CoSp(αCoSp)													
A (αA)													
Hereditary ovalocytosis													
Pos													
Neg													
Glucose-6-phosphate dehydrogenase													
G6PD Normal	0·843	0·833	1·000		0·986	0·847	0·909	0·977	0·996	0·946	1·000	1·000	1·000
G6PD Deficient	0·157	0·167	0·000		0·014	0·153	0·091	0·023	0·004	0·054	0·000	0·000	0·000

6-Phosphogluconate dehydrogenase										
6PGD A	0·957	0·946	0·959	0·973	0·995	0·982	1·000	0·948	0·930	0·924
6PGD C	0·043	0·054	0·041	0·027	0·005	0·018	0·000	0·052	0·029	0·071
6PGD Elcho	0·000	0·000	0·000	0·000	0·000	0·000	0·000	0·000	0·041	0·004
Phosphoglucomutase										
PGM$_1^1$	0·738							0·904	0·913	0·925
PGM$_1^2$	0·249							0·096	0·087	0·075
PGM$_1^6$	0·010							0·000	0·000	0·000
PGM$_1^7$	0·003							0·000	0·000	0·000
Adenylate kinase										
AK^1	0·995	0·997	0·989	1·000	0·986	1·000	0·991			
AK^2	0·005	0·003	0·004	0·000	0·014	0·000	0·000			
AK^3	0·000	0·000	0·007	0·000	0·000	0·000	0·009			
Peptidase B										
Pep B^1										
Pep B^2										
Pep B^6										

NOTE: All data for Malayan aborigines, Malays, Chinese, and Indians were obtained from published and unpublished material from our group (see bibliography), except that haemoglobin results for Malays, Chinese, and Indians were combined frequencies obtained from Vella (1962) and our group. The gene frequencies for Batak were combined results from McDermid *et al* (1973), Lie-Injo *et al* (1973b), and Lie-Injo *et al* (1974). Data on Thais were from northern Thailand: Hb E, from the review by Flatz (1967b); G6PD deficiency, from Flatz and Sringam (1964); 6PGD, from Tuchinda *et al* (1968); and PGM and AK, from Sanpitak *et al* (1972). The Thai variant of 6PGD was excluded because it was not found in the northern part of Thailand.

Table 3: Frequencies of alleles of serum protein systems

System	Negrito	Senoi	Aboriginal Malay	Malay (in Malaysia)	Chinese (in Malaysia)	Indian (in Malaysia)	Batak North Sumatra Indonesia	Minangkabau	Thai	Maeo	Yaeo	Burmese	Vietnamese	Aranda	Nunggubuyu	Tiwi
Haptoglobin																
Hp^1	0·050	0·257	0·391	0·230	0·285	0·090	0·290	0·216	0·260	0·210	0·190	0·190	0·309	0·232	0·302	0·404
Hp^2	0·950	0·743	0·609	0·770	0·715	0·910	0·710	0·784	0·740	0·790	0·810	0·810	0·691	0·768	0·698	0·596
Transferrin																
Tf^C	0·985	0·985	0·985	0·977	0·966	1·000	0·951	0·992	0·946	0·985	0·960	0·987		0·981	0·791	0·829
Tf^{DChi}	0·015	0·015	0·015	0·023	0·034	0·000	0·044	0·008	0·054	0·015	0·040	0·013		0·000	0·000	0·000
Tf^B	0·000	0·000	0·000	0·000	0·000	0·000	0·005	0·000	0·000	0·000	0·000	0·000		0·000	0·000	0·000
Tf^{D1}	0·000	0·000	0·000	0·000	0·000	0·000	0·000	0·000	0·000	0·000	0·000	0·000		0·019	0·209	0·171
Immunoglobulin G																
Gm 1, 3, 5, 13, 14	0·646	0·989	0·934													
Gm 1, 21	0·333	0·006	0·037													
Gm 1, 2, 21	0·021	0·000	0·029													
Gm 1, 5, 6	0·000	0·006	0·000													
Inv (1+)	0·209	0·315	0·187						0·343				0·454			
Inv (1−)	0·791	0·685	0·813						0·657				0·546			

NOTE: Data on Malayan aborigines came from published and unpublished material from our group, with the exception of the haptoglobin and transferrin data for aboriginal Malays, which were combined results from Kirk and Lai (1961) and our group. Haptoglobin and transferrin data for Malays, Chinese, and Indians were combined results from Kirk and Lai (1961) and Steinberg et al (1961); those for Batak were combined results from McDermid et al (1973) and Lie-Injo et al (1974); those for Minangkabau were from Lie-Injo et al (1974); and those for Thais were from Kirk and Lai (1961). Data on Burmese came from Than-Than-Sint and Mya-Tu (1973) and haptoglobin frequencies for Vietnamese came from Nguyen Van Hung (1967b).

Tables 2 and 3 also list available data for other racial groups in South East Asia. The intention is not to give a complete tabulation of data but to show the population groups for which suitable data are available for studying genetic relationships and genetic distance using blood genetic characteristics.

Abnormal haemoglobin and thalassaemia Hb E is characteristic and widely distributed in South East Asia. Its distribution in different racial groups has been discussed in detail by Lie-Injo (1964, 1969) and by Flatz (1967b), and tabulated by Livingstone (1967). Structural studies by Blackwell *et al* (1970, 1971, 1972) have shown that the Hb E found in different populations in South East Asia is apparently identical.

The high frequencies of Hb E in the Temiar and Semai Senoi in the Malay Peninsula equal those found in northeast Thailand. Gene frequencies for Hb E approach $0 \cdot 3$ for the Temiar in certain villages in Kelantan, Malaysia and for the Khmer in Surin, Thailand. In Thailand, although the Hb E frequency is generally high, in certain areas and among certain aboriginal groups Hb E occurs at a very low frequency or not at all. For instance, Hb E is not found in the hill tribes in northern Thailand and Laos, the Miao and Yao and the Lahu and Lissu. Flatz (1967b) noted that its distribution follows that of the Austroasiatic (Mon-Khmer) language group. The frequency is high in northeast Thailand and northern Cambodia and decreases in all directions. A cline starting high in northeast Thailand and northern Cambodia and decreasing southward into Sumatra, Indonesia is evident, with the exception of the Senoi aborigines. In the Batak of Medan, North Sumatra, Indonesia the gene frequency is only $0 \cdot 005$ (Lie-Injo *et al* 1973b), while in the Batak from the island of Samosir in North Sumatra no abnormal haemoglobins have been found (McDermid *et al*, 1973). Hb E appears to have been introduced in the Batak only recently. The cline from north to south seems to reflect a population migration in that direction.

The Negritos have a relatively low frequency of Hb E. In fact, the Negritos found to have Hb E lived in the area bordering that inhabited by the Senoi, who are known to intermarry considerably with the Negritos, and who probably introduced the Hb E in the Negritos. No Hb S was found in the Negritos, in agreement with the finding of Polunin and Sneath (1956) that none of the Negritos examined had sickle cells in their blood.

It is also interesting that the Temuan and Jakun, both belonging to the aboriginal Malay group, have relatively low frequencies of Hb E and appreciable frequencies of Hb CoSp, as is the case with the Malays. This finding is in agreement with the idea that they are more closely related to the Malays than to the Senoi. No Hb CoSp has been found so far in the Temiar and Semai Senoi.

Affinities of the people in North Sumatra to the Malays and aboriginal Malays in the Malay peninsula are shown by the occurrence of Hb CoSp and Hb A_2 Indonesia (Lie-Injo *et al*, 1971b) in appreciable frequencies in both countries, although Hb A_2 Indonesia is very rare in the Malayan aborigines (Lie-Injo, 1970), probably because it has only recently been introduced in this group. It is possible that both Hb A_2 Indonesia and Hb CoSp are widespread in South East Asia but that they have been overlooked due to the low concentration in the blood. That Hb CoSp is common in Thailand and Hong Kong can be concluded from the finding that Hb H disease in these countries is often associated with this abnormal haemoglobin (Fessas *et al*, 1972; Wasi *et al*, 1972). The frequency in the general population has, however, not been determined in South East Asia except in Malaysia and in North Sumatra, Indonesia.

The relationship among the South East Asian populations is further shown by the widespread occurrence of alpha- as well as beta-thalassaemia in South East Asia (Lie-Injo, 1969). However, thalassaemia frequencies are more difficult to assess. Frequencies of beta-thalassaemia have usually been determined from the number of persons with an increased amount of Hb A_2, but it is known that the Hb A_2 level may be influenced by different, non-genetic factors. Alpha-thalassaemia frequencies have been determined only for the newborn period, during which the presence of Hb Bart's in appreciable amounts was thought to represent alpha-thalassaemia. However, recently Lie-Injo (1972, 1973) pointed out that Hb Bart's in South East Asian newborns may not always indicate alpha-thalassaemia. In the Malayan aborigines beta-thalassaemia is rare and may have been introduced by intermarriage with Chinese (Bolton and Lie-Injo, 1969).

Hereditary ovalocytosis (elliptocytosis)   Although the aboriginal Malays are more like the Malays with respect to abnormal haemoglobin frequencies, they are more like the Senoi than the Malays with respect to gene frequencies for hereditary ovalocytosis (elliptocytosis). The Temuan and Jakun aboriginal Malays have very high frequencies of hereditary ovalocytosis (Baer *et al*, 1976), as have the Senoi (Lie-Injo *et al*, 1972a), while the frequency in Malays is very low. It is interesting that the frequency in aboriginal Malays is much higher than that in Senoi, and that the Semai Senoi in Pahang, which is geographically nearer to the aboriginal Malays in the south, have a higher frequency of hereditary ovalocytosis than the Semai Senoi in Perak, which is farther away. The high frequency of hereditary ovalocytosis in the aboriginal Malay group equals that found in central Sulawesi (Celebes), Indonesia, where Bonne and Sandground (1939) reported that slightly less than half of the Toradja living around Lake Lindu had ovalocytosis.

Erythrocyte enzymes   Twelve different enzymes were studied.

1. Glucose-6-phosphate dehydrogenase (G6PD) deficiency: The South East Asian distribution of G6PD deficiency, which more or less follows that of Hb E, has been reviewed and discussed in detail by Lie-Injo (1969). The frequency of G6PD deficiency is high in Thailand and among the Malayan aborigines, especially the Senoi. A high frequency of 24·2 per cent was also found among the Muruts in Sabah. In the aboriginal Malays the frequency is lower than in the Senoi but much higher than in the Malays. In North

Sumatra the frequency is low. As with Hb E, in certain aboriginal groups G6PD deficiency occurs at very low frequencies or is absent. This is true of the Lahu and Lissu and the Miao in northern Thailand, and of the Negritos in Malaysia, indicating that G6PD deficiency as well as Hb E either has not been introduced or has been introduced fairly recently in these groups. There are different types of G6PD deficiency in South East Asia (Kirkman and Lie-Injo, 1969; Panich and Sungate, 1973). There are suggestions that Hb E, hereditary ovalocytosis, and G6PD deficiency may be subject to selective forces of the balanced type. The possible role of malaria in the distribution of Hb E and G6PD deficiency in South East Asia was discussed by Lie-Injo (1969).

2. *6-phosphogluconate dehydrogenase (6PGD):* The common 6PGD alleles are PGD^A and PGD^C. The Chinese and Malays in Malaysia resemble Europeans in their PGD^C gene frequencies, that is, around 0·03. The Malayan aborigines generally have higher frequencies, resembling those found in Thais (Tuchinda *et al*, 1968; Giblett and Scott, quoted in Giblett, 1969), Batak (McDermid *et al*, 1973), and Vietnamese and Khmer (Bowman *et al*, 1971). Low frequencies found in Minangkabau (Lie-Injo *et al*, 1974), and in Malayo-Polynesians and Mon-Khmer (Bowman *et al*, 1971) resemble the low frequencies found in Indians (Ananthakrishnan and Kirk, 1969; Das *et al*, 1970b; Blake *et al*, 1970a). Perhaps these low frequencies are evidence for affinities of these different ethnic groups to the Indians. An unusual variant of 6PGD found in Thailand, and designated 6PGD Thai (Tuchinda *et al*, 1968), has also been found in Malaysia (Lie-Injo and Welch, 1972); it may have been introduced from the north into the Malay Peninsula. 6PGD Elcho, which is found in appreciable frequencies on Elcho Island in Australia (Blake and Kirk, 1969), has not yet been found in South East Asia.

3. *Phosphoglucomutase (PGM):* Two loci for PGM are known, PGM_1 and PGM_2. Variants for the PGM_2 locus are rare, while the PGM_1 locus shows polymorphism. Only variants of locus 1 have so far been found in South East Asia. The frequencies of $PGM_1{}^1$ reported for different population groups in South East Asia generally do not differ much. However, in Malayan aborigines the frequencies of $PGM_1{}^1$ vary considerably, ranging from 0·508 to 0·899. The low frequency of 0·508 in the Semai in Pahang is very low compared to those for all populations that have been examined, and resembles the 0·51 found in Norwegian Lapps (Monn, 1969) and the 0·43 found in Habbanite Jews (Mourant and Tills, 1967). The affinity between the Thais and the Chinese is shown by the presence of $PGM_1{}^6$ in both populations, while $PGM_1{}^7$ is found in the Malayan aborigines, the Malays, and the Thais.

4. *Adenylate kinase (AK):* The usual allele determining the AK type in all populations examined is AK^1. The AK^2 gene is found in relatively high frequencies in Caucasians and Indians but it is either present at low frequencies or absent in the people of South East Asia who have been

examined. Populations in North Sumatra have low frequencies or absence of AK^2 (McDermid *et al*, 1973; Lie-Injo *et al*, 1974). AK^2 has also not been found in the Mon-Khmer in Vietnam (Bowman *et al*, 1971). The very low frequencies of AK^2 resemble those found in Mongoloids, in contrast to the high frequencies found in Indians and Caucasians, suggesting very little Caucasian or Indian admixture. In the Malays and Malayan aborigines the frequency is somewhat higher than that found in most of the other populations examined in South East Asia (Welch *et al*, 1971; Chan, 1971). It would be interesting to examine the Burmese, the Mons, and the Tavoyans in Burma, and several other aboriginal population groups, who show Indian influence in their *cde* blood group frequency (Ikin *et al*, 1969; Mya-Tu *et al*, 1971). The Malayan aborigines and other populations examined in Malaysia and North Sumatra do not have the AK^3 gene but Bowman *et al* (1971) found it in the Khmer (Cambodians) and Mon-Khmer (Stieng) in Vietnam.

5. *Acid phosphatase:* Only the alleles p^a and p^b are present in the Batak from Samosir, North Sumatra (McDermid *et al*, 1973), as is also the case in most populations in South East Asia (Lai and Kwa, 1968; Chan, 1972) the Oceania (Lai and Kariks, 1968; Sinnett *et al*, 1970; Kirk *et al*, 1973). The frequency of p^b in the Batak resembles that in Chinese in Singapore and is slightly lower than that in Malays (Blake *et al*, 1973). Acid phosphatase has not been examined in other aboriginal groups.

Only a few populations in South East Asia have been studied for enzymes other than those mentioned above. Either these other enzyme systems did not show variation or variants were rare. Their significance in the study of population affinities is not yet clear.

6. *Lactate dehydrogenase (LDH):* Variants are usually very rare. However, Indians in India (Das *et al*, 1970a), in Singapore (Blake *et al*, 1973), and in Malaysia (Lie-Injo *et al*, 1973c) have appreciable frequencies of LDH Calcutta and LDH Madras. In Malays and Chinese other LDH variants are found at low frequencies. No LDH variation was found among the Malayan aborigines in Malaysia and the Batak in North Sumatra. The LDH system also does not show variation in Australian Aboriginals of the Northern Territory in Australia (Kirk *et al*, 1969). Possibly, the LDH variants have only recently been introduced and have not penetrated into the gene pools of the Malayan aborigines, the Batak, or the Australian Aboriginals. Other aboriginal groups in South East Asia have not been studied for LDH variants. The LDH system is not listed in Table 1 because there is still some uncertainty regarding the identity of variants found in Malays and Chinese in Malaysia compared to those found in Singapore (McDermid *et al*, 1973; Lie-Injo *et al*, 1973c).

7. *Phosphohexose isomerase (PHI), catalase, and carbonic anhydrase (Ca):* These systems also have not shown any variation in the Malayan aborigines in Malaysia and the Batak in North Sumatra. In Malays (Lie-Injo *et al*, 1971a),

Filipinos (Lie-Injo, 1967), Indonesians (Lie-Injo and Poey-Oey, 1970), and the Chamorros from the Mariana Islands in Micronesia (Tashian et al, 1963) Ca_{1c} was found in appreciable frequencies, indicating that these populations are related.

8. Soluble malate dehydrogenase (S-MDH): A slow variant was found in a mother and her daughter among 56 Temuan aborigines examined (Baer et al, 1976). The other aboriginal groups have not been examined for S-MDH yet.

9. Adenosine deaminase (ADA): Was examined in Batak and showed a gene frequency of 0·088 for ADA^2 (McDermid et al, 1973), which is comparable to frequencies found in northern Thailand (Sanpitak et al, 1972) and in Oceania (Omoto, 1972a), while the ADA^2 frequency is slightly higher in Filipinos (Detter et al, 1970) and in Malays in Malaysia (Welch et al, 1975). The rest was ADA^1. Study of ADA in the Malayan aborigines has not yet been completed.

10. Peptidase B (Pep B): Has been examined in the Malayan aborigines, and Pep B 2–1 and Pep B 6–1 were found at low frequencies (Welch, 1973). Pep B 6–1 was earlier reported by Blake et al (1970b) in Australian Aboriginals. If the Pep B 6 variant in the Malayan aborigines is really identical to that found in the Australians, this may be evidence for a relationship between the two populations. No variant was found in the Batak from Samosir, North Sumatra (McDermid et al, 1973). Pep B has not been examined in other aboriginal groups in South East Asia.

11. Phosphoglycerate kinase (PGK): Was examined in the Batak of Samosir, North Sumatra (McDermid et al, 1973) and did not show any variation. This was also the case in Chinese, Malays, and Indians in Singapore (Blake et al, 1973) and in Chinese in Taiwan (Chen and Giblett, 1972). In contrast, the frequency of variants is relatively high in Micronesians and New Guineans in certain areas (Omoto and Blake, 1972).

12. Diaphorase: Was examined in Malays, Chinese, and Indians in Malaysia (Lie-Injo et al, 1972b), and in Chinese and Malays in Singapore (Blake et al, 1973). Variants were rare. It has not been examined in the aboriginal groups.

Serum proteins   A total of six types of serum protein was studied.

1. Haptoglobin (Hp): The Hp^1 and Hp^2 alleles are found in all population groups. The world distribution of haptoglobin genes has been discussed by Barnicot (1961), Kirk and Lai (1961), and Kirk (1968a). The frequency of Hp^1 is generally high in American Indians and Africans. In Europe the Hp^1 gene frequency ranges from 0·34 to 0·46. It is rather low in Asiatics. The haptoglobin gene frequencies in the Malayan aborigines show an interesting pattern. In the Semai Senoi, the gene frequency of Hp^1 is within the range 0·23 to 0·29 generally found in South East Asia, as seen in Thais, Chinese,

Malays, Indonesians in Java, and Batak in North Sumatra. The Vietnamese have a somewhat higher frequency of $0 \cdot 32$ (Nguyen Van Hung, 1967b). In 224 Temuan of the Aboriginal Malay group examined by Baer *et al* 1976 and Hp^1 gene frequency of $0 \cdot 37$ resembles that in Europeans. However, a large percentage (21 per cent) of the persons examined had ahapto-globinaemia, a condition probably at least partly due to malaria, which is endemic in the area examined by Baer *et al*. This finding agrees with the high frequency reported by Kirk and Lai (1961) in 66 Proto-Malays examined in Malaysia. The Hp^1 gene frequency for the aboriginal Malays is higher than that for the other populations in Malaysia and nearby areas, and Kirk (1968a) postulated that it is part of a cline of steadily increasing Hp^1 values as one moves from the Asiatic mainland through the islands of Indonesia to Micronesia and Polynesia. In the Negritos, the Hp^1 gene frequency of $0 \cdot 05$ is the lowest so far reported in any population, even lower than the low frequencies seen in Tamils ($0 \cdot 09$) and Irulas ($0 \cdot 07$) from India (Kirk and Lai, 1961). This low Hp^1 gene frequency in the Negritos is quite different from the high frequencies of Hp^1 seen in populations in Africa, and it is especially noteworthy that in the Pygmies, who aré thought to be related to the Negritos, the Hp^1 gene frequency is as high as $0 \cdot 40$ (Giblett *et al*, 1966). The unusually low Hp^1 gene frequency in the Negritos may be due to the Negritos having a different origin or to genetic drift. Examples of significant differences between the haptoglobin gene frequencies in small inbred communities and the surrounding populations have been mentioned by Kirk and Lai (1961).

2. Transferrin (Tf): The world distribution of transferrin genes has been discussed by Kirk and Lai (1961), Kirk *et al* (1964), and Kirk (1968b). Transferrin C is common to all populations. The most common variants are the slow-moving D_1 and D_{CHI}. The D_1 variant is found in Africans and in Australian Aboriginals, whereas the D_{CHI} variant is found throughout South East Asia and is considered a Mongoloid characteristic. The gene frequency for Tf D_{CHI} in Malayan aborigines ($0 \cdot 015$ in all main groups) is low compared to the frequencies found in most other populations in South East Asia; it is similar to those in the Miao (Kirk and Lai, 1961), the Burmese (Than-Than-Sint and Mya-Tu, 1973), and the Minangkabau (Lie-Injo *et al*, 1974). The fast moving Tf B variants, usually found in Europe at low frequencies, are very rare in inhabitants of Africa and of the Pacific area. The Batak from North Sumatra are exceptional in having the gene for Tf B: Tf B was found both in the Batak from Samosir examined by McDermid *et al* (1973) and in the Batak from Medan examined by Lie-Injo *et al* (1974). Other exceptional populations in Asia and the Pacific area having the Tf B gene are the Pathans in West Pakistan (Kirk and Lai, 1961) and several isolated groups in Australia (Kirk, 1965).

3. Immunoglobulin G (Gm and Inv antigens): Gm and Inv allotypic markers have been found the most useful for population affinity studies. However, very little work on immunoglobulin types has been carried out in South

East Asia. Some data were reported for Thai people tested only for Gm (1) and Gm (2) and Inv (1) (Phansomboon and Singhprasert, 1970); for Vietnamese examined for Gm(1), Gm(2), Gm(5), and Inv (1) (Nguyen Van Hung, 1968); and for Indians and Chinese in Malaysia (Steinberg et al, 1961). The Malayan aborigines have been tested for Gm(1), Gm(2), Gm(3), Gm(5), Gm(6), Gm(13), Gm(14), Gm(21), and Inv (1), and those positive for Gm(6) have also been tested for Gm(24). The Gm phenogroup of the Semai is almost entirely Gm^{1,3,5,13,14}; a very low frequency of Gm^{1,5,6} may possibly be due to African admixture and a very low frequency of Gm^{1,21} may be due to Negrito admixture. If the assumption that the presence of Gm^{1,21} and Gm^{1,5,6} is due to admixture with other populations is correct, the Semai are unique in having only Gm^{1,3,5,13,14}. The aboriginal Malays also have a very high frequency of Gm^{1,3,5,13,14} with some Gm^{1,21} and Gm^{1,2,21}. The Negritos have a very high frequency of Gm^{1,21}, which is not found in Africa, in marked contrast to the African Pygmies to whom they are thought to be related. The Inv(1) frequencies of the aboriginal Malays and the Negritos do not differ much but the Inv (1) frequency of the Semai group is significantly higher and is similar to that of the Thais (Phansomboon and Singhprasert, 1970). A higher frequency was also found in the Vietnamese (Nguyen Van Hung, 1968).

4. Group specific component (Gc): The common Gc alleles are *Gc*^{1} and *Gc*^{2}, and the gene frequency for *Gc*^{1} is usually higher than that for *Gc*^{2}. Other variants are rare. The distribution of the group specific component in selected populations in South and South East Asia, including Malaysia and Thailand, and in Oceania was discussed by Kirk *et al* (1963). Further studies were carried out in Thailand by Tuchinda *et al* (1968), who described an unusual variant designated Gc Bangkok in a Thai family. Gc Aborigine (Gc Ab) which is found in Australia and New Guinea and other parts of Melanesia (Kirk, 1965), is not found in South East Asia. Group specific components have not been examined in Malayan aboriginal groups.

5. Serum albumin: The number of known serum albumin variants is rapidly increasing. When we reviewed the serum albumin system in 1971 (Lie-Injo *et al*, 1971c), at least five rapidly-migrating and ten slowly-migrating albumin variants were known, and more have since been described. At least four of the variants displayed polymorphic frequencies in certain populations. Very little work on serum albumin has been carried out in South East Asia, but recently our group described four different variants in various populations in Malaysia and Indonesia (Lie-Injo *et al*, 1971c; Welch and Lie-Injo, 1972): albumin Gombak was found at low frequencies in Malaysia in Malayan aborigines, Malays, and Indians; albumin Medan was found in Medan, Indonesia in Batak and Minangkabau, and in Malaysia in Malays; albumin Sentul was found in Malaysia in Indians; and albumin Kuala Lumpur was found in Malaysia in Chinese. A slow-moving albumin variant described in Indians by McDermid (1971) may be the same as albumin Gombak. Four of 488 persons examined in North

Sumatra were found to have a serum albumin variant (Lie-Injo *et al*, 1974). Probably serum albumin variants are not very rare in South East Asia, and further studies may show definite distribution patterns among different populations in the area.

6. *Other serum proteins:* Other serum proteins examined on a very limited scale are the enzymes pseudocholinesterase, protease inhibitor, and ceruloplasmin. The pseudocholinesterase (E) system was examined in Thais and the $E_1{}^a$ variant was found to be absent (Altland *et al*, 1967); in Filipinos $E_1{}^a$ was found at a low frequency of $0 \cdot 002$ (Morrow and Motulsky, 1965). The Australian Aboriginals also have low frequencies (Horsfall, 1963, quoted in Kirk, 1965). In contrast, Indians (Motulsky and Morrow, 1968) and Europeans (reviewed by Giblett, 1969) have higher frequencies. Pseudocholinesterase has not been examined in aboriginal populations in South East Asia. Protease inhibitor (Pi) has been studied in South East Asia among the Batak in Samosir, North Sumatra (McDermid, 1971). The common Pi allele, *Pi*m, was present at a frequency of $0 \cdot 973$, and the atypical allele, *Pi*s, at a frequency of $0 \cdot 027$. In a study among Malays (Lie-Injo and Ganesan in progress), we found the atypical variant at a frequency of $0 \cdot 015$. (We also found another slow-moving, still unidentified variant.) These figures are higher than those for New Guineans and Australian Aboriginals (quoted by McDermid *et al*, 1973). Ceruloplasmin phenotypes were also examined in the Batak of Samosir and several unidentified variants were encountered (McDermid *et al*, 1973).

Relationships based on other polymorphisms

Earwax types: Human cerumen type may be categorised as wet or dry; the allele for the wet type is dominant. The world distribution of the dry type was reviewed by Petrakis *et al* (1971): the dry allele is prevalent among Mongoloid populations of Asia and among American Indians; the wet type is prevalent among Europeans, American Caucasians, Negroes, and natives of New Guinea. Petrakis *et al* found the gene frequency of the dry type in the Malayan aboriginals of different groups to be $0 \cdot 261$, and Baer *et al* (1976) found a frequency in the Temuan group of $0 \cdot 339$. Petrakis *et al* obtained data on cerumen types in the Middle East and South East Asia and found frequencies for the dry type that were intermediate between the high values in the northern Orient and the low values in Caucasians and Negroes. They noticed that there was a cline in earwax types such that high frequencies in Mongolian Asia decrease as one moves into the Middle East, South East Asia, and Europe. They postulated that this cline reflects an introduction of the dry allele into indigenous populations during migrations from central and eastern Asia to the south and west.

Taste sensitivity: Taste sensitivity is usually tested using phenylthiocarbamide (PTC) or phenylthiourea (PTU), and the allele for being a taster is dominant to that for being a nontaster. Considerable differences in percentages of tasters and nontasters in different parts of the world have been reported. In general, the Negroid and Mongoloid populations have low frequencies of nontasters, less than 15 per cent, and Caucasian populations have frequencies of approximately 30 per cent. Persons who are extremely sensitive to PTC have been reported among Ainu, Japanese, Koreans, and Australian Aboriginals (Lugg, 1966, 1968), and a third allele, for extreme sensitivity to PTC, has been proposed by Richkov and Bordina (1969, quoted by Boobphanirojana et al, 1970) based on the finding of extreme sensitivity to PTC in a Siberian population. In South East Asia such extremely sensitive persons have not been described. Lugg (1957) examined the taste sensitivity of Kintak Bong Negritos and Semai populations in Malaysia and found that 18 per cent of the Negritos and 4 per cent of the Semai were nontasters. He concluded that the Negritos differed significantly from the Africans to whom they were thought to be related, and that the low frequency of the Semai resembled that of the Chinese. Baer et al (1976) found 21 per cent of Temuan to be nontasters. This percentage is much higher than that for the Semai, and is also higher than that for the Malays (Thambipillai, 1955; Lugg and White, 1955) and the Thai (Boobphanirojana et al, 1970); it resembles that found in the Negritos.

Colour blindness: X-linked red-green blindness is a collective term for different types of colour blindness. However, the majority of reports give only overall frequencies for red-green blindness. In northern Thailand, Flatz (1967a) found a 5·2 per cent frequency of colour blindness among Thais and a significantly lower frequency of 2·2 per cent among a small number of Miao tribesmen. He viewed this finding as support for the selection-relaxation theory proposed by Post (1962). Post believed that the incidence of red-green colour blindness was very low among hunter-gatherer populations, and higher among agricultural peoples due to a relaxation of selection among the agriculturists. Baer et al (1976) found a frequency of 8·1 per cent in Temuan, which is higher than that found in Thais. Adam et al (1969), who found an overall frequency of red-green blindness of 5·6 per cent in Thais and 5·7 per cent in Chinese, drew attention to the problems of carrying out such studies accurately.

Dermatoglyphics: Very few dermatoglyphic studies have been carried out in aboriginal groups in South East Asia. In the Malayan aboriginals some work was carried out by Hughes (1963, 1964) on the fingertip prints from Temiar Senoi and Kensiu Negritos. Recently dermatoglyphic studies of complete handprints were carried out by Q. B. Welch in more than 400 Malayan aboriginals of different groups. The results are still being analysed. Part of the work was reported in the 1971 Annual Report of the University of California International Center for Medical Research, San Francisco, California. Preliminary results show that Malayan aborigines in general are entirely different from Caucasians, and that the Semai and Temuan groups are very similar to each other.

Genetic distance analysis

Genetic relationships can be evaluated using separate genetic systems. However, as the preceding discussions show, quite contradictory results may be obtained with different systems. Relationships can also be determined using the combined information obtained from the concurrent study of a number of systems, and an index of genetic distance so derived will naturally be of greater value. A number of methods of calculating the genetic distance have recently been developed. Using the method of Cavalli-Sforza and Edwards (1967), the genetic distances for the main groups of Malayan aboriginals and adjacent populations, as well as for several Australian Aboriginal populations were examined.

In one attempt, frequencies of alleles for the ABO, MN, and Rh blood groups were used (Table 4). These three blood group systems were chosen because they appear to be the most useful for studying population affinities, and are the ones most studied in different populations. In another attempt, the Hb, G6PD, 6PGD, PGM, Hp, and Tf systems were employed (Table 5). For purposes of comparison, one should in fact select the same population groups for each attempt. However, this would considerably reduce the number of populations available for analysis because, for example, for the Burmese sufficient data are available on blood groups but not on biochemical genetic markers. Conversely, for the Batak data for many biochemical genetic traits are available but data on blood groups are incomplete. Therefore, available data were utilised as much as possible. Choosing groups of Australian Aboriginals was complicated by the fact that gene frequencies of different markers differ considerably in different areas in Australia. After consultation with Dr R. L. Kirk, the Nunggubuyu were chosen as representative of northern Australia, and the Aranda as representative of central Australia. I also included the Tiwi as representative of Aboriginals from Bathurst Island, because there are speculations that inhabitants of that island are of Negrito ancestry. The data for these three Aboriginal groups were kindly provided by Dr Kirk.

The distance matrices in Tables 4 and 5 showed Negritos to be close to Malays, Thais, Batak, and Chinese. However, a large discrepancy appeared: blood group analysis (Table 4) showed Negritos and Indians to be far apart, whereas enzyme and serum protein analysis (Table 5) showed them to be very close. Results from Table 4 were compatible with those from Table 5 for both the Senoi and the aboriginal Malays. In general, the Malayan aboriginals showed affinities to all other South East Asian populations studied, including the Chinese; the Indians and Burmese stood apart.

All three Australian Aboriginal groups were clearly separated from the South East Asian populations according to distance analysis of blood groups and of enzymes and serum proteins. Apart from the distances among themselves, they showed the smallest distance from the Chinese (except the Tiwi, who were closest to the Negritos on the basis of blood groups). The distance of the Australian Aboriginals from the Indians was definitely greater than that from the Chinese, but that does not mean that they are closely related

Table 4: Matrix of genetic distances (Cavalli-Sforza) based on blood groups

	Negrito	Senoi	Aboriginal Malay	Malay	Chinese	Indian	Burmese	Thai	Javanese	Filipinos	Aranda	Nunggubuyu
Senoi	0·3295											
Aboriginal Malay	0·3226	0·1244										
Malay	0·2060	0·2183	0·2202									
Chinese	0·2504	0·2243	0·2262	0·0907								
Indian	0·4073	0·3854	0·4007	0·3099	0·3587							
Burmese	0·4581	0·3375	0·3267	0·3163	0·3271	0·1947						
Thai	0·2096	0·2217	0·2112	0·0960	0·1497	0·3533	0·3499					
Javanese	0·2242	0·1941	0·1724	0·0789	0·3526	0·3526	0·3414	0·0874				
Filipino	0·2971	0·1968	0·2058	0·1310	0·1479	0·3612	0·3546	0·1625	0·0988			
Aranda	0·4864	0·5361	0·5347	0·3983	0·3686	0·5544	0·5633	0·4651	0·4225	0·3879		
Nunggubuyu	0·5477	0·5365	0·5374	0·4360	0·3951	0·5804	0·5575	0·5011	0·4565	0·4123	0·1306	
Tiwi	0·3807	0·5274	0·5529	0·4162	0·4378	0·5597	0·6571	0·4635	0·4364	0·4195	0·3597	0·4357

Table 5: Matrix of genetic distances (Cavalli-Sforza) based on haemoglobin, erythrocyte enzyme, and serum protein systems

	Negrito	Senoi	Aboriginal Malay	Malay	Chinese	Indian	Batak	Thai	Aranda	Nunggubuyu
Senoi	0·3829									
Aboriginal Malay	0·3262	0·3139								
Malay	0·1848	0·3334	0·1742							
Chinese	0·2405	0·3689	0·1966	0·1014						
Indian	0·1588	0·4287	0·3627	0·2101	0·2344					
Batak	0·2401	0·3983	0·2308	0·1167	0·1017	0·2382				
Thai	0·2874	0·2374	0·1839	0·1924	0·1879	0·3402	0·2495			
Aranda	0·2707	0·5007	0·2908	0·2102	0·2374	0·2512	0·2171	0·3719		
Nunggubuyu	0·4412	0·5952	0·4191	0·3814	0·3920	0·4205	0·3814	0·4881	0·2571	
Tiwi	0·4481	0·5823	0·3756	0·3628	0·3685	0·4319	0·3514	0·4699	0·2251	0·1288

to the Chinese. In fact, blood group distribution differs greatly, the Mongoloid groups in South East Asia having relatively high B and M frequencies, the Australian Aboriginals having practically no B and high N instead of M. Nevertheless, genetic distance analysis did give evidence that they are relatively closer to the Mongoloids of South East Asia than to the Indians. External visible characteristics point toward just the opposite relationship: in their physical appearance, the Australian Aboriginals resemble not the Mongoloids, but the Indians, who have Caucasoid characteristics and have been classified as one of the Caucasoid races (Cole, 1965), with which the Australian Aboriginals are thought to share a common ancestry. Omoto (1972b) suggested that the evolution of the 'visible' characters is different from that of the 'invisible' characters. It may also be that the change in blood genetic characteristics, under the influence of genetic drift, took place after the physical characteristics were well established.

Blood group distance analysis showed that, apart from their distances toward the other Australian groups, the Tiwi from Bathurst Island are closest to the Negritos. However, enzyme and serum protein distance analysis did not yield the same result.

Since both Hb E and G6PD deficiency may be subject to selective forces of the balanced type due to malaria, they may be unsuitable for genetic distance analysis. However, Fix and Lie-Injo (1975) found that genetic distance analysis by the procedure of Cavalli-Sforza and Edwards (1967) of eight different villages of a Semai population in Pahang, Peninsular Malaysia, using Hb E, hereditary ovalocytosis, and ABO blood group systems, showed a fair agreement with results on degrees of closeness of migrational ties between the villages derived from parent-offspring birthplace analysis. That agreement is probably due to the fact that these genetic markers, if they were selected for by malaria, were all subject to more or less the same degree of selection because they are located fairly close together. This may not be true of populations that are geographically widely separated. In any case, to eliminate possible erroneous results due to their inclusion in the distance analysis, we have in a third attempt (Table 6) carried out distance analysis based on gene frequencies of alleles of blood groups and of enzyme and serum protein systems combined, but have omitted the Hb and G6PD systems. Results showed that the Malays, Thais, and Chinese were very close together, as expected. The Negritos were closest to the Malays, closer in fact than to the Senoi and aboriginal Malays. The Senoi and aboriginal Malays were close to each other and to the Malays, Chinese, and Thais. The Indians stood apart. The three Australian Aboriginal groups clearly formed a separate group, but apart from the distances among themselves they were generally closest to the Chinese and Malays. Of the three Australian Aboriginal groups, the Aranda were closest to the Mongoloid populations of South East Asia. The results of distance analysis with or without the Hb and G6PD systems were broadly similar, but omitting Hb and G6PD did bring the Senoi more in line with the other South East Asian populations and made their difference from the Indians more obvious.

Table 6: Matrix of genetic distances (Cavalli-Sforza) based on blood groups, erythrocyte enzyme, and serum protein systems combined

	Negrito	Senoi	Aboriginal Malay	Malay	Chinese	Indian	Thai	Aranda	Nunggubuyu
Senoi	0·4069								
Aboriginal Malay	0·4411	0·2615							
Malay	0·2754	0·2645	0·2585						
Chinese	0·3352	0·2656	0·2689	0·1186					
Indian	0·4290	0·4323	0·5041	0·3640	0·4189				
Thai	0·3057	0·2615	0·2743	0·1384	0·1622	0·4232			
Aranda	0·5418	0·5983	0·5598	0·4305	0·4199	0·6070	0·5194		
Nunggubuyu	0·6916	0·6797	0·6383	0·5639	0·5421	0·7153	0·6360	0·2884	
Tiwi	0·5740	0·6612	0·6242	0·5360	0·5581	0·7056	0·5923	0·4243	0·4543

Acknowledgments   The author would like to thank Drs A. Baer, Q. B. Welch, A. Fix and J. Ganesan for permission to quote unpublished data; and Dr Mary Claire King and Ms. Vicki Tamaradze for computing the genetic distances for this study; and the University of California, San Francisco Computer Center for machine time.

This work was supported by the University of California International Center for Medical Research (UC ICMR) through research grant AI-10051 and by research grant HL-10486, both from the National Institutes of Health, U.S. Public Health Service.

References

ADAM, A., M. PUENPATOM, V. DAVIVONGS and S. WANGSPA   1969   Anomaloscopic diagnoses of red-green blindness among Thais and Chinese. *Human Heredity*, 19:509.

ALTLAND, K., F. EPPLE and H. W. GOEDDE   1967   Pseudocholinesterase-variants in Thailand and Japan. *Humangenetik*, 4:127.

ANANTHAKRISHNAN, R. and R. L. KIRK   1969   The distribution of some serum protein and enzyme group systems in two endogamous groups in S. India. *Indian Journal of Medical Research*, 57:1011.

BAER, A., L. E. LIE-INJO, Q. B. WELCH and A. N. LEWIS   1976   Genetic factors and malaria in the Temuan. *American Journal of Human Genetics*, 28:179–188.

BARNICOT, N. A.   1961   *Haptoglobin and Transferrins. Genetical Variation in Human Population.* Pergamon Press, Oxford and London.

BLACKWELL, R. Q., H. J. YANG, C. S. LIU and C. C. WANG   1970   Structural identification of haemoglobin E in Filipinos. *Tropical and Geographical Medicine*, 22:112.

——, L. E. LIE–INJO and M. I. WENG   1971   Structural identification of a haemoglobin E in Malayan ethnic groups. *Tropical and Geographical Medicine*, 23:294.

——, K. ARNOLD, A. SCHIPUL and M. I. WENG   1972   Structural identification of haemoglobin E in Montagnards of Vietnam, Vietnamese, and Cambodians. *Tropical and Geographical Medicine*, 24:73.

BLAKE, N. M. and R. L. KIRK   1969   New genetic variant of 6-phosphogluconate dehydrogenase in Australian Aborigines. *Nature*, 221:278.

——, R. L. KIRK and A. J. BAXI   1970a   The distribution of some enzyme group systems among Marathis and Gujaratis in Bombay. *Human Heredity*, 20:409.

——, R. L. KIRK, W. H. P. LEWIS and H. HARRIS   1970b   Some further peptidase B phenotypes. *Annals of Human Genetics*, 33:301.

——, E. M. McDERMID, R. L. KIRK, Y. W. ONG and M. J. SIMONS   1973   The distribution of red cell enzyme groups among Chinese and Malays in Singapore. *Singapore Medical Journal*, 14:2.

BOLTON, J. M. and L. E. LIE-INJO   1969   Hb E-beta thalassemia in the West Malaysian Orang Asli (Aborigines). *Medical Journal of Malaya*, 24:36.

BONNE, C. and J. H. SANDGROUND   1939   Echinostomiasis in Celebes veroorzaakt door het eten van zoetwatermosselen. *Geneeskundig tijdschrift voor Nederlandsch-Indie*, 79:2116.

BOOBPHANIROJANA, P., M. CHETANASILPIN, C. SAENGUDOM and G. FLATZ   1970   Phenylthiocarbamide taste thresholds in the population of Thailand. *Humangenetik*, 10:329.

BOWMAN, J. E., P. E. CARSON, H. FRISCHER, R. D. POWELL, E. J. COLWELL, L. J. LEGTERS, A. J. COTTINGHAM, S. C. BOONE, and W. W. HISER   1971   Hemoglobin and red cell enzyme variation in some populations of the Republic of Vietnam with comments on the malaria hypothesis. *American Journal of Physical Anthropology*, 34:313.

BOYD, W. C.   1950   *Genetics and the races of man; an introduction to modern physical anthropology.* Little, Brown, Boston.

CAVALLI-SFORZA, L. L. and A. W. F. EDWARDS   1967   Phylogenetic analysis models and estimation procedures. *American Journal of Human Genetics*, 19:233.
CHAN, K. L.   1971   Human red cell adenylate kinase polymorphism in West Malaysian populations. *Human Heredity*, 21:173.
——   1972   Human red cell acid phosphatase polymorphism in Malays, Chinese and Indians of West Malaysia. *Malaysian Journal of Science*, 1A:13.
CHEN, S. H. and E. R. GIBLETT   1972   Phosphoglycerate kinase: additional variants and their geographical distribution. *American Journal of Human Genetics*, 24:229.
CHIN, J.   1964   Absence of Di^{a+} in Malayan Aborigines. *Nature*, 201:1039.
COLBOURNE, M. J., E. W. IKIN, A. E. MOURANT, H. LEHMANN and H. THEIN   1958   Haemoglobin E and Diego blood group antigen in Sarawak and Burma. *Nature*, 181:119.
COLE, F. C.   1945   *The peoples of Malaysia*. Van Nostrand, New York.
COLE, S.   1965   *Races of man*. British Museum (Natural History), London.
DAS, S. R., B. N. MUKHERJEE, S. K. DAS, R. ANANTHAKRISHNAN, N. M. BLAKE and R. L. KIRK   1970a   LDH variants in India. *Humangenetik*, 9:107.
——, B. N. MUKHERJEE, S. K. DAS, N. M. BLAKE and R. L. KIRK   1970b   The distribution of some enzyme group systems among Bengalis. *Indian Journal of Medical Research*, 58:866.
DETTER, J. C., G. STAMATOYANOPOULOS, E. R. GIBLETT, and A. G. MOTULSKY   1970   Adenosine deaminase: racial distribution and report of a new phenotype. *Journal of Medical Genetics*, 7: 356.
DUNN, F. L.   1967   The current status of ethnographic, genetic, and other biomedical research among the primitive ethnic groups of South-east Asia. In *The biology of human adaptability*, P. T. Baker and J. S. Weiner (eds), pp. 533–63. Clarendon Press, Oxford.
DURAISAMY, G. and R. D. AMARASINGHAM   1971   The ABO blood group frequency distribution of Kuala Lumpur based on a blood donor sample. *Medical Journal of Malaya*, 25:257.
FARINAUD, E.   1941   Contribution à l'étude des populations de l'Indochine méridionale francaise d'après la répartition des groups sanguins. *Bulletin of Social Anthropology of Paris*, 2:75.
FESSAS, P., L. E. LIE-INJO, S. NA-NAKORN, D. TODD, J. B. CLEGG and D. J. WEATHERALL   1972   Identification of slow-moving haemoglobins in haemoglobin H disease from different racial groups. *Lancet*, 1:1308.
FIX, A. G. and L. E. LIE-INJO   1975   Genetic microdifferentiation in the Samai Senoi of Malaysia. *American Journal of Physical Anthropology*, 43:47.
FLATZ, G.   1967a   Die Verbreitung erblicher Farbsehstörungen in der Bevölkerung Nordthailands. *Humangenetik*, 3:328.
——   1967b   Hemoglobin E: Distribution and population dynamics. *Humangenetik*, 3:189.
—— and S. SRINGAM   1964   Glucose-6-phosphate dehydrogenase deficiency in different ethnic groups in Thailand. *Annals of Human Genetics*, 27:315.
FOURQUET, R.   1957   Distribution des groupes sanguin et des types Rh dans deux ethnies du Vietnam. *Revue d'hématologie*, 12:328.
GIBLETT, E. R.   1969   *Genetic markers in human blood*. F. A. Davis, Philadelphia.
——, A. G. MOTULSKY and G. R. FRASER   1966   Population genetic studies in the Congo. 4. Haptoglobin and transferrin serum groups in the Congo and in other African populations. *American Journal of Human Genetics*, 18:553–58.
GREEN, R.   1949   Anthropological blood groups among the Sakai. *Bulletin of the Raffles Museum*, Ser. B, 4:130.
HALL, D. G. E.   1966   *A history of South-East Asia*. second edition. Macmillan, London.
HUGHES, D. R.   1963   Senoi Temiar, dermatoglyphic data. *Man*, 83.
——   1964   Kensiu Negritos: dermatoglyphic data with comparative notes. *Man*, 94.
IKIN, E. W., H. LEHMANN, A. E. MOURANT and H. THEIN   1969   The blood groups and haemoglobin of the Burmese. *Man*, 4:118.
KIRK, R. L.   1965   Population genetic studies of the indigenous peoples of Australia and New Guinea. *Progress of Medical Genetics*, 4:202.

—— 1968a *The haptoglobin groups in man.* Monographs in human genetics, No. 4. Karger, Basel, New York.

—— 1968b The world distribution of transferrin variants and some unsolved problems. *Acta geneticae medicae et gemellologiae (Rome),* 17:613.

—— and L. Y. C. LAI 1961 The distribution of haptoglobin and transferrin groups in South and South-East Asia. *Acta Geneticae (Basel),* 11:97.

——, H. CLEVE and A. G. BEARN 1963 The distribution of the group specific component (Gc) in selected populations in South and South East Asia and Oceania. *Acta Genetica (Basel),* 13:140.

——, W. C. Parker and A. G. BEARN 1964 The distribution of the transferrin variants D_1 and D_{Chi} in various populations. *Acta Geneticae, (Basel),* 14:41.

——, N. M. BLAKE, L. Y. C. LAI and D. R. COOKE 1969 Population genetic studies in Australian Aborigines of the Northern Territory. The distribution of some serum protein and enzyme groups among the Malag of Elcho Island. *Archaeology and Physical Anthropology in Oceania,* 4:238.

——, E. M. McDERMID, N. M. BLAKE, R. L. WIGHT, E. H. YAP and M. J. SIMONS 1973 The distribution of red cell enzyme and serum protein groups in a population of Dani (Pit River, West Irian). *Humangenetik,* 17:345.

KIRKMAN, H. N. and L. E. LIE-INJO 1969 Variants of glucose–6–phosphate dehydrogenase in Indonesia. *Nature,* 221:959.

KURISU, K. 1970 Multivariate statistical analysis on the physical interrelationship of native tribes in Sarawak, Malaysia. *American Journal of Physical Anthropology,* 33:229.

LAI, L. Y. C. and J. KARIKS 1968 Red cell acid phosphatases in the Baining population of New Britain (New Guinea). *Archaeology and Physical Anthropology in Oceania,* 3:143.

—— and S. B. KWA 1968 Red cell acid phosphatase types in some populations of South-East Asia. *Acta Geneticae (Basel),* 18:45.

LEBAR, F. M., G. C. HICKEY and J. K. MUSGRAVE 1964 *Ethnic Groups of Mainland Southeast Asia.* Human Relation Area Files Press, New Haven.

LIE-INJO, L. E. 1964 Haemoglobinopathies in East Asia. *Annals of Human Genetics,* 28:101.

—— 1965 Hereditary ovalocytoses and haemoglobin E-ovalocytosis in Malayan Aborigines. *Nature,* 208:1329.

—— 1967 Red cell carbonic anhydrase Ic in Filipinos. *American Journal of Human Genetics,* 19:130.

—— 1969 Distribution of genetic red cell defects in South-East Asia. *Transactions of the Royal Society of Tropical Medical Hygiene,* 63:664.

—— 1970 Hb B_2 in West Malaysia. *S.E. Asian Journal of Tropical Medicine and Public Health,* 1:58.

—— 1972 Small haemoglobin components accompanying Hb Bart's in newborns. *Medical Journal of Malaysia,* 27:120.

—— 1973 Haemoglobin Bart's and slow-moving haemoglobin components in newborns. The homozygous state for the slow-moving X components in a Malay boy. *Acta Haematologica,* 49:25.

—— and J. CHIN 1964 Abnormal haemoglobin and glucose-6-phosphate dehydrogenase deficiency in Malayan Aborigines. *Nature,* 204:291.

—— and G. DURAISAMY 1972 The slow-moving haemoglobin X components in Malaysians. *Human Heredity,* 22:118.

—— and H. G. POEY-OEY 1964 Glucose-6-phosphate dehydrogenase deficiency in Indonesia. *Nature,* 204:88.

—— and —— 1970 Phosphoglucomutase, carbonic anhydrase and catalase in Indonesians. *Human Heredity,* 20:215.

—— and T. S. TI 1964 Glucose-6-phosphate dehydrogenase deficiency in Malayans. *Transactions of the Royal Society of Tropical Medicine and Hygiene,* 58:500.

—— and Q. B. Welch 1972 Electrophoretic variants of 6-phosphogluconate dehydrogenase (6PGD) and phosphohexose isomerase (PHI) in different racial groups in Malaysia. *Human Heredity,* 22:338.

——, J. CHIN and T. S. TI 1964 Glucose-6-phosphate dehydrogenase deficiency in Brunei, Sabah and Sarawak. *Annals of Human Genetics,* 28:173.

——, J. M. BOLTON and H. H. FUDENBERG 1967 Haptoglobins, transferrins and serum gamma-globulin types in Malayan Aborigines. *Nature*, 215:777.

——, C. G. LOPEZ and H. G. POEY-OEY   1968a   Erythrocyte and leukocyte phosphoglucomutase in Chinese. *American Journal of Human Genetics*, 20:101.

——, H. G. POEY-OEY and R. J. MOSSBERGER   1968b   Haptoglobins, transferrins, and hemoglobin B₂ in Indonesians. *American Journal of Human Genetics*, 20:470.

——, D. A. McKAY and S. GOVINDASAMY   1971a   Genetic red cell abnormalities in Trengganu and Perlis (West Malaysia). *S.E. Asian Journal of Tropical Medicine and Public Health*, 2:133.

——, W. PRIBADI, F. WESTENDORP BOERMA, G. D. EFREMOV, J. B. WILSON, C. A. REYNOLDS and T. H. J. HUISMAN   1971b   Hemoglobin A₂-Indonesia or $\alpha_2\delta_2{}^{69(E13)Gly \rightarrow Arg}$. *Biochimica et Biophysica acta*, 229:335.

——, L. R. WEITKAMP, E. N. KOSASIH, J. M. BOLTON and G. L. MOORE   1971c   Unusual albumin variants in Indonesians and Malayan Aborigines. *Human Heredity*, 21:376.

——, A. FIX, J. M. BOLTON and R. H. GILMAN   1972a   Haemoglobin E-hereditary elliptocytosis in Malayan Aborigines. *Acta Haematologica (Basel)*, 47:210.

——, M. LOO and K. F. FOO   1972b   Diaphorase activity and variants in normal adults and newborns. *British Journal of Haematology*, 23:419.

——, A. BAER, A. N. LEWIS and Q. B. WELCH   1973a   Hemoglobin Constant Spring (slow-moving hemoglobin X components) and hemoglobin E in Malayan Aborigines. *American Journal of Human Genetics*, 25:382.

——, E. N. KOSASIH and A. SIREGAR   1973b   Abnormal haemoglobin, glucose 6-phosphate dehydrogenase deficiency, and hereditary ovalocytosis in North Sumatra. *S.E. Asian Journal of Tropical Medicine and Public Health*, 4:1.

——, C. G. LOPEZ and J. GANESAN   1973c   Lactic dehydrogenase variants in different racial groups in Malaysia. *Human Heredity*, 23:487.

——, E. N. KOSASIH and G. TANN   1974   Variation of several erythrocyte enzymes and serum proteins in Indonesians from North Sumatra. *Humangenetik*, 22:331.

LIVINGSTONE, F. B.   1967   *Abnormal Hemoglobins in Human Populations; a Summary and Interpretation*. Aldine, Chicago.

LUGG, J. W. H.   1957   Taste thresholds for phenylthiocarbamide of some population groups. II. The thresholds of two uncivilized ethnic groups living in Malaya. *Annals of Human Genetics*, 21:244.

——   1966   Taste thresholds for phenylthiocarbamide of some population groups. III. The thresholds of some groups living in Japan. *Annals of Human Genetics*, 29:217.

——   1968   Taste thresholds for phenylthiocarbamide of some population groups. IV. The thresholds of some Australian Aboriginal and South Korean subjects. *Annals of Human Genetics*, 32:43.

—— and J. M. WHITE   1955   Taste thresholds for phenylthiocarbamide in some population groups: I. The thresholds of some civilized ethnic groups living in Malaya. *Annals of Human Genetics*, 19:290.

McDERMID, E. M.   1971   Serum albumin variation in Indian populations. *Vox Sanguinis*, 21:462.

——, N. M. BLAKE, R. L. KIRK, E. N. KOSASITH [*sic*] and M. J. SIMONS   1973 The distribution of serum protein and enzyme groups among the Batak of Samosir Island (Sumatra, Indonesia). *Humangenetik*, 17:351.

MONN, E.   1969   Red cell phosphoglucomutase (PGM) types of Norwegian Lapps: characteristic gene frequencies and variant types. *Human Heredity*, 19:264.

MORROW, A. and A. G. MOTULSKY   1965   Population genetics of pseudocholinesterase variants studied with a rapid screening test. *Clinical Research*, 13:266.

MOTULSKY, A. G. and A. MORROW   1968   Atypical cholinesterase gene $E_1{}^a$: rarity in Negroes and most Orientals. *Science*, 159:202.

MOURANT, A. E.   1954   *The distribution of the human blood groups*. Blackwell, Oxford.

—— and D. TILLS   1967   Phosphoglucomutase frequencies in Habbanite Jews and Icelanders. *Nature*, 214:810.

——, A. C. KOPEC and K. DOMANIEWSKA-SOBCZAK   1958   *The ABO blood groups; comprehensive tables and maps of world distribution*. Blackwell, Oxford.

MYA-TU, M., MAY-MAY-YI and THIN-THIN-HLIANG   1968   Blood groups of the

Inthas and Tavoyans of Burma. *Union of Burma and Journal of Life Sciences*, 1:353.
——, —— and —— 1971 Blood groups of the Burmese population. *Human Heredity*, 21:420.

NGUYEN VAN HUNG 1967a Das MNS-Blutgruppensystem in Vietnam. *Deutsche Gesundheitswesen*, 22:1755.

—— 1967b Die Verteilund der Haptoglobintypen und Gc-Merkmale in einer Stichprobe aus Vietnam. *Deutsche Gesundheitswesen*, 22:856.

—— 1968 Untersuchungen zur Frequenz der Faktoren Gm(a), Gm(x), Gm(f) und Inv(l) in Vietnam. *Folia Haematologica*, 89:80.

OMOTO, K. 1972a The distribution of red cell adenosine deaminase phenotypes in Oceania. *Japanese Journal of Human Genetics*, 16:166.

—— 1972b Polymorphisms and genetic affinities of the Ainu of Hokkaido. *Human Biology in Oceania*, 1:278.

—— and N. M. BLAKE 1972 Distribution of genetic variants of erythrocyte phosphoglycerate kinase (PGK) and phosphohexose isomerase (PHI) among some population groups in southeast Asia and Oceania. *Annals of Human Genetics*, 36:61.

PANICH, V. and T. SUNGATE 1973 Characterization of glucose-6-phosphate dehydrogenase in Thailand: the occurrence of 6 variants among 50 G-6-PD deficient Thai. *Humangenetik*, 18:39.

PETRAKIS, N. L., U. PINGLE, S. J. PETRAKIS and S. L. PETRAKIS 1971 Evidence for a genetic cline in earwax types in the Middle East and Southeast Asia. *American Journal of Physical Anthropology*, 35:141.

PHANSOMBOON, S. and P. SINGHPRASERT 1970 The Gm and Inv factors of the Thai people. *Vox Sanguinis*, 18:274.

——, E. W. IKIN and A. E. MOURANT 1949 The ABO, Rh and MN blood groups of the Siamese. *American Journal of Physical Anthropology*, 7:563.

POLUNIN, I. and P. H. A. SNEATH 1956 Studies of blood groups in Southeast Asia. *Journal of the Royal Anthropological Institute of Great Britain and Ireland*, 83:215.

POST, R. H. 1962 Population differences in red and green color vision deficiency: a review and a query on selection relaxation. *Eugenics Quarterly*, 9:131.

SANGER, R., R. J. WALSH and M. P. KAY 1951 Blood types of natives of Australia and New Guinea. *American Journal of Physical Anthropology*, 9:171.

SANPITAK, N., H. DELBRUCK, J. MUANGINTRA, B. WINYAR and G. FLATZ 1972 Polymorphism of erythrocyte phosphoglucomutase, adenylate kinase and adenosine deaminase in northern Thailand. *Humangenetik*, 14:330.

SIMMONS, R. T. and J. J. GRAYDON 1951 A comparison of the blood groups, subgroups, M-N and Rh types found in Java with those found in other parts of Indonesia, together with a summary of the evidence for north-south gradients in the values for the blood genes q, m and R¹. *Medical Journal of Australia*, 1:173.

—— and J. J. GRAYDON 1971 Population genetic studies in Australian Aborigines of the Northern Territory: blood group genetic studies of populations at 16 localities including Arnhem Land and Groote Eylandt. *Human Biology in Oceania*, 1:23.

——, ——, N. M. SEMPLE and R. GREEN 1950 The A₁A₂BO, M-N and Rh blood groups in southern Chinese: Hak-Kas, Cantonese and Hokkiens. *Medical Journal of Australia*, 2:917.

SINNETT, P., N. M. BLAKE, R. L. KIRK, L. Y. C. LAI and R. J. WALSH 1970 Blood serum protein and enzyme groups among Enga speaking people of the Western Highlands, New Guinea, with an estimate of genetic distances between clans. *Archaeology and Physical Anthropology in Oceania*, 5:236.

SKEAT, W. W. and C. O. BLAGDEN 1906 *Pagan races of the Malay Peninsula*, 2 volumes. Macmillan, London.

STEINBERG, A. G. and L. E. LIE-INJO 1972 Immunoglobulin G allotypes in Malayan Aborigines. *Human Heredity*, 22:254.

——, L. Y. C. LAI, G. H. VOS, R. BHAGWAN SINGH and T. W. LIM 1961 Genetic and population studies of the blood types and serum factors among Indians and Chinese from Malaya. *American Journal of Human Genetics*, 13:355.

SULLIVAN, L. R. 1918 Racial types in the Philippine Islands. *Anthropological Papers of the American Museum*, 23:61.

—— 1921 A few Andamanese skulls with comparative notes on Negrito craniometry. *Anthropological Papers of the American Museum*, 23:175.

TASHIAN, R. E., C. C. PLATO and T. B. SHOWS JR.   1963   Inherited variant of erythrocyte carbonic anhydrase in Micronesians from Guam and Saipan. *Science*, 140:53.

THAMBIPILLAI, V.   1955   Taste threshold for phenyl-thio-urea in Malay school children. *Annals of Human Genetics*, 20:232.

THAN-THAN-SINT and M. MYA-TU   1973   Haptoglobin and transferrin distribution in the Burmese. *Human Heredity*, 23:267.

TUCHINDA, S., D. L. RUCKNAGEL, S. NA-NAKORN and P. WASI   1968   The Thai variant and the distribution of alleles of 6-phosphogluconate dehydrogenase and the distribution of glucose 6-phosphate dehydrogenase deficiency in Thailand. *Biochemical Genetics*, 2:253.

VELLA, F.   1962   Abnormal haemoglobins, thalassaemia and erythrocyte glucose-6-phosphate dehydrogenase deficiency in Singapore and Malaya. *Oceania*, 32:219.

WASI, P., S. NA-NAKORN, P. POOTRAKUL and V. PANICH   1972   Incidence of haemoglobin Thai: a re-examination of the genetics of α-thalassaemic diseases. *Annals of Human Genetics*, 35:467.

WELCH, Q. B.   1973   Peptidase B variants among the Semai, Temuan, Semelai, and Jakun groups of West Malaysian Orang Asli. *Human Heredity*, 23:482.

—— and L. E. LIE-INJO   1972   Serum albumin variants in three Malaysian racial groups. *Human Heredity*, 22:503.

——, L. E. LIE-INJO and J. M. BOLTON   1971   Adenylate kinase and malate dehydrogenase in four Malaysian racial groups. *Humangenetik*, 14:61.

——, —— and ——   1972   Phosphoglucomutase and carbonic anhydrase in West Malaysian Aborigines. *Human Heredity*, 22:28.

——, L. E. LIE-INJO and J. GANESAN   1975   Erythrocyte Adenosine Deaminase in Malaysians. *Human Heredity*, 25:69.

WILLIAMS-HUNT, P. D. R.   1952   *An introduction to the Malayan Aborigines*. Government Press, Kuala Lumpur.

The biological origin of Australian Aboriginals

An examination of blood group genes and gene frequencies for possible evidence in populations from Australia to Eurasia

Roy T. Simmons*

THIRTY FIVE YEARS ago I, together with my colleagues, set out to map the blood group genes of the Australian Aboriginals living in varying numbers in most Australian states. From this initial gambit flowed single and then multiple surveys of the peoples in many parts of south and east Asia and the Pacific. In all, we have published some 90 papers on racial blood group genetics and we have another 10 in press, or in preparation. Thus, we have produced serological maps of the genes in many blood group systems for the Aboriginal people of Australia and for the peoples of Polynesia, Melanesia, Indonesia, Micronesia and to a lesser extent some of the populations in South East and other parts of Asia. It seems appropriate therefore to this symposium on 'The Biological Origin of the Australians' that I should review the blood groups and gene frequencies of the original Australians in relation to the groups and frequencies in the areas where it has been suggested they may have originated, and to extend this to the areas through which the possibly initial few had to pass to reach Australia, to see if our data and that of other serologists provide an answer, or even clues to the solution of the problem of their biological origin.

To make such an examination possible Tables 1 and 2 have been prepared listing blood group gene frequencies and phenotype percentages for Australian and other populations to the north of Australia. The limited number of studies quoted have been selected in some instances according to numbers tested and also to show similarities or differences in genes and gene frequencies in member groups of the same population. In addition to the author's own papers on Australian Aboriginals, data have been taken from the summary publication by Kirk (1965).

Australian Aboriginals

The A_1A_2BO blood groups: More than 10,000 Aboriginals have been tested for the ABO blood groups and out of the possible groups O, A_1, A_2, B, A_1B and A_2B only groups O and A_1 have been found in unmixed Aboriginals

---

* Dr Simmons died in February, 1975.

over the greater part of Australia. However, group B with a remarkable frequency of 0·23 has been found in 47 apparently unmixed Bentinck Islanders in the Gulf of Carpentaria. The number tested represented most of the surviving members of this population which had been isolated from any other contact for centuries. They possessed only the O and B genes, the A gene apparently having been lost in the various population decimations suffered by these people, or alternatively, the founder group lacked A when it initially reached Bentinck Island.

The larger Mornington Island slightly north of Bentinck has a small amount of A, a trace of B and an O frequency of 0·93. These two islands appear to provide a classic example of microevolution in Man. Simmons et al (1962) discussed at length the findings and possible historical background of these island-dwelling Aboriginals.

To the northeast on Cape York is the Mitchell River mission settlement and here A, B and O genes are found, with B again having a high frequency of 0·14. Elsewhere in Australia only occasional examples of B have been recorded in apparently unmixed Aboriginals, but mostly where B has been found admixture is known, or is physically evident. We accept that B is an introduced gene and occurs mostly in the north of Australia. The highest values for the A gene are found in central Australia and these values extend into Western Australia and the Northern Territory. The highest peaks of O (0·85–0·96) are found in and around Cape York and in the islands of the Gulf of Carpentaria.

Subgroup A_2 is uniformly absent in unmixed Aboriginals in all parts of Australia.

The MNSs blood groups: The gene n frequencies of Aboriginals throughout Australia are mostly high and in the range 0·65–0·80 and it has been shown that in the same locality the frequency may vary in the same tribe and even markedly in adjacent tribes. However, the Gulf of Carpentaria area presents four main exceptions to the above. At Bentinck Island we found $n = 0·50$, Mornington Island $n = 0·49$, Robinson River $n = 0·52$ and Roper River $n = 0·54$, and these are low Australian frequencies for n. The principal explanation we offer is that (as for Bentinck) their numbers were established from a small initial breeding pool in each of the four areas.

The S gene of the MNS system is found to be absent in all parts of Australia in unmixed Aboriginals. In the Cape York area we found no S in about 1000 unmixed Aboriginals. Simmons and Graydon (1971) found no S in 1195 Aboriginals of the Northern Territory, but in 49 which were known to be admixed there were 27 who were S-positive.

Simmons and Cooke (1969) found no S-positive in 179 Elcho Island Aboriginals; however, four admixed Aboriginals were S positive. Of these four, one was A_2, three were of group B and one was Rh negative (rh), all introduced genes.

It can be said in relation to the S blood group that it has been widely introduced into Australia by admixture mostly with Caucasians, and its presence when detected by laboratory testing, is certainly proof of racial admixture. The Australian Aboriginal is possibly unique in the world as a race in not possessing the S blood group antigen.

The Rh blood groups: Of the possible Rh blood groups Rh_0, Rh_1, Rh_2, Rh_z, rh, rh', rh'' and rh_y unmixed Aboriginals possess only Rh_0, Rh_1, Rh_2 and Rh_z. In the same area in Western Australia notably in Dampier Land rh' has been found twice where group B was also found in apparently unmixed Aboriginals. Elsewhere in Australia the rh' blood group has been uniformly absent. We regard r' as an introduced gene.

The R^0 gene has a range in Australia of approximately 0–0·43, R^1 ranges from about 0·44–0·94, R^2 from 0·05–0·44 while R^z ranges from 0–0·26. In some areas of Western Australia R^z has been found as the homozygous genotype $R^z R^z$ (Simmons et al, 1953). (A similar finding has been reported in some American Indian tribes.) The R^z gene which is rare in Caucasians has a wide distribution in most areas of Australia.

Note should be taken of the remarkably high frequency for R^0 of 0·43 at Bentinck Island, also a finding of 0·13 on the mainland around the Gulf of Carpentaria with low frequencies in some areas, and a complete absence in others in the Northern Territory and at Groote Eylandt in the Gulf. The highest frequency we found in Western Australia was 0·21 slightly northwest of the central area in the Nangatara tribe, while the lowest was 0·02 in the Nangata further south.

There are $Rh_1{}^u(D^u)$ variants of both high grade and low grade found around Australia. They occur about once in 200 blood samples tested with anti-Rh_0 (D) testing serum. These variants possess varying amounts of the Rh_0(D) blood group antigen and are inherited.

Other blood groups: Table 2 shows the results of tests made for the blood group antigens P_1, Le[a] (Lewis), Lu[a] (Lutheran), K (Kell), Fy[a] (Duffy), Jk[a] (Kidd) and Di[a] (Diego).

In Australia P_1 percentages are mostly from 20–50 with some higher and some lower.

Le[a] percentages vary from 0–20; Le[a] is absent in many tribes and occurs in less than 10 per cent in most others.

Lu[a] is consistently absent.

Fy[a] occurs mostly as 100 per cent, but some tribes fall as low as 96 per cent. However, most tribes have been shown by us to possess Fy[b] when an anti-Fy[b] serum was used in testing along with anti-Fy[a] serum. Initially only anti-Fy[a] serum was available for testing.

K is uniformly absent except where admixture is present.

The Di[a] antigen has been found in only one case, and was introduced probably by admixture with a Chinese. Where tested for the Di[b] antigen all were found to be positive.

Papua New Guinea, Irian Jaya and Schouten Island

The A_1A_2BO blood groups: The ABO blood groups found universally in this area are O, A_1, B and A_1B. In over 20,000 blood samples tested subgroup

A_2 has only been confirmed in two or three families and they probably represented mutations from A_1 as admixture was shown to be most unlikely. Over the whole area there is, as in Australia, wide variation in gene frequencies for the same gene between series belonging to the same linguistic group from adjacent villages, and between series belonging to different linguistic groups. Examples of such variation came from two extensive surveys made by Simmons *et al* (1961; 1972) in the Eastern Highlands District of New Guinea, and by Giles *et al* (1966) which covered populations in the Markham River Valley in the Morobe District. The range for the ABO gene frequencies in the two areas are:

	Eastern Highlands	Markham River Valley
A	0·055–0·326;	0·076–0·363
B	0·050–0·343;	0·025–0·336
O	0·579–0·747;	0·461–0·799

From the results given in Table 1 it will be noticed that both the pygmies of the Wissellakes and the people of Schouten Island have a lower *A* frequency and increased *O*.

The MNSs blood groups: New Guinea is characterised by extremely high values for gene *n*, and the almost complete absence of the combination mS. For the other three combinations the frequency ranges in the same two areas are as follows:

ms	0·018–0·127;	0·034–0·186
nS	0·004–0·173;	0·033–0·253
ns	0·773–0·973;	0·601–0·925

The *S* gene is found throughout the New Guinea area with a range of 0–0·54. Only a few populations lack the gene.

The pygmies and peoples of Schouten Island have slightly more *m* than the other populations listed.

The Rh blood groups: Only three genes R^0, R^1 and R^2 are found in the former Trust Territory of New Guinea but the R^z gene occurs in low frequency at Schouten Island, in Irian Jaya and in Papua, (as also in other parts of Melanesia including New Britain, New Ireland, Bougainville, the British Solomon Islands and the New Hebrides). The Eastern Highlands and Markham Valley Rh gene ranges are as follows:

R^0	0 –0·133;	0 –0·067
R^1	0·775–0·981;	0·845–0·979
R^2	0·011–0·117;	0·004–0·130

$Rh_1{}^u$ (D^u) variants of high grade and low grade occur in small numbers in all the Melanesian populations.

Tables 1 and 2 show that three populations including pygmies selected in Irian Jaya and the people of Schouten Island exhibit genetic characteristics similar to those listed for the New Guinea populations above.

Other blood groups: P_1 occurs in all Melanesian populations and has a fairly wide range of variation.

Le^a while absent in the New Guinea Highlands and in the Irian Jaya pygmies does occur in all other Melanesian populations from low frequency to 30 per cent.

Lu^a is consistently absent as is K and Di^a.

Fy^a is mostly 100 per cent or close to it. The Fy^b allele also occurs in Melanesians.

Jk^a is present in Melanesians and the frequency varies.

In a recent paper Simmons (1973) discussed blood group genetic patterns and heterogeneity in New Guinea.

Indonesia and the Philippines

The four series summarised in Tables 1 and 2 consist of Malays from Java and another series from 20 other islands in Indonesia. The next is for Filipinos from Leyte and Samar who were described as Filipinos proper subjected to many influences (the descendents of the Malays Christianised by the Spaniards). The Filipinos sampled in Manila were described as heterogeneous people who in general possessed elements from Malaya, Indonesia and India by way of Malaya, as well as admixture with resident Spaniards, itinerant Portuguese and other Europeans who have traded with the islands.

The A_1A_2BO blood groups: All the series have the genes A_1 (no A_2), B and O. Of the four peoples listed only the Indonesians from 20 other islands show a slightly lower A_1 and higher O than the other three.

In a recent report Hawkins *et al* (1973) have tested 150 Toba Bataks of North Sumatra and found one A_2 in 20 of group A and one A_2B in 4 of group AB.

The MNSs blood groups: In this system there is a higher frequency of m compared with Melanesians and Australian Aboriginals. Our data for the S gene in the Indonesian-Philippines area are inadequate, but the S antigen range appears to be between 7 and 20 per cent. The Javanese have $m = 0 \cdot 63$ which is the highest of the four peoples listed while m for 20 other islands falls to $0 \cdot 44$, however, the general MN pattern is similar in all of the four series.

The Rh blood groups: The Rh genes R^0, R^1, R^2 and R^z are present in all four peoples listed. There is a slight drop in R^1 values compared with Melanesians and R^z is present in each survey. The Indonesian and Philippines Rh results are very uniform.

Other blood groups: Other blood group data for the peoples of Indonesia and the Philippines are totally inadequate, but in both areas P_1, Le^a, Fy^a and Jk^a are present while Lu^a, K and Di^a are generally absent. However, occasional examples of Lu^a and K have been encountered recently in Malays by Lopez and Case (unpublished), and these are probably introduced genes. Hawkins *et al* (1973) also demonstrated the presence of the *Fy^b* gene in Toba Bataks in Sumatra and found 1 of 57 persons tested to be Lu(a+).

Malayan aborigines

Three populations from West Malaysia are listed in Tables 1 and 2, namely, Negritos, Senoi and aboriginal Malays. The results in the ABO system present a pattern similar to that broadly seen in New Guinea, Indonesia and the Philippines. The genes A_1, B and O are present and A_2 is absent.

In the MNS system values for m are higher than those reported above and are all about $0 \cdot 73$.

In the Rh system the Negritos have a high R^0 of $0 \cdot 27$ and a lower R^1 of $0 \cdot 63$ while the findings for Senoi and aboriginal Malays are each identical with R^0 of $0 \cdot 01$ and R^1 of $0 \cdot 93$ and $0 \cdot 94$. The only exception is that the aboriginal Malays have a low frequency of R^z not found in the other two peoples.

In the other blood group systems data are inadequate, but we do know P_1 varies from 72–80 per cent, which is a very high frequency, while Fy^a varies from 80–90 per cent.

It seems from the three major blood group systems that it could be said the Negritos, Senoi and aboriginal Malays are from the same basic stock, and would relate closely to the Indonesian–Malay people discussed in the previous section.

Some populations in Borneo

There are three main groups in Borneo namely, Dayak, Malay and Chinese. The Chinese are derived from migrations during very recent times, the Malays as a whole have been described as such only in the last 500 years. Many of the Dayaks (Dayak means 'inland chap') notably the Sea Dayaks (Ibans) are relatively newcomers too. All three groups overlap, intermix and relate in varying, complex and often uncertain degrees.

The main blood group data available for Borneo relates to Land Dayaks, Sea Dayaks, Melanaus, Kedayans, and Bruneis. The Bruneis are classified as 'Malays', the Kedayans as intermediate between Malay and 'Dayak' but with a majority of Malay associations. The Melanaus are balanced towards the Dayak but may become 'Malay' apparently by marriage. The Land Dayaks and Sea Dayaks are directly Dayak.

The A_1, B and O gene frequencies are fairly similar in pattern to those listed for Malays in Indonesia and the Philippines. No examples of A_2 were recorded in any survey.

In the MNSs system four of the six surveys listed m or mS with values from $0 \cdot 61$–$0 \cdot 67$ which again is the usual finding for Malays and Malayan aborigines.

In the Rh system the genes found were R^0, R^1 and R^2 in six surveys, while in three surveys R^z was also identified which was the previous finding in five out of seven surveys on various Malay people.

In other blood group systems the data are inadequate, but P_1 was found in 71–75 per cent (high percentages as in Malayan aborigines), and Le^a in 14–18 per cent of the individuals tested.

From all the above blood group results it would appear that the Borneo populations tested to date can be bracketed with the Malay peoples of Indonesia, Malaya and the Philippines.

Indo-China and Southern China

The blood group genetic patterns are much the same in Thailand, Cambodia, Laos and Southern China. Two surveys on Thais and two on Southern Chinese are listed in Tables 1 and 2 as representative of the peoples in general. The gene frequencies in Indo-China and Southern China show the expected variations in the recorded data, which is far from adequate for most of the blood group systems now available for study.

In China the A frequency is usually slightly more than $0 \cdot 20$ while B is usually slightly less than $0 \cdot 20$. In India and South East Asia B has usually a slightly higher value than A.

In the MN system we find the Asian higher m than n frequency with m values usually above $0 \cdot 6$.

In the Rh system all four genes R^0, R^1, R^2 and R^z are present with R^1 values around $0 \cdot 7 - 0 \cdot 8$. Both in Thais and Southern Chinese very occasional examples of the Rh-negative gene r are found and this is probably an introduced gene at some earlier date.

Hawkins and Simons (1973) have recently tested Chinese living in Singapore and report finding the r' gene in two siblings. This may be an introduced gene and not part of the original Chinese genetic make-up, but they point out that it is possible the r' gene may have a higher frequency in Chinese than has hitherto been recognised, and recommend further family studies.

The same authors also found one Rh negative gene r in 700 Chinese studied in Singapore. In 1944 and in 1951 three subjects with the r gene were found in 240 Chinese tested in New York. Obviously, the Mongoloid peoples possess a low frequency of this Rh gene which is common in Caucasoids, and most frequent of all in the Basque population.

Hawkins (1973) has published recently a comprehensive review of blood genetic markers in Chinese populations sampled in various parts of the world.

The sub-division: Australoid or archaic Caucasoid

Montagu (1951) lists the possible representatives of this ethnic group as follows:

Australian	Australia
Veddah	Ceylon
Pre-Dravidian	India
Ainu	Japan, Hokkaido and Sakhalin Islands.

In relation to the four peoples Montagu said:

Into this sub-division fall four of the most interesting groups of mankind, the Australian Aboriginals, the Veddahs of Ceylon, the Pre-Dravidian peoples of India, and the Ainu of Japan. These four groups bear a close resemblance to one another, and to the so-called 'white' or Caucasoid peoples. The evidence of their physical characters, of their geographic distribution, and of pre-history, suggests a considerable antiquity for these four groups, while from their physical characters alone it seems clear that their nearest affinities are with the Caucasoids, and that they are best regarded as a Caucasoid sub-division. (1951:318)

It is proposed in the following section to examine the Ainu, the southern Indian and pre-Dravidian peoples, and the Veddahs of Ceylon (now called Sri Lanka).

The Ainu of Hokkaido, Northern Japan: Simmons *et al* (1953) reported the results of their blood group genetic studies on 271 Ainu and 159 Ainu-Japanese. This investigation was made primarily to search for a possible blood group genetic link between Ainu and Australian Aboriginals.

The ABO gene frequencies for Ainu, Ainu-Japanese and Japanese are very similar. As in all populations examined to date subgroup A_2 is absent.

For the MNS blood groups the Ainu and Ainu-Japanese frequencies are almost identical, while the Japanese have a higher *m* frequency of $0 \cdot 55$ compared with about $0 \cdot 40$ for the former.

The Rh genes present in Ainu, Ainu-Japanese and Japanese differ from all the South East Asian and Pacific peoples examined to data and which are listed in Table 1. In Ainu-Japanese the Rh genes R^0, R^1, R^2, r, r' and r'' were found, while in Japanese R^0 was not found in several surveys, but R^1, R^2, R^z, r, r' and r'' have been identified. Thus, the Rh gene pattern which now includes r, r' and r'' has completely changed. The most unusual finding in Ainu and Ainu-Japanese has been the frequency for r'' of $0 \cdot 20$ and $0 \cdot 14$ respectively. This unusual frequency for r'' has been confirmed subsequently by Misawa and Hayashida (1968) who recorded r'' as $0 \cdot 17$ for Ainu-Japanese. In the same 120 Ainu-Japanese they also found Fy (a+) 100 per cent, K absent, and Jk^a with a frequency of $0 \cdot 29$ compared with a frequency of $0 \cdot 38$ for Japanese. They also found the Le^a frequency to be $0 \cdot 60$ which is similar to the frequency of $0 \cdot 59$ given by Simmons *et al* (1953).

The limited data we have for other blood group systems do not provide additional material useful for comparison. The Le^a phenotype percentages of 34 and 37 are the highest recorded in Table 2.

The ABO, MNS and Rh genes and gene frequencies are so similar in the Ainu and Japanese that it seems obvious the Japanese of today possess a substantial Ainu component acquired no doubt many centuries ago.

The Australian Aboriginals do not possess group B, or S of MNS while the Ainu possess both in quite high frequencies, in fact, $26 \cdot 2$ per cent of the Ainu possess *B* which gives a frequency of $0 \cdot 212$, and $47 \cdot 9$ per cent are S positive with frequencies for *mS* of $0 \cdot 012$ and *nS* of $0 \cdot 277$.

The Ainu clearly possess the Rh genes R^1, R^2, r and r''; the r'' being in a remarkably high frequency of $0 \cdot 20$ not found in any other race. By contrast the Australian Aboriginals possess R^0, R^1, R^2 and R^z. Only two examples of $r'r'$ have been found in many thousands of Rh tests made all around Australia. The r' gene may well have been introduced to the Aboriginals.

It seems fair to say that while the Ainu and Japanese very clearly relate to one another, no such blood group genetic relationship can be claimed between the Ainu and Australian Aboriginals, even though both peoples have been listed by Montagu and many others as each belonging to the Australoid or Archaic Caucasian classification.

Southern Indian and pre-Dravidians: Extensive testing for the ABO blood groups has been carried out in India and to a much smaller extent for some of the other blood group systems. Detailed reviews have appeared in Bhalla (1966) and Majumdar (1961). For the pre-Dravidian or Veddoid tribes of south India more limited information is available but blood group studies have been carried out by Lehmann and Cutbush (1952) and Kirk *et al* (1962) on tribal populations in the Nilgiri Hills, by Simmons *et al* (1953) for the Chenchu of Guntur and Kurnool Districts and by Sarkar and Banerjee (1959) and Saha *et al* (1974) for the Kadar of Kerala. These authors have summarised also earlier work on some of these and other related groups.

In Lehmann and Cutbush's (1952) study the Veddoids as represented by the Paniyans differ from other southern Indians in having a higher frequency of *A* than *B* while the Irulas, another Veddoid tribe, have about equal *A* and *B*. Their North-Indid neighbours the Todas have one of the highest *B* frequencies (0·484) recorded. However, 200 Todas tested by Pandit in 1934 gave a much lower *B* frequency of 0·278 and close to that of the Kotas. Then, to further complicate the picture another North-Indid community, the Kotas (86 tested) who also live in the Nilgiris have only the *B* and *O* genes. The Indid Badagas another aboriginal group in the Nilgiris showed frequencies between the North-Indids and the Veddoids which fitted their physical appearance as a possible mixture of the two peoples.

The MN frequencies follow those of the rest of India with high *m* and lower *n*. A total of 161 Veddoid Irulas, Kurumbas and Paniyans had an *m* frequency of 0·74 and *n* of 0·26. The respective frequencies in the three groups were almost identical in that *m* ranged from 0·72–0·77. No *S* frequencies were given.

A total of 156 Veddoids were Rh tested by Lehmann and Cutbush but no gene frequencies were published. It was said that no examples of Rh_0 were found, while 14 examples of Rh_z were identified and this chromosome was present in all three groups of the Veddoid peoples studied.

Tests with anti-rh″ (E) showed an E frequency of 0·22 for Veddoids, 0·14 for the Indid Badagas, 0·09 for Canarese, Telegus and Tamils while the North-Indid Kotas and Todas had a frequency of 0. It will be recalled that the Kotas also had no *A* gene while the Todas had *A* 0·18 and *B* a very high 0·48. It would seem that here we have another fine example of genetic drift.

It was suggested by Lehmann and Cutbush that a mixture of Kotas (North-Indids) and Veddoids who present two opposites would result in what is found today in south India. They also suggested that a mixture of Kota and European blood would result in the type of blood distribution seen today in the Todas and the so-called 'Aryan' population strata of north India.

While these suggestions fit present day gene frequency findings it seems most unlikely that the present blood group gene frequencies for less than 90 Kotas would truly represent the frequencies the Kotas would have possessed many centuries ago.

Mourant (1954) quotes P_1, Lu^a and Fy^a results of Lehmann and Cutbush (1952) as a personal communication. The P_1 results for the Veddoid peoples range from 54–75 per cent. For three of the other peoples in the Nilgiri Hills the P_1 range was from 45–57 per cent.

In the Veddoids Fy^a ranged from 75–93 per cent, while in the other tribes the range was 66–92 per cent. No example of Lu^a was found in the Veddoids or in any of the other tribes tested.

Our own studies of the Chenchu of Guntur and Kurnool Districts were published by Simmons *et al* (1953).

For the ABO blood groups the gene frequencies found were A 0·22, B 0·27 and O 0·54. Of 37 individuals of group A and AB all except one were of subgroup A_1 and A_1B: the one exception found was of subgroup A_2B. In the case of the MNS blood groups for the Chenchu the gene frequencies were: mS 0·21, ms 0·32, nS 0·21, ns 0·25. In this survey 67·6 per cent of the samples were anti-S positive while in the survey by Prasad *et al* (1949) 58·9 per cent of Indians were S positive and their frequencies were: mS 0·29, ms 0·31, nS 0·06, ns 0·34. The S percentages were both very high.

The S distribution shows a degree of similarity in the two studies, but in Chenchu nS was higher. The m frequency was greater than 0·60 as in other Asian populations.

The Rh gene frequencies found were: R^0 0, R^1 0·69, R^2 0·07, r 0·07, r' 0·16. In our series we found R^0 and R^z absent. R^1 was slightly higher than the Indian series of both Wiener *et al*, 1945 and Prasad *et al*, 1949, R^2 about the same, r (the Rh negative gene) lower, and r' very much higher. While we found no examples of high grade Rh$_0$^{u} (D^u) variants we unfortunately did not test the rh' samples for D^u. The high r' frequency in a small Chenchu community may be true as was the very high r'' frequency we found in Ainu and which was subsequently confirmed by Japanese workers.

The Veddahs of Ceylon: Until 1962 the only data relative to the Veddahs who, for some time have been subjected to varying amounts of inbreeding with their Sinhalese and Tamil neighbours appeared to be those of Hill (1937) who tested 5 Veddahs in Ceylon and found 2 of group B and 3 of group O, while Lehmann *et al* in 1955 (Mourant, 1958) reported testing 9 Veddahs in Singapore who had come from Ceylon. They found 5 of group B and 4 of group O. Thus, in 14 Veddahs 7 were of group B and 7 were of group O.

Subsequently, there were two reports on the Veddahs of Ceylon, one by Wickremasinghe *et al* (1963) and the other by Kirk *et al* (1962). The survey by Kirk and his associates covered also the Tamils, Todas, Kurumbas and Irulas of South India, and the Sinhalese, Tamils, Wanni castes and Veddahs of Ceylon. Tests were made for the ABO, MNSs and Rh blood groups with limited tests for other blood group systems, together with a survey of gamma globulin groups, abnormal haemoglobins, haptoglobins and transferrins. Only the blood group genetic results of the extensive survey by Kirk *et al* (1962) will be used in the present examination of blood group genes and gene frequencies found in the above peoples.

As seen from Table 1 the Veddahs have a high B frequency of $0·28$, a feature common in south Indian populations also. The Veddahs, however, have a very low A frequency of $0·06$.

Veddahs have a lower m frequency in the MNS system, the range of $0·40–0·57$ falling below the range in south India of $0·60–0·86$. The mS frequency in Veddahs of $0·11$ is low also. For the Rh blood groups the R^1 gene has a value of $0·77$ in Veddahs, R^2 was low and R^z r or r' was not found. R^0 was present.

On the basis of the small number of Veddahs tested as distinct from all the Indian and Ceylon populations blood grouped, it has been shown that they have the lowest A and m gene frequencies and possess only three Rh genes, namely, R^0, R^1 and R^2, and these differences distinguish them from all the populations of south India and Ceylon examined here. The Veddahs therefore have been placed in a separate section in Table 3 as presently being distinct from all the populations listed in sections 1 to 4 of this table.

On the basis of the blood group genetic data presently available it appears that the Veddoids, and other aboriginal peoples of south India relate most closely to the Indian population, and neither they nor the Veddahs relate in any obvious blood group genetic make-up to the distant Ainu, or to the even more distant Australian Aboriginals.

Conclusions

The purpose of the present paper has been to look for a blood group genetic link especially between the peoples accepted by the anthropologists as being of the sub-division known as Australoid or Archaic Caucasoid, and having representatives in this ethnic group such as Australian Aboriginals, the Ainu of Japan, the pre-Dravidian peoples of southern India and the Veddahs of Ceylon. At the same time other populations located between Australia and Eurasia have been examined to see if possible pockets of Australian-type populations are still detectable genetically, anywhere on the route the Australians must have used on their journey to Australia, possibly 30,000 years ago. Southern India has been suggested by some as their possible place of origin.

In recent decades we have realised that blood group genetic change is a continuing process, that genetic drift, founder affect, microevolution are terms now used by geneticists to explain the differences encountered in the distribution of genes and gene frequencies, between peoples even of the same racial group in adjacent villages. It therefore seems unreal in 1974 to look for blood group genetic relationships suggested between peoples of apparently the same ethnic group, and separated in time by many thousands of years.

Table 1 shows that there is evidence of three gradients between Asia and Australia in the gene frequency values recorded for B of ABO, m of MNSs and R^1 of the Rh system. Simmons and Graydon (1951) first drew attention to these gradients.

The highest values of B are in Asia about $0 \cdot 27$ falling away to zero in unmixed Australian Aboriginals.

The highest m values are in Asia about $0 \cdot 60$ and decrease to their lowest values in Papua New Guinea often less than $0 \cdot 10$.

The lowest values of R^1 are generally in the order of $0 \cdot 50$–$0 \cdot 60$ in Asia and increase to $0 \cdot 80$–$0 \cdot 90$ in Papua New Guinea, Indonesia and Malayan aboriginals. The Australian R^1 values are usually in the range of $0 \cdot 50$–$0 \cdot 60$.

It will be seen from Table 3 that based on the presence or absence of certain genes five rough classifications of the various peoples examined have been made as follows:

1.   The Australian Aboriginals;

2.   The peoples of New Guinea, Indonesia, the Philippines, Malaya, Borneo and Thailand. The Micronesians not examined in this paper would also fall into this group;

3.   The Ainu would group with the Japanese and possibly with the Chinese;

4.   The aboriginal peoples of southern India group with the Indian population;

5.   The Veddahs of Ceylon appear to be a distinct people when compared with other groups in south India and Ceylon.

Another group not considered in this examination are the Polynesians who would be grouped with the American Indians based on the absence of subgroup A_2 and B of the ABO system, and the presence of the S antigen of MNSs. The presence of the S antigen separates them from the Australian Aboriginals who lack A_2, B and S.

Australian Aboriginals are unique in that unmixed Aboriginals over almost the entire continent lack A_2 and B of the ABO system, S of the MNS system and the Rh negative genes r, r' (with two exceptions in one area of Western Australia) and r''. Aboriginals of Bentinck Island and Mitchell River have high B frequencies and these people appear physically to be unmixed. These are exceptions.

No blood group genetic evidence has been found to suggest a migration route for the Australians on their journey to Australia. Neither has blood group genetic evidence been found to suggest a relationship for the Australian Aboriginals with the Ainu of Hokkaido, Northern Japan, with the pre-Dravidian aboriginal peoples of south India or with the Veddahs of Ceylon.

The Ainu also failed to show any blood group genetic relationship with any of the Australoid peoples listed here.

A study of the blood group genes of the Pacific peoples shows that there is no blood group genetic evidence that the African Negroes or Negrillos ever entered the Pacific. The Asian, Oceanic and Australian Negritos* are,

---

* Negrito is Spanish for "Little Negro".

in fact, part of each local populace. The Asian, and Oceanic Negritos lack A_2 of the ABO system, the Rh-negative gene r (cde) and the sickle-cell trait of the Africans, while the unmixed Australian Negritos also lack B of the ABO system and S of the MNSs system.

Our studies have included some isolated Negritos (Murrayians) in Victoria and many of this type selected by Professor Birdsell in Western Australia, and their genetic pattern was identical with other Australians. In addition, our pygmy (Negrito) studies in Papua and New Guinea including West Irian, like those made by others on Malayan Negritos have shown that these smaller people are simply part of the local population and lack blood group marker genes from Africa.

Our studies have not been a complete loss, however, in that we have assisted in providing a blood group genetic map of the Pacific peoples, and for them at least, we have made blood transfusion a safer procedure in return for their blood samples.

Finally, it must be said that our 35 years of blood group genetic research have unfortunately failed to provide us with any clues, at least obvious to us, as to 'The Biological Origin of the Australians'.

Table 1: Comparison of blood groups and gene frequencies in Australian Aboriginals and other populations

Population or Linguistic Group	Authors	ABO Gene Frequencies				MNSs Gene Frequencies				Rh Gene Frequencies						
		A_1	A_2	B	O	mS	ms	nS	ns	R^0	R^1	R^2	R^z	r	r'	r''
Australia: Aboriginals																
Northern Territory	Simmons and Graydon (1971)	·214	0	·002	·783	0	·265	0	·734	·044	·650	·250	·055	0	0	0
Western Australia	Birdsell, Simmons, and Graydon (1974)	·253	0	·001	·746	0	·255	0	·744	·084	·626	·210	·054	0	·024	0
Gulf of Carpentaria																
Bentinck Is.	Simmons, Graydon and Tindale (1964)	0	0	·228	·772	0	·500	0	·500	·426	·521	·053	0	0	0	0
Mornington Is.		·059	0	·008	·932	0	·511	0	·488	·095	·652	·243	·009	0	0	0
Mainland		·103	0	·044	·852	0	·308	0	·692	·134	·666	·199	0	0	0	0
New Guinea																
Eastern Highlands	Simmons et al (1961 and 1972)	·218	0	·114	·668	·001	·039	·050	·908	·032	·906	·060	0	0	0	0
Irian Jaya																
Asmat	Simmons et al (1967)	·209	0	·138	·658	0	·023	·036	·940	·013	·952	·034	0	0	0	0
Khogir		·227	0	·128	·645	0	·043	·028	·928	0	·850	·149	0	0	0	0
Pygmies	Graydon et al (1958)	·075	0	·139	·786	0	·102	·007	·891	·030	·850	·119	0	0	0	0
Schouten Island	Nijenhuis and van der Hoeven (1956)	·101	0	·120	·780	0	·265	·039	·696	·011	·929	·057	·003	0	0	0
Indonesia																
Malays, Java	Simmons and Graydon (1951)	·178	0	·180	·642		·632	·368		·065	·837	·086	·012	0	0	0
20 other islands		·130	0	·133	·737		·435	·565		·04	·81	·13	·02	0	0	0
Philippines																
Negritos	Polunin and Sneath (1953)	·19	0	·08	·73		·510		·490	·03	·88	·08	·01	0	0	0
Malays (Filipinos)	Simmons and Graydon (1945)	·152	0	·181	·671											
Filipinos	Walsh et al (1954)	·155	0	·158	·687	·012	·528	·023	·437	·066	·807	·110	·018	0	0	0

Malayan Aborigines																
Negritos	Polunin and Sneath (1953)	·16	0	·10	·74	·08	·65	·06	·21	·27	·63	·10	0	0	0	0
Senoi		·05	0	·24	·71	·07	·65	·04	·24	·01	·93	·07	0	0	0	0
Aboriginal Malays		·12	0	·20	·68	·03	·75	·01	·21	·01	·94	·04	·01	0	0	0
Borneo																
Land Dayaks	Graydon *et al* (1952)	·171	0	·295	·518	·624		·376		·021	·867	·112	0	0	0	0
Sea Dayaks		·225	0	·141	·611	·452		·548		·033	·885	·070	·012	0	0	0
Melanaus		·129	0	·185	·661	·02	·44	0	·54	·036	·899	·055	·010	0	0	0
Kedayans		·319	0	·164	·535	·04	·57	·10	·29	·035	·876	·070	·019	0	0	0
Bruneis (Malays)		·17	0	·24	·62	·63		·37		·107	·732	·161	0	0	0	0
Land Dayaks	Polunin and Sneath (1953)	·21	0	·31	·48	·01	·66	0	·33	·07	·85	·08	0	0	0	0
Thailand	Phansomboon *et al* (1949)	·148	0	·257	·595	·662		·338		·111	·756	·112	·022	0	0	0
	Simmons *et al* (1954)	·180	0	·249	·571	·045	·595	·040	·320	·050	·820	·130	0	0	0	0
China																
Southern	Simmons *et al* (1950)	·168	0	·141	·692	·630		·370		·040	·760	·195	·005	0	0	0
	Miller *et al* (1950 and 1951)	·195	0	·162	·643	·033	·574	·011	·382	·029	·691	·197	0	·083	0	0
Ainu																
Hokkaido	Simmons *et al* (1953)									$R^{\circ}+r$						
Northern Japan		·285	0	·212	·512	·012	·385	·277	·326	·037	·556	·210	0		0	·197
Ainu-Japanese		·266	0	·208	·526	·030	·387	·227	·356	·065	·553	·227	0		·020	·135
Combined series	Rh frequencies as calculated by Mourant (1954)									R° ·025	·566	·212	0	·017	·006	·174
Japanese	Furuhata (ABO), Yamanaka (MN), Cited by Boyd (1939). Rh by Chown *et al* (1946)	·259	0	·173	·564	·553		·447		0	·580	·307	·004	·080	0	·029

Table 1: continued

Population or Linguistic Group	Authors	A_1	A_2	B	O	mS	ms	nS	ns	R^0	R^1	R^2	R^z	r	r'	r''
		ABO Gene Frequencies				MNSs Gene Frequencies				Rh Gene Frequencies						
Southern India																
Dravidian-speaking Aborigines																
North Indids																
Kotas	Lehmann and Cutbush (1952)	0		·293	·777	·190	·674	·085	·051							
Todas		·180		·484	·349	·276	·474	·130	·120							
Indids																
Badagas		·124		·152	·718	·239	·410	0	·351							
Veddoids																
Irulas		·217		·244	·563	·301	·414	0	·285							
Paniyans		·427		·094	·445	·281	·486	0	·233	0	+	+	+	]	Not stated	
Paniyans	Ayappan (Boyd, 1939)	·461		·078	·447											
Dravidians																
Munda, Santal and Oraon	Malone and Lahiri (Boyd, 1939)	·227		·289	·493											
Todas	Pandit (Boyd, 1939)	·157		·278	·545											
Goa																
Pre-Dravidian region	Mahratta (Boyd, 1939)	·208		·254	·540											

Population	Reference															
S. India and Ceylon																
Tamil (low caste and untouchables)	Bais and Verhoef (Boyd, 1939)	·155		·218	·616											
South India																
Chenchu	Simmons et al (1953)	·222	*	·275	·536	·216	·326	·210	·248	0	·692	·073	0	·072	·163**	0
Indians																
Bengal, Bihar	Prasad et al (1949), Wiener et al (1945)		*			·288	·312	·060	·340	·042	·566	·104	0	·247	·038	0
Bombay		·185	*	·261	·583					·034	·562	·060	0	·266	·044	0
Indians (South)	Venkataramiah and Rao (Mourant 1954)									·042	·571	·137	·009	·242	0	0
South India	Kirk et al (1962)															
Tamils		·176		·194	·630	·38	·32	·13	·17	·012	·636	·055	0	·268	·026	0
Todas		·198		·378	·424	·21	·58	·07	·14	·019	·593	·006	0	·346	·036	0
Kurumbas		·112		·134	·753	·43	·39	·07	·11	0	·651	·252	·016	·081	0	0
Irulas		·149		·226	·625	·17	·55	·03	·25	0	·487	·174	·027	·312	0	0
Ceylon																
Sinhalese		·188		·165	·647	·16	·42	·09	·33	·038	·650	·082	0	·217	·013	0
Tamils		·164		·227	·608	·25	·41	·12	·22	·024	·707	·117	0	·152	0	0
Wanni		·140		·152	·707	·24	·44	·14	·18	0	·689	·089	·007	·214	0	0
Veddahs		·061		·247	·692	·11	·29	·14	·46	·196	·765	·039	0	0	0	0

* Subgroup A_2 was found in all three surveys and apparently was not tested in the other surveys.

** Coombs tests for low-grade Rh_0^u (D^u) were not possible at the time. High-grade D^u were absent.

Table 2: Comparison of other blood group phenotypes in Australian Aboriginals and other populations

Population or Linguistic Group	Authors	Phenotype Percentage						
		P_1	Le^a	Lu^a	K	Fy^a	Jk^a	Di^a
Australia: Aboriginals								
Northern Territory	Simmons and Graydon (1971)	27·4	7·3	0	0	98·9		0
Western Australia	Birdsell, Simmons and Graydon (1974)	32·4	6·9	0	0	99·8		
Gulf of Carpentaria								
Bentinck Is.	Simmons, Tindale and Birdsell (1962)	10	10			100	69	
Mornington Is.		27	0			100	61	
New Guinea								
Eastern Highlands	Simmons *et al* (1961 and 1972)	35	0*	0	0	100	60	0
Irian Jaya								
Pygmies	Graydon *et al* (1958)	63·8	0	0	0	90		0
Schouten Is.	Nijenhuis and van der Hoeven (1956)	42·8	0	0	·55	100		
Indonesia and the Philippines	Various papers but data inadequate	+	+	0	0	+	+	0
Malayan Aborigines								
Negritos	Polunin and Sneath (1953)	76		0	0	80		
Senoi		79		1	0			
Aboriginal Malays		72		0	0	90		
Borneo								
Melanaus	Graydon *et al* (1952)	75	18					
Kedayans		71	14					
Land Dayaks	Polunin and Sneath (1953)	74		1	0			

* Le^a is present in all Melanesian populations except those in the New Guinea Highlands; it occurs elsewhere from low frequencies up to 30%.

Thailand Bangkok	Simmons et al (1954)	30	23	0	98
Chinese Southern	Miller et al (1951)	27	23·5	0	99
Ainu Hokkaido, Northern Japan	Simmons et al (1953)	72	34		96
Ainu-Japanese			37	0	100
South India Chenchu	Simmons et al (1953)	74	9		100
Kotas	Lehmann and Cutbush (Mourant, 1954)	50		0	92
Todas		45		0	66
Badagas		57		0	93
Irulas		54		0	75
Kurumbas		75		0	75
Paniyans					
Todas	Kirk et al (1962)	71	19		
Irulas		81	5		
Kurumbas		79	10		
Tamils		70	17	0	79
Ceylon Sinhalese		78	18	0	
Tamils		62	22		
Wanni		69			
Veddahs		83	13	0	

Table 3: Summary of blood group antigens found in populations from Australia to Eurasia

Population	A₁	A₂	B	O	A₁B	A₂B	M	N	S	Rh₀	Rh₁	Rh₂	Rhz	rh	rh′	rh″	P₁	Leᵃ	Luᵃ	K	Fyᵃ	Jkᵃ	Diᵃ
Australia	+	−	−	+	−	−	+	+	−	+	+	+	+	−	−	−	+	+	−	−	+	+	−
New Guinea	+	−	+	+	+	+	+	+	+	+	+	+	+	−	−	−	+	+	−	−	+	+	−
Indonesia	+	−	+	+	+	+	+	+	+	+	+	+	+	−	−	−	+	+	−	−	+	+	−
Philippines	+	−	+	+	+	+	+	+	+	+	+	+	+	−	−	−	+	+	−	−	+	+	−
Malayan Aborigines																							
Negritos and Senoi	+	−	+	+	+	+	+	+	+	+	+	−	−	−	−	−	+	−	−		+		
Aboriginal Malays	+	−	+	+	+	+	+	+	+	+	+	−	−	−	−	−	+	−	−		+		
Borneo																							
Melanaus	+	−	+	+	+	+	+	+	+	+	+	+	−	−	−	−	+	+					
Kedayans	+	−	+	+	+	+	+	+	+	+	+	+	+	−	−	−	+	+					
Thailand	+	−	+	+	+	+	+	+	+	+	+	+	−	−	−	−	+	+	−		+		
Southern Chinese	+	−	+	+	+	+	+	+	+	−	+	+	−	+	−	−	+	+	−	−	+	+	−
Ainu	+	−	+	+	+	+	+	+	+	−	+	−	−	+	−	−	+	+	−	−	+	+	−
Ainu-Japanese	+	−	+	+	+	+	+	+	+	+	+	−	−	+	+	+	+	+	−	−	+	+	−
Japanese	+	−	+	+	+	+	+	+	+	−	+	+	+	+	−	+	+	+	−	−	+	+	−
Indians Three localities	+	+	+	+	+	+	+	+	+	+	+	+	−	+	+	−	+	+	−	−	+		
Southern India																							
Chenchu	+	+[1]	+	+	+	·	+	+	+	−	+	−	−	+	−	−	+	+		−	+		
Tamils	+	+[1]	+	+	+	·	+	+	+	−	+	−	−	+	+	−	+	+		−	+		−
Todas	·	·	+	+	+	·	+	+	+	+	+	−	−	+	+	−	+	+					
Kurumbas	·	·	+	+	+	·	+	+	+	−	+	−	−	+	−	−	+	+					−
Irulas	+	−	+	+	+	·	+	+	+	−	+	+	+	+	−	−	+	+				−	−
Ceylon																							
Sinhalese	+	·	+	+	+	·	+	+	+	+	+	−	−	+	+	−	+	+			+		−
Tamils	+	·	+	+	+	·	+	+	+	+	+	+	+	+	−	−	+	+			+		
Wanni	+	·	+	+	+	·	+	+	+	−	+	+	−	−	−	−	+						
Ceylon Veddahs	+	·	+	+	·	·	+	+	+	+	+	+	−	−	−	−	+						−

The five sections in this table indicate the presence or absence of genetic markers in various populations. A sixth section could comprise Polynesians and Amerindians who lack *B* but have *S* of MNSs.

1. In the surveys indicated by a dot no tests for subgroup A₂ were apparently made.

References

BHALLA, V. 1966 Blood group distribution pertaining to ABO, MNSs and Rh–Hr systems in the Indian subcontinent. *Anthropologie*, 4:67–86.

BIRDSELL, J. B., R. T. SIMMONS and J. J. GRAYDON 1974 Microdifferentiation in blood group gene frequencies among 28 Aboriginal tribal isolates in Western Australia. Unpublished manuscript with Australian Institute of Aboriginal Studies, Canberra.

BOYD, W. C. 1939 Blood groups. *Tabulae Biologicae*, 17:113.

CHOWN, B., Y. OMAKURA and R. F. PETERSON 1946 The Rh types of Canadians of Japanese race. *Canadian Journal of Research*, E24:135.

GILES, E., E. OGAN, R. J. WALSH and M. A. BRADLEY 1966 Blood group genetics of natives of the Morobe District and Bougainville, Territory of New Guinea. *Archaeology and Physical Anthropology in Oceania*, 1:135.

GRAYDON, J. J., N. M. SEMPLE, R. T. SIMMONS and S. FRANKEN 1958 Blood groups in pygmies of the Wissellakes in Netherlands New Guinea with anthropological notes by H. J. T. Bijlmer. *American Journal of Physical Anthropology*, 16:149.

——, R. T. SIMMONS, N. M. SEMPLE, L. J. CLAPHAM, E. H. WALLACE and T. HARRISSON 1952 Blood genetics of various populations in Borneo. *Medical Journal of Australia*, 1:694.

HAWKINS, B. R. 1973 The distribution of blood genetic markers in immigrant Chinese populations. *Acta geneticae medicae et gemellologiae*, 22:139–66.

HAWKINS, B., M. ELLIOT, E. N. KOSASIH and M. J. SIMONS 1973 Red cell genetic studies of the Toba Bataks of North Sumatra. *Human Biology in Oceania*, 2:147–54.

—— and M. J. SIMONS 1973 Evidence for the existence of the Rhesus complex Cde(r') in a Chinese. *Vox Sang*, 25:286–87.

HILL, W. C. O. 1937 Blood groups of Veddahs. *Nature*, 140:548.

KIRK, R. L. 1965 *The distribution of genetic markers in Australian Aborigines*. The Australian Institute of Aboriginal Studies, Canberra.

——, L. Y. C. LAI, G. H. VOS, R. L. WICKREMASINGHE and D. J. B. PERERA 1962 The blood and serum groups of selected populations in South India and Ceylon. *American Journal of Physical Anthropology*, 20:485.

LEHMANN, H. and M. CUTBUSH 1952 Sub-division of some Southern Indian communities according to the incidence of sicklecell trait and blood groups. *Transactions of the Royal Society of Tropical Medicine*, 46:380.

MAJUMDAR, D. N. 1961 *Races and cultures of India*. 4th Edition. Asia Publishing House, Bombay.

MILLER, E. B., R. E. ROSENFIELD and P. VOGEL 1951 On the incidence of some of the newer agglutinogens in Chinese and Negroes. *American Journal of Physical Anthropology*, 9:115.

——, H. D. TANNER and C. HSU 1950 The P factor and its variants. *Journal of Laboratory and Clinical Medicine*, 36:230.

MISAWA, S. and Y. HAYASHIDA 1968 On the blood groups among the Ainu in Shizunai, Hokkaido. *Proceedings of the Japanese Academy*, 44:83.

MONTAGU, M. F. A. 1951 *An introduction to physical anthropology*. Charles C. Thomas, Springfield, Illinois.

MOURANT, A. E. 1954 *The distribution of the human blood groups*. Blackwell Scientific Publications, Oxford.

——, A. C. KOPEC and K. DOMANIEWSKA-SOBCZAK 1958 *The ABO blood groups*. Blackwell Scientific Publications, Oxford.

NIJENHUIS, L. E. and J. A. VAN DER HOEVEN 1956 Blood group frequencies in Papuans from Biak (Isles of Schouten). *Vox Sang*, 1:241.

PHANSOMBOON, S., E. W. IKIN and A. E. MOURANT 1949 The ABO, Rh and MN blood groups of the Siamese. *American Journal of Physical Anthropology*, 7:563.

POLUNIN, I. and P. H. A. SNEATH 1953 Studies of blood groups in South-East Asia. *Journal of the Royal Anthropological Institute*, 83:215.

PRASAD, C. H., E. W. IKIN and A. E. MOURANT 1949 The Rh and MNS blood groups of some students from India. *American Journal of Physical Anthropology*, 7:553–58.

SAHA, N., R. L. KIRK, SHAILA SHANBHAG, S. H. JOSHI and H. M. BHATIA   1974
Genetic studies among the Kadar of Kerala. *Human Heredity*, 24:198–218.

SARKAR, S. S. and A. R. BANERJEE   1959   ABO blood groups. In *A physical survey of the Kadar of Kerala*, pp. 71–78. Memoir No. 6, Department of Anthropology, Government of India.

SCHEBESTA, P.   1952   Die Negrito Asiens. *Studies of the Institute of Anthropologie*, 6:496. Cited by Polunin and Sneath (1953).

SIMMONS, R. T.   1973a   Blood group genetic patterns and heterogeneity in New Guinea. *Human Biology in Oceania*, 2:63.

——   1973b   The distribution of blood group genetic markers in Melanesians. *Journal Australasian College of Biomedical Scientists*, September:64.

—— and D. R. COOKE   1969   Population genetic studies in Australian Aborigines of the Northern Territory: blood group genetic studies in the Malag of Elcho Island. *Archaeology and Physical Anthropology in Oceania*, 4:252.

—— and J. J. GRAYDON   1945   Blood groups, subgroups, M, N types and Rh subtypes in Filipinos. *Medical Journal of Australia*, 2:325.

—— and ——   1951   A comparison of the blood groups, subgroups, M–N and Rh types found in Java with those found in other parts of Indonesia, together with a summary of the evidence for north–south gradients in the values for the blood genes q, m and R[1]. *Medical Journal of Australia*, 1:173.

—— and ——   1971   Population genetic studies in Australian Aborigines of the Northern Territory: blood group genetic studies on populations sampled at 16 localities including Arnhem Land and Groote Eylandt. *Human Biology in Oceania*, 1:23.

——, D. C. GAJDUSEK and M. K. NICHOLSON   1967   Blood group genetic variations in inhabitants of West New Guinea, with a map of the villages and linguistic groups of South West New Guinea. *American Journal of Physical Anthropology*, 27:277.

——, J. J. GRAYDON and J. B. BIRDSELL   1953   High R^z frequency in the blood of Australian Aborigines. *Nature*, 172:500.

——, —— and S. SRINGAM   1954   A blood group genetical survey in Thais, Bangkok. *American Journal of Physical Anthropology*, 12:407.

——, —— and N. B. TINDALE   1964   Further blood group genetical studies on Australian Aborigines of Bentinck, Mornington and Forsyth Islands and the mainland, Gulf of Carpentaria, together with frequencies for natives of the Western Desert, Western Australia. *Oceania*, 35:65.

——, N. B. TINDALE and J. B. BIRDSELL   1962   A blood group genetical survey in Aborigines of Bentinck, Mornington and Forsyth Islands, Gulf of Carpentaria. *American Journal of Physical Anthropology*, 20:303.

——, J. J. GRAYDON, N. M. SEMPLE and G. W. L. D'SENA   1953   A genetical survey in Chenchu, South India: blood, taste and secretion. *Medical Journal of Australia*, 1:497.

——, ——, —— and R. GREEN   1950   The A_1A_2BO, MN and Rh blood group in Southern Chinese: Hak-Kas, Cantonese and Hokkiens. *Medical Journal of Australia*, 2:917.

——, ——, —— and S. KODAMA   1953   A collaborative genetical survey in Ainu: Hidaka, Island of Hokkaido. *American Journal of Physical Anthropology*, 11:47.

——, ——, D. C. GAJDUSEK, M. P. ALPERS and R. W. HORNABROOK   1972   Genetic studies in relation to kuru. II. Blood group genetic patterns in kuru patients and populations of the Eastern Highlands of New Guinea. *American Journal of Human Genetics*, Supplement, November 24:39.

——, ——, V. ZIGAS, L. L. BAKER and D. C. GAJDUSEK   1961   A blood group genetical survey of the kuru region and other parts of Papua-New Guinea. *American Journal of Tropical and Medical Hygiene*, 10:639.

WALSH, R. J., O. KOOPTZOFF, D. DUNN and R. Y. ATIENZE   1954   Blood groups of Filipinos. *Oceania*, 25:61.

WICKREMASINGHE, R. K., E. W. IKIN, A. E. MOURANT and H. LEHMANN   1963   The blood groups and haemoglobins of the Veddahs of Ceylon. *Journal of the Royal Anthropological Institute*, 93:117–25.

WIENER, A. S., E. B. SONN and R. B. BELKIN   1945   Distribution and heredity of the human blood properties in a series of A, B, M, N, P and R[h]. *Journal of Immunology*, 50:341–48.

Serum protein and enzyme markers as indicators of population affinities in Australia and the Western Pacific

R.L. Kirk

RECENT RESEARCH has demonstrated that approximately 10 per cent of randomly selected gene loci controlling biochemical traits in Man show polymorphic variation and that nearly all gene loci reveal the presence of rare mutant forms with frequencies of 1 per 1000 or less (Harris, 1970; Harris and Hopkinson, 1972). The ability to detect such genetic variants provides a powerful tool for tracing population affinities, although there are limitations which will be discussed below.

The use of specific genetic markers as tracers of population affinities is clear-cut in those cases where the marker in question achieves a reasonable frequency, of the order of 5 to 10 per cent. A classic example is the Diego (a) blood group discovered by Layrisse et al (1955) in Venezuelan Indians, but then found to be widely though not universally distributed in other Amerindian populations as well as in Mongoloid populations in east and southeast Asia but absent in almost all other parts of the world. Its occurrence in fringe populations such as the Oraons of the Chota Nagpur plateau in India clearly demonstrates the penetration of Mongoloid genes into tribal populations of northeast India (Vos and Kirk, 1961), a conclusion supported by the detection of other gene markers for Mongoloid populations in the Oraons (Kirk et al, 1962a).

Of course, there are several factors which limit interpretations of population affinities based on the presence or absence of specific markers such as Di(a). Firstly, a marker which is of low frequency in the original population will have a correspondingly low probability of transmission to a new population, the probability being dependent on the number of persons involved in the biological interpopulation contact. Secondly, a specific marker introduced as a single event into a new population will face the probability of extinction or survival in the same way as a new mutant. Kimura and Ohta (1969) have given an expression for survival time in populations of limited size, and Li (1975) has discussed the time needed for a new mutant to achieve any particular frequency in similar populations. Thirdly, the possibility exists that the particular form of the marker being considered arose as independent mutations which survived in both populations. In such a situation the inference of biological interpopulation contact would be incorrect. Finally, the marker concerned in the populations under study may be phenotypically but not genetically identical.

The refinement of criteria for the identification of specific genetic markers now makes it less likely that markers with superficially similar phenotypic appearances will be confused. Techniques such as electro-focusing, crossed immuno-electrophoresis, gradient electrophoresis, differential response to inhibitors or the reaction kinetics for various substrates, as well as the primary sequencing of protein structure in those cases where it can be accomplished, make it possible to state with more certainty whether or not the same mutational site was involved. Where identity seems certain and where other evidence suggests biological interpopulation contact could occur, then the most economical hypothesis is that the variant gene was not an independent mutation but was introduced from outside. Where more than one such marker can be demonstrated in the two populations the argument for such biological contact between the populations is strengthened.

The search for specific genetic markers in Australian Aboriginal and related populations was begun by my laboratory nearly 15 years ago. Some attention has been given to genetic variants of red cell antigens but the difficulties associated with the production and distribution of specific anti-sera have restricted this approach. Thus Vos and Kirk (1962) demonstrated a variant of the E antigen of the Rh blood group system with high frequency among Aboriginals in the Western Desert region of Australia but with decreasing frequency to the north and northeast. This antigen, E^T, has not been tested for outside Australia. Similarly, the red cell antigen N^A defined by Booth (1971) has been charted in many parts of Papua New Guinea and a few other parts of the world but not so far in Australia. Booth and his colleagues (Booth et al, 1970) have also studied the absence of the so-called Gerbich(a) antigen in populations in Papua New Guinea, but again this work still remains to be extended to Australia and many other populations in the area.

Because of the limitations in studying specific red cell antigen markers my own studies were focussed initially on serum protein variants. During the last seven years however they have been expanded to include an ever increasing number of red cell enzyme systems and the evidence gained from these serum protein and enzyme studies is outlined below under the individual systems.

Serum protein groups

(a) Haptoglobin: The haemoglobin-binding protein haptoglobin (Hp) present in serum shows polymorphic variation under the control of two alleles, Hp^1 and Hp^2, in all human populations. In addition, a number of rarer alleles have been reported sporadically from many parts of the world (Kirk, 1968a). Some individuals cannot be typed for Hp and these are referred to as HpO. The majority of such cases are due to environmental rather than genetic causes. The frequencies of the Hp^1 and Hp^2 alleles are of value in genetic distance studies and merit more detailed analysis in relation to possible selective factors. Curtain *et al* (1965) have discussed this for some populations in New Guinea.

Specific markers in the Hp system are notable for their almost complete absence in Australian Aboriginals (Nicholls *et al*, 1965 reported two cases of Hp 'Johnson' in Pintubi), complete absence in New Guinea and all other Pacific Island populations so far studied.

(b) Transferrin: The iron-binding protein transferrin (Tf) is of great interest in the present context. Unlike Hp it is not universally polymorphic, but more than 20 alleles at the Tf locus are known and a number of these are polymorphic in geographically restricted human populations. Variant alleles of this type are potentially valuable in assessing human population affinities.

Initial reports (Bennett *et al*, 1961; Kirk and Lai, 1961; Kirk *et al*, 1962b; Kirk, 1965) indicated a widespread distribution of the slow-moving Tf variant D_1 in Australia, New Guinea and South East Asian populations. More careful electrophoretic studies however showed that the slow-moving variant in South East Asian populations was D_{Chi}, a variant with an electrophoretic mobility almost identical with that of D_1 (Kirk *et al*, 1964). The distribution of D_{Chi} has now been charted in some detail (Kirk, 1968b) and it is found in all Mongoloid populations, including the Ainu of Hokkaido (Omoto and Harada, 1972) as well as in the Oraons of Chota Nagpur and the Veddahs of Ceylon (Kirk *et al*, 1964). So far TfD_{Chi} has not been reported from any part of Australia, New Guinea, Fiji or the New Hebrides: on the contrary, TfD_1 is widely distributed in nearly all populations tested in these areas, the variant sometimes reaching frequencies of nearly 50 per cent in the Western Desert areas of Australia (see Figure 1).

Of particular interest is the widespread distribution of TfD_1 variants in black African populations (Kirk, 1968b). The older view that Melanesians had African affinities has now been abandoned by some authorities (cf. Howells, 1973), but the widespread distribution of TfD_1 in Melanesian and black African populations supports the older view. Wang and his colleagues (Wang *et al*, 1967) have examined the molecular structure of TfD_1 from American Negro and Australian Aboriginal sources and have concluded that the amino acid substitution is identical in both cases. The TfD_1 variant therefore arose either in a population ancestral to ones which have contributed to modern black Africans, Australian Aboriginal and Melanesian populations, or the variants in the two areas stemmed from independent and unrelated mutations affecting the same codon at the Tf locus. Other evidence to be discussed later suggests the former possibility is more likely.

The transferrin locus gives rise also to a number of other mutants which have become established in various populations. In the area of immediate interest three other specific transferrin variants have been described. The first, Tf B_{Lae} (Lai, 1963) was detected near Lae in the Markham River Valley area in New Guinea but has been detected also in New Britain and

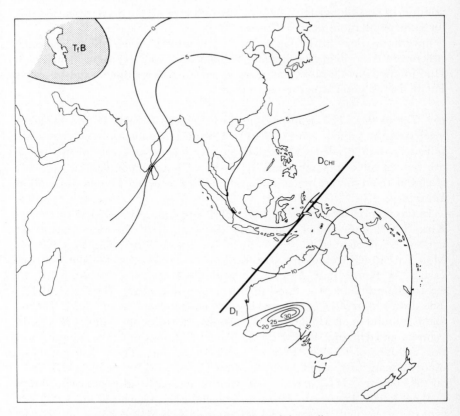

Figure 1   Isogenes for Transferrin alleles in Asia and Australia.

other places in the Markham River Valley but only rarely in neighbouring populations outside the Markham Valley (Curtain *et al*, 1965). Gene flow between New Britain and the neighbouring coastal area of New Guinea is demonstrated in this instance. Even more restricted distributions of another TfB variant in Cape York have been described (Kirk, 1973) and for a distinct slow-moving variant TfD$_{Manus}$ among the Manus and Usiai of Manus Island (Malcolm *et al*, 1972). This latter variant so far has not been described in any other population in the Western Pacific, but it is necessary to express the caution that some of the previously described TfD$_1$ cases could have been Tf D$_{Manus}$ if critical comparisons had been made.

(c) Group specific component: This α_2-globulin in human serum exists in polymorphic forms in all human populations and is controlled by genes closely linked to those controlling serum albumin. In addition to the common alleles Gc^1 and Gc^2 a number of rare alleles have been identified, and one of these is of special interest in the present context. The specific gene marker GcAborigine was detected first in the population at Aurukun in Cape

York (Cleve *et al*, 1963) and we were able to show that it was absent among populations in south and southeast Asia though present in Australia and New Guinea (Kirk *et al*, 1963 a & b). Subsequent studies have confirmed its presence in New Guinea and also in the New Hebrides (Cleve and Kirk, 1967; Kenrick, 1967).

Unfortunately, accurate typing of phenotypes involving $Gc^{Aborigine}$ is difficult and relatively few studies of its distribution have been undertaken, despite its implication in possible susceptibility to the neurological disorder, Kuru, amongst the Fore of the Eastern Highlands in Papua New Guinea. Kitchin *et al* (1972) have completed the only detailed survey outside Australia and some of their data is reproduced in Figure 2 with corresponding distribution for Australia and related areas being shown in Figure 3.

It seems clear that $Gc^{Aborigine}$ is an Australian-Melanesian gene marker with a distribution in the southwest Pacific very similar to that for TfD_1. The frequency variations are not highly correlated: TfD_1 for example has its highest frequency in the Western Desert area of Australia, a region where $Gc^{Aborigine}$ is virtually absent. This widespread distribution in Melanesia and Australia raises the possibility that $Gc^{Aborigine}$ may be identical with Gc^Y, another Gc variant allele detected in black Americans, and present also in black African populations (Kitchin and Bearn, 1966; McDermid and Vos, 1971). In conjunction with Dr Cleve our group has examined the possibility further, using antigen-antibody crossed immuno-electrophoresis (McDermid and Cleve, 1972). They concluded that the Gc variants found in Australian Aboriginals, New Guineans, South African Bantu and black Americans may represent products of the same gene mutation. Though the evidence is not quite so convincing as for the comparison of TfD_1 in Negroes and Australian Aboriginals, it lends further support to the view that Australians and Melanesians share with Africans some common genes not found in any other racial groups.

(d) Albumin: Though genetic variants of serum albumin have been reported for some time in the medical literature, the first demonstration that such variants could be polymorphic in human populations was by Melartin and Blumberg (1966) for the Naskapi Indians in North America. Subsequently a large number of variant alleles have been described, mostly rare, but sometimes achieving polymorphic frequency (Weitkamp *et al*, 1973). Of these numerous variant alleles two occur in New Guinea, but no albumin variants have been found in Australian Aboriginals in more than 2000 sera examined. Weitkamp *et al*, (1969) first reported a number of cases of Albumin New Guinea in samples from the Markham River Valley, near Popondetta, from Russel Island and four cases of Albumin^{Uinba} from the village of Uinba in the Western Highlands. No further examples of Albumin^{Uinba} have been detected but McDermid (1971 and unpublished) has found Albumin New Guinea from a number of localities in the coastal areas of Papua New Guinea. The distribution of these variants in other parts of the Pacific, except for Australia, has not yet been studied in detail.

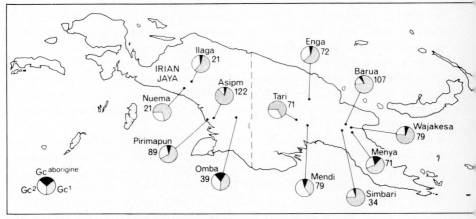

Figure 2   Gc alleles in New Guinea (from Kitchin *et al*, 1972).

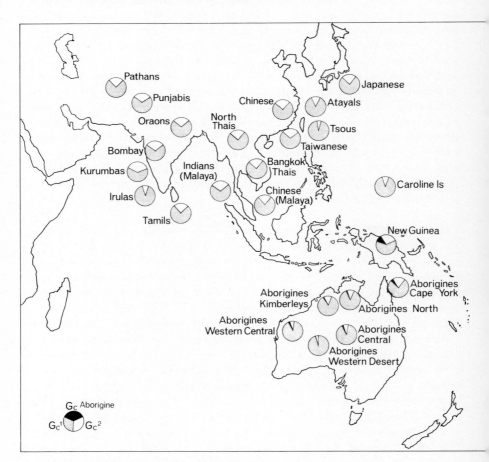

Figure 3   Gc alleles in Asia and Australasia.

(e) Other serum protein systems: Of the remaining serum protein systems my laboratory has carried out intensive studies only for the protease inhibitor (Pi) types. No specifically localised variants have been detected and the system appears to be uninformative. The other systems which are of very great significance, however, are those involving the immunoglobulin groups. Our earlier work in conjunction with Dr A. G. Steinberg (Steinberg and Kirk, 1965, 1970; Vos *et al*, 1963) revealed the discriminatory power of the gammaglobulin (Gm) group system in Australia, New Guinea and other areas in south and southeast Asia, and to a lesser extent of the Inv system (Steinberg *et al*, 1972). The power of the Gm system has been exploited also for studying relationships between human populations by several other investigators including Dr Schanfield, Dr Erna van Loghem, and Dr Curtain. Curtain *et al*, (1976) review this work in the present volume.

Leucocyte antigens

The histocompatibility antigens which can be detected by serological methods on the surface of white cells and platelets are complex genetically but are being studied vigorously at the present time. They fall into two HL-A groups, the 1st and 2nd loci, which are closely linked with a recombination frequency of the order of $0 \cdot 5$–$1 \cdot 0$ per cent.

Between 1970 and 1972 a major international effort provided data on the distribution of the HL-A types from populations around the world, and the results appeared last year in the volume 'Histocompatibility Testing— 1972'. By combining the information on the HL-A types from world populations it is possible to measure genetic distances and construct phylogenetic trees (Piazza and Viganotti, 1973). A tree based on information from two closely linked loci alone is likely to be subject to considerable error, but even bearing this limitation in mind it is clear that Australian Aboriginals, New Guineans and Fijians are related, and are involved closely through their HLA antigens with at least one of the Mongoloid populations, in this case an Eskimo population.

The populations sampled in the Australasian area perforce were restricted: in Australia people from the Western Desert, the Waljbiri in central Australia and a small group from the north of the Northern Territory. In New Guinea two populations were sampled, one on KarKar Island off the north coast, and the other in the Eastern Highlands. In Fiji the sample was from Fijians on Viti Levu. All these populations show an HL-A pattern completely different from that in Caucasians, as well as some differences between themselves, although it is the factors they either lack or have in common which is of greatest interest. Figure 4, taken from Forbes *et al*, (1973) illustrates diagrammatically these patterns for two of the Australian populations and the Highland and coastal populations in New Guinea. At the 1st locus HL-A 1 and HL-A 3 and at the 2nd locus HL-A 5, 7, 8 and 12 and W 5, 14 and 17 are virtually absent from Australian and New Guinean samples though present in the Caucasian controls, whilst HL-A 9 at the first locus and HL-A 13, W 10, 15 and 22 at the second locus

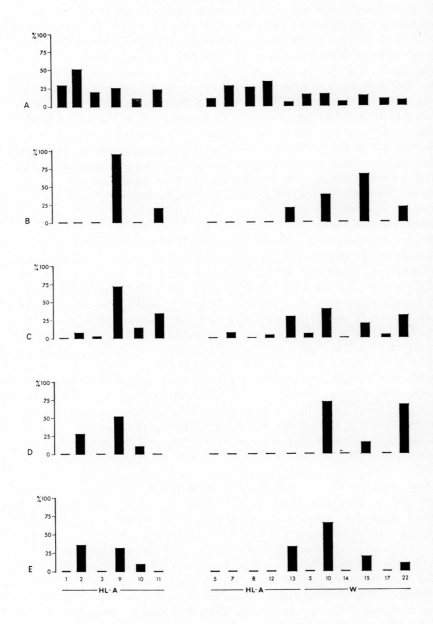

A = Australian Caucasians. B = New Guineans (Highlands). C = New Guineans (Coastal). D = Australian Aboriginals (Western Desert). E = Australian Aboriginals (Northern Territory).

Figure 4 Comparison of HL-A frequencies in Australia and New Guinea (from Forbes *et al*, 1973).

are more frequent than in Caucasians. Similar results were obtained for the Waljbiri by Bashir *et al*, (1973) and they conclude that the overall distribution of the histocompatibility antigens in the Waljbiri and New Guineans suggests that they originated from a common stock.

Red cell enzyme systems

Methods are available now for detecting genetically controlled differences in a large number of enzymes present in red cells and the exploitation of these techniques during the last ten years has yielded results of great interest to the students of evolution both in Man and other animals, and in plants.

My laboratory has been largely responsible for data in the Australian, New Guinean, Western Pacific and southeast Asian area, with important additional contributions from Dr Lie-Injo's and Professor Morton's laboratories as well as more limited contributions from others. I have selected a number of examples from this rapidly growing wealth of data, much of it still unpublished, to illustrate the present theme.

(a) Acid phosphatase: Three alleles are present in Caucasian populations, p^a, p^b and p^c, but all of the area under consideration is characterised by the absence of the p^c allele except in a few isolated cases. Indians have a low frequency of p^c although it appears to be absent in the tribal populations of the Nilgiris and among the Kadar of Kerala (unpublished and Saha *et al*, 1974). New Guinean populations have a high frequency of p^b, and this appears to be the only gene present in central Australia (Kirk *et al*, 1971). The low frequency of the p^a allele in the north of Australia suggests it may have been a post-Pleistocene introduction, as well it may have been also into parts of New Guinea.

No specific marker genes have been detected in the Australian-New Guinea, Western Pacific area, although the absence of one is of interest. Black Africans and derivative populations in America possess a fourth allele, p^r, at the acid phosphatase locus. We have failed to detect it in many thousands of persons tested in Australia, New Guinea and the Western Pacific, although Bayoni-Sioson (1971) has reported it in the Philippines. Recently our laboratory has identified a few examples of the p^r allele in the Banks and Torres Islands, but further study, including a reinvestigation of the Philippine claim, will be needed.

(b) 6-Phosphogluconate dehydrogenase (6PGD): Nearly all populations in the world are polymorphic for the two common alleles PGD^A and PGD^C. In addition a number of more locally distributed alleles have been reported and these have been summarised recently by us (Blake *et al*, 1974).

One of these rarer alleles, PGD^{Elcho}, detected first in samples from the Malag of Elcho Island (Blake and Kirk, 1968) promised to be important as a genetic marker for contact between Arnhem Land populations and non-Australian groups. However, we have been unsuccessful in detecting PGD^{Elcho} in Sumatra, Irian Jaya, Papua New Guinea or elsewhere in Australia outside Arnhem Land. Recently we were excited by the possibility that a variant with relatively high frequency among the Kadar in south India was PGD^{Elcho}, but closer examination showed it to be a distinctive allele restricted to the Kadar population (Saha *et al*, 1974).

What is of interest, however, is the very high frequency of the PGD^C allele in New Guinea and some of the Western Pacific areas, although PGD^C is not a specific marker allele. In the Western Carolines the PGD^C frequency is 10 per cent (Blake *et al*, 1973), in the Admiralty Islands 20 per cent (Malcolm *et al*, 1972) and unpublished results for New Guinea give frequencies ranging from less than 1 to 30 per cent with higher frequencies tending to be in Irian Jaya. The PGD^C frequency in Fiji is 18 per cent, and in Australia ranges from less than 1 to 8 per cent.

(c) Phosphoglucomutase: The complex isozyme pattern produced by the enzyme phosphoglucomutase is under the control of alleles at three independent gene loci. The gene products from only two of these loci however are detectable in red cell lysates so that population data are restricted almost entirely to variations at the PGM_1 and PGM_2 loci. A large number of alleles has now been identified at both these loci and their distribution in the south and east Asian, Western Pacific and Australasian area has been summarised recently by Blake and Omoto (1975).

Two common alleles at locus 1, $PGM_1{}^1$ and $PGM_1{}^2$ are polymorphic in all human populations, but additional alleles occur either sporadically or in some populations with polymorphic frequency. This is true in the Western Pacific-New Guinea area, and two alleles $PGM_1{}^3$ and $PGM_1{}^7$ are of special interest. My laboratory has found $PGM_1{}^3$ at many localities in India, South East Asia, many areas of New Guinea and in the Western Carolines and Fiji. It has been reported also in Chinese and Japanese populations. So far we have not detected $PGM_1{}^3$ in any part of the Australian continent (see Figure 5). In parts of New Guinea and Micronesia the frequency of $PGM_1{}^3$ reaches 9–11 per cent respectively, but elsewhere in the areas mentioned above values are low. By contrast $PGM_1{}^7$ is polymorphic in the Western Carolines, reaching values of 8 per cent, and has been reported sporadically for South East Asia, Japan and for two localities in India. It is absent completely in New Guinea and Fiji, and also in Australia.

The distributions of $PGM_1{}^3$ and $PGM_1{}^7$ considered together suggest that Micronesians have genetic links with South East Asia and also with New Guinea – a view supported in both cases by other evidence. The diff-erential distribution of the two alleles in Micronesia and New Guinea is, however, puzzling and suggests that the population movement has been largely a secondary push from New Guinea into Western Micronesia, taking in the $PGM_1{}^7$ allele, followed by a movement from South East Asia into Micronesia bringing in the $PGM_1{}^3$ allele. This allele, in spite of achieving a frequency of 10 per cent in its Micronesian environment, has not moved into New Guinea. Incidentally, neither allele is present in Australia.

The second locus of PGM is monomorphic in nearly all human popula-tions except in black Africa. However, New Guinea and Australia possess

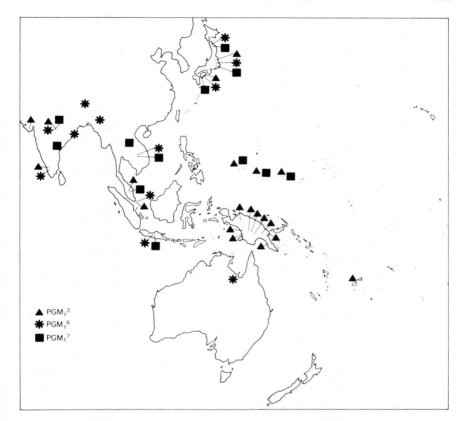

Figure 5 Rare PGM locus 1 alleles in Asia and the Western Pacific.

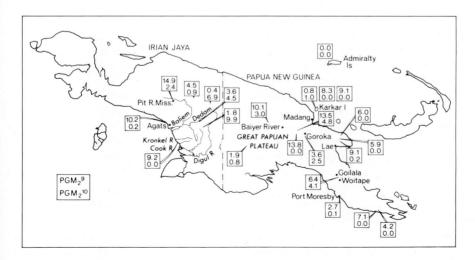

Figure 6 Percentage of rare PGM locus 2 alleles in New Guinea.

alleles with interesting geographic distributions. In New Guinea, two alleles ($PGM_2{}^9$ and $PGM_2{}^{10}$) are found widely distributed in many parts of the island (see Figure 6) and although there appear to be higher frequencies of both alleles in Highland areas and among speakers of Papuan languages, there is a wide distribution of both $PGM_2{}^9$ and $PGM_2{}^{10}$ in some coastal populations. What is of special interest is, with one exception, the complete absence of these alleles in Micronesia and in Australia. The single Aboriginal with a $PGM_2{}^{10}$ allele belonged to the Malag, whose traditional home is the north-eastern corner of Arnhem Land. This genetic link between the Malag and New Guinea is supported by evidence from the presence of another specific marker gene in both places to which reference will be made in the next section.

The other 2nd locus PGM allele which achieves polymorphic frequency in the area is $PGM_2{}^3$, previously reported in England, and also in Negroes and Asiatic Indians but with an unstated frequency (Hopkinson, 1968). We have recently detected a wide distribution in central Australia. Although it has its highest concentration in the Waljbiri, it occurs also in the Aranda and Bidjandjadjara (Pitjantjatjara) people and two cases have been found further north. This localised distribution in the centre provides a marker useful for mapping gene flow out of the area, a process which I believe has been in progress in Australia for a considerable period of time.

(d) Peptidase B: A number of specific peptidases can be identified by using appropriate peptide substrates, and they have been given arbitrary designations A, B, C, etc. One of these, Peptidase B, is of value as a gene marker for gene exchange between New Guinea and Australia, whilst another, Peptidase A, is interesting because of the absence in Australia and New Guinea of the variant *Pep A²* allele which achieves a frequency of up to 10 per cent in black Africans.

On the positive side, we have identified a new allele, *Pep B⁶*, at several localities in Arnhem Land, and further study revealed that all the individuals concerned with one exception belonged to the Nunggubuyu linguistic group, and even the single exceptional case belonged to the neighbouring Malag, where as noted previously the $PGM_2{}^{10}$ allele also has been detected (Blake *et al*, 1970). In tests throughout many parts of Asia, Australia and the Western Pacific we have found examples of *Pep B⁶* only among the Asmat on the south coast of Irian Jaya.

Which way did the gene flow proceed? The evidence is equivocal, but though it could be from Asmat to Nunggubuyu, the probability favouring this direction is not very great.

Very recently Welch (1973) in Dr Lie Injo's laboratory has reported the *Pep B⁶* allele in two populations in Malaysia. If this observation is confirmed it raises the possibility that the *Pep B⁶* allele was introduced to both the Asmat and Nunggubuyu by Malay trepangers, whose boats are known to have frequented these coasts. Of equal interest is the more recent report of a *Pep B⁶* allele amongst the Kadar of south India (Saha *et al*, 1974). This suggests a possibly far wider distribution of this allele at some time in the past.

By coincidence perhaps, we have detected the presence of another specific Peptidase allele, $Pep\ B^7$, in the Waljbiri in central Australia. This time, although the $Pep\ B^7$ allele has a frequency of 5 per cent in the Waljbiri, only a single case has been reported elsewhere, i.e. in a Luridja man, a close neighbour of the Waljbiri (Blake et al, 1970).

(e) Phosphoglycerate kinase: The enzyme phosphoglycerate kinase is controlled by a locus on the X-chromosome and is considered to be genetically invariant, except in rare instances. This is not the case however, in the Western Pacific and New Guinea.

A variant allele PGK^2 was described first in samples from New Guinea (Chen et al, 1971) and PGK^2 was also found in 1 of 6 samples from Samoa (Chen and Giblett, 1972). These authors described also a single case of another variant allele, PGK^4, in New Guinea. My own laboratory has studied the distribution of PGK variants in the area under present discussion, and the distribution of these two alleles is quite different. PGK^2 appears to be distributed in the Western Pacific as well as in the coastal areas of New Guinea and achieves a mean gene frequency of 8 per cent in the Western Carolines (Blake et al, 1973). It is present in Fiji but absent on Manus Island and KarKar Island. It is present only sporadically in the Eastern Highlands of Papua New Guinea. It has not been detected elsewhere in the entire area. PGK^4 on the other hand has not been found outside New Guinea, and appears to have its highest frequency of about 2 per cent in the Eastern Highlands. Further study of Western Pacific populations is currently in progress.

Conclusions

The patterned spread of genes across Asia, the Western Pacific and Australia provides us with a chart indicating the movement of peoples, either singly or in groups, across tribal and geographic boundaries. How long in the past such exchanges occurred we can guess at only vaguely but at least we can attempt some kind of ranking from the earliest period to the present.

It is tempting to assume that in Australia and New Guinea and other parts of Melanesia there was first of all a common substratum population which shared not only some genes within its borders, but also derived these from a common ancestor of present-day black Africans. Such genes were the transferrin D_1 and the group-specific protein Gc Aborigine: in course of time others may be found which form a firmer bond between these distantly related populations.

About 8000 to 10,000 years ago rising sea levels separated New Guinea from Australia and the populations in both these areas since then have pursued divergent courses with only relatively minor exchanges between them. Indeed, even at the time the water barrier became reality it is probable that Australian populations were already undergoing genetic differentiation: if we accept the evidence of contrasting skull morphology from sites in southeast Australia this could have been in process for at least 10,000 years before the end of the Pleistocene. During the Recent period Melanesians were shaped by a new wave of migrants who brought with them not only a vastly different technology but also an array of genes not present before. Australia too may have witnessed the arrival of new migrants in the same period for when agriculture was taking hold to the north, a new microlith industry was revolutionising the stone tool kit of Australians. These innovators possibly were producing other social changes reflected now in the linguistic differences between Pama-Nyungen across the centre and south of the continent and the diversified language families of the north.

The developments in Melanesia and the likely relationships with Polynesia and Micronesia as evidenced by linguistic relationships and scant archaeological discoveries have been summarised by Howells in his recent book *The Pacific Islanders* (1973). The genetic marker distribution is adding support to some of the hypothetical movements outlined by the linguists and archaeologists, and in particular we now have genetic evidence for links between Melanesia and Micronesia, and between the latter area and South East Asia. Unfortunately Polynesia remains almost completely uncharted by the techniques of genetic marker analysis. We are filling some of the gaps for the western outliers at the present time, but the islands of the main Polynesian bloc remain to be investigated.

Let us look, however, in more detail at Australia itself. Populations in the centre are today distinctly different in genetic constitution from those in the north. The north has remained a close point of contact with New Guinea and this influence is present not only in anthroposcopic traits but also in certain specific genes such as blood group B, the acid phosphatase allele p^a and the gammaglobulin marker $Gm^{1,5,13,14}$, all of which are absent in central Australia but present in New Guinea. Nor is the genetic differentiation in Australia between centre and north due only to absence of specific markers, which it could be argued is due to loss in small breeding populations. Some markers in the centre are absent in the north, the most notable cases being the phosphoglucomutase $PGM_2{}^3$ and the peptidase $Pep\ B^7$ alleles.

Finally, what do genetic markers have to tell about the possible ancestral homeland(s) of the Australian Aboriginals? The links with populations ancestral to present-day black Africans have been mentioned above. The evidence for such links will be more convincing if further specific alleles confined to these populations can be discovered. On the contrary side specific markers in present-day black African populations, such as the acid phosphatase p^r, the phosphoglucomutase $PGM_2{}^2$ and the peptidase $Pep\ A^2$ alleles have not been found in Australia (or anywhere in the Western Pacific), the only exception being the presence of p^r in the Banks and Torres Islands and possibly in the Philippines.

The Veddoids? When I began my investigations 15 years ago I was searching for specific markers which might link Australian Aboriginals with the Veddahs of Ceylon and the 'Veddoid' populations of south India. So far no specific markers common to any of these sets of populations have been found. By contrast, the Veddahs of Ceylon do have some gene markers in common with groups in southeast Asia, particularly Tf D_{Chi} and the abnormal haemoglobin Hb E. The 'Veddoids' of south India, however, have neither of these markers, possessing the abnormal haemoglobin HbS and having no transferrin variants in the populations which I have studied. It is only in the north east of India that the transferrin allele Tf D_{Chi} is found and HbE is not uncommon among tribal populations such as the Oraons, Konda Reddi and Koya Dora.

Ainu? No specific markers have been reported which link Ainu with Australian Aboriginals. The recent studies of Omoto and Misawa (1976) reveal the Ainu to possess Mongoloid markers and not to be closely related to Melanesian or Australian Aboriginal populations.

Caucasians? The white populations of Europe and the modern populations of India possess a number of specific markers which distinguish them from non-white populations; amongst these markers are the adenylate kinase AK^2 (found with low frequency also in Africa), the p^c acid phosphatase and the transferrin B_2 alleles. None of these is found in Australian Aboriginals or in the Western Pacific.

Malayan Aboriginals? The evidence based on specific markers is at present almost non-existent. The recent report (Welch, 1973), referred to earlier, of a $Pep\ B^6$ allele in Aboriginal populations in West Malaysia needs further investigation. In any case it appears to be a recent introduction into Australia for it is confined almost entirely to the Nunggubuyu of Arnhem Land and to one restricted area of Irian Jaya in New Guinea. Other specific markers remain to be discovered. But aboriginals in West Malaysia do possess markers in common with Mongoloid populations in the same area and this suggests that gene exchange has been taking place in a way which has modified considerably the structure of Malaysian Aboriginal populations from that which they must have had originally.

The totality of our knowledge, despite intensive studies in the last decade and a half, is still very meagre. This is true both for the coverage of the populations in Australia and throughout the Western Pacific and South East Asia, but also for the gene loci sampled. The serum proteins and enzymes reported here represent only a small fraction of the proteins under the control of the genome of Man. When the techniques available now can be applied more widely, say to an array of 100 or more products of our genes, it may be possible to give firmer answers to the question posed by this symposium than is possible at this point in time.

Acknowledgements: Many persons both in Australia and overseas have contributed to the work on which the present paper is based: to them all I express my thanks. In particular during the last few years I am indebted to N. M. Blake, E. M. McDermid, R. Taylor, Elizabeth Robertson, Kathryn Sims, Christine Hayes, Ann Montagner and Marjorie Coggan for helpful discussions and excellent assistance in Canberra.

References

BASHIR, H. V., J. M. MACQUEEN, D. B. AMOS, J. J. GUINAN, J. M. JOHNSTONE, J. V. M. BROTHERTON, B. BOETTCHER and C. J. ASHTON   1973   A study of the HL–A system in an Australian Aboriginal population. In *Histocompatibility Testing 1972*. J. Dausset and J. Colombani (eds). Munksgaard, Copenhagen.

BAYANI-SIOSON, P. S.   1971   Biochemical polymorphism in Filipino populations 3. Qualitative and quantitative differences in acid phosphatase of red cells. *Acta medicae Phillipina*, 7: 101–06.

BENNETT, J. H., C. C. AURICHT, A. J. GRAY, R. L. KIRK and L. Y. C. LAI   1961   Haptoglobin and transferrin types in the Kuru region of Australian New Guinea. *Nature*, 189:68–69.

BLAKE, N. M. and R. L. KIRK   1968   A new genetic variant of 6-phosphogluconate dehydrogenase in Australian Aborigines. *Nature*, 221:278.

——, ——, W. H. P. LEWIS and H. HARRIS   1970   Some further peptidase B phenotypes. *Annals of Human Genetics*, 33:301–05.

——, K. OMOTO, R. L. KIRK and D. C. GAJDUSEK   1973   Variation in red cell enzyme groups among populations of the Western Caroline Islands, Micronesia. *American Journal of Human Genetics*, 25:413–21.

—— and ——   1975   Phosphoglucomutase types in the Asian-Pacific area: a critical review including new phenotypes. *Annals of Human Genetics*, 38:251–373.

——, N. SAHA, E. M. McDERMID, R. L. KIRK and G. G. CRANE   1974   Additional electrophoretic variants of 6-phosphogluconate dehydrogenase. *Humangenetik*, 21:347–54.

BOOTH, P. B.   1971   Anti-N^A, an antibody subdividing Melanesian N. *Vox Sang*, 21:522–30.

——, J. A. ALBREY, J. WHITTAKER and R. SANGER   1970   The Gerbich blood group system. A useful genetic marker in certain Melanesians of Papua and New Guinea. *Nature*, 228:462.

CHEN, S. H., L. A. MALCOLM, A. YOSHIDA and E. R. GIBLETT   1971   Phosphoglycerate kinase: an x-linked polymorphism in Man. *American Journal of Human Genetics*, 23:87–91.

——, and E. R. GIBLETT   1972   Phosphoglycerate kinase: additional variants and their geographic distribution. *American Journal of Human Genetics*, 24:229–30.

CLEVE, H., R. L. KIRK, C. PARKER and A. G. BEARN   1963   Two genetic variants of the Group-Specific component of human serum: Gc Chippewa and Gc Aborigine. *American Journal of Human Genetics*, 15:368–79.

—— and ——   1967   On the distribution of the Gc variant Gc Aborigine in Melanesian populations; determination of the Gc-type in sera from Tongariki Island, New Hebrides. *Acta Geneticae*, 17:511–17.

CURTAIN, C. C., D. C. GAJDUSEK, C. KIDSON, J. G. GORMAN, L. CHAMPNESS and R. RODRIGUE   1965   Haptoglobins and transferrins in Melanesia. *American Journal of Physical Anthropology*, 23:363–79.

——, E. VAN LOGHEM and M. S. SCHANFIELD   1976   Immunoglobulin markers as indicators of population affinities in Australasia and the Western Pacific. In *The origin of the Australians*, R. L. Kirk and A. G. Thorne (eds), pp 347–364. Australian Institute of Aboriginal Studies, Canberra.

DAUSSET, J. and J. COLAMBANI   1973   *Histocompatibility Testing—1972*, J. Dausset and J. Colombani (eds). Munksgaard, Copenhagen.

FORBES, J. F., H. BASHIR, R. CROSS, M. ALPERS, A. TING and P. J. MORRIS   1973   Leucocyte antigen studies in Australia and New Guinea. In *The human biology of Aborigines in Cape York*, R. L. Kirk (ed). Australian Institute of Aboriginal Studies, Canberra.

HARRIS, H.   1970   *The principles of human biochemical genetics*. North-Holland Publishing Company, Amsterdam and London.

—— and D. A. HOPKINSON   1972   Average heterozygosity per locus in man: an estimate based on the incidence of enzyme polymorphisms. *Annals of Human Genetics*, 36:9–20.

HOPKINSON, D. A.   1968   Genetically determined polymorphisms of erythrocyte enzymes in man. *Advanced Clinical Chemistry*, 2:37.

HOWELLS, W. W.   1973   *The Pacific Islanders.* Weidenfeld and Nicholson, London.
KENRICK, K. G.   1967   Gc-Aborigine in a New Guinea population. *Acta Genetica et Statistica Medica*, 17:222–25.
KIMURA, M. and T. OHTA   1969   The average number of generations until extinction of an individual mutant gene in a finite population. *Genetics*, 63:701–09.
KIRK, R. L.   1965   *The distribution of genetic markers in Australian Aborigines.* Australian Institute of Aboriginal Studies, Canberra.
——   1968a   *Haptoglobin groups in Man.* Monographs in Human Genetics No. 4, Karger, Basel.
——   1968b   The world distribution of transferrin variants and some unsolved problems. *Acta geneticae medicae et gemellologiae*, 17:613–40.
——   1973   Genetic studies of Cape York populations. In *The human biology of Aborigines in Cape York*, R. L. Kirk (ed). Australian Institute of Aboriginal Studies, Canberra.
—— and L. Y. C. LAI   1961   The distribution of haptoglobin and transferrin groups in South and South East Asia. *Acta Genetica et Statistica Medica*, 11:97–105.
——, ——, G. H. VOS and L. P. VIDYARTHI   1962a   A genetical study of the Oraons of the Chota Nagpur Plateau (Bihar, India). *American Journal of Physical Anthropology*, 20:375–85.
——, ——, ——, R. L. WICKRAMASINGHE and T. E. PEREIRA   1962b   The blood and serum groups of selected populations in South India and Ceylon. *American Journal of Physical Anthropology*, 20:485–97.
——, H. CLEVE and A. G. BEARN   1963a   The distribution of Gc types in sera from Australian Aborigines. *American Journal of Physical Anthropology*, 21:215–23.
——, —— and ——   1963b   The distribution of the Group Specific component (Gc) in selected populations in South and South East Asia and Oceania. *Acta Genetica et Statistica Medica*, 13:140–49.
——, C. PARKER and A. G. BEARN   1964   The distribution of the transferrin variants D_1 and D_{Chi} in various populations. *Acta Genetica*, 14:41–51.
——, N. M. BLAKE, P. M. MOODIE and J. TIBBS   1971   The distribution of some serum protein and enzyme groups among populations at various localities in the Northern Territory of Australia. *Human Biology in Oceania*, 1:54–76.
KITCHIN, F. D. and A. G. BEARN   1966   The electrophoretic patterns of normal and variant phenotypes of the Group Specific (Gc) components in human serum. *American Journal of Human Genetics*, 18:201–14.
——, ——, M. ALPERS and D. C. GAJDUSEK   1972   Genetic studies in relation to Kuru. III. Distribution of the inherited serum Group-Specific protein (Gc) phenotypes in New Guineans: an association of Kuru and the Gc Ab phenotype. *American Journal of Human Genetics*, 24:572–75.
LAI, L. Y. C.   1963   A new transferrin in New Guinea. *Nature*, 198:589.
LAYRISSE, M., T. ARENDS and S. DOMINGUEZ   1955   Nuevo grupo sanguineo encontrado en descentientes de indios. *Acta medica Venezolena*, 3:132–35.
LI, W. H.   1975   The first arrival time and mean age of a deleterious mutant gene in a finite population. *American Journal of Human Genetics*, 27:274–86.
MALCOLM, L. A., D. G. WOODFIELD, N. M. BLAKE, R. L. KIRK and E. M. MCDERMID   1972   The distribution of blood, serum protein and enzyme groups on Manus (Admiralty Islands, New Guinea). *Human Heredity*, 22:305–22.
MCDERMID, E. M. and G. H. VOS   1971a   Variants in human serum albumin and caeruloplasmin in populations from Australia, New Guinea, South Africa and India. *Australian Journal of Experimental Biology and Medical Science*, 49:309–12.
—— and ——   1971b   Serum protein groups of South African Bantu. 2. α_1-antitrypsin, group-specific component and further observations on haptoglobin and caeruloplasmin. *South African Journal of Medical Science*, 36:63–68.
—— and H. CLEVE   1972   A comparison of the fast migrating Gc-variant of Australian Aborigines, New Guinea indigenes, South African Bantu and Black Americans. *Human Heredity*, 22:249–53.
MELARTIN, L. and B. S. BLUMBERG   1966   Albumin-Naskapi: a new genetic variant of serum albumin. *Science*, 153:1664–66.
NICHOLLS, E. M., H. B. M. LEWIS, D. W. COOPER and J. H. BENNETT   1965   Blood group and serum protein differences in some central Australian Aborigines. *American Journal of Human Genetics*, 17:293–307.

Oмото, K. and S. Harada   1972   The distribution of polymorphic traits in the
    Hidaka Ainu. II. Red cell enzyme and serum protein groups. *J. Faculty of Science,
    University of Tokyo*. Section 5, 4:171–211.
—— and S. Misawa   1976   The genetic relations of the Ainu. In *The origin of the
    Australians*, R. L. Kirk and A. G. Thorne (eds), pp. 365–76. Australian Institute of
    Aboriginal Studies, Canberra.
Piazza, A. and C. Viganotti   1973   Evolutionary trees and HL–A poly-
    morphism. In *Histocompatibility testing—1972*, J. Dausett and J. Colombani (eds).
    Munksgaard, Copenhagen.
Saha, N., R. L. Kirk, Shaila Shanbhag, S. H. Joshi and H. M. Bhatia   1974
    Genetic studies among the Kadar of Kerala. *Human Heredity*, 24:198–218.
Steinberg, A. G. and R. L. Kirk   1965   Quoted in R. L. Kirk (1965).
—— and ——   1970   Gm and Inv types of Aborigines in the Northern Territory
    of Australia. *Archaeology and Physical Anthropology in Oceania*, 5:163–72.
——, D. C. Gajdusek and M. Alpers   1972   Genetic studies in relation to Kuru.
    B. Distribution of human gamma globulin allotypes in New Guinea populations.
    American Journal of Human Genetics, 24 supplement:S95–110.
Vos, G. H. and R. L. Kirk   1961   The Di^a and Js^a and V blood groups in South
    and South East Asia. *Nature*, 189:321–22.
—— and ——   1962   Naturally occurring anti-E which distinguishes a variant
    of the E antigen in Australian Aboriginals. *Vox Sang*, 7:22–32.
——, —— and A. G. Steinberg   1963   The distribution of the Gamma
    Globulin types Gm(a), Gm(b), Gm(x) and Gm-like in South and South East
    Asia and Australia. *American Journal of Human Genetics*, 15:44–52.
Wang, A. C., H. E. Sutton and I. D. Scott   1967   Transferrin D$_1$: identity in
    Australian Aborigines and American Negroes. *Science*, 156: 936–37.
Weitkamp, L. R., D. C. Shreffler and J. Saave   1969   Serum albumin variants
    in New Guinea indigines. *Vox Sang*, 17:237.
——, E. M. McDermid, J. V. Neel, J. M. Fine, C. Petrini, L. Bonazzi, V. Ortali,
    F. Porta, R. Tanis, D. J. Harris, T. Peters, G. Ruffini and E. Johnston   1973
    Additional data on the population distribution of human serum albumin genes;
    three new variants. *Annals of Human Genetics*, 37:219–26.
Welch, Q. B.   1973   Peptidase B variants among the Semai, Temuan, Semelai
    and Jakun groups of West Malaysian Orang Asli. *Human Heredity*, 23:482–86.

Immunoglobulin markers as indicators of population affinities in Australasia and the Western Pacific

C.C. Curtain, Erna van Loghem and M.S. Schanfield

SINCE THE DISCOVERY of Gm(a) by Grubb and Laurell (1956) at least thirty immunoglobulin markers have been reported. Each marker belongs to a specific locus, identified with a region of either the light or heavy polypeptide chains which make up the immunoglobulins. The main markers and their loci are listed in Table 1. It can be seen that two nomenclatures are in use. In this paper the alphabetical will be used in preference to the numerical nomenclature which was proposed by the WHO Scientific Group on Genes, Genotypes and Allotypes of Immunoglobulins (1965). The reasons for this were given by Curtain *et al* (1971). It can be seen from Table 1 that neither nomenclature indicates the genetic relationships between the markers or their molecular localisation. As a consequence, we feel that the present state of the nomenclature is one of the barriers standing between the non-specialist and an appreciation of the significance of the immunoglobulin marker systems. To the physical anthropologist this significance lies in the knowledge that the markers are inherited in different combinations or allo-groups in different ethnic groups (Steinberg, 1969). The distribution of these allogroups is set out in Table 2. It is clear that not only do all the races tested have allogroups not found in the others but also that no two have the same array of markers. There is no other human genetic system with such a distinctive distribution of alleles. A general review of the genetic markers of the human immunoglobulins will be found in Grubb (1970).

It was appreciated quite early that data on the immunoglobulin markers could contribute to our understanding of the relationships between the populations of Australasia and the Western Pacific. The first study was published by Vos, Kirk and Steinberg (1963) covering a wide range of populations in the region and a number of others followed in the ensuing decade. Their data and other early observations are summarised in Table 3. Tabulation and discussion of the data is complicated by the fact that each study has added new markers and differences even exist between contemporary studies. Thus, of Friedlaender and Steinberg (1970), Steinberg and Kirk (1970), Schanfield (1971) and Curtain *et al* (1971, 1972) only the latter two gave results for Gm(g), and Gm(z) was tested only by Curtain and his

Table 1: The Gm, A_2m and Inv markers and their localisation on the immunoglobulin chains of human serum

System	Gm			Inv	A_2m
Locus	IgG1(γ_1)	IgG2(γ_2)	IgG3(γ_3)	L chain (κ)	IgA2(α_2)
Nomenclature					
—alphabetic[a]	a x f z	n	g b^0 b^1 b^3 b^4 b^5 s t c^3 c^5	1 a b	1,2
—numerical[b]	1 2 3,4 17	23	21 11 5 12 13 14 10 15 16 6 24	1 2 3	1,2

[a] nomenclature used in this paper.
[b] nomenclature proposed by the WHO Scientific Group on Genes, Genotypes and Allotypes (1965).

Table 2: Distribution of the Gm gene allogroups in different ethnic groups

	IgG1 Locus	IgG3 Locus
Negroes	za	$b^0 b^1 b^3 b^4 b^5$
	za	$b^0 b^1 c^3 c^5$
	za	$b^0 s\ b^3 b^5$
	za	$b^0 b^1 c^3 b^4 b^5$
Caucasians	f	$b^0 b^1 b^3 b^4 b^5$
	za	g
	zax	g
Mongoloids	fa	$b^0 b^1 b^3 b^4 b^5$
	za	$b^0 stb^3 b^5$
	za	g
	za	g
Australian Aboriginals	za	g
	zax	g
	za	$b^0 b^1 b^3 b^4 b^5$ [a]
Melanesians (MN and NAN)[b,c]	fa	$b^0 b^1 b^3 b^4 b^5$
(NAN)	za	$b^0 b^1 b^3 b^4 b^5$
(MN and NAN)	za	g
(MN and NAN)	zax	g

[a] In Northern Australian Aboriginals only.
[b] MN, Melanesian speaking; NAN non-Austronesian-speaking.
[c] Selected Melanesian sera have been tested for b^4 and b^5. These markers always occur when b^0, b^1 and b^3 are present.

colleagues. Testing for Gm(z) permits detection of *Gm*ab in Gm(afb) heterozygotes and the use of Gm(g) reagents reveals *Gm*ag in heterozygotes with either *Gm*ab or *Gm*afb. Finally, only Curtain *et al* (1972) included Gm(n) and Am(1), the markers at the IgG2 and IgA$_2$ loci respectively. Because of these differences we have summarised the data in a series of separate tables. Tables 4–7 summarise the already published data for Australian and Melanesian populations for the markers at the IgG1, IgG2, IgG3 and K chain loci. In Tables 8 and 9 we present new, unpublished data. In Table 8a are given the frequencies of the A$_2$m(1) and A$_2$m(2) types in different Gm genotypes of selected Australian Aboriginal and New Guinea populations. In Table 8b the overall A$_2$m frequencies are given. In Table 9 are presented new data for the IgG1, IgG2, IgG3, A$_2$m and K chain loci in the Melanesian (MN) and non-Austronesian (NAN) speaking populations of New Guinea. These will be published *in extenso* by Schanfield *et al* (in prep.). The map, Figure 1, gives the general location of the MN and NAN language groups in Melanesia.

It is possible to draw some clear-cut conclusions from the mass of data presented in the tables. In New Guinea, Giles, Ogan and Steinberg (1965) were the first to note that differences existed between the MN and NAN speakers with respect to the Gm markers they could test for (Table 3). At the same time it became clear that the New Guinea populations differed markedly from the Australian Aboriginals tested by Vos, Kirk and Steinberg (1963), Flory (1964) and Nicholls *et al* (1965) principally in the absence of Gm(ab) from the Western Desert populations and its low and variable

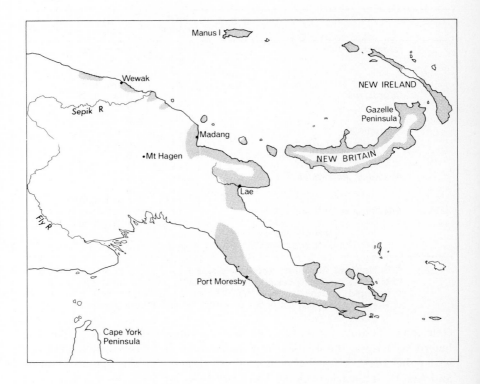

Figure 1   Map of New Guinea showing location of Melanesian-speaking (MN) groups (shaded) the non-Austronesian (NAN) speaking groups occupying the remaining areas. This is adapted from Capell (1969) which gives further detailed maps locating many of the linguistic groups mentioned in the Tables. There is insufficient data available at present to attempt correlation of markers with Capell's sub-groupings of MN and NAN. This possibility should, however, be borne in mind in future work.

frequency amongst the others (Table 4). Flory (1964) also found a Gm(b) frequency of $0 \cdot 10$ in her Cape York and Mornington Island populations, suggesting a 15 per cent Caucasian admixture. Gm(c) was absent in both Australia and New Guinea. Later work confirmed these impressions and extended the number of markers studied. The present position is that in New Guinea the IgG1 and IgG3 markers z, f, a, x, g and all the b factors are found, whilst s, t, c^3 and c^5 are absent. At the IgG2 locus Gm(n) is found and both A_2m markers occur. The K-chain complex Inv(1,a) occurs generally in low frequency. Amongst the Australian Aboriginal populations the f, s, t, c^3 and c^5 markers are absent – all the others are present. Amongst the New Guinea populations it seems that Gm(fa;n;b), $A_2m(1)$ and Gm(fa;n;b), $A_2m(2)$ are probably Austronesian markers and Gm(za;n;b), $A_2m(1)$ is a common non-Austronesian marker. Within the limitations of the earlier surveys the same may be said of, respectively, Gm(fa;b) and Gm(za;b). In some parts of New Guinea a clear cut distinction between the MN and NAN groups with respect to the Gm factors may be obscured by gene flow. This is particularly evident in the Markham Valley and the Gazelle Peninsula of New Britain. Schanfield (1971) found that all of the MN speaking Markham Valley groups which he examined had an appreciable frequency of Gm^{zab} (0·43–0·63), the mean frequency (0·53) being higher than that of Gm^{fab} (0·34) (Table 4b). On the other hand, the only NAN population examined (Waffa) had a Gm^{fab} frequency of only 0·06 and Gm^{zab} frequency of 0·21. In New Britain on the other hand Curtain et al (1971) found that whilst the Gm^{fab} frequency was high (0·27 0·79) amongst the MN speaking Tolai, Kilenge and Kove the NAN Sulka (0·65) also fell within this range. The Gm^{zab} frequency was quite low in all the groups tested (0–0·05). Possibly in the Markham Valley many of the present day MN populations arose from a mixture of MN speakers with an earlier pre-Austronesian stock. Admixture probably also occurred in New Britain between the adjacent Sulka and Tolai populations. Amongst the NAN speakers considerable heterogeneity is evident with respect to the $Gm^{za;n;b}$ allogroup which is found in very high frequency (0·75) amongst the Gogodara of the Fly Delta and in much lower frequency in the Western Highlands (Curtain et al, 1972). In the latter populations $Gm^{za;(n-);g}$ occurs in very high frequency. The $Gm^{za;n;b}$ allogroup has so far not been found in any other part of the world and may be a valuable marker in the south-west Pacific. Schanfield (1971) found high frequencies of $Gm^{(z)a;b}$ amongst several southern New Guinea populations including the Asmat (0·84) in Irian Jaya and the Yonggom (0·81) and Awin (0·73) of the Fly River. Steinberg et al (1972) also reported some high $Gm^{z;ab}$ frequencies from the Western District and south west coast of New Guinea (Table 5).

The extensive new data in Table 9 indicate a cline in Gm and Am allogroups across New Guinea. All of the south coast NAN-speakers, up to the mountains, have high frequencies of $Gm^{za;n;b}$ A_2m^1 and low frequencies of $Gm^{za;g}$ A_2m^1 and $Gm^{zax;g}$ A_2m^1. The north coast people have a high frequency of $Gm^{za;g}$ [$A_2m(1)$ was not tested in these, to any extent]. The highland populations are in between and reflect these differences depending on where they are. Many populations have $Gm^{fa;n;b}$ A_2m^1 or A_2m^2, which we regard as a Melanesian marker, in varying frequencies. The MN-speakers are variable, but almost universally have high frequencies of $Gm^{fa;b}$ and higher Inv^1 frequencies.

Looking at the data for the Australian Aboriginal populations, three striking points emerge. The first is the heterogeneity of the data, the second is the absence of any IgG1 and IgG3 markers other than Gm(a), (x) and (g) from the Western and Central Desert peoples and the third is the extensive occurrence of $Gm^{za;n;b}$ A_2m^1 amongst the peoples of the Gulf of Carpentaria. The latter is the allogroup which occurs in such high frequency amongst the NAN populations of southern New Guinea. It is tempting to assume that the Gm^{ab} allogroup detected in a range of Northern Territory Aboriginal populations by Steinberg and Kirk (1970) is in fact $Gm^{za;n;b}$. These authors concluded that the presence of Gm^{ab} was due to New Guinea admixture; up to 30 per cent of the genotypes of the groups they studied could have been derived from New Guinea. A similar conclusion could be drawn from the finding by Vos, Kirk and Steinberg (1963) of Gm(ab) in the people of the Kimberley. At the IgA_2 locus all the Australian Aboriginal populations tested have a markedly higher A_2m^1 frequency than the New Guinea groups (Tables 8b and 9) other than those living in the southern districts.

The Inv (κ chain locus) data are relatively uninformative. Except in Bougainville the $Inv^{1,a}$ frequencies are low and variable (Table 7) with a tendency to be lower amongst the NAN speakers. Amongst Australian Aboriginals the frequencies are very variable with no consistent pattern, except that the northern populations tend to have somewhat high $Inv^{1,a}$ frequencies.

To attempt a summary in terms of what is known of the history of the region we might postulate that the earliest people possessed the Gm allogroups $Gm^{za(n-);g}$, and $Gm^{zax(n-)g}$ and a very high frequency of A_2m^1. Today these people are represented by the Central and Western Desert Aboriginals. These gene complexes are also found in high frequency amongst some of the NAN-speaking New Guinea Highland populations with the balance of the gene pool being made up by $Gm^{za;n;b}$ and $Gm^{za;(n-);b}$, mostly with A_2m^1. These two allogroups were probably brought to New Guinea by later pre-Austronesian migrants. The rather common occurrence of $Gm^{za;(n-);g}A_2m^2$ in New Guinea – (Tables 8,9) – Asia and American Indians (Schanfield, unpublished) suggests that it might be a very old gene. Today these later pre-Austronesians are represented by the south coast population in which we noted high $Gm^{za;n;b}$ frequencies. Diffusion occurred of this allogroup, but not of $Gm^{za;(n-);b}$ to the Australian mainland. Indeed some of the Aboriginal populations tested have strikingly similar immunoglobulin gene frequency distributions to some of the adjacent New Guinea people. Figure 2 shows a phylogenetic tree constructed using the method of Cavalli-Sforza and Edwards (1967) and the data from Table 7 for the IgG1, IgG2 and IgG3 markers for Aboriginals from the Gulf of Carpentaria, Cape York Peninsula and NAN-speakers from the Western District and the Western Highlands of New Guinea. It can be seen that the Weipa and Western District populations are the most similar on the one hand and the mainland and Western Highland populations the most similar on the other. This is probably not so much due to a direct affinity between the populations so paired but to similar rates of flow of $Gm^{za;n;b}$ from a common source. It may be possible that the people populating these areas came from a common source at a similar time i.e. more recently than the more peripheral populations in central Australia and northern New Guinea. This of course is an alternative to the theory of gene flow from New Guinea. Simmons et al (1962) have suggested an earliest date of 3500 years ago for the last colonisation of Bentinck Island. Assuming that these people, who have a high frequency of $Gm^{za;n;b}$, have remained isolated for the whole of this period

Phenogroups

Population	Gm[a]	Gm[b]	Gm[ax]	Gm[f]	Gm[ab]	Inv[1]	Inv[b]	Sample size
Melanesia								
Markham Valley[a]								
(MN)[a]	0·105	0·000	0·001	—[b]	0·894	0·070	0·930	948
(NAN)[a]	0·411	0·000	0·074	—[b]	0·515	0·115	0·885	573
Bougainville (NAN)[a] (Solomon Is.)	0·109	0·000	0·057	—	0·832	0·413	0·587	148
New Guinea Eastern Highlands								
(Kukukuku, NAN)	0·150	0·000	0·150	—	0·700	0·070	—	—
West Irian (NAN)[c]	0·000	0·000	0·020	—	0·010	0·070	—	—
(MN)[d]	0·150	0·000	0·007	0·820	0·023	0·079	—	134
Ceylon								
Sinhalese[c]	0·545	0·252	0·203	—	0·000	—	—	159
Tamils[c]	0·603	0·236	0·161	—	0·000	—	—	108
Wanni Castes[c]	0·437	0·408	0·155	—	0·000	—	—	98
Veddahs[c]	0·364	0·596	0·040	—	0·000	—	—	52
India								
Oraons[c]	0·182	0·297	0·018	—	0·503	—	—	124
Todas[c]	0·204	0·755	0·041	—	0·000	—	—	99
Kurumbas[c]	0·392	0·538	0·070	—	0·000	—	—	52
Irulus[c]	0·358	0·527	0·115	—	0·000	—	—	74
Malaya								
Malays[c]	0·166	0·000	0·063	—	0·772	—	—	156
Chinese[c]	0·233	0·000	0·028	—	0·741	—	—	149
Thailand								
Thais[c]	0·220	0·000	0·073	—	0·707	—	—	163

[a] Giles *et al* (1965).

[b] Steinberg (1967) reported that, after retesting the same samples, 63·2% of the Gm(a + b +) individuals in the MN Markham Valley population were Gm(3)+ (3 = f) and that 38·5% of the Gm(a + b +) individuals of the NAN population were Gm(3)+.

[c] Kirk (1965) quoting Steinberg and Gajdusek (unpublished).

[d] Van Loghem and den Butter (unpublished).

[e] Vos *et al* (1963).

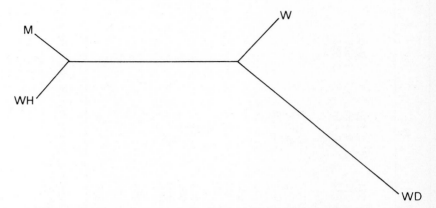

Figure 2 Phylogenetic tree constructed by the method of Cavalli-Sforza and Edwards
(1967) using frequencies of the markers at the IgG1 IgG2 and IgG3 loci for mainland
Aboriginals (M), Weipa Aboriginals (W), Western Highland New Guineans (WH) and
Western District New Guineans (WD). The pairwise distances were calculated to be

M–W	.3386	W–WH	.3655
M–WH	.1203	W–WD	.3395
M–WD	.5803	WH–WD	.5316

this would indicate that this allogroup has been in the region for at least
3500 years. The later-arriving Austronesian peoples appear to have had
little influence on the Australian gene pool, although their influence on New
Guinea was profound. To some extent the lack of influence on Australia
might have been because their major impact was on the north coast of New
Guinea and the Melanesian Islands. However, Melanesian speakers exist
along the eastern end of the south coast. Many of these people, notably the
Motu, were competent seafarers and it is surprising that they did not leave
their mark on the Australian mainland in the form of the $Gm^{fa;n;b}$ complex.
The same may be said of the Malay trepangers who visited our northern
coast for some centuries before the arrival of the white man.

Much more work is needed to fill in the picture presented above. In terms
of number of samples and factors tested our knowledge of the New Guinea
populations is far superior to those of Australia. Nothing for example, is
known of the southwards flow of the $Gm^{za;n;b}$ complex in Australia although
we know that it does not occur in the Central and Western Desert peoples.
It might be argued that the further south we go the less chance we have of
finding people of pure Aboriginal stock. It is in this situation that the
immunoglobulin markers are very valuable because of the unique ethnic
distribution of the various allogroups. The most likely admixture amongst
southern Aboriginal populations is with Caucasians who lack the $Gm^{za;n;b}$
allogroup. The latter if it is present could, in the light of our present knowledge, have only come from New Guinea. As an example of the practic-
ability of this approach we can cite Steinberg's (1973) finding of the
African $Gm^{za;b}$ allogroup in significant frequency (2 per cent) amongst

Ashkenazic Jews living in the U.S.A. This complex probably diffused into the ancient Jewish populations in the Middle East and has survived the 2000 years of the Diaspora in the Ashkenazic Jews. Similarly, we might expect $Gm^{za;n;b}$ to survive 200 years of white contact with Aboriginals and to be traceable in southern Aboriginal populations if it had existed among them.

Acknowledgements: The authors are most grateful to Miss Gerda de Lange for her excellent technical assistance and to Miss Robyn Ballantyne who computed the data for the phylogenetic tree in Figure 2.

The field work of C.C.C. was partly supported by U.S. Public Health Service Grant H.E. 10040–01.

Table 4: Distribution of Gm allogroups at the IgG1, IgG3 and κ chain loci amongst Aboriginals of the Western Desert, Central, Kimberley and Northern regions of Australia.

	No.	Gm			Inv[1]
		a	ax	ab[1], b[3], b[4]	
Western Desert[a]	289	·73	·27	0	—
Central Region[b]	84	·79	·21	0	·208
Kimberley[a]	268	·58	·25	0·17	—
Northern Region[b]	96	·64	·26	0·10	·144
Central Region[c]					
Aranda	77	·78	·22	0	·35
Anmatjera	16	·66	·34	0	·34
Walpari	41	·62	·38	0	·24
Bidjandjadjara	84	·71	·29	0	·18
Pintubi	35	·61	·39	0	·17
Loridja	48	·74	·26	0	·20
Cape York and Mornington Island[d]	103	·67	·21	(·03, ·10[e])	—

[a] Vos *et al* (1963).
[b] Steinberg and Kirk (1970).
[c] Nicholls, Lewis, Cooper and Bennett (1965).
[d] Flory (1964).
[e] As Gm(b).

Table 5: Distribution of Gm allogroups in Melanesia

District, language and place	Size of sample	Gene complex frequencies				References
		za;g	zax;g	za;b	fa;b	
New Britain						
Tolai, Vunalia Village	48	.183	.275	.042	.500	
Tolai, Kuraip Village	39	.118	.357	.000	.525	
Tolai, Rakunai Village	17	.451	.285	.000	.265	
Tolai, Vunalaka Village	18	.289	.238	.000	.472	
MN Tolai, Nordup Village	40	.017	.258	.013	.712	
Tolai, Vairiki Village	56	.128	.274	.000	.598	
Tolai, Ralmalmal Village	68	.225	.106	.015	.654	Curtain *et al* (1971)
Tolai, Bunamin Village	55	.248	.342	.102	.611	
NAN Sulka, Mope Village	54	.165	.141	.046	.648	
Baining, Gaulim Village	43	.307	.483	.000	.209	
New Guinea						
Western Highlands						
NAN Kuman, Minj	101	.724	.083	.183	.010	
Enga, Laiagam	185	.787	.070	.143	.000	
Western District						
NAN Gogodara, Balimo	99	.091	.000	.909	.000	
Central District						
MN Motu, Porebada	38	.013	.000	.105	.882	
Papua New Guinea						
Eastern Highlands						
NAN Simbari	235	.471	.064	.373	.091	
	206	.553	.043	.343		
Southern Highlands						
NAN Onabasulu	317	.781	.024	.166	.029	
	231	.342		.652	.006	
Huli	149	.507	.067	.426		
Western District						
NAN Biami	245	.227		.773		Steinberg, Gajdusek and Alpers (1972)
Olsobip	92	.538		.462		
Irian Jaya						
NAN Southwest Coast	262	.130	.015	.853	.002	
Northwest Coast Mungai	120	.058		.008	.933	
Rennell and Bellona Islands	142	.270	.142		.588	

Population	n					Reference
[MN]						
[...]				·46	·36	Schanfield (1971)
Itsingats	66	·24		·46	·30	
Paguap	90	·132		·478	·389	
Singas	87	·13		·58	·29	
Yanuf	41	·10		·48	·42	
Yatsing	67	·21		·43	·37	
Total	537	·134		·527	·339	
New Britain — MN						
Kilenge	74	·10			·90	Schanfield (1971)
Fiji — MN						
Viti Levu	271	·611	·138	·103	·238	
Lau Islands	74	·43	·11		·46	
Total Fiji	345	·572	·132	·020	·286	
Total MN speakers	956	·290	·047	·314	·349	
Markham — NAN						
Waffa	138	·568	·160	·213	·059	
Fly River — NAN						
Yonggom	91	·17	·02	·81		
Awia	133	·256	·011	·733		
Total	224	·221	·103	·766		
Agats — NAN						
Asmat	179	·122	·1034	·843	·015	Schanfield (1971)
Total NAN speakers	541	·277	·057	·651		
Bougainville — MN						
Urvava	108	·082	·028	·000	·890	
Torau	243	·050	·029	·000	·920	
Nasioi	237	·089	·021	·000	·890	
Siaui	226	·019	·073	·000	·908	
Kwaio	451	·044	·017		·939	
NAN						Friedlaender and Steinberg (1970)
Lau	143	·180	·040	·031	·748	
Baegu	147	·197	·007		·796	
Nasioi	161	·104	·038		·858	
Aita	307	·490	·091		·419	
Nagovisi	386	·022	·023		·953	

Table 6: Distribution of the Inv allotypes in Melanesia

Place	No.	Inv¹ (Inv¹,ᵃ)	Invᵇ (Inv¹⁻,ᵃ⁻)	Reference
New Guinea				
Markham Valley				
MN	948	·070	·930	Giles *et al* (1965)
NAN	573	·115	·885	
Solomon Islands				
Bougainville				
NAN	148	·413	·587	Friedlaender and Steinberg
MN	351	·362	·638	(1970)
NAN	463	·438	·562	
New Britain				
MN	376	·140	·860	
NAN—Sulka	54	·056	·944	
—Baining	42	·190	·810	
New Guinea				
Western Highlands				
NAN	286	·019	·981	Curtain *et al* (1971)
Western District				
NAN	99	·075	·925	
Central District				
MN	38	·263	·737	
Eastern Highlands				
NAN	246	·014	·986	
Southern Highlands	380	·016	·984	Steinberg *et al* (1972)
Western Highlands				
NAN	337	·104	·986	
Markham Valley				
MN	537	·032	·968	
NAN	141	·104	·986	
Western District				
NAN	224	·034	·961	Schanfield (1971)
Irian Jaya				
(Asmat) NAN	178	·076	·924	
New Britain				
MN	74	·126	·880	
Fiji				
MN	271	·126	·874	

Table 7: Frequencies of Gene Complexes at IgG1, IgG2, and IgG3 loci in Australian Aboriginals compared with New Guineans.

	za;(n—);g	zax;(n—);g	za;(n—);b	za;n;b	fa;(n—);b	fa;n;b
			Australian Aboriginals			
Mornington Island	·631	·068	·015	·286	·000	·000
Bentinck Island	·087	·000	·000	·913	·000	·000
Mainland	·742	·091	·000	·167	·000	·000
Weipa	·281	·059	·000.	·660	·000	·000
Western Desert[a]	·797(·019)	·152(·032)	·000	·000	·000	·000
			New Guineans			
New Britain						
Tolai Vunalia (MN)	·183	·275	·000	·042[b]	·086	·414
Tolai Kuraip (MN)	·118	·357	·000	·000	·054	·471
Tolai Rakunai (MN)	·451	·285	·000	·000	·000	·265
Tolai Vunulaka (MN)	·289	·238	·000	·000	·152	·321
Tolai Nordup (MN)	·017	·258	·013[b]	·000	·228	·484
Tolai Vairiki (MN)	·128	·274	·000	·000	·124	·474
Tolai Ralmalmal (MN)	·225	·106	·000	·015[b]	·180	·474
Tolai Bunamin (MN)	·248	·342	·000	·000	·038	·371
Tolai Koulon (MN)	·231	·147	·000	·011[b]	·063	·549
Sulka Mope (NAN)	·165	·141	·039	·007	·158	·490
Baining Gaulim (NAN)	·307	·483	·000	·000	·000	·209
Western Highlands						
Minj (NAN)	·724	·083	·036	·147	·006	·005
Western District						
Balim (NAN)	·91	·000	·164	·745	·000	·000
Central District						
Motu (MN)	·013	·000	·000	·105[b]	·437	·445

[a] The frequencies given in parentheses are for za;n;g and zax;n;g, respectively, which were found only in this population.
[b] A gene complex carrying the opposite Gm(n) type may occur, although there is no evidence for it.
All data from Curtain *et al* (1972).

Table 8a: $A_2m(1)$ and $A_2m(2)$ types in different Gm genotypes[a] of Australian Aboriginals and New Guineans

		$A_2m(1+2-)$	$A_2m(1+2+)$	$A_2m(1-2+)$
GULF OF CARPENTARIA				
Weipa	(N = 28)			
zag/zag		2	–	–
zaxg/za(x)g		3	–	–
zag/zanb		7	2	–
zanb/za(n)b		8	6	–
Bentinck Island	(N = 46)			
zag/zanb		8	–	–
zanb/za(n)b		26	12	–
WESTERN AUSTRALIA				
Western Desert	(N = 70)			
zag/zag		44	–	–
zang/za(n)g		–	2	–
zaxg/za(x)g		18	1	–
zax(n)g/za(x)ng		–	5	–
NEW BRITAIN				
Tolai Vunalia	(N = 48)			
zag/zag		1	–	–
zaxg/za(x)g		8	–	–
zanb/za(n)b		1	–	–
zag/fab		2	–	–
zag/fanb		1	8	–
zaxg/fab		1	2	–
zaxg/fanb		–	12	–
zanb/fa(n)b		–	2	–
fanb/fanb		–	–	10
Tolai Nordup	(N = 40)			
zaxg/za(x)g		3	–	–
zag/fanb		–	1	–
zaxg/fab		1	2	–
zaxg/fanb		5	7	–
zanb/fa(n)b		–	1	–
fab/fab		1	1	1
fanb/fa(n)b		1	4	12
NEW GUINEA				
Western District				
Balimo	(N = 99)			
zag/zag		2	–	–
zag/zab		2	–	–
zag/zanb		3	8	1
zab/zab		3	–	–
zanb/za(n)b		27	42	11
Central District				
Motu	(N = 38)			
zanb/za(n)b		–	1	–
zag/fab		1	–	–
zanb/fa(n)b		–	5	1
fab/fab		1	4	2
fanb/fa(n)b		–	6	17

[a] Markers between brackets (in some genotypes with Gm(x) and Gm(n)) indicates that homozygosity cannot be demonstrated.

Table 8b: Gene frequencies of $A_2m(1)$ and $A_2m(2)$ in Australian Aboriginals and New Guineans

		Gene frequencies	
		$A_2m(1)$	$A_2m(2)$
Gulf of Carpentaria			
Weipa	N = 28	·86	·14
Bentinck Island	N = 46	·87	·13
Western Australia			
Western Desert	N = 70	·94	·06
New Guinea—New Britain			
Tolai Vunalia	N = 48	·54	·46
Tolai Nordup	N = 40	·47	·53
New Guinea—Mainland			
Western District Balimo	N = 99	·63	·37
Central District Motu	N = 38	·26	·74

Table 9: Immunoglobulin allogroups in New Guinea populations

Column allele systems (stacked header): IgG2 / IgG1 / IgG3 / IgA$_2$

Population	N	−za g A_2m^1	−za g A_2m^2	−zax g A_2m^1	n za b A_2m^1	−za b A_2m^1	n za b A_2m^2	−za b A_2m^2	n fa b A_2m^1	−fa b A_2m^1	n fa b A_2m^2	−fa b A_2m^1	Others	Inv^1
Papuan Speakers														
Western District														
Yonggom	246	·241	·005	·032	·535	·180	—	—	·005	—	—	—	·002	·051
Awin	27	·222	·037	—	·741	—	—	—	—	—	—	—	—	·057
Suki	21	·190	·024	—	·568	—	—	—	—	—	—	—	—	·024
Southern Highlands District														
Foi[a]	194	·103	·013	·015	·869	—	—	—	—	—	—	—	—	·039
Gulf District														
Kovio or Kukukuku[a,b]	46	·435		·022	(	·337	)	(	(		·206	)		·033
Central District														
Towade/Kuni[a,b]	41	·821		·048	(	—	)	(	(		·131	)		·036
Fuyuge[a,b]	98	·684		·076	(	·056	)	(	(		·184	)		·046
Fuyuge	56	·527	·045	·062	·125	—	—	·018	·027		·179	·018		·063
Suku-Sikube[a,b]	32	·750		·031	(	·031	)	—	(		·187	)		·016
Koiari/Maria/Obres	56	·411	·036	—	·312	·009		·009	·071		·134	·009	·009	·059
Milne Bay District														
Gwoira?	19	·658	·105	·079	—	—	—	—	·026		·131	—		—
Northern District														
Doriaidi	23	·174	·022	—	·261	—	—	—	·109	·022	·413	—		·039
Boli	16	·594	·031	—	—	—	—	—	·062	—	·250	—	·063[c]	·028
Berigi	12	·08	·04	—	·71	—	—	—	·08	—	·58	—		—
Binandere[a,b]	19	·316		—	(	·263	)	—	—	—	·421	—		·024
Guhu-Samane or Tawade	57	·114	·009	—	·052	—	—	·017	·158	·043	·579	·026		·208
Guhu-Samane	48	·510	·104	·062	·229	·010	·010	—	—	—	·052	—	·021[c]	·021
Hanjara[a,b]	34	(·456		·088	(	·206	)	(	(		·250	)		·094

	n													
Morobe District														
Bia	80	·075	·019	—	·300	·100	·025	·006	·087	·031	·287	·069		·157
Kene	95	·710	·068	·021	·079	·026	—	(	·010	—	·058	·026	·005[c]	·062
Kene/Kunimaipa[a,b]	73	(·541	)	·123	(	·164	)	)	(	·171	(	)		·028
Kunimaipa[a,b]	27	·464	)	·071	(	·339	)	)	(	·125	(	)		·018
Wiri	102	·613	·034	·059	·132	·054	·005	)	(	·103	)			·036
Wiri[a,b]	61	(·459	)	·041	(	·131	)	)	(	·369	)			·098
Watut[a,b]	215	(·674	)	·044	(	·249	)	)	(	·032	)			·056
Eastern Highlands														
Kamano[a]	33	·651	·106	·091	·091	(	—	)	·061	—	(	)		—
East Sepik														
Abelam[a,b]	112	(·924	)	·009	(	·036	)	)	(	·031	(	)		·046
Iatmul[a,b]	21	(·905	)	—	(	·095	)	)	(	—	(	)		—
Melanesian Speakers														
Central District														
Motu	123	·012	—	—	(·150	)	·008	)	(·130	)	(·700	)		·203
Milne Bay District														
Mixed	70	·200	·021	·021	·021	·014	—	)	·043	·041	·550	·028	·093	·099
Kikukuia	49	·010	—	—	·122	·010	·020		·245	·041	·510	·031	·010	·110
Morobe District														
Atsera	80	·262	·025	—	·156	·044	·012	·006	·094	·081	·206	·112		·052
Madang District														
Graged[a,b]	32	(·094	)	·047	(	·125	)	)	·734	(	)			·190
West New Britain														
Kilengi	53	·094	·019	·019	·047	·019	·019	(	·198	·066	·462	·066		·109
Kove[a,b]	68	(·162	)	—	(	·052	)	)	(	·787	(	)		·101

[a] Not tested for Gm(n).

[b] Not tested for A₂m(1 or 2).

[c] n, za, g A₂m(1) allogroup.

General Notes

All samples were tested for Gm(a, x, z, f, g, b^0, b^1, b^3, b^5, c^3, c^5, s and t) and Inv(1).
The allogroup frequencies in this table are gene counting estimates. They thus may differ slightly from maximum likelihood estimates.

References

CAPELL, A.   1969   *A survey of New Guinea languages.* Sydney University Press, Sydney.

CAVALLI-SFORZA, L. L. and A. W. F. EDWARDS   1967   Phylogenetic Analysis: Models and estimation procedures. *American Journal of Human Genetics*, 19:233–57.

CURTAIN, C. C., E. VAN LOGHEM, A. BAUMGARTEN, T. GOLAB, J. GORMAN, C. F. RUTGERS and C. KIDSON   1971   The ethnological significance of the gamma-globulin (Gm) factors in Melanesia. *American Journal of Physical Anthropology*, 34: 257–72.

——, ——, H. H. FUDENBERG, N. B. TINDALE, R. T. SIMMONS, R. L. DOHERTY and G. VOS   1972   Distribution of the immunoglobulin markers at the IgG1, IgG2, IgG3, IgA₂ and κ-chain loci in Australian aborigines: Comparison with New Guinea populations. *American Journal of Human Genetics*, 24:145–55.

FLORY, L. L.   1964   Serum factors of Australian aborigines from North Queensland. *Nature*, 201:508–09.

FRIEDLAENDER, J. S. and A. G. STEINBERG   1970   Anthropological significance of gamma globulin (Gm and Inv) antigens in Bougainville Island, Melanesia. *Nature*, 228:59–61.

GILES, E., E. OGAN and A. G. STEINBERG   1965   Gamma-globulin factors (Gm and Inv) in New Guinea: anthropological significance. *Science*, 150:1158–60.

GRUBB, R.   1970   *The genetic markers of human immunoglobulins.* Springer, New York.

—— and A.-B. LAURELL   1956   Hereditary serological human serum groups. *Acta pathologica microbiologica scandinavica*, 39:390–98.

KIRK, R. L.   1965   Population genetic studies of the indigenous peoples of Australia and New Guinea. *Progress medical Genetics*, 4:202–41.

NICHOLLS, E. M., H. B. M. LEWIS, D. W. COOPER and J. H. BENNETT   1965   Blood group and serum protein differences in some Central Australian aborigines. *American Journal of Human Genetics*, 17:293–307.

SCHANFIELD, M. S.   1971   *Population studies on the Gm and Inv antigens in Asia and Oceania.* Ph.D. Thesis, University of Michigan, Ann Arbor.

——, P. B. BOOTH, R. HORNABROOK, J. SAAVE, G. WOODFIELD and H. H. FUDENBERG   Immunoglobulin allotypic markers in several areas of Papua New Guinea. (In preparation.)

SIMMONS, R. T., N. B. TINDALE and J. B. BIRDSELL   1962   A blood group genetical survey in Australian aborigines of Bentinck, Mornington and Forsyth Islands, Gulf of Carpentaria. *American Journal of Physical Anthropology*, 20:303–20.

STEINBERG, A. G.   1967   Genetic variations in human immunoglobulins: The Gm and Inv types. In *Advances in Immunogenetics*, T. J. Greenwalt (ed), pp. 75–98. Lippincott, Philadelphia.

——   1969   Globulin polymorphisms in man. *American Review of Genetics*, 3:25–52.

——   1973   The Gm and Inv allotypes of some Ashkenazic Jews living in northern U.S.A. *American Journal of Physical Anthropology*, 39:409–12.

—— and R. L. KIRK   1970   Gm and Inv types of aborigines in the Northern Territory of Australia. *Archaeology and Physical Anthropology in Oceania*, 5:163–72.

——, D. C. GAJDUSEK and M. ALPERS   1972   Genetic studies in relation to Kuru. V. Distribution of human gamma globulin allotypes in New Guinea populations. *American Journal of Human Genetics*, 24:S95–110.

VOS, G. H., R. L. KIRK and A. G. STEINBERG   1963   The distribution of the gamma globulin types Gm(a), Gm(b), Gm(x) and Gm-like in South and Southeast Asia and Australia. *American Journal of Human Genetics*, 15:44–52.

W.H.O.   1965   Scientific Group on Genes, Genotypes and Allotypes of Immuno-globulins. Notation for genetic factors of human immunoglobulins. *Bulletin World Health Organisation*, 33:721–24.

The genetic relations of the Ainu

K. Omoto and S. Misawa

THE AINU of Northern Japan, the aboriginal group who once inhabited also Sachalin and the Kurile Islands, are now almost confined in their distribution to Hokkaido, the northernmost island of Japan. They number about 16,000 but of these the full-blooded Ainu are believed to be only a few percent. For anthropological study, the District of Hidaka in the southern part of Hokkaido is almost the only place at the present time where a reasonable number of Ainu subjects can be studied.

During the period 1966–1971 we carried out genetic surveys of the Ainu as a part of the Japanese IBP Human Adaptability project (Anthropological Study and Adaptability of the Ainu: Watanabe, 1975). The details of the results for the 40 genetic systems listed in Table 1 have been published in a series of publications (Misawa and Hayashida, 1968, 1970; Omoto, 1970, 1972; Omoto and Harada, 1968, 1969, 1972).

The present paper will review briefly the characteristics of the distribution of genetic markers in the Ainu and examine the genetic affinities of the Ainu with other population groups, including the Australian Aboriginals. This is important, since beside the well known 'Caucasoid' theory of Ainu affinities, the theory which postulates the special affinity of the Ainu to the Australian Aboriginals has been proposed by several anthropologists, particularly by those in the Soviet Union. Also, the craniometric comparison between Ainu and the Australian Aboriginal skulls led Yamaguchi (1967) to conclude that the Ainu and the Australian Aboriginals are both derived from a generalised upper Palaeolithic or Mesolithic population of Asia, but later differentiated independently under the impact of different population histories and environmental conditions. The question then arises whether we can pick up some particular gene markers which eventually provide evidence of the ancient genetic link between these two groups. They are now distantly separated geographically but they are both peripheral populations of the East Asiatic continent, and if the view often held in zoogeography that peripheral populations tend to preserve primitive characters holds true, it will be of interest to find out if there are any markers which are present specifically in both the Ainu and the Australian Aboriginals.

Table 1: Genetic marker systems examined in the Ainu

Red cell antigens	Serum proteins	Red cell enzymes	Miscellaneous
1. ABO	1. Haptoglobin	1. Acid phosphatase	1. Red-green colour vision
2. MNS	2. Transferrin	2. Phosphoglucomutase (PGM$_1$)	2. PTC taste sensitivity
3. P	3. Gc	3. Phosphoglucomutase (PGM$_2$)	3. Cerumen
4. Lewis	4. Cholinesterase (E$_1$)	4. 6-PGD	4. INH metabolism‡
5. Rh	5. Cholinesterase (E$_2$)	5. AK*	
6. Duffy	6. α_1-antitrypsin (Pi)	6. ADA	
7. Kell	7. Albumin*	7. G-6PD*	
8. Kidd	8. Ceruloplasmin	8. LDH*	
9. Diego	9. Ag	9. MDH*	
	10. Gm†	10. PHI*	
	11. Inv†	11. PGK*	
		12. NADH-Dia*	
		13. Pep A*(?)	
		14. Pep B*	
		15. Pep D*	
		16. Es D	

* Loci with no variation detected.
† Matsumoto and Miyazaki (1972).
‡ Investigation by Sunahara et al (1961).

A total of more than 500 Ainu and 1000 non-Ainu Japanese individuals from various parts of the District of Hidaka were examined during the 1966–1970 surveys. However, not all these samples could be investigated for all the polymorphic systems and the actual number of Ainu samples used for calculation of gene frequencies varied from about 100 to more than 500. Close relatives and those with uncertain Ainu descent were excluded in those cases where the information was available.

Attempts were made to estimate the amount of cumulative gene flow from the non-Ainu Japanese populations. On the basis of official family records and information obtained from informants such as teachers and old men in the Ainu village, the average amount of non-Ainu admixture has been estimated in this sample group at about 40 per cent (Omoto and Harada, 1972). Since the information referred to above covers the time range of approximately the last 100 years, and since it is known that the drastic increase in hybridisation began to take place about 100 years ago, we used for the phylogenetic analyses corrected gene frequencies calculated by Bernstein's method on the assumption of 40 per cent Japanese admixture to give values for a hypothetical, ancestral Ainu population.

Genetic profile of the Ainu

The findings from the genetic surveys are described briefly in the following sections.

1. Red cell antigen groups : The gene frequencies for nine systems examined in our investigations are presented in Table 2 together with those for Japanese from central Japan and Ryukyuan, the inhabitants of the Ryukyu Islands, the chain of islands extending from southern Kyushu of the Japanese main islands to the north eastern tip of Taiwan. In Table 2 results are presented separately for Ryukyuan from Okinawa and Miyako and from the Ishigaki Islands.

The most outstanding feature of the Ainu is the high frequency of the alleles *NS* and *r″* compared to the Japanese and Ryukyuan series. Furthermore, both the alleles *P* and *Jk^a* have a lower frequency than in Japanese, but the Ryukyuan are more similar to the Ainu. It is interesting that *Di^a* is present in a frequency which is slightly higher than in Japanese, and this is true also for the Ryukyuan from Ishigaki Island.

The first comprehensive study of red cell antigen groups of the Ainu was made about 20 years ago by Dr R. T. Simmons and his colleagues in the same area of Hokkaido as we made our surveys (Simmons *et al*, 1953). Some discrepancies are notable between Dr Simmons' and our results, among which one of the most important is the occurrence of K(+) type among the Ainu, since this type is lacking in virtually all the Mongoloid and Pacific peoples. While Simmons and his colleagues reported K(+) in 15 per cent and 8 per cent respectively of pure and mixed Ainu, we failed to observe this phenotype among 532 Ainu. The gene frequencies of the ABO system are also different, in particular with respect to the *B* frequency. Simmons *et al* reported a

Table 2: Frequency distribution of red cell antigen groups among four population groups in Japan

		Ainu[1]		Japanese[2]	Ryukyuan—1 (Okinawa, Miyako)[3]	Ryukyuan—2 (Ishigaki)[4]
A_1BO	$p(A_1)$	0·2511	(0·2451)*	0·2601	0·2702	0·2404
	$q(B)$	0·1618	(0·1580)	0·1675	0·1590	0·1780
	$r(O)$	0·5871	(0·5969)	0·5724	0·5708	0·5816
MNSs	MS	0·0628	(0·0732)	0·0472	0·0801	0·1007
	Ms	0·3980	(0·3592)	0·4562	0·4232	0·4355
	NS	0·1032	(0·1656)	0·0096	0·0216	0·0493
	Ns	0·4360	(0·4020)	0·4870	0·4751	0·4145
P	P	0·1468	(0·1100)	0·2020	0·2076	0·1408
Lewis	Le^a	0·5324	(0·5701)	0·4758	0·4315	0·4665
	R^z	0·0032	(0·0037)	0·0025	0·0045	0·0165
	R^1	0·5311	(0·4553)	0·6448	0·5902	0·6068
	R^2	0·2213	(0·2039)	0·2474	0·2401	0·2786
Rh	R^0	0·0000	(0·0000)	0·0099	0·0078	0·0094
	r^y	0·0000	(0·0000)	0·0000	0·0000	0·0000
	r'	0·0462	(0·0703)	0·0100	0·0403	0·0194
	r''	0·1382	(0·2001)	0·0454	0·0811	0·0101
	r	0·0600	(0·0667)	0·0400	0·0360	0·0592
Duffy	Fy^a	0·9020	(0·9178)	0·8783	0·8409	0·8092
Kell	K	0·0000	(0·0000)	0·0000	0·0000	0·0000
Kidd	Jk^a	0·3312	(0·2840)	0·4020	0·3108	0·1977
Diego	Di^a	0·0398		0·0279	—	0·0328

* In parentheses are corrected values on the basis of estimated 40% Japanese admixture.

References: (1) Misawa & Hayashida (1968, 1970).
(2) Furuhata (1966).
(3) Nakajima et al (1967).
(4) Misawa (1974).

considerably higher B frequency than that of the Japanese, while our figure is almost identical to that of the Japanese.

It may be argued that these discrepancies are explained by the different degree of non-Ainu admixture between the two sample groups of the Ainu (it was much easier to obtain considerable numbers of full blood Ainu 20 years ago!). However, it seems unlikely that an allele with a frequency of about 8 per cent will completely disappear as the result of 40 per cent gene flow from Japanese who do not possess this allele. Our samples contained also a considerable number of relatively pure Ainu individuals and we still failed to detect $K(+)$ type among them. It is possible in the Ainu population that gene frequencies vary markedly from village to village. If the $K(+)$ type has rather a restricted distribution among the Ainu population our failure to detect it may simply be an accident of sampling at the village level.*

In other blood group systems the Ainu gene frequencies are quite similar to those for the Japanese. But it is interesting to note that the overall pattern of gene frequencies of the Ainu seems to show a closer similarity to the Ryukyuan than to the Japanese. In particular, the occurrence of r'' allele in considerable frequency among Ryukyuan of Okinawa and Miyako Islands is of interest, since this allele is known to be extremely rare in most of the other populations of the world.

2. *Red cell enzyme and serum protein groups*: Gene frequencies are summarised in Table 3, together with those of Japanese and Ryukyuan. In the red cell acid phosphatase system the gene P^c is absent, and the frequency of P^a is slightly higher than that of Japanese, approaching the value found in Ryukyuan. For locus 1 of phosphoglucomutase the allele $PGM_1{}^1$ has a higher frequency than in Japanese, and in the adenylate kinase system the gene AK^2 is absent, as in most East Asiatic and Pacific populations.

Among the serum protein systems, for haptoglobin the allele frequency for Hp^1 is found to be among the lowest in the world, the estimated value in a hypothetical ancestral Ainu population being approximately $0 \cdot 10$. A tentative study of Hp sub-typing showed that the allele Hp^{1F} was uncommon in the Ainu as in most Mongoloid populations so far examined.

The finding of serum transferrin variants among the Ainu is of importance, since the variant allele D_{Chi} is found mostly in Mongoloid populations while the allele D_1 occurs in populations of Africa and parts of Oceania. A relatively high frequency of heterozygous Tf CD persons (14 out of 466 unrelated samples) was found in the Ainu. Using control samples of known Tf types it was possible to determine that the TfD found among the Ainu is indistinguishable from TfD_{Chi} and is not TfD_1.

In other enzyme and serum protein systems essentially similar gene frequencies were observed for the Ainu and Japanese. The serum

---

* In subsequent discussions Dr Simmons has commented on this problem. He suggested that the antiserum used for the K blood group typing in the earlier study of Simmons *et al* might have been inadequate and the reported occurrence of $K(+)$ antigen among the Ainu is now to be regarded as doubtful.

Table 3: Gene frequencies of serum protein and red cell enzyme systems in Ainu, Japanese and Ryukyuan populations

		Ainu[1]	Japanese[2]	Ryukyuan[3]
Hp	Hp[1]	0·1623 (0·0992)*	0·2570	0·2495
Tf	C	0·9829 (0·9790)	0·9903	0·9925
	D$_{Chi}$	0·0150 (0·0187)	0·0085	0·0070
	Others	0·0021 (0·0023)	0·0012	0·0005
Gc	Gc[2]	0·2505 (0·2555)	0·2431	0·3064
ACP	p[a]	0·2249 (0·2834)	0·2113	0·2702
	p[b]	0·7751 (0·7166)	0·7887	0·7298
PGM$_1$	PGM$_1$[1]	0·8220 (0·9084)	0·7795	0·7210
	PGM$_1$[2]	0·1780 (0·0916)	0·2175	0·2604
	PGM$_1$[3]	0·0000 (0·0000)	0·0002	0·0039
	PGM$_1$[7]	0·0000 (0·0000)	0·0016	0·0147
	Others	0·0000 (0·0000)	0·0013	0·0000
PGD	PGD[A]	0·9575 (0·9877)	0·9123	0·9211
	PGD[C]	0·0425 (0·0123)	0·0877	0·0789
AK	AK[2]	0·0000 (0·0000)	0·0000	0·0000

* In parentheses are corrected values on the basis of estimated 40% Japanese admixture.

References: (1) Omoto and Harada (1972).
              (2) Summarized from various sources (See Omoto *et al* 1973).
              (3) Omoto *et al* (1973).

cholinesterase atypical gene (E_1^a) is absent in the Ainu as in most Mongoloid populations.

3. Gm and Inv allotypes : The serum samples used in our studies were examined by Matsumoto and Miyazaki (1972) for Gm(1), Gm(2), Gm(4), Gm(5), Gm(13), Gm(15), Gm(16), Gm(21) and Inv(1). The frequencies of the Gm phenogroups of the Ainu were very similar to those of Japanese except for the occurrence in low frequency of $Gm^{2,21}$ in the Ainu. This phenogroup so far has not been found in other populations. The frequency of Inv^1 of the hypothetical, ancestral population of the Ainu was estimated at 0·17. This value is much lower than that for Japanese with a value of 0·29.

4. Other polymorphic systems : Among the other genetic traits examined it is interesting to note that red-green colour blindness is virtually absent in the Ainu, while it is present in about 5 per cent of the non-Ainu boys in the same area. Also the incidence of the PTC non-tasters in the Ainu (ca. 5 per cent) is among the lowest values in the world. For ear-wax the wet cerumen type occurs in approximately 50 per cent of the Ainu. It is postulated that the dry cerumen type already occurred in considerable frequency in the ancestral Ainu population (Omoto, 1970). Finally, according to Sunahara and his colleagues (1963), the frequency of slow-inactivator type for INH metabolism among the Ainu is similar to that in Japanese and other Mongoloid populations.

From this brief summary of the genetic traits investigated in the Ainu it is clear that the distribution of genetic markers overall is remarkably similar to those in Japanese and even more similar to the Ryukyuan. There is no system in which a particularly close affinity can be postulated between the Ainu and European populations. Also, there is no marker indicating an ancient link to the Australian Aboriginals. So far as the systems used in the present comparison are concerned, the Ainu are likely to be more closely related to Mongoloid groups of East Asia than to any other major racial groups.

Genetic distance analyses

It is generally agreed that multivariate analysis is superior in phylogenetic studies to simple comparison of gene frequencies from system to system. However, one drawback of this approach is that the 'racial marker' genes such as Di^a, TfD_{Chi} and others because of their low frequencies usually make only a negligible contribution when assessing the similarity between populations.

The results of the application of genetic distance analysis and construction of phylogenetic trees following the method of Cavalli-Sforza and Edwards (1967) to the problem of the genetic origins of the Ainu have been published already (Omoto, 1972, 1973b). It was shown, in agreement with the conclusion obtained in the last section, that the Ainu have the closest genetic affinity to Japanese and belong to the East Asiatic Mongoloid cluster group.

This work has been extended here using data for 16 genetic loci, namely, nine red cell antigen systems: *ABO, MNS, Rh, Fy, Di, Jk, P, Le, K* and seven serum protein and red cell enzyme systems: *Hp, Tf, Gc, AcP, PGM$_1$, PGD, AK.* The matrix of genetic distances calculated for 18 populations for which gene frequency data were available from published reports are shown in Table 4. Data for the Australian Aboriginals were taken mostly from Kirk (1965, 1973) and Kirk *et al* (1971, 1972). In Tables 4 and 5, Australian Aboriginals—1 refers to the northern populations from Cape York Peninsula and Arnhem Land, while Australian Aboriginals—2 refers to those from Central and Western Australia. In Table 5 the distances from the Ainu to other populations are arranged roughly in increasing order. It is evident that the Ryukyuan and Japanese have the closest distance values to the Ainu. The Ryukyuan show a slightly smaller distance to the Ainu than do the Japanese. Chinese (mainly Taiwan-Chinese), Thai and Formosan aborigines (Takasago tribes) show moderately close distances to the Ainu. On the other hand it should be noted that the distances to the Malays and Indonesians are relatively large; they are even larger than the distance from the Ainu to Australian Aboriginals from Cape York Peninsula and Arnhem Land (Australian Aboriginals—1). However, since only incomplete data was available for some blood group loci for Malays and Indonesians the present results should be considered with reserve. It is interesting also that New Guineans have a slightly larger distance to the Ainu than either of the Australian Aboriginal populations.

Table 4: The matrix of genetic distances among 18 populations based on data for 16 polymorphic loci

		1 Ainu	2 Japanese	3 Ryukyuans	4 Chinese	5 Formosan aborigines	6 Malays	7 Indonesians	8 Thais	9 Eskimos	10 N. American Indians	11 Lapps	12 English	13 S. African Bantu	14 Micronesians	15 New Guineans	16 Australian Aboriginals—1	17 Australian Aboriginals—2
Japanese	2	0·4001																
Ryukyuans	3	0·3793	0·1800															
Chinese	4	0·4762	0·2064	0·2372														
Formosan aborigines	5	0·5945	0·3412	0·4063	0·3032													
Malays	6	0·9280	0·7179	0·7966	0·7357	0·6506												
Indonesians	7	0·9207	0·6799	0·7812	0·7213	0·6737	0·2996											
Thais	8	0·5590	0·3296	0·3901	0·2523	0·2651	0·6352	0·6690										
Eskimos	9	0·8649	0·7051	0·7170	0·6756	0·6394	0·8863	0·9073	0·6972									
N. American Indians	10	0·8934	0·7646	0·7502	0·7482	0·7844	0·8908	0·8789	0·7905	0·6054								
Lapps	11	0·8505	0·7171	0·6948	0·7320	0·7375	0·8455	0·8510	0·7538	0·8604	0·7206							
English	12	0·7303	0·6416	0·6132	0·6701	0·7188	0·8376	0·8300	0·7378	0·9502	0·7874	0·4815						
S. African Bantu	13	1·1800	1·0386	1·0487	1·0567	1·0879	0·9457	0·9512	1·0728	1·2633	1·0241	0·8919	0·7763					
Micronesians	14	0·7315	0·4768	0·5710	0·4937	0·4212	0·6202	0·5585	0·4830	0·7160	0·8374	0·8314	0·8385	1·0953				
New Guineans	15	1·0118	0·8778	0·9125	0·8932	0·8801	1·0566	0·9651	0·9363	0·7883	0·9058	1·0109	1·0874	1·3112	0·7238			
Australian Aboriginals—1	16	0·8347	0·6263	0·6817	0·6207	0·7037	0·8862	0·7871	0·6630	0·7548	0·8040	0·9048	0·9495	1·1224	0·6117	0·7541		
Australian Aboriginals—2	17	0·9461	0·7808	0·8608	0·8087	0·8731	1·0023	0·8833	0·8622	0·8234	0·9236	1·0719	1·1151	1·2758	0·6879	0·7879	0·4398	
Asiatic Indians	18	0·6870	0·5661	0·5477	0·5575	0·6245	0·6755	0·7314	0·5878	0·8007	0·6991	0·5044	0·4216	0·8444	0·7527	1·0190	0·8447	1·0316

Table 5: Genetic distances between Ainu and 17 other populations based on data for 16 polymorphic loci

Ryukyuan	0·3793
Japanese	0·4001
Chinese	0·4762
Thais	0·5590
Formosan aborigines	0·5945
Asiatic Indians	0·6870
Micronesians	0·7315
English	0·7303
Lapps	0·8505
Eskimos	0·8649
N. American Indians	0·8934
Malays	0·9280
Indonesians	0·9207
Australian Aboriginals—1	0·8347
Australian Aboriginals—2	0·9461
New Guineans	1·0118
S. African Bantu	1·1800

Conclusions

The present analysis indicates that on the basis of gene frequency data for 16 loci the Ainu may have a closer genetic affinity to the Mongoloid groups of East Asia than to any other racial groups. Neither the affinities to Caucasoid or Australoid groups, nor the concept of a 'racial island' (Koganei, 1927) of the Ainu have been substantiated in this study.

The explanation that the similarity in gene frequencies can be ascribed to gene flow into the Ainu from surrounding Mongoloid populations cannot be supported. Firstly, since gene flow must affect all genetic loci it is unlikely that only certain polymorphic loci will show resemblance to Mongoloids due to gene flow. Secondly, although cultural influences of the Japanese on the Ainu may date back well into protohistoric times, the inter-marriage between the two populations may have been limited before 1868, when Hokkaido came under the Japanese government control. Thus, while the estimate of 40 per cent for the accumulated genes descended from Japanese may be an underestimate, it is unlikely that the hypothetical non-Mongoloid characters in the original gene pool have now disappeared completely. Moreover, there are a number of loci which show gene frequencies unique to the Ainu population at the present time: high frequencies of NS and r'' (cdE), a low frequency of Hp^1, and the occurrence of the $Gm^{2,21}$ phenogroup. These may indicate indirectly that the present Ainu population retains a considerable part of the ancestral gene pool.

A more plausible interpretation may be that the genetic similarity of the Ainu to the Mongoloid groups has a real phylogenetic basis: the Ainu and the East Asiatic Mongoloid groups are both derived from a common basic stock, but later differentiated under different population histories and have been differently affected by various evolutionary factors. This interpretation is consistent with the results of recent multivariate analyses of Ainu crania by Howells (1966) and Yamaguchi (1967). Their conclusions seem to indicate that the Ainu are a survival population from a series of upper Palaeolithic or Mesolithic populations of East Asia, including the Jomon people of Japan.

It should be pointed out, however, that certain properties of the morphological traits make them rather inadequate for use in studies of phylogenetic relationship between populations. Firstly, the genetic basis is obscure in most anthropometric characters and many of them are known to be subject to secular change: they may show a significant difference in two populations common by descent but different in the way of life or in cultural stage. Those characteristics of the Ainu such as the ruggedness of the face, tendency to dolichocephaly, rather developed supra-orbital arch, the edge-to-edge bite etc., are generalised characters probably possessed by most population groups of Man at a certain stage of human evolution. Therefore, the occurrence of such characters in a population cannot be a definite clue to the link by descent with any of the present races of Man. The concept of 'Cro-Magnon-like' appearance of the skull is misleading.

A further problem in the use of morphological traits which may be relevant to this discussion lies in the 'visible' nature of somatoscopic characters. A marked dissimilarity in visible characters, on the one hand, tends to become a reproductive barrier between human populations as is the case for language. On the other hand it is through 'visible' characters that assortative mating mostly takes place. Therefore, particularly in a small population such as the Ainu, a certain complex of somatoscopic characters could have attained a predominant incidence through inbreeding and assortative mating. Probably this will explain some of the predominant somatoscopic features of the Ainu, such as hairiness (Omoto, 1973a).

As the well known hypothesis by Coon, Garn and Birdsell (1950) postulates, the specialised morphological characters of the Mongoloid group, which may be called for simplicity's sake the 'later' Mongoloid, may have been formed as the result of selection by the extremely cold climatic conditions which occurred somewhere in north east Asia during the last glacial period. During the postglacial, and especially after the Neolithic period, probably this population began to grow rapidly in size and spread through almost the whole of Asia, absorbing aboriginal proto-Mongoloid populations. Also, the selective forces induced by the environments newly formed must have affected the genetic composition of the later Mongoloid populations.

The Ainu, on the other hand, due to their geographically peripheral position and possibly also to the barriers mentioned above probably remained relatively unaffected by the later Mongoloid populations. Since they have undergone almost certainly only slight changes in their subsistence economy since Mesolithic times until quite recently, generalised morphological characters were preserved. On the other hand, limited gene flow as well as small population size may have decreased the variability and promoted the uniqueness of the Ainu, both in genetic and non-genetic characters including culture. The effect of random genetic drift must have been strong, since the Ainu community used to be small-sized. They lived throughout the whole of Hokkaido Island, except the most mountainous interior, being scattered in small settlements called *kotan*, which were mostly made up of not more than 20 households (see for example, Watanabe, 1964). Also, the 'bottle-neck' effect may have played a great role. A drastic decrease in the Ainu population number was recorded during the period of 1822–1855. In the western half of Hokkaido the reduction was almost 50 per cent, and a number of Ainu settlements were annihilated. Epidemic diseases such as smallpox, measles, tuberculosis and Asiatic cholera introduced from the *Wajin*, namely, Japanese immigrants, were probably the main causes for this population decrease (see Kodama, 1970).

The blood group study carried out before World War II showed a marked local difference of ABO blood group gene frequencies among the Ainu populations of different districts of Hokkaido (see Tanaka, 1959). Unfortunately, such a study cannot be repeated since it is almost impossible now to obtain Ainu series of reasonable size in districts other than Hidaka. In the absence of evidence for selective factors it is safe to consider at present that the unique frequencies mentioned above found for a number of gene loci in the Ainu population are accounted for by random genetic drift.

The similarity observed in gene frequencies between the Ainu and the Ryukyuan is interesting since both groups are believed to be relatively unaffected representatives of the aboriginal populations of Japan. It was Baelz (1911) who claimed on the basis of somatoscopic similarities such as hairiness and facial appearances that the Ainu and the Ryukyuan are closely related. This classic view has long been rather ignored by Japanese anthropologists but certainly it is a stimulating theory worthy of special study. The collection of more genetic data from various islands of Ryukyu is in progress and this data together with more data for the Koreans will shed further light on the problem of the biological formation of the present Japanese.

Acknowledgements: This study was partly supported by the Japan Society for the Promotion of Sciences. We thank Dr Hideo Matsumoto for providing us with his unpublished data of Takasago tribes of Formosa. Thanks are also due to Professor Kazuro Hanihara and Dr Hideo Miyahara for their valuable advice in the computation of genetic distance using HITAC 8800/8700 at the University of Tokyo.

References

BAELZ, E. VON   1911   Die Riu-Kiu-Insulaner, die Aino und andere kaukasier-ähnliche Reste in Ostasien. *Korrespondenz-Blatt der Deutschen Gesellschaft für Anthropologie, Ethnologie und Urgeschichte*, 42:187–91.

CAVALLI-SFORZA, L. L. and A. W. F. EDWARDS   1967   Phylogenetic analysis: models and estimation procedures. *American Journal of Human Genetics*, 19:233–57.

COON, C. S., S. M. GARN and J. B. BIRDSELL   1950   *Races: a study of the problems of race formation in man*. Thomas, Springfield.

FURUHATA, T.   1966   *Hemotypology*, 2nd edition. Igaku Shoinu, Tokyo.

HOWELLS, W. W.   1966   The Jomon population of Japan. A study by discriminant analysis of Japanese and Ainu crania. *Papers of the Peabody Museum*, 57(1):1–43.

KIRK, R. L.   1965   *The distribution of genetic markers in Australian Aborigines*. Australian Institute of Aboriginal Studies, Canberra.

——   1973   *The human biology of Aborigines in Cape York*. Australian Institute of Aboriginal Studies, Canberra.

——, N. M. BLAKE, P. M. MOODIE and G. J. TIBBS   1971   Population genetic studies in Australian Aborigines of the Northern Territory. *Human Biology in Oceania*, 1:54–76.

——, ——, D. R. COOKE and D. G. JOSE   1972   The distribution of some serum protein and enzyme groups among Aboriginal populations in Queensland. *Human Biology in Oceania*, 1:207–14.

KODAMA, S.   1970   *Ainu: historical and anthropological studies*. Hokkaido University, School of Medicine, Sapporo.

KOGANEI, R.   1927   Zur Frage der Abstammung der Aino und ihre Verwandtschaft mit anderen Völkern. *Anthropologische Anz.*, 4:201–07.

MATSUMOTO, H. and T. MIYAZAKI   1972   Gm and Inv allotypes of the Ainu in Hidaka area, Hokkaido. *Japanese Journal of Human Genetics*, 17:20–26.

MISAWA, S.   1974   Unpublished data.

—— and Y. HAYASHIDA   1968   On the blood groups among the Ainu in Shizunai, Hokkaido. *Proceedings of the Japanese Academy*, 44:83–88.

—— and ——   1970   On the blood groups among the Ainu in Niikappu, Hokkaido. *Journal of the Anthropological Society of Nippon*, 78:177–86.

NAKAJIMA, H. *et al*   1967   The distribution of several serological and biochemical traits in East Asia II. *Japanese Journal of Human Genetics*, 12:29–37.

OMOTO, K.   1970   The distribution of polymorphic traits in the Hidaka Ainu. I. Defective colour vision, PTC taste sensitivity and cerumen dimorphism. *Journal of the Faculty of Science, University of Tokyo, Sec. V. Vol. III*, Part 5:337–55.

——   1972   Polymorphisms and genetic affinities of the Ainu of Hokkaido. *Human Biology in Oceania*, 1:278–88.

——   1973a   The Ainu: a racial isolate? *Israel Journal of Medical Science*, 9:1285–90.

——   1973b   Blood protein polymorphisms and the problems of the genetic affinities of the Ainu. *Proceedings of the 9th International Congress of Anthropological Ethnological Science*, Mouton, The Hague (in press).

—— and S. HARADA   1968   Red cell and serum protein types in the Ainu population of Shizunai, Hokkaido. *Proceedings of the 8th International Congress of Anthropological Ethnological Science*, 1:206–09.

—— and ——   1969   Polymorphism of red cell acid phosphatase in several population groups in Japan. *Japanese Journal of Human Genetics*, 14:143–53.

—— and ——   1972   The distribution of polymorphic traits in the Hidaka Ainu. II. Red cell enzyme and serum protein groups. *Journal of the Faculty of Science, University of Tokyo, V* 4:171–211.

——, K. ISHIZAKI, S. HARADA, S. AKAISHI, T. KUDO and K. TAKAHASHI   1973   The distribution of serum protein and red cell enzyme types among blood donors of Okinawa Island, the Ryukyus. *Journal of the Anthropological Society of Nippon*, 81:159–73.

SIMMONS, R. T., J. J. GRAYDON, N. M. SEMPLE and S. KODAMA   1953   A collaborative genetical survey in Ainu: Hidaka, Island of Hokkaido. *American Journal of Physical Anthropology*, 11:47–81.

SUNAHARA, M., M. URANO and M. OGAWA   1961   Genetical and geographic studies on isoniazid inactivation. *Science*, 134:1530.

TANAKA, T.   1959   A study on the Japanese from the standpoint of the blood groups. *Japanese Journal of Criminology*, 25:37–67 Supplement. (In Japanese with English summary.)

WATANABE, H.   1964   The Ainu: a study of ecology and the system of social solidarity between man and nature in relation to group structure. *Journal of the Faculty of Science, University of Tokyo, V* 2:1–164.

WATANABE, S. (ed)   1975   Anthropological and genetic studies on the Ainu. In *Anthropological and genetic studies of Japanese*, S. Kondo, E. Matsunaga and S. Watanabe (eds). University of Tokyo Press, Tokyo.

YAMAGUCHI, B.   1967   *A comparative osteological study of the Ainu and the Australian Aborigines*. Australian Institute of Aboriginal Studies, Canberra.

Genetics and Evolutionary Relationships

Human microdifferentiation in the Western Pacific

N.E. Morton and B. Keats

POPULATION STRUCTURE is a linear change in the frequency of heterozygotes from the value expected under panmixia. The definition traces to Wright (1921), who developed correlational and variance aspects, including multiple alleles and polysomy (Wright, 1938, 1951). 'This concept of Wright has enormously simplified population genetics, and its validity under a great variety of conditions is one of the great discoveries of mathematical biology' (Morton and Yasuda, 1963). It was left to Malécot (1948) to exploit the probabilistic interpretation in terms of kinship. Every year other measures of population structure are invented, which invariably reduce to some function of kinship. Any further analysis to describe isolation by distance, evolution of structure, or genetic topology is an operation on kinship, whether predicted from migration and genealogy or bioassayed from polymorphisms, metrics or isonymy.

Kinship

To approach microdifferentiation from the standpoint of kinship, let q_{ki} be the frequency of gene A^k in the ith population and $Q_k = \sum w_i q_{ki}$ be the regional frequency, where w_i is the contribution of population i to the region ($\sum w_i = 1$). For random pairs of gametes from populations i and j, the frequency of heterozygotes is $H_{ij} = 1 - \sum q_{ki}q_{kj}$. Under regional panmixia the frequency of heterozygotes is $H_0 = 1 - \sum Q^2_k$. By definition, kinship relative to the region is

(1) $\quad \varphi_{ij} \equiv (H_0 - H_{ij})/H_0 = (\sum q_{ki}q_{kj} - \sum Q^2_k)/(1 - \sum Q^2_k)$

For $H_{ij} \leqslant H_0$ we may consider φ_{ij} the probability that a random gene in i be identical by descent with a random gene in j. More generally, within the region φ_{ij} is the correlation between the gene pools of i and j, and the expected covariance of the kth gene frequency in populations i and j is $Q_k(1 - Q_k) \varphi_{ij}$. Thus identity by descent, correlation between gametes, and covariance of gene frequencies are intimately related.

Three properties of kinship are especially important in studying micro-differentiation. First, kinship φ_{ijR} within a region R is related to kinship φ_{ijT} within a larger collective T as

$$(2) \qquad\qquad \varphi_{ijR} = \frac{\varphi_{ijT} - \varphi_R}{1 - \varphi_R},$$

where φ_R is the kinship of random gametes from the region relative to T. This is Wright's hierarchical description of population structure. Secondly, kinship declines approximately exponentially with distance d,

$$(3) \qquad\qquad \varphi(d) \doteq (1 - L)ae^{-bd} + L$$

where a, b, L are the parameters of Malécot (1948).* In terms of the hierarchical model, $\varphi_R = -L/(1 - L)$. Thirdly, kinship increases in time according to

$$(4) \qquad \varphi^{(t)} \doteq \left[\frac{1}{4\,N_e\,m_e + 1}\right] [1 - e^{-(2m_e + 1/2N_e)t}]$$

where N_e is the evolutionary size of the population and m_e is the linearised systematic pressure (Morton et al, 1971a). This property is most useful when kinship is predicted from migration and genealogy, whereas the other properties can be studied either from predictions or by phenotype bioassay.

Populations of the Western Pacific

Anthropologists on Pacific islands have collected data suitable for kinship analysis, but neither their work nor the large body of material from the western Carolines by Gajdusek and collaborators has yet been published in detail. An extensive study of Pingelap and Mokil atolls in the eastern Carolines was conducted by Morton and collaborators (reviewed in Morton, 1973a). A smaller study by Pollock et al (1972) on Namu atoll in the Marshalls and two surveys of Micronesia (Imaizumi and Morton, 1970; Morton and Lalouel, 1973) complete the kinship record for Oceanic populations (Table 1). The studies agree in showing kinship roughly equivalent to first cousins between random members of the same island (a) relative to all Micronesia. Decline of kinship (b) is slow, with no substantial decrease at distances of 100 km. Regular phenotypes (polymorphisms), metrics, and clan isonymy are in good agreement. The suggestion of Wright (1951), that human kinship is unlikely to exceed 0·02 even in isolates, is much too cautious.

The evolutionary size of Oceanic populations is substantially smaller than their current census size (Table 2). This is because of population 'bottlenecks' during famines which followed typhoons and other disasters. Undoubtedly restricted numbers of founders produced the same effect, with the consequence that archipelagos populated from settlers on one atoll are expected to show as much drift as a small island. For example, phenotype bioassay gives a kinship of 0·0446 for random Marshallese, relative to all

* It is important to note that these parameters are characteristic of the local population: if demes are combined into tribes, prefectures, or other units larger than the breeding group, a and b will both be reduced.

Table 1: Parameters of isolation by distance (after Morton, 1973a,):
$$\varphi(d) = (1 - L)\, ae^{-bd} + L$$

Population	Source	L	a	b
Oceania				
Micronesia	phenotypes	— ·0081	·0463	·0023
	metrics	— ·0133	·0569	·0016
	cognates	·1531	1	·0029
Pingelap/Mokil with others	phenotypes	— ·0103	·0565	·0069
	metrics	— ·0021	·0884	·0069
	cognates	·3440	1	·0045
	migration	0	·0606	·0120
	clans	— ·0121	·0540	·0111
Marshalls	migration	0	·0431	·0005
New Guinea				
Bougainville	phenotypes	?	·0765	·1050
	migration	0	·0588	·0954
New Guinea	phenotypes	— ·0098	·0444	·0519
Australian Aboriginals	phenotypes	— ·0235	·0641	·0013

Micronesia. This is much greater than predicted from migration at the current population size, despite widespread voyaging which tended to fuse the scattered gene pool, as reflected both by anthropological accounts and the small value of b in Table 1 (Pollock *et al*, 1972; Morton and Lalouel, 1973). There seems little doubt that the Marshalls were populated from a small number of founders.

Natives of New Guinea show as much local kinship (a) as atoll dwellers, but the decline with distance (b) is much more precipitate, giving substantial decrease at 10 km and virtual abolition of measurable kinship at 100 km (Table 1). Clearly migrational distances are less in New Guinea than in Oceania, both because of geographic obstacles and hostility of neighbouring villages. Australian Aboriginals have comparable values of local kinship (a) but much slower decline with distance (b), like Oceanic populations. Evidently geographic and social obstacles to long-distance migration were much less serious in Australia than in New Guinea, as the tradition of long treks and 'walk-abouts' suggests.

Table 2: Parameters of kinship evolution (after Morton, 1973b)

Population	Source for m_e	Evolutionary size, N_e	Systematic pressure, m_e	Limiting kinship, φ
Oceania				
Pingelap	migration	87	·027	·0938
Mokil	migration	82	·076	·0341
Namu	genealogy	114	·045	·0468
Other				
Northeastern Brazil	genealogy	124	·308	·0065
Alpine isolates	migration	390	·092	·0060
Switzerland	migration	594	·160	·0021
Switzerland	genealogy	1499	·203	·0008

There are no estimates of evolutionary size and systematic pressure for New Guinea and Australia. However, the Malécot parameters suggest larger groups in New Guinea with less mobility than in Australia. This is of course only the genetic consequence of what anthropologists like Yengoyan (1968, 1970) have observed in Australia: small groups of 20 to 70 people, searching for food and water over an area of several hundred square miles with a kinship system that tends to provide access to resources by minimising hostility in group encounters. Among the swidden agriculturalists of New Guinea, inhabiting self-sufficient areas of higher density, peaceful relations with other groups are less advantageous and the social organisation fosters defence against encroachment.

Simulation of kinship

Two kinds of population structure have been predicted by a migration matrix. The simplest is a population subdivided by an exogamy rule into clans, moieties, and sections. Morton et al (1971b) considered a population of 160 adults of reproductive age with 5 per cent immigration from the outside world. The various marriage rules have almost no effect on random kinship in such a population, but inbreeding is increased by sections and circulating connubia relative to an undivided population, although not of course by comparison with group endogamy. If, as is likely, the society does not always follow an idealised system, the genetic effects must be even smaller than under this model. Therefore marriage rules appear to have a negligible effect on kinship, compared with population size and migration.

More complex structure has also been simulated, usually by estimating a migration matrix for actual populations. The number of tribes in the Western Pacific is too large for this method, but we may use a more abstract model. Suppose a region is composed of three populations, each of evolutionary size N_e and exchanging a proportion $k/2$ of its members with each of the other populations, called steppingstones. In addition, a proportion m is replaced each generation by immigrants from outside the region. Treating the local Australian population as a mob of several bands, we took $N_e = 98$ from Table 2 and $m = 0 \cdot 02$ from the suggestion of Tindale (1953) that $7 \cdot 5$ per cent of marriages contracted among Australian Aboriginals prior to appreciable White influence were intertribal. A similar value is indicated for New Guinea (Friedlaender, 1971) and Oceania (Table 2).

Malécot (1948) deduced that systematic pressure is

(5) $$m_e \doteq \sqrt{m(m + 2k)}$$

Equation 4 gives for local kinship

$$a \doteq \frac{1}{4 N_e m_e + 1}$$

These relations allow us to estimate

(6) $$m_e \doteq (1 - a)/4a N_e$$
$$k \doteq (m_e^2 - m^2)/2m$$

Only the effective size N of the population is undetermined. However, Morton et al (1971a) found that the ratio $C = N_e/N$ is insensitive to changes in N. Therefore by simulating structure with a migration matrix at a trial value N_0, with corresponding local kinship a_0, we can determine $N = a_0(1 - a) N_0/a(1 - a_0)$ and verify other parameters under the model.

Table 3 gives these results. The systematic pressure due to migration is many orders of magnitude greater than mutation and selection rates determined from amino-acid substitution. The possibility of inferring selection pressure from geographical distribution of gene frequencies is remote, unless the agent of selection (malaria, etc.) can be determined on other evidence. The chance of making a critical test of neutral mutation is negligible.

The inbreeding coefficient is close to local kinship on the assumption that mating between a given pair of populations is random. Under the population structure of the Western Pacific elimination of deleterious 'recessive' genes must have been largely through inbreeding, not heterozygote disadvantage as has been suggested for farming and industrial populations (Morton, Crow and Muller, 1956). The effective size is less than the evolutionary size. Oceania, New Guinea, and Australia do not differ much in local kinship, evolutionary size, or systematic pressure. However, stepping-stone distances are hundreds of kilometres in Oceania and Australia but only a few kilometres in New Guinea. The genetic structure reflects the main features of ecology and social organisation.

Other indices of structure

If x_i is the vectorial deviation of population i from the regional mean, then $x_i x_j'$ is a measure of *affinity* (similarity) and $(x_i - x_j)(x_i - x_j)'$ is a measure of *divergence* (dissimilarity). Kinship, correlation, and Wright's F statistics are examples of affinity, while genetic distance typifies divergence. Affinity decreases with geographic distance, and divergence increases. Affinity between a population and its founders (or between two populations with a common origin) decreases with time, whereas divergence increases (Figure 1). Of course, affinity within a contemporary population or between two independent populations under migration increases with time, just as divergence does, a circumstance that has led to confusion between kinship and distance (Cavalli-Sforza, 1973). The two concepts have a simple relation, since

$$(x_i - x_j)(x_i - x_j)' = x_i x_i' + x_j x_j' - 2 x_i x_j'$$

In words, the divergence between two populations is the sum of their internal affinities, minus twice their cross-affinity. In the case of kinship,

(7) $$D_{ij} = \varphi_{ii} + \varphi_{jj} - 2 \varphi_{ij}$$

where D_{ij} is the genetic distance. It is easy to show that Mahalanobis' distance equals D_{ij} except for a proportionality constant which is a function of genetic covariances (Morton, 1973a). Kullback (1968) derived Mahalanobis' distance from information theory, and so genetic distance has a strong theoretical foundation.

Table 3: Simulation of kinship

Parameter	Oceania	New Guinea	Australian Aboriginals	Northeastern Brazil	Switzerland	Alpine isolates
Assumed:						
long-range migration, m	·04	·02	·02	·20	·10	·05
local kinship, a	·0580	·0600	·0641	·0050	·0025	·0069
Malecot exponent, b	·0054	·0841	·0013	·0021	·0185	·0643
stepping-stone migration, k	·0123	·0500	·0420	·3024	·0881	·0560
effective size, N	75	87	85	75	491	372
Predicted at $t = \infty$:						
kinship with stepping-stone, ϕ_m	·0080	·0354	·0346	·0034	·0009	·0027
inbreeding coefficient, x	·0568	·0580	·0620	·0040	·0022	·0064
stepping-stone distance, $D = \ln(a/\phi_m)/b$	364	6	475	180	54	14
Verified by equation 4:						
evolutionary size, N_e	80	108	98	178	649	447
systematic pressure, m_e	·0509	·0362	·0371	·2825	·1549	·0806

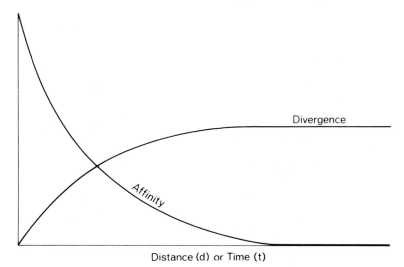

Distance (d) or Time (t)

Figure 1   Affinity and divergence.

There is, however, a slight disadvantage to D_{ij}. Applying equation 3, we see that

$$(8) \qquad D_{ij} \doteq 2a\,(1 - e^{-bd})(1 - L)$$

The scalar L is no obstacle to microtaxonomy, but for comparison of different structures, it is better to use the hybridity,

$$(9) \qquad \theta_{ij} = \frac{\varphi_{ii} + \varphi_{jj} - 2\,\varphi_{ij}}{4 - \varphi_{ii} - \varphi_{jj} - 2\,\varphi_{ij}}$$

which has expectation

$$E(\theta_{ij}) = \frac{a(1 - e^{-bd})}{2 - a(1 + e^{-bd})}$$

and therefore is invariant with respect to L. Hybridity has a simple genetic meaning. If H_2 is the heterozygosity in the F_2 between two populations. then the F_1 heterozygosity is

$$(10) \qquad H_1 = (1 + \theta_{ij})\, H_2$$

and the heterozygosity in the two parental populations is

$$H_0 = (1 - \theta_{ij})\, H_2$$

This property is appealing, but since $1 - L$ within a region is not much different from unity, in theory and practice there is little to choose between θ_{ij} and $D_{ij}/4$.

Nei (1973) has devised a set of statistics based on local homozygosis, $\sum q_{ki}\, q_{kj}$. He calls $H_T = 1 - \sum Q^2_k$ the gene diversity of the total population, and $D_{ST} = \sum w_i\, q^2_{ki} - \sum Q^2_k$ the gene diversity between populations. Then $G_{ST} = D_{ST}/H_T$ is the relative measure of gene differentiation.

It is easy to show that

$$G_{ST} = \frac{\varphi_0 - \varphi_R}{1 - \varphi_R}$$

where

$$\varphi_0 = \sum_{i,k} w_i \, q_{ki}^2$$

and

$$\varphi_R = \sum Q_k^2$$

Thus G_{ST} is the mean kinship within populations, relative to the region, which is identical to the F_{ST} of Wright (1921), the φ of Morton *et al* (1971c), and the R_{ST} of Workman *et al* (1973). In terms of Malécot parameters, equation 3 gives $G_{ST} = (1 - L) a + L$ (Morton, Miki and Yee, 1968). As the mean of the diagonal of a kinship matrix, G_{ST} summarises a symmetrical matrix of rank n by a scalar, and therefore less completely than the Malécot parameters, which give not only G_{ST} but also the decline of the off-diagonal entries with distance.

Latter (1972) proposed the statistic

$$\varphi^* \equiv \frac{2\,\theta}{1 + \theta}$$
$$= \frac{\varphi_{ii} + \varphi_{jj} - 2\,\varphi_{ij}}{2(1 - \varphi_{ij})} \doteq \frac{a(1 - e^{-bd})}{1 - ae^{-bd}}$$

In the absence of systematic pressure $a = 1$, and then $\varphi^* = a$. However, systematic pressure from migration, mutation, and perhaps selection is ubiquitous, and so φ^* seems poorly motivated. He also suggested an 'index of mutational divergence'

$$\gamma_{ij} = 1 - \frac{2\,\varphi_{ij}}{\varphi_{ii} + \varphi_{jj}}$$
$$\doteq 1 - e^{-2\mu t} \doteq 2\,t\,\mu$$

for $\varphi_{ij} = \sum q_{ki} q_{kj}$, where μ is the mutation rate per generation since the population separated t generations (or years) ago. This would be appropriate for populations of uniform size if migration and selection pressure were negligible relative to mutation. As Table 2 shows, the condition does not hold within our species, and probably within any species, although it may apply to higher taxa over phylogenetic sequences short enough so that $1 - e^{-2\mu t} \doteq 2\,\mu\,t$.

Clearly all these indices of population structure are simple functions of the kinship matrix.

Genetic topology

Studies of population structure have two objectives: (1) to compare different structures, for example with respect to Malécot parameters, and (2) to describe kinship among populations within a region. The latter is called *genetic topology*. It commonly takes the form of a two-dimensional graph, which gives more detail than summary indices like Malécot parameters or F statistics, but sacrifices some of the information in the kinship matrix (φ_{ij}) in order to demonstrate its main features. In one type of graph each population is represented by a point, with similar populations tending to cluster. Diversity among populations is maximised by taking the axes as the principal components of the centroid-adjusted kinship matrix (Lalouel, 1973). The other type of graph is a bifurcating tree in which more similar populations are separated by shorter paths. The logical structure is not altered by rotating any branch 180°, so that $A(BC) = A(CB) = (BC)A$. A tree constructed on affinity or divergence, without phylogenetic assumptions, is called a *dendrogram*. A tree constructed on the assumption of evolution with binary fission but no migration is called a *cladogram*. The main axis of a dendrogram is distance or hybridity, which in a cladogram may be converted to time since divergence began on the assumption of uniform drift. There are many competing algorithms for constructing a tree, which can be objectively compared in terms of the cophenetic correlation between observed and expected distance or hybridity. Numerical taxonomy (Sokal and Sneath, 1963) and recent genetic experience (e.g. Martin, 1973) have urged caution in interpreting a dendrogram as a cladogram, especially at the subspecific level (Morton and Lalouel, 1973).

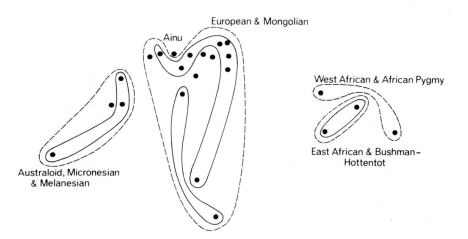

Figure 2 Principal components of hybridity in 25 races (after Imaizumi *et al*, 1973).

Imaizumi *et al* (1973) studied the genetic topology of 25 polymorphisms in 25 populations with the results shown in Figure 2. The Western Pacific is a distinct cluster of populations, with greatest affinity to the Mongoloids of South East Asia.

To examine the topology of this region more closely we chose 13 polymorphisms in 17 populations, mostly from the Western Pacific (Figure 3). The gene frequencies are set out in Table 4. Because of a question raised by Latter (1973), kinship was calculated from gene frequencies by two methods. In the first, each system was treated separately and the kinship estimates pooled, with equal weights (Table 5). In the second, the quantities $\sum_k Q_k^2$ and $\sum_k q_{ki}\, q_{kj}$ were averaged over systems and kinship was computed from these means. These estimates will be called within and among systems, respectively.

The principal components analysis is almost indistinguishable for the two methods, with a correlation of $0\cdot935$ within systems and $0\cdot926$ among systems. The Ainu cluster with the Mongoloid populations, and there is no similarity between Melanesians and Negroids (Figure 4).

A tree representation conserves these features, but the cophenetic correlation is reduced to $0\cdot783$ within systems and $0\cdot808$ among systems. Figure 5 gives the former tree as a cladogram, assuming exponentially linear differentiation from the first split 100,000 years ago. Comparison with the principal components plot, which conserves more of the information in the kinship matrix, makes one properly cautious about a phylogenetic interpretation. The most striking feature of these analyses is the diversity among Australoids, Micronesians, Melanesians, and Polynesians, which may indicate a small founder population, a long time span, or both.

Significance of polymorphism

Inspection of Table 6 shows that mean kinship within populations is about $0\cdot05$ for systems like Gc, PGM_1, ABO, Tf, and Inv, but reaches much higher values for Gm, Fy, and Rh. Imaizumi *et al* (1973) reported similar values for world populations. This variation may be due to differences among loci in rates of mutation, selection pressure, time since last fixation, stochastic departure from equilibrium, or power to detect genetic differences by electrophoretic or antigenic methods. The alternatives to a null hypothesis of uniformity are so numerous that the fact of variability gives no information about the relative importance of selection and neutral mutation.

The mean kinship for these systems is about $0\cdot15$, with a variance that is minimal for the estimator φ_1 given by equation 1. The estimator

$$\varphi_{ij2} = \left\{ \sum_{k=1}^{A} q_{ki}\, q_{kj}/Q_k - 1 \right\}/(A - 1)$$

and the Malécot estimator $(1 - L)\, a + L$ give similar means with slightly larger variances. The largest error is associated with regional homozygosity.

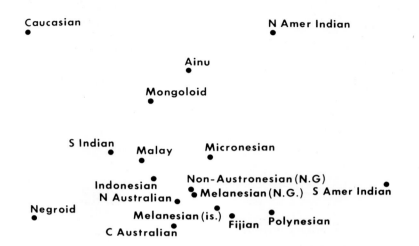

Figure 3 Geographic locations of the 17 populations.

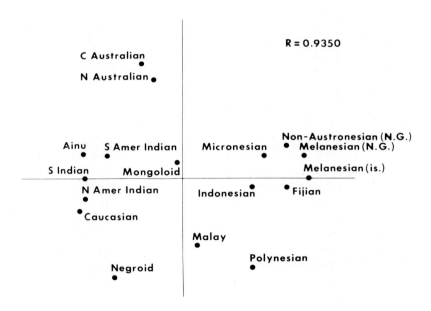

Figure 4 Principal components of kinship within systems.

Table 4: Gene frequencies

	North Australian Aboriginals	Central Australian Aboriginals	Non-Austronesian (New Guinea)	Melanesian (New Guinea)	Melanesian (Islanders)	Micronesian	Polynesian	Indonesian	Fijian	South American Indians	North American Indians	Negroid	Caucasian	Mongoloid	Ainu	Malay aboriginals	South Indian
A	138	281	218	086	181	199	338	140	340	000	096	178	279	186	285	120	224
B	002	000	114	124	106	095	000	180	055	000	004	114	061	170	212	200	218
O	860	719	668	790	713	706	662	680	605	1000	900	708	660	644	503	680	558
MS	000	000	001	013	000	000	014	014	009	320	159	093	237	041	012	028	276
Ms	291	228	040	272	175	463	500	446	342	400	611	487	305	566	385	748	474
NS	000	000	051	072	025	009	048	000	009	150	021	044	071	014	277	010	130
Ns	709	772	908	643	800	528	438	540	640	130	209	376	387	379	326	214	120
R^z	041	055	000	000	003	000	000	003	000	020	000	000	001	005	000	000	009
R^1	689	619	907	861	882	786	465	892	816	410	282	029	422	759	556	846	570
R^2	151	316	061	139	090	182	486	060	140	540	570	043	167	195	210	056	137
R^0	119	010	032	000	020	032	027	045	044	030	148	739	019	041	037	098	042
r'^y	000	000	000	000	000	000	000	000	000	000	000	000	001	000	000	000	000
r'	000	000	000	000	005	000	022	000	000	000	000	071	005	000	000	000	000
r''	000	000	000	000	000	000	000	000	000	000	000	000	003	000	197	000	000
r	000	000	000	000	000	000	000	000	000	000	000	118	382	000	000	000	242

Inv[a]	260	370	075	250	362	206	393	142	375	420	200	319	102	277	168	350	147
Inv[b]	740	630	925	750	638	794	607	858	625	580	800	681	898	723	832	650	853
Fy[a]+	977	965	1000	1000	929	1000	470	1000	965	730	747	061	421	902	722	700	735
Fy[a]-	023	035	000	000	071	000	530	000	035	270	253	939	579	098	278	300	265
K+	000	000	000	000	003	000	000	000	002	000	000	003	046	000	111	000	065
K-	1000	1000	1000	1000	997	1000	1000	1000	998	1000	1000	997	954	1000	889	1000	935
Phs[a]	011	000	245	148	175	060	175	465	176	050	669	160	360	220	320	344	292
Phs[b]	989	1000	755	852	825	940	825	535	824	950	331	839	600	780	680	654	708
Phs[c]	000	000	000	000	000	000	000	000	000	000	000	001	040	000	000	002	000
PGD[A]	934	952	906	883	795	939	810	903	824	990	971	943	979	934	958	975	993
PGD[C]	052	046	094	117	205	061	190	097	176	010	029	057	021	066	042	025	007
PGD[E]	014	002	000	000	000	000	000	000	000	000	000	000	000	000	000	000	000
PGM$_1^1$	909	906	966	929	902	707	797	765	692	850	890	781	765	750	822	682	721
PGM$_1^2$	091	094	034	071	098	166	198	232	298	150	110	219	235	250	178	308	279
PGM$_1^3$	000	000	000	000	000	068	005	000	010	000	000	000	000	000	000	000	000
PGM$_1^7$	000	000	000	000	000	059	000	003	000	000	000	000	000	000	000	010	000
Tf[C]	812	905	938	951	972	991	999	990	991	1000	969	973	995	991	983	977	998
Tf[D]	188	095	062	049	023	009	000	010	009	000	027	027	001	007	015	023	002
Tf[B]	000	000	000	000	005	000	001	000	000	000	004	000	004	002	002	000	000
Gc[1]	868	900	493	622	759	892	753	720	753	820	850	840	722	675	750	840	682
Gc[2]	112	078	339	278	193	108	247	280	247	180	150	160	278	325	250	160	318
Gc[Ab]	020	022	168	100	048	000	000	000	000	000	000	000	000	000	000	000	000
Hp[1]	316	198	697	538	702	461	648	376	589	420	370	559	376	280	162	233	160
Hp[2]	684	802	303	462	298	539	352	624	411	580	630	441	624	720	838	767	840
Gm[5]	000	000	000	000	000	000	000	000	000	000	000	000	633	000	000	000	537
Gm[1]	636	794	070	013	062	158	069	122	065	784	778	611	220	452	795	166	368
Gm[1,2]	265	206	143	000	028	018	074	073	051	210	198	000	147	148	000	063	024
Gm[1,5]	099	000	787	987	910	812	857	805	881	002	024	347	000	400	026	771	071
Gm[1,5,6]	000	000	000	000	000	012	000	000	000	000	000	042	000	000	000	000	000
Gm[2]	000	000	000	000	000	000	000	000	000	000	000	000	000	000	179	000	000

Table 5: Kinship (upper trimat) and hybridity (lower trimat) within systems

	N. Aust	C. Aust	NAN	MN (NG)	MN (Is)	Micro	Poly
N. Australian	·1647	·1402	·0014	− ·0186	− ·0294	− ·0080	− ·09?
C. Australian	·0188	·1706	− ·0227	− ·0398	− ·0369	− ·0103	− ·09?
Non-Austronesian	·0884	·0983	·1656	·1211	·1197	·0578	·01?
Melanesian (N.G.)	·0885	·0957	·0196	·1349	·1270	·0861	·04?
Melanesian (Is.)	·0990	·1000	·0226	− ·0080	·1514	·0722	·07?
Micronesian	·0706	·0711	·0376	·0140	·0267	·0879	·02?
Polynesian	·1316	·1279	·0736	·0462	·0392	·0502	·14?
Indonesian	·0956	·0997	·0368	·0239	·0390	·0240	·06
Fijian	·0990	·0955	·0362	·0085	·0121	·0183	·03?
S. American Indian	·0560	·0434	·1253	·1040	·1115	·0786	·09?
N. American Indian	·0886	·0887	·1328	·1326	·1405	·1097	·12
Negroid	·1073	·1334	·1456	·1434	·1335	·1143	− ·00?
Caucasian	·1029	·0902	·1265	·1374	·1390	·1145	·09?
Mongoloid	·0562	·0505	·0632	·0511	·0621	·0295	·06?
Ainu	·0817	·0625	·1252	·1264	·1345	·0991	·11?
Malay	·1029	·1041	·0926	·0590	·0726	·0390	·04?
S. Indian	·0797	·0662	·1206	·1160	·1307	·0850	·10?

Table 6: Parameters of population structure by system

Genetic system	Mean kinship ϕ_1	Mean kinship ϕ_2	Mean hybridity θ	Regional homozygos ΣQ^2
ABO	·0620	·0583	·0319	·5498
MNS	·1618	·1610	·0910	·3931
Rh	·2336	·0971	·0620	·4561
Inv	·0582	·0582	·0313	·6154
Fy	·3798	·2572	·1347	·6610
K	·0682	·0682	·0406	·9733
Phs	·1583	·1555	·0921	·6444
PGD	·0509	·0516	·0281	·8575
PGM_1	·0481	·0458	·0246	·6936
Tf	·0650	·0676	·0411	·9357
Gc	·0501	·0384	·0206	·6272
Hp	·1271	·1270	·0694	·5138
Gm	·4406	·5928	·3269	·3552
Mean	·1464	·1368	·0765	·6366
Standard deviation	·1307	·1506	·0824	·1936

* Because of failure of 3—parameter iteration to converge L was taken
mean for other systems or from Imaizumi *et al* (1973), whichever g
smaller variance.

Ind	Fiji	SA Ind	NA Ind	Neg	Cauc	Mong	Ainu	Malay	S. Ind
− ·0533	− ·0476	·0524	·0062	− ·0333	− ·0224	− ·0033	·0142	− ·0643	− ·0021
− ·0629	− ·0438	·0723	·0006	− ·0964	·0051	·0113	·0487	− ·0692	·0252
·0646	·0772	− ·0875	− ·0776	− ·1275	− ·0732	·0210	− ·0760	− ·0504	− ·0880
·0724	·0954	− ·0697	− ·1010	− ·1442	− ·1199	− ·0063	− ·1009	·0076	− ·0969
·0529	·1132	− ·0722	− ·1048	− ·0993	− ·1081	− ·0233	− ·1063	− ·0143	− ·1178
·0449	·0694	− ·0385	− ·0791	− ·1074	− ·0949	·0046	− ·0668	·0187	− ·0575
·0038	·0702	− ·0446	− ·0737	·0406	− ·0171	− ·0228	− ·0713	·0383	− ·0660
·0972	·0588	− ·0794	− ·0073	− ·1206	− ·0566	·0157	− ·0411	·0392	− ·0287
·0262	·1198	− ·0761	− ·1010	− ·0922	− ·0975	·0016	− ·0847	·0160	− ·0793
·1014	·1046	·1422	·0537	·0159	·0512	·0124	·0402	− ·0261	·0534
·0774	·1304	·0565	·1747	·0584	·0907	·0070	·0683	·0078	·0703
·1251	·1208	·0838	·0749	·1742	·0372	− ·0669	− ·0165	·0296	− ·0112
·0979	·1243	·0618	·0553	− ·0004	·1717	− ·0055	·1149	− ·0250	·1070
·0265	·0404	·0431	·0584	·0885	·0610	·0327	·0156	·0164	·0314
·0890	·1154	·0595	·0600	·1061	·0365	·0467	·1592	− ·0254	·1274
·0313	·0490	·0771	·0727	·0666	·0864	·0263	·0821	·0995	·0013
·0733	·1034	·0450	·0506	·0937	·0279	·0281	·0131	·0591	·1311

Local homozygosity Σq^2	Malecot parameters a	b	L	$(1-L)a+L$
·5777	·0644	·0008	− ·0098*	·0552
·4913	·2050	·0003	− ·0395	·1736
·5832	·1499	·0002	− ·0687	·0915
·6378	·0617	·0019	− ·0040	·0579
·7898	·2996	·0003	− ·0265*	·2810
·9751	·0728	·0010	− ·0059	·0673
·7007	·1738	·0006	− ·0199	·1574
·8648	·0608	·0003	− ·0116	·0499
·7083	·0588	·0005	·0082	·0511
·9399	·0830	·0004	− ·0111	·0728
·6458	·0401	·0031	− ·0001*	·0402
·5756	·1501	·0004	− ·0262	·1278
·6393	·6362	·0007	− ·0695	·6109
·7024	·1582	·0008	− ·0231	·1413
·1491	·1621	·0008	·0231	·1569

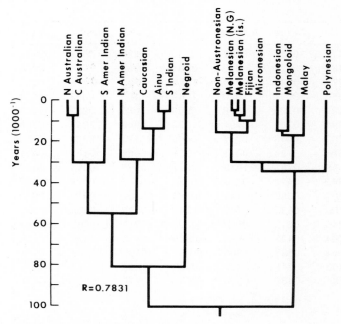

Figure 5   Cladogram from kinship within systems.

Kinship among systems is

$$\varphi = \frac{\cdot 7024 - \cdot 6366}{1 - \cdot 6366} = \cdot 1811$$

which is greater than any of the estimates based on system means.

If we allow for monomorphisms at 72 per cent of loci (Harris and Hopkinson, 1972) the regional homozygosis becomes

$$\cdot 72(1) + \cdot 28(\cdot 6366) = \cdot 8982$$

and local homozygosis is

$$\cdot 72(1) + \cdot 28(\cdot 7024) = \cdot 9167$$

Kinship among systems remains virtually unchanged at ·1817. Thus kinship within a region is much less affected by preferential sampling of polymorphisms than is random homozygosis. The bias noted by Latter (1973) for the more polymorphic loci to give higher estimates of kinship is eliminated by taking means of homozygosis among systems. Our results suggest this bias is not large for human races, and is therefore negligible for local populations. Because estimates of homozygosis are so unstable, we prefer to express population structure in terms of kinship.

In recent years theoretical population genetics has devoted much attention to the controversy between Darwinian advocates of selection and non-Darwinian proponents of neutral mutation (Lewontin, 1973). The question at issue concerns the systematic pressure for a species not undergoing introgressive hybridisation,

$$(11) \qquad\qquad k \equiv U + pS$$

where U is the mutation rate for neutral and advantageous alleles, and p is the proportion of these that are advantageous, with mean advantage S (Morton, 1973b). We want to know the fraction pS/k of systematic pressure which is selective, an inquiry that may usefully be pursued if, and only if, the selection pressure S is large relative to the mutation rate and the systematic pressure k is measurably great.

Unfortunately, this condition may be met for only a small fraction of loci. Several calculations indicate that the expressed genetic load in Man cannot exceed unity, and therefore the typical systematic pressure must be less than 10^{-4} per locus per generation (Morton, 1975). An independent approach takes an amino acid substitution rate of 10^{-9} per year for a gene of 500 codons with a generation time of 20 years, for a systematic pressure of 10^{-5}. If there is synergism, the systematic pressure is even smaller. It may be larger if much selection is in response to transient conditions and does not lead to fixation. However, even if such transient selection is 100 times greater than pressure toward fixation, it is too small to be measured. The great controversy over non-Darwinian evolution is beginning to founder for lack of critical evidence.

These considerations do not preclude generations of intense selection, but they do mean that most loci are nearly neutral most of the time. It seems likely, therefore, that most gene frequency variation in the Western Pacific is neutral. In the remainder, we are unlikely to be able to demonstrate the selective forces involved. This should encourage investigation of any system where special considerations suggest that selection may be important, at the same time that it discourages attempts to find a selective explanation for most gene frequency variation.

We have seen that evolutionary size of populations in the Western Pacific is small. The simplest explanation is that, to a greater extent than in Eurasia, the present day distribution reflects settlement by a small number of founders, with restricted subsequent introgression. This was probably typical of pre-agricultural and swidden Man, and of Europe before the Roman empire, and so the Western Pacific is of special interest for study of population structure.

References

ANANTHAKRISHNAN, R.   1972   Further studies on the distribution of some serum protein and enzyme groups in South India. *Humangenetik*, 15:172–76.
—— and R. L. KIRK   1969   The distribution of some serum protein and enzyme group systems in two endogamous groups in South India. *Indian Journal of Medical Research*, 57:1011–17.
ARENDS, T., L. R. WEITKAMP, M. L. GALLANGO, J. V. NEEL and J. SCHULTZ   1970   Gene frequencies and microdifferentiation among the Makiritare Indians. II. Seven serum protein systems. *American Journal of Human Genetics*, 22:526–32.

BLAKE, N. M., K. OMOTO, R. L. KIRK and D. C. GAJDUSEK   1973   Variation in red cell enzyme groups among populations of the Western Caroline Islands, Micronesia. *American Journal of Human Genetics*, 25:413–21.

BOWMAN, J. E., P. E. CARSON, H. FRISCHER and A. L. DE GARAY   1966   Genetics of starch-gel electrophoretic variants of human 6-phosphogluconate dehydrogenase. Population and family studies in the United States and in Mexico. *Nature*, 210: 811–13.

BRANDTZAEG, B. and J. MOHR   1961   On the genetics of the Gm serum system. *Acta Genetica (Basel)*, 11:111–25.

CAVALLI-SFORZA, L.   1973   Analytic review: some current problems of human population genetics. *American Journal of Human Genetics*, 25:82–104.

—— and W. F. BODMER   1971   *The genetics of human populations*. W. H. Freeman & Company, San Francisco.

CHOPRA, V. P.   1970   Studies on the serum groups in the Kumaon region, India. *Humangenetik*, 10:35–43.

CLEVE. H.   1973   The variants of the Group-Specific Component. *Israel Journal of Medical Science*, 9:1133–46.

——, R. L. KIRK, D. C. GAJDUSEK and J. GUIART   1967   On the distribution of the Gc variant Gc Aborigine in Melanesian populations: determination of Gc types in sera from Tongariki Island, New Hebrides. *Acta Genetica (Basel)*, 17:511–17.

CURTAIN, C. C., E. VAN LOGHEM, A. BAUMGARTEN, T. GOLAB, J. GORMAN, C. F. RUTGERS and C. KIDSON   1971   The ethnological significance of the gamma-globulin (Gm) factors in Melanesia. *American Journal of Physical Anthropology*, 34: 257–71.

——, ——, H. H. FUDENBERG, N. B. TINDALE, R. T. SIMMONS, R. L. DOHERTY and G. VOS   1972   Distribution of the immunoglobulin markers at the IgG_1, IgG_2, IgG_3, IgA_2 and κ-chain loci in Australian Aborigines: comparison with New Guinea populations. *American Journal of Human Genetics*, 24:145–55.

DOUGLAS, R., J. J. JACOBS, G. E. HOULT and J. M. STAVELEY   1962   Blood groups, serum genetic factors, and haemoglobins in Western Solomon Islanders. *Transfusion*, 2:413–18.

FRIEDLAENDER, J. S.   1971   Isolation by distance in Bougainville. *Proceedings of the National Academy of Science, U.S.A.*, 68:704–07.

—— and A. G. STEINBERG   1970   Anthropological significance of gamma-globulin (gm and Inv) antigens in Bougainville Island, Melanesia. *Nature*, 228: 59–61.

GERSHOWITZ, H., M. LAYRISSE, Z. LAYRISSE, J. V. NEEL, C. BREWER, N. CHAGNON and M. AYRES   1970   Gene frequencies and microdifferentiation among the Makiritare Indians. I. Eleven blood group systems and the ABH-1e secretor traits: a note on Rh gene frequency determinations. *American Journal of Human Genetics*, 22:515–25.

GRAYDON, J. J., R. T. SIMMONS, N. M. SEMPLE, J. L. CLAPHAM and E. H. WALLACE   1952   Blood genetics of various populations in Borneo. *Medical Journal of Australia*, 1:694–702.

HAINLINE, J., P. CLARK and R. J. WALSH   1969   ABO, Rh and MNS blood typing results and other biochemical traits in the people of the Yap Islands. *Archaeology and Physical Anthropology in Oceania*, 4:64–71.

HARRIS, H. and D. A. HOPKINSON   1972   Average heterozygosity per locus in man: an estimate based on the incidence of enzyme polymorphisms. *Annals of Human Genetics*, 36:9–20.

IMAIZUMI, Y. and N. E. MORTON   1970   Isolation by distance in New Guinea and Micronesia. *Archaeology and Physical Anthropology in Oceania*, 5:218–35.

——, —— and J. M. LALOUEL   1973   Kinship and race. In *Genetic structure of populations*, N. E. Morton (ed), pp. 228–33. University Press, Hawaii, Honolulu.

JENKINS, T., A. ZOUTENDYK and A. G. STEINBERG   1970   Gammaglobulin groups (Gm and Inv) of various Southern African populations. *American Journal of Physical Anthropology*, 32:197–218.

KIRK, R. L.   1964   Population genetic studies of the indigenous peoples of Australia and New Guinea. In *Progress in Medical Genetics*, A. G. Steinberg and A. G. Bearn (eds). Grune & Stratton, New York and London.

——, N. M. Blake, P. M. Moodie and G. J. Tibbs   1971   Population genetic studies in Australian Aborigines of the Northern Territory. *Human Biology in Oceania*, 1:54–76.

——, H. Cleve and A. G. Bearn   1963   The distribution of the Gc-types in sera from Australian Aborigines. *American Journal of Physical Anthropology*, 21:215–23.

——, —— and ——   1963   The distribution of the group specific component (Gc) in selected populations in south and southeast Asia and Oceania. *Acta Genetica et Statistica Medica (Basel)*, 13:140–49.

Kullback, S.   1968   *Information theory and statistics*. Dover Publications, New York.

Lalouel, J. M.   1973   Topology of population structure. In *Genetic structure of populations*, N. E. Morton (ed), pp. 139–52. University Press, Hawaii, Honolulu.

Latter, B. D. H.   1972   The island model of population differentiation: a general solution. *Genetics*, 73:147–57.

——   1973   Measure of genetic distance between individuals and populations. In *Genetic structure of populations*, N. E. Morton (ed), pp. 27–39. University Press, Hawaii, Honolulu.

Lewontin, R.   1973   Population genetics. In *Annual Review of Genetics VII*, pp. 1–17. Palo Alto, U.S.A.

Lie-Injo, L. E. and H. G. Poey-Oey   1970   Phosphoglucomutase, carbonic anhydrase and catalase in Indonesians. *Human Heredity*, 20:215–19.

Malcolm, L. A., D. G. Woodfield, N. M. Blake, R. L. Kirk and E. M. McDermid   1972   The distribution of blood, serum protein and enzyme groups on Manus Island (Admiralty Islands, New Guinea). *Human Heredity*, 22:305–22.

Malécot, G.   1948   *Les mathématiques de l'hérédité*. Masson, Paris.

Martin, A. O.   1973   An empirical comparison of some descriptions of population structure in a human isolate. In *Genetic structure of populations*, N. E. Morton (ed), pp. 195–202. University Press, Hawaii, Honolulu.

Morton, N. E.   1973a   Kinship and population structure. In *Genetic structure of populations*, N. E. Morton (ed), pp. 66–71. University Press, Hawaii, Honolulu.

——   1973b   Kinship and molecular evolution. In *Genetic structure of populations*, N. E. Morton (ed), pp. 263–67. University Press, Hawaii, Honolulu.

——   1975   Kinship, fitness and evolution. In *The role of natural selection in human evolution*, F. M. Salzano (ed), pp 133–54, North Holland, Amsterdam.

——, J. F. Crow and H. J. Muller   1956   An estimate of the mutational damage in man from data on consanguineous marriages. *Proceedings of the National Academy of Science*, 42:855–63.

——, D. E. Harris, S. Yee and R. Lew   1971a   Pingelap and Mokil Atolls: migration. *American Journal of Human Genetics*, 23:339–49.

——, Y. Imaizumi and D. E. Harris   1971b   Clans as genetic barriers. *American Anthropologist*, 73:1005–10.

—— and J. M. Lalouel   1973   Bioassay of kinship in Micronesia. *American Journal of Physical Anthropology*, 38:709–19.

——, C. Miki and S. Yee   1968   Bioassay of population structure under isolation by distance. *American Journal of Human Genetics*, 20:411–19.

—— and M. Yamamoto   1973   Blood groups and haptoglobins in the Eastern Carolines. *American Journal of Physical Anthropology*, 38:695–98.

—— and N. Yasuda   1963   The genetical structure of human populations. In *Les deplacements humain. Aspects methodologiques de leur mesure*, J. Sutter (ed), pp. 185–203. Entretiens de Monaco en Sciences Humaines.

——, S. Yee, D. E. Harris and R. Lew   1971c   Bioassay of kinship. *Theoretical population biology*, 2:507–24.

Mourant, A. E.   1954   *The distribution of the human blood groups*. Blackwell, Oxford.

Nei, M.   1973   The theory and estimation of genetic distance. In *Genetics of population structure*, N. E. Morton (ed), pp. 45–54. University Press, Hawaii, Honolulu.

Omoto, K.   1973   Polymorphic traits in peoples of Eastern Asia and the Pacific. *Israel Journal of Medical Science*, 9:1195–215.

Pollock, N., J. M. Lalouel and N. E. Morton   1972   Kinship and inbreeding on Namu Atoll (Marshall Islands). *Human Biology*, 44:459–73.

POLUNIN, I. and P. H. A. SNEATH   1953   Studies of blood groups in South-East Asia. *Journal of the Royal Anthropological Institute*, 83:215–51.

ROPARTZ, C., P. Y. ROUSSEAU, L. RIVAT, H. BAITSCH, H. RITTER, F. J. PINKERTON and L. E. MERMOD   1964   Les groupes de gamma-globulines Gm et Inv parmi la population d'Honolulu (Hawaii). *Acta Genetica* (Basel), 14:25–35.

SALZANO, F. M., A. G. STEINBERG and M. A. TEPFENHART   1973   Gm and Inv allotypes of Brazilian Cayapo Indians. *American Journal of Human Genetics*, 25:167–77.

SCHANFIELD, M. S. and H. GERSHOWITZ   1973   Non-random distribution of Gm haplotypes in East Asia. *American Journal of Human Genetics*, 25:567–74.

SCOTT, E. M., I. W. DUNCAN, V. EKSTRAND and R. C. WRIGHT   1966   Frequency of polymorphic types of red cell enzymes and serum factors in Alaskan Eskimos and Indians. *American Journal of Human Genetics*, 18:408–11.

SIMMONS, R. T. and J. J. GRAYDON   1971   Population genetics studies in Australian Aborigines of the Northern Territory. *Human Biology in Oceania*, 1:23–53.

——, J. J. GRAYDON, D. C. GAJDUSEK, M. P. ALPERS and R. W. HORNABROOK   1972   Genetic studies in relation to Kuru. II. Blood group genetic patterns in Kuru patients and populations of the Eastern Highlands of New Guinea. *American Journal of Human Genetics*, 24 supplement S39–71.

——, ——, and P. BROWN   1965   Blood group genetic variations in natives of the Caroline Islands and in other parts of Micronesia. *Oceania*, 36:132–70.

——, ——, N. M. SEMPLE, J. B. BIRDSELL, J. D. MILBOURNE and J. R. LEE   1952   A collaborative genetical survey in Marshall Islanders. *American Journal of Physical Anthropology*, 10:31–54.

——, ——, —— and S. KODAMA   1953   A collaborative genetical survey in Ainu: Hidaka, Island of Hokkaido. *American Journal of Physical Anthropology*, 11:47–82.

——, ——, —— and C. N. D. TAYLOR, 1951   Blood, taste and secretion: a genetical survey in Maoris. *Medical Journal of Australia*, 1:425–31.

SOKAL, R. R. and P. H. A. SNEATH   1963   *Principles of numerical taxonomy*. W. H. Freeman, San Francisco.

STEINBERG, A. G.   1973   Contribution of the Gm and Inv allotypes to the characterisation of human populations. *Israel Journal of Medical Science*, 9:1249–56.

—— and R. GOLDBLUM   1965   A genetic study of the antigens associated with the Gm(b) factor of human gamma globulin. *American Journal of Human Genetics*, 17:133–47.

—— and S. KAGEYAMA   1970   Further data on the Gm and Inv allotypes of the Ainu: Confirmation of the presence of Gm[2,17,21] phenogroup. *American Journal of Human Genetics*, 22:319–25.

—— and R. L. KIRK   1970   Gm and Inv types of Aborigines in the Northern Territory of Australia. *Archaeology and Physical Anthropology in Oceania*, 5:163–72.

—— and N. E. MORTON   1973   Immunoglobulins in the Eastern Carolines. *American Journal of Physical Anthropology*, 38:699–702.

——, J. V. UNDEVIA and M. A. TEPFENHART   1973   Gm and Inv studies of Parsi and Irani in India: report of a new polymorphic haplotype Gm[1,3,21]. *American Journal of Human Genetics*, 25:302–09.

TINDALE, N. B.   1953   Tribal and intertribal marriage among the Australian Aborigines. *Human Biology*, 25:169–90.

VOS, G. H., R. L. KIRK and A. G. STEINBERG   1963   The distribution of the gamma globulin types Gm(a), Gm(b), Gm(x) and Gm-like in south and south east Asia and Australia. *American Journal of Human Genetics*, 15:44–52.

WALTER, H. and M. BAJATZADEH   1971   Investigations on the geographical variability of the human transferrins. *Humangenetik*, 12:267–74.

WEITKAMP, L. and J. V. NEEL   1970   Gene frequencies and microdifferentiation among the Makiritare Indians. III. Nine erythrocyte enzyme systems. *American Journal of Human Genetics*, 22:533–37.

WORKMAN, P. L., H. HARPENDING, J. M. LALOUEL, C. LYNCH, J. D. NISWANDER and R. SINGLETON   1973   Population studies on southwestern Indian tribes VI. In *Genetic structure of populations*, N. E. Morton (ed), pp. 166–94. University Press Hawaii, Honolulu.

WRIGHT, S.   1921   Systems of mating. II. The effects of inbreeding on the genetic composition of a population. *Genetics*, 6:124–43.

——   1938   The distribution of gene frequencies in population of polyploids. *Proceedings of the National Academy of Science*, 24:372-77.

——   1951   The genetic structure of populations. *Annals of Eugenics*, 15:323–54.

YENGOYAN, A. A.   1968   Demographic and ecological influence on Aboriginal marriage sections. In *Man the hunter*, R. B. Lee and I. De Vore, pp. 185–99. Aldine Publishing Company, Chicago.

——   1970   Demographic factors in Pitjantjatjara social organization. In *Australian Aboriginal anthropology: modern studies in the social anthropology of the Australian Aborigines*, R. M. Berndt (ed), pp. 70–91. The University of Western Australia Press, Nedlands, W. A.

Comparative genetic studies between some groups of Australian Aboriginals and certain tribal peoples of India

L.D. Sanghvi

PROBLEMS OF THE ORIGIN and evolution of Man have continued to engage the attention of scientists from different disciplines during the last hundred years. The input of scientific work and the excitement that has been generated are, however, not commensurate with the results obtained so far. Accurate methods of skull and body measurements were developed in the last century and extensive data of hundreds of populations all over the world were collected. The cephalic index and several other analytical methods were marshalled towards a solution of these problems, and these efforts culminated in several active schools of thought leading to important developments in this field. This century has witnessed the growth of human population genetics and we are currently in an active phase of evaluation of what contribution it has made and can make towards a better understanding of these old problems.

My own interest in this field has been indirect. I was intrigued by the genetic diversity found in the castes and tribes in India (Sanghvi, 1953, 1966). One of the social mechanisms which maintained this diversity was the rigid endogamous nature of these population units. The force of culture in this respect was sufficiently strong to overcome the religious and other influences, and an enormous mass of people who moved into the country from outside during historical times had to accept this aspect of culture. It provided wide scope for their absorption at various hierarchical levels without disturbing the basic endogamous nature of the indigenous groups and provided adequate guidelines and flexibility to these incoming peoples for setting up their own endogamous units.

In studying this general problem we found it useful to make use of some composite measure of genetic distance to help in understanding the biological relationships among these endogamous groups. In the computation of genetic distance equal weights are attached generally to each allele and it is assumed that by increasing the number of alleles, it will be possible to arrive at a set of relationships which will reflect the past history of the populations under consideration. The chief limitation in this approach continues to be a lack of knowledge about the selective values of alleles.

The work on the sickle-cell, thalassemia and G-6-PD alleles had demonstrated that specific agents in the environment, such as malarial parasites, have determined to a great extent their current frequency as well as their rise and fall spread over hundreds of generations. The alleles at other loci, such as for the ABO blood groups, were originally assumed to be neutral and were useful therefore in detecting relationships such as those of European Gypsies with India. Gradually evidence was received regarding their adaptative nature and the idea about their utility in long term racial analysis became suspect. For this reason the question of determining the adaptative nature of alleles became of importance. However, direct studies in the search for these parameters have turned out to be of limited value and there was a need to search for alternative approaches.

One such approach is to examine the extent of allelic variability between populations in a given region and between regions. Contrasts in the behaviour of individual alleles in such a set of comparisons may indicate the importance of selective or other controlling factors. It is this approach I wish to explore in the present paper in relation to tribal populations in India and Australia. This analysis is important not only from the point of view of understanding the evolution of genetic divergence between human populations but also because of the postulated ancestral relationship between Indian and Australian Aboriginal peoples.

During the last century there were speculations about the common origin of some indigenous people of peninsular India and the Australian Aboriginals. These views were reviewed earlier by Thurstone (1909) and more recently by Birdsell (1972). Guha (1937), one of the students of Dixon at Harvard provided a racial classification of India based on his extensive anthropological studies. He formalised this old idea by coining a term 'Proto-Australoid' to designate these indigenous people of India presumed to have racial affinities with Australian Aboriginals. I am quoting below his views, which have formed the basis for the populations selected in this analysis.

> Among the aboriginal Indian population, specially those of Central and Southern India, there are many who show a marked development of the supra-orbital ridges along with a sunken nasal root, but in the majority however, this trait is not pronounced, though in the shape of the head, the form of the nose, the projection of the face, skin colour and structure of hair no significant differences are observed.
>
> If we compare these tribes with the Veddas of Ceylon, and the aborigines of Australia, we find that in the shape of the head and the face, the form of hair and, skin colour, the three are essentially alike, though the Australians are taller and show larger absolute dimensions of head than the other two. The Veddas are closer to the Australians, than to the Indian tribes, who are the smallest of the three. Among the Australians also the brow ridges are more marked and the body hair is more profuse. In all these characters there seems to be a regular gradation, the shortest and the smallest being the Indian tribes, then come the Veddas, and lastly the Australians. We may assume then that all the three belong essentially to the same stock, the Indian tribes retaining the more basic characters, and the two extra-Indian groups

having developed some of the features in a more marked manner. The most appropriate term to apply to them therefore is Proto-Australoid which shows best the genetic relationships between the three.

The whole of the Central and Southern Indian tribes belong essentially to this type, though pertaining to different linguistic families. The same can be said of the tribes of Western India and the partially reclaimed groups in the Gangetic Valleys who form the outer layer of the Hindu social system at the present times. The Bhils, Kols, Badagas, Korwa, Karwar, Munda, Bhumij and Malpaharias living in the Central Indian highlands and the Chenchus, Kurumbas, Malayans and Yeruvas of South India may be regarded as some of the representatives of this race, though the amount of admixture with other types specially the Negritos, in each of these tribes is not uniform. It is certainly stronger among the tribes living in the marginal areas of S. India than among the Central Indian groups.

We have no definite evidence as to the times of the respective drifts of these races into India but judging from their distribution, the Proto-Australoids appear to be later, whose pressure it may be presumed, the more primitive Negritos were not able to withstand and were gradually driven off to less hospitable regions. In the process of this expansion, the Proto-Australoids unquestionably have absorbed a large amount of their blood in varying proportions, to which must be ascribed some of the differences noticeable in these tribes—specially between those of the Central Indian highlands and the Southern Indian hills.

The study material

Populations in India: In an earlier paper (Sanghvi, 1966) I analysed the genetic data on a set of six tribes of Gujarat in Western India in relation to their adaptation to local environments. The morphological and historical evidence indicated that these six tribes were sub-sections of the Bhil tribe, going under different names and having separated from the original stock for various reasons, which may be geographical (isolation), social (various degrees of Hinduisation) or economic (various transitional stages to plough cultivation). Bhils belong to an ancient tribal group to which references are found in early Sanskrit literature beginning at least from 2nd or 3rd century B.C. They are distributed over a large area and all over the extent of their geographical distribution there are a number of smaller tribal groups, with many cultural traits in common with the surrounding Bhils. Two of the six tribes, viz. Dhanka and Gamit were considered part of the Bhil tribe in the 1901 Census but were recognised as separate tribes in the 1931 Census.

I have now extended this earlier study in India by addition of fresh data on four more tribes which were studied in Maharashtra. These tribes have been taken as a southward extension of the Bhils, primarily on the basis of geographical contiguity and similarity of certain cultural traits.

Table 1 gives the list of these ten tribes in western India and their numerical strength according to the 1931 Census, and the primary centres of their location is shown in Figure 1.

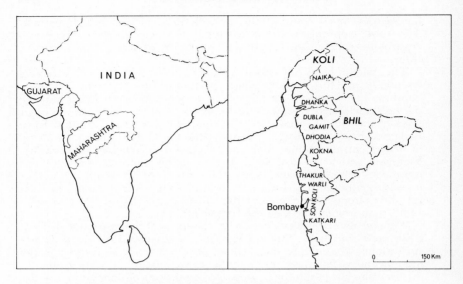

Figure 1 Location of tribes of Western India included in the study.

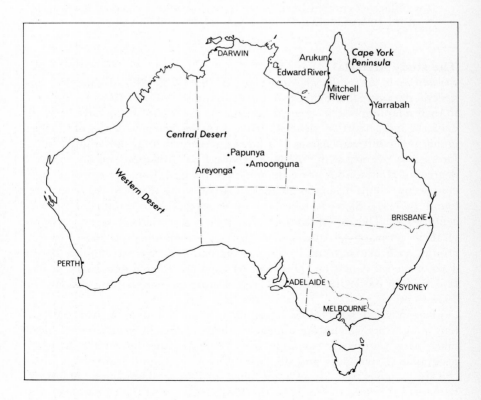

Figure 2 Localities for Australian Aborigines included in the study.

Table 1: Numerical strength of ten tribes of Western India

Tribe (Abbreviation)	Numerical strength (1931 Census)
Gujarat	
Bhil (Bh)	776,975
Naika (Na)	101,954
Dhanka (Dk)	34,622
Dubla (Du)	83,527
Gamit (Ga)	11,933
Dhodia (Dd)	140,000
Maharashtra	
Kokna (Ko)	65,792
Thakur (Th)	116,591
Warli (Wa)	206,551
Katkari (Ka)	87,748

Data on the A_1, A_2, B, O, MN and Rh blood groups, ABH secretion, PTC tasting, red-green colour vision and Hb-S were used in the present analysis. Data on the six tribes of Gujarat were given in the earlier paper (Sanghvi, 1966) and are not reproduced here. Data on the four tribes of Maharashtra are given in Table 2. These were collected by me and the staff of the former Human Variation Unit to whom appropriate credit is given at the end of the paper.

Populations in Australia: The Australian populations were taken from four localities in Cape York together with five tribes from three localities in central Australia and a further population from the Western Desert in Western Australia. The locations of these populations is given in Figure 2 and they are described in more detail by Sanghvi *et al* (1971). In the analysis Cape York has been considered to be one region and central Australia another. The data for the ABO, MN, Rh, P and Le blood groups and for the Hp, Tf, Gm and Gc serum protein types is given in the paper referred to above and is not reproduced here.

Table 2: Percent allelic frequencies in four tribes of Western India

Allele	Kokna	Thakur	Warli	Katkari
A_1	22·67	17·77	21·99	17·58
A_2	3·46	4·32	1·98	2·75
B	15·26	21·50	20·04	24·17
O	58·61	56·41	55·99	55·50
R_1	70·19	82·05	80·54	85·10
R_2	9·81	6·28	4·39	4·10
R_0	4·12	1·00	3·59	—
R_z	—	0·22	—	—
Rh(d)	15·88	10·46	11·48	10·80
M	50·78	63·77	48·51	50·00
Se	46·05	53·36	54·49	49·65
PTC(T)	34·30	32·73	28·22	30·14
R—G	—	1·00	3·92	1·38
Hb—S	2·11	—	8·25	4·01

Method of analysis: In order to obtain a satisfactory measure of allelic variability two approaches are available. For applying the powerful procedures of analysis of variance, it is necessary to use angular transformation so that the variance will be independent of the allelic frequencies. Estimation of rare genes has posed some problems in practice and it is here that angular transformation inflates them considerably. An alternative approach is to run a x^2-test directly on the Maximum-likelihood gene frequency estimates without resorting to angular transformation. I had applied this procedure in my previous analysis of six tribes of Gujarat.

In the present analysis, I have used the same procedure to measure allelic variability at various levels. Allelic data from Gujarat provided variability within this region and was compared with similar data from Maharashtra. The same data on ten tribes provided a measure of variability between these two regions in Western India. Similarly, the data from Australia provided variability estimates within each region and of total variability. The interaction values between regions as well as between India and Australia could be provided approximately by subtraction from the total variability. A modified procedure for calculating interaction was devised by V. Balakrishnan of my group and is given in the appendix. In the present study, comparisons are based directly on x^2 values. Their probabilities for appropriate degrees of freedom can also provide a measure of their variability.

Variability in Indian tribes

Table 3 gives the allelic variability (as chi-square values) of ten tribes of Western India. The allelic complexes r, r' and r″ at the Rh locus have been combined together to give one value Rh(d).

Table 3: Allelic variability of ten tribes in Western India (expressed as chi-square values)

Allele	Within Gujarat (5 d.f.)	Within Maharashtra (3 d.f.)	Between regions (1 d.f.)	Total variability (9 d.f.)
A	6·14	1·05	0·25	7·36
A_2	0·83	0·98	3·76	5·77
B	9·41	2·59	0·01	12·03
O	1·38	0·23	0·12	1·73
R_1	6·90	7·70	4·51	18·72
R_2	4·70	3·59	0·17	8·49
R_0	2·35	5·58	21·70	26·90
R_z	6·80	0·66	1·68	12·39
Rh(d)	8·19	1·40	1·44	10·51
M	6·76	6·02	0·01	12·79
Se	5·14	1·76	2·12	8·99
PTC(T)	3·62	1·02	0·05	4·68
R—G	4·07	5·39	0·07	9·32
Hb—S	9·84	10·67	12·81	31·14

Gujarat: The data relating to six tribes of Gujarat were published earlier (Sanghvi, 1966). The alleles were broadly divided into three arbitrary categories, viz. high, moderate and low variability. The alleles A_2, O and R_0 were in the low variable category; B, $Rh(d)$ and Hb-S were in the high variable category and the remaining alleles, viz. A_1, M, R_1, R_2, R_Z, Se, PTC and R-G, the gene for red-green colour vision defect, were in the intermediate category. It will be seen that allelic variability is independent of the loci with multiple alleles.

Maharashtra: When the same criteria are applied to the data of four tribes in Maharashtra, it turns out that A_2 and O continue to be in the low variable category and Hb-S, in the high variability class. In the intermediate group, R_1, R_2, M and R-G have retained their position. The main switch is by the B and $Rh(d)$ alleles which are in the low variable group in Maharashtra. A_1, R_Z, PTC and Se which were in the intermediate position in Gujarat have moved to the low variable position in Maharashtra.

Between regions: The two values of x^2 which deserve special attention with respect to variability between Gujarat and Maharashtra are for R_0 ($21 \cdot 70$) and Hb-S ($12 \cdot 81$). Hb-S continues to show consistent variability not only within each region but also between regions. A somewhat unexpected finding is for the R_0 complex. Its values are consistently higher in Gujarat than in Maharashtra with somewhat larger variation in the latter. It shows a geographical gradient with values declining from north to south. There is a corresponding relationship with the R_1 allele, but it is not so marked.

Total variability: If we look now at the last column of Table 3 it will be seen that the A_2, O and PTC alleles are least variable and consistently so within each region as well as between the two regions. In contrast, Hb-S is the most variable allele at each level. R_1 is comparable to Hb-S, but its variability is not so marked. Finally, R_0 shows high variability between the two regions and shows a gradient. Environmental effects are marked for Hb-S as well as for R_0 and R_1 alleles at the Rh locus.

Variability in Australian Aboriginals

Table 4 gives the allelic variability (as chi-square values) of 10 populations of Australian Aboriginals. These data were earlier analysed for genetic distance (Sanghvi *et al*, 1971).

Cape York: The highest value of x^2 in the series is $20 \cdot 45$ for the M allele and the dividing line is taken at half way giving a class of moderate variability and another one of low variability to make it comparable with the variability in the central and Desert region (see below). With this criterion, A, B, O, R_Z, M, Gm^a and Gm^x fall in the moderate and the rest in the low variability class. The variability within this region is about twice the variation found within the Indian regions.

Central Australia and Western Desert: Variability in the central and Desert region is much higher than in Cape York. Here I have taken the same

Table 4: Allelic variability of ten populations of Australian Aboriginals (expressed as chi-square values)

Allele		Within Cape York (3 d.f.)	Within Desert (5 d.f.)	Between regions (1 d.f.)	Total variability (9 d.f.)
A		11·84	7·00	68·95	84·01
B		12·09	4·61	16·20	44·39
O		16·48	7·15	48·85	67·57
R_1		2·48	5·71	29·77	37·90
R_2		0·02	4·55	70·25	76·02
R_0		2·60	3·37	28·48	34·48
R_z		13·47	5·06	8·37	22·92
M		20·45	25·85	8·39	54·78
P_1		0·19	35·21	1·55	34·71
Le^a		4·63	7·09	21·65	33·05
Gm	a	19·38	11·14	5·03	34·32
	b	7·09	0·00	13·78	31·27
	x	20·32	11·14	9·39	38·89
Gc	1	1·53	4·10	43·04	47·88
	2	1·75	5·06	36·43	42·17
	Ab	3·12	25·76	4·87	26·85
Hp^1		2·21	14·23	2·89	20·12
Tf		5·84	18·92	2·04	27·88

criterion as in the Cape York with values more than 21 falling in the high variability class. The alleles M, P_1 and $Gc^{Ab.}$ fall in the high variability class. The alleles Gm^a, Gm^x, Hp^1 and Tf^D occupy the intermediate position and the rest are in the low variable group. It may be noted that M shows high variability in both regions and Gm^a, Gm^x show intermediate variability. On the other hand, A, B, O and R_z which showed intermediate variability in Cape York are less variable in the centre and Desert region and the situation is reversed for Hp^1 and Tf^D. Sharpest contrast is shown by Gc^{Ab} which has high variability in the centre and Desert and low in Cape York.

Between regions: Variability between the two regions of Australia is very striking and is considerably more than the regions in India. Many factors must be operating to bring about this differentiation. Very high variability is shown by A and R_2 alleles. The alleles O, R_1, R_0, Gc^1, and Gc^2 show high variability. Intermediate variability is shown by B, Le and Gm^b alleles. The remaining alleles show low variability. It is interesting to note that the R_2 complex, which showed low variability within each region, shows the largest contrast between the two regions. This is due to high values of the R_2 allele in the centre and Desert region which is almost balanced by low values of R_0 and R_1. A similar situation is reflected by the A allele which attains very high values in the centre and Desert. Here the balance is maintained primarily by O. Similarly, the high value of Gc^1 in the centre and Desert is compensated by low values of Gc^2.

Table 5: Allelic variability between India and Australia
(expressed as chi-square values)

Allele	Between India and Australia (1 d.f.)	Total variability (19 d.f.)
A	1·50	93·12
B	186·94	213·22
O	61·94	121·46
M	217·97	271·07
R_1	37·35	95·15
R_2	97·21	209·19
R_0	3·13	65·37
R_z	63·32	106·66

Total variability: The last column in Table 4 shows the total variability. The alleles A, O, and R_2 are highly variable and this is primarily due to their differentiation between the two regions. Amongst the alleles which are moderately variable, the same is true for Gc^1 and Gc^2. In contrast, the allele M shows high variability within regions but low variability between the regions.

Variability between India and Australia

A comparison of allelic variability between India and Australia is feasible for the ABO, MN and Rh loci for which common data are available. For the ABO locus, the A_2 allele does not exist in Australia and this is the case also for the $Rh(d)$ complex. The remaining alleles are compared in Table 5.

It will be seen from the last column of this table that the total variability is high for all the alleles and is particularly marked for B, M and R_2. Variability between India and Australia falls in four broad categories: B and M show greatest differences in the series; O, R_2 and R_z show high variation; R_1 shows moderate difference and A and R_0 show very little difference.

Discussion

The criteria adopted for comparing variability at various levels, i.e. within regions, between regions and between India and Australia are arbitrary and are primarily based on the range of variation of chi-square values in each category under consideration. Although this procedure is not entirely satisfactory, it is sufficiently useful to show the nature and extent of variability of each allele. Almost every allele under consideration has its own individuality if one takes into account its behaviour pattern in different regions and in different continents.

If we consider eight alleles for which comparative data are available for India and Australia, it will be seen that there are no alleles which are consistently more variable or which are consistently less variable. The largest range of variation is found between India and Australia, where the variation is lowest for A and R_0 and highest for B and M. This implies that the mean values of A and R_0 in the two continents have remained close to one another whereas those of *B* and *M* have moved greatly apart. Other alleles are spread between these two extremes.

I might point out another significant feature of this variation. In the Indian tribes, the alleles A_2 and $Rh(d)$ are consistently present whereas they are not found in the Australian Aboriginals. Earlier Kirk (1961) reported a positive correlation between these two alleles. Is their absence due to genetic drift or is there something in the Australian environment which is working against these alleles? The *B* allele also shows a similar behaviour in Australia, but in India it seems to be one of the most needed alleles. This is in contrast to the behaviour of the *A* allele which is more common in the centre and Desert area of Australia but less so in Cape York and in India. In view of this, the search for appropriate weights for individual alleles to be used in genetic distance analysis for problems of racial origins has not so far been rewarding.

Acknowledgements: Field work in the tribes of Maharashtra was initiated in 1953 jointly by me as Chief of the former Human Variation Unit and the late Professor G. M. Kurulkar of the Department of Anatomy, G. S. Medical College, Bombay. Mr P. K. Sukumaran, Mr D. S. Varde and Dr J. V. Undevia of the Human Variation Unit participated in the field work and carried out the laboratory studies. Thanks are due to Mr V. Balakrishnan of the Epidemiology Division for giving me assistance in the calculations involved in this study.

References

BIRDSELL, J. B.   1972   The problem of the evolution of human races: classification or clines? *Social Biology*, 19:136–62.

GUHA, B. S.   1937   An outline of the racial ethnology of India. In *An outline of the field sciences of India*, pp. 125–39. Indian Science Congress Association, Calcutta.

KIRK, R. L.   1961   Blood group interaction and the world distribution of the ABO gene p² and the Rh gene r(cde). *American Journal of Human Genetics*, 13: 224–32.

SANGHVI, L. D.   1953   Comparison of genetical and morphological methods for a study of biological differences. *American Journal of Physical Anthropology*, 11: 385–404.

——   1966   Genetic adaptation in man. In *The biology of human adaptability*. P. T. Baker and J. S. Weiner (eds), pp. 305–28. Clarendon Press, Oxford.

——, R. L. KIRK and V. BALAKRISHNAN   1971   A study of genetic distance among some populations of Australian Aborigines. *Human Biology*, 43:445–58.

THURSTONE, E.   1909   *Castes and tribes of Southern India*. Vol. I. Government Press, Madras.

Appendix

A method to study allelic variability

V. Balakrishnan

In the foregoing paper Sanghvi has pointed out that the usual procedure of giving equal weights to each allele in the computation of genetic distance is not an ideal one since it does not distinguish the alleles whose frequencies are less variable over environmental ranges from the ones whose frequencies are subject to greater adaptation to local environments. He suggested that it might be possible to distinguish between the two types of alleles under some circumstances and proposed as a measure of variability the heterogeneity Chi-square determined from the allelic frequencies. Applying this method to study the allelic variability in several tribes of Gujarat, he found that A_2, O and R_0 are less variable than B, Hb-S and $Rh(d)$ in the environments in which these tribes live.

Sanghvi has tried to extend this analysis to different populations living over a gradation of environments. It is possible that if we consider two sets of populations with populations in each set nearer to each other but living in two types of environments, those alleles which are more useful for racial analysis will show less variability within each set and greater variability between the two sets, while those alleles which are more susceptible to environmental variation will show more variability within each set but less variability between the subsets living in similar environments. The data presented by Sanghvi above do not fully satisfy the above theoretical formulation of the conditions; the present method of analysis was developed during the analysis of this data.

Method

Let $a(i, j, k)$, $i = 1, \ldots m$; $j = 1, \ldots, n$, be the percent allelic frequency in population k of subset j of set i. The maximum value of k need not be the same for all values of (i, j).

For subset j of set i, let

Total $\quad = A(i, j) = \sum_k a(i, j, k)$,

Mean $\quad = a(i, j)$,

Sum of squares $= S(i, j) = \sum_k a^2(i, j, k)$, and

Adjusted SS $\quad = V(i, j) = S(i, j) - A(i, j)a(i, j)$.

For set i, let

Total $\quad = A(i) = \sum A(i, j)$,

Mean $\quad = a(i)$,

Sum of squares $= S(i) = \sum S(i, j)$, and

Adjusted SS $\quad= V(i) = S(i) - A(i)\, a(i).$

For subset j (over all sets), let

Total $\quad\quad\quad = A(j) = \sum_i A(i, j),$

Mean $\quad\quad\quad = a(j),$
Sum of squares $= S(j) = \sum_i S(i, j),$ and

Adjusted SS $\quad= V(j) = S(j) - A(j)\, a(j).$

For all populations, let

Total $\quad\quad\quad = A = \sum_i A(i) = \sum_j A(j),$

Mean $\quad\quad\quad = a,$
Sum of squares $= S = \sum_i S(i) = \sum_j S(j),$ and

Adjusted SS $\quad= V = S - Aa.$

Setting up a 2-way table with $a(i, j, k)$ in one row and $100 - a(i, j, k)$ in the other row, the Chi-square value for differences between populations over subset j of set i is

$$x^2(k/i, j) = 100\, V(i, j)/a(i, j)(100 - a(i, j)) ,$$

Analogously, the Chi-square value for differences between populations over set i is

$$x^2(k/i) = 100\, V(i)/a(i)(100 - a(i)) ,$$

the Chi-square value for differences between populations over subset j (over all sets) is

$$x^2(k/j) = 100\, V(j)/a(j)(100 - a(j)) ,$$

and the Chi-square value for differences between all populations is

$$x^2(k) = 100\, V/a(100 - a) .$$

Under some circumstances, it may be found that $x^2(k/i, j)$ is greater than $x^2(k/i)$ or $x^2(k/j)$. Rarely, it may even happen that one particular $x^2(k/i, j)$ is greater than the corresponding $x^2(k/i)$ or $x^2(k/j)$. Hence, it is not possible to get the Chi-square value for differences between populations over subsets in set i by subtraction as $x^2(k/i) - \sum_j x^2(k/i, j)$. Similarly, it is not possible to get the Chi-square value for differences between populations over the sets for a particular j by subtraction as $x^2(k/j) - \sum_i x^2(k/i, j)$.

These difficulties may be avoided by using the analysis of variance technique to get the appropriate adjusted sum of squares and then calculate the Chi-square value as above. Let

$$V(j/i) = V(i) - \sum V(i, j) \quad \text{and} \quad V(i/j) = V(j) - \sum V(i, j) .$$

Then, the Chi-square value for differences between populations over the subsets within set i is $x^2(j/i) = 100\, V(j/i)/a(i)(100 - a(i))$ and the Chi-square value for differences between populations over the sets for a particular subset j is

$$x^2(i/j) = 100\, V(i/j)/a(j)(100 - a(j)) .$$

Now, let $V_1(i) = V - V(i)$ and $V_1(j) = V - V(j)$. Then, the Chi-square value for differences between populations over sets is $x^2(i) = 100\, V_1(i)/a(100 - a)$ and the Chi-square value for differences between populations over subsets (over all sets) is $x^2(j) = 100\, V_1(j)/a(100 - a)$.

Discussion

Let the number of populations in subset j of set i be $K(i, j)$ and let $K(i) = \sum_j K(i, j)$, $K(j) = \sum_i K(i, j)$ and $K = \sum_i K(i) = \sum_j K(j)$. For each allele, the total degrees of freedom may be partitioned in two different ways, since

$$K - 1 = \sum_i \sum_j (K(i, j) - 1) + m(n - 1) + (m - 1)$$
$$= \sum_i \sum_j (K(i, j) - 1) + n(m - 1) + (n - 1) .$$

We thus have the following table for each allele.

Table 1: Two different partitionings of the total Chi-square

Source	Chi-square		
	Number	d.f.	Value
Between Populations			
A			
Over subset j of set i	mn	$K(i, j) - 1$	$\chi^2(k/i, j)$
Over subsets of set i	m	$n - 1$	$\chi^2(j/i)$
Over set i	m	$K(i) - 1$	$\chi^2(k/i)$
Over sets	1	$m - 1$	$\chi^2(i)$
All	1	$K - 1$	$\chi^2(k)$
B			
Over subset j of set i	mn	$K(i, j) - 1$	$\chi^2(k/i, j)$
Over sets for subset j	n	$m - 1$	$\chi^2(i/j)$
Over subset j	n	$K(j) - 1$	$\chi^2(k/j)$
Over subsets	1	$n - 1$	$\chi^2(j)$
All	1	$K - 1$	$\chi^2(k)$

Remembering that i stands for a racially homogeneous group and j stands for a particular environment, an allele will be more useful than another in racial analysis if it shows larger Chi-square values over sets and over sets for particular subsets. On the other hand, an allele will be more susceptible to environmental influences if it shows larger Chi-square values over subsets and over subsets in particular sets. While studying microevolution within a set i of racially near populations, that allele which shows a smaller Chi-square over subsets in that set will be more useful. A larger Chi-square value for an allele over a particular subset in a set would indicate a greater susceptibility of that allele to small local environmental changes.

Once the alleles have been grouped in this manner, the problem arises of how to assign proper weights to different alleles while computing genetic distances. Usually genetic distance is most useful in studying the relationships between populations which are not far apart racially. In this case, if the populations also share a common environment, one method may be to weight each allele with the reciprocal of the square root of the heterogeneity Chi-square over the populations. In Indian conditions, this may be appropriate in the study of interrelationships among the tribes of a region or the castes of a region. In a study of the interrelationships of the tribes and castes of a region, the appropriate weight may be the product of the square root of the Chi-square over the two sets and the reciprocal of the square root of the heterogeneity Chi-square over the populations in each set. It is not clear yet how such weights could be incorporated in the definition of an index of genetic distance.

While the method has been developed with this genetic application in mind, it may be useful in other fields also. For example, one of the problems in the etiology of cancer is to pick out from a group of cancers those which are more associated with particular environmental factors. Let us consider the group of cancers of the Oral Cavity, Oropharynx, Hypopharynx and Oesophagus (upper 1/3). There are indications that tobacco use, either smoking or chewing, has some influence in the development of these cancers. Another factor may be atmospheric pollution found in greater degree in urban areas. The data will consist of percentages of the different cancers in subsets determined by smoking (S and NS), chewing (C and NC) and place of residence (U and R).

Those cancers giving larger Chi-square values in each category specified by the smoking and chewing classifications would appear to be more associated with urban-rural differences. Those cancers giving larger Chi-square values over chewing categories would appear to be more associated with chewing tobacco. Similarly, those cancers giving larger Chi-square values over smoking categories would appear to be more associated with smoking tobacco. Again, those cancers giving larger Chi-square values over chewing categories within each smoking category would appear to be influenced more by chewing tobacco than by smoking it. The analysis of the data by the method suggested here may thus lead to some interesting hypotheses.

Genetic distance analysis of some New Guinea populations

An evaluation

P.B. Booth and H.W. Taylor

ALTHOUGH ONLY about one fifth of the New Guinean populations separable by language differences have been the subjects of genetic surveys, and although most of the surveys have dealt only with a restricted number of red cell antigens, the data which has been accumulated is quite formidable. Several of the more recent surveys have included tests for an extended series of markers, relating to blood groups, serum proteins and red cell enzymes, and have thus produced an even more indigestible mass of information. It may well be that this will be of greatest value to future workers, who will be able to study the changes wrought by time, and relate them to known events. But here and now we must interpret, as best we can, results obtained from population samples that were obtained, often with great difficulty, from remote places, and tested tediously and exactingly in the laboratory.

The mathematical exercises necessary for genetic distance analysis need but slight effort compared to the work which necessarily precedes them, and thus there was no excuse for not trying this approach, which if successful promised to be of use in several ways, as set out below. If, on the other hand, analyses produced results which appeared to lack meaning when examined in the light of other known facts, then fuel would be provided for critics of the method, and its application to small and semi-isolated populations, such as are commonly found in New Guinea, would be at least dubious.

It seemed of some importance that this point be settled, and that the New Guinea data, derived in many instances from surveys inevitably less than perfect in sample size and subject selection, would provide an adequately stern test. In the event, the correlation of the results of genetic distance analyses with linguistic classification, and with time-scales derived from lexico-statistical methods, was quite astonishingly good, and from these results one can begin to descry where some critics are in error. This point will be returned to later, as first the aims of the genetic distance analyses, and the results, must be detailed.

In this paper examples are given of the four main facets of our investigations to date. Only the first of these was decided upon *ab initio*, the others arising as the work progressed, in a continuing process. Briefly, the questions concerning genetic distance analysis to which we have sought answers are:

1.   Does it correspond with, and thus support, known, suspected or postulated inter-relationships of the populations under study?

2.   Can it help explain the discrepancies between the results of red cell antigen and 'other loci' testing which it itself brings to light?

3.   Does it correlate with time-scales derived from linguistic work?

4.   Would the use of information on a limited number of blood group systems, such as abounds in New Guinea, produce worth-while results?

Method

The method of analysis adopted derives minimum length genetic networks from the calculated gene frequencies, using the computer programme TREE (Edwards, 1969) modified for use with the Digital PDP11 computer, and to select any or all of 15 populations and seven loci.

Pair-wise chord distances, d, (Cavalli-Sforza and Edwards, 1967) directly representable in Euclidean space are first calculated. (These are related to the mean kinship coefficient, f_θ, (Cavalli-Sforza, 1969), by the formula $f_\theta = \pi^2 d^2/2n$ where n is the total number of alleles less the total number of loci). An initial cluster analysis is performed (Edwards and Cavalli-Sforza, 1965), using the pair-wise distances, and the networks are derived from this according to the minimum net length procedure of Cavalli-Sforza and Edwards (1967). The network figures included here were drawn to scale on polar graph paper, with genetic distances along the radius. Thus the sum of the radial distances of any two populations from their common node gives the pair-wise distance. The primary segment of the net, joining the two nodes giving rise to the two initial clusters, is arbitrarily drawn through the origin, with the nodes equidistant from the origin. The method does not give information concerning the initial split, apart from the internodal distance.

Correspondence with other data

If analysis results correlated well with linguistic, cultural or anthropological postulates, then it was felt that some mutual confirmation would be provided. Additionally, some confidence that the population sample tested was satisfactory would be generated. Lack of correlation would suggest either that the analysis was inappropriate, that the genetic data were unsatisfactory, or that the other information used as a yard-stick should be critically re-examined. It was supposed that genetic distance analysis might sometimes reveal unexpected affinities between population groups, and when this occurred further investigations would be warranted to establish whether, if the surveys were themselves adequate, the convergencies were accidental or not.

Figure 1 shows the network derived from *ABO*, *MNSs* and *Rh* gene frequencies for nine Highland populations, selected rather at random for their geographical distribution and probable diversity. It can be seen that the primary split separates the three most westerly populations, those of Lake

Kopiago, Oksapmin and Telefolmin, from the rest, while on the other branch the two populations north of the Bismarck Divide here called Bundi and Simbai (speaking respectively Gende-Biyom and Maring) are associated, as are the three members of the Central Language Family (Jimi, Enga and Chimbu) occupying territory to the south of the Divide. Siane, of the East-Central Language Family, occupies an anomalous position, and this has been commented upon before (Booth, 1974) as occurring when comparisons are made between populations speaking languages of the Central and East Central Families.

It is clear that in general the results of this genetic analysis are in accord with linguistic and geographical considerations, but the convergence of Bundi and Simbai gene frequencies has not previously been noted. This may well represent an accidental convergence within a framework of generally similar gene frequencies in the area, but it is interesting in that one might have expected the Maring people of the Simbai Valley to be associated genetically, as they are linguistically and culturally, with the Jimi Valley groups to their south. About 20 per cent of Simbai marriages are said to be with Jimi Valley Maring speakers, (Buchbinder and Clark, 1971), whereas although western Bundi clans intermarry with Jimi Valley people, this only amounts to one per cent of all Bundi marriages (Malcolm, Booth and Cavalli-Sforza, 1971). In each area about 30 per cent of marriages are endogamous, and the main outside contribution of women to the Bundi population comes from the Chimbu area.

However, Chimbu is closely associated, on blood group data, with Jimi, of the same Central Highlands Linguistic Family. It was found that the subjects tested and here called Jimi included a high proportion of Narak and Kandawo speakers, who together with the Maring form the Jimi language sub-family (Wurm, 1964).

A special case of seeking and finding, by distance analysis, some corroboration of genetic similarity in otherwise apparently dissimilar populations has already been reported (Booth and Hornabrook, 1973). After eight New Guinean populations, selected only by availability of samples, had been tested for their MNᴬSZ blood groups, cluster analysis was performed, using the genetic distances. Three main clusters could be distinguished. One comprised the Tolai of New Britain and Motu from around Port Moresby, another three Highland-affiliated populations (Kutubu, Watut and Kunimaipa), while the third cluster consisted of the Guhu-Samane of the middle Waria, the Atzera of the Markham Valley, and the Takia of Karkar Island. The point is that this last cluster, though composed of widely separated groups speaking both Austronesian and non-Austronesian languages, contains the only populations then dealt with which possessed a high proportion of Gerbich negative subjects. There is no known link between Gerbich and MNS, so the link is between the populations themselves. This is of course clearly evident on the Gerbich results, but had these not been available, the association of the three populations revealed by MNᴬSZ analysis would have been most surprising.

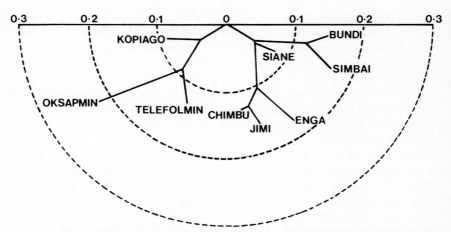

Figure 1 Minimum length genetic net for nine New Guinea Highland populations, derived from *ABO, MNSs* and *Rh* gene frequencies.

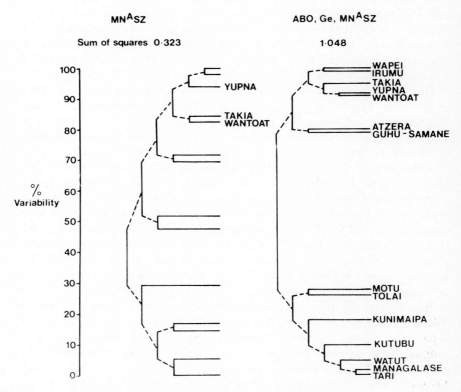

Figure 2 Cluster analyses for 14 populations, using blood group data as indicated on the figure. The populations occupy the same positions on each diagram, except for Yupna, Takia and Wantoat, which alter as shown. The upper seven populations are those with significant numbers of Gerbich negative subjects.

More recently, the results of testing a further six populations have become available, and Figure 2 shows cluster analyses performed on all 14 populations, firstly using MN^{A}SZ data, and secondly using the same plus ABO and Gerbich results. As in the previous eight populations analysis, it can again be seen that those containing significant numbers of Gerbich negative subjects (now increased from three to seven) cluster together when their MN^{A}SZ groups are considered, and that though, as might be expected, addition of ABO and Gerbich data increases the efficiency of the separations, the result is essentially the same. It is perhaps of interest that Atzera and Guhu-Samane, the populations with the highest Ge(a−) incidence, separate quite markedly from the other 'Gerbich negative' populations (Wapei, Irumu, Wantoat, Yupna and Takia) on the MN^{A}SZ system alone. The Motu and Tolai cluster can be seen to change place, when ABO and Gerbich data are included, and a rather similar situation occurred when the eight populations were analysed. It seems likely that this uncertainty arises because the populations included cannot be thought really to have a common ancestry, and the indications from cluster analysis are of three, and possibly four, main lines of descent.

These would be:

1.   The Austronesian Motu and Tolai.

2.   The Highland-affiliated populations of Kunimaipa, Watut, Managalase, Kutubu and Tari, with the former being on cluster analysis to some extent the odd man out, perhaps because of proximity to and inter-marriage with Guhu-Samane.

3.   Atzera and Guhu-Samane, which seem linguistically, but not genetically strange bed-fellows.

4.   A rather heterogenous group, comprising Wantoat, Irumu, Yupna, Wapei and Takia. The first three of these populations occupy territory close to the Atzeran people, and it is conceivable that the other two might have had contact with, or represent the remnants of, some other population(s) having a basically similar genetic pattern, still detectable in the analyses. The common occurrence of Gerbich negative subjects in Torricelli Range peoples, and on Karkar Island, is not otherwise readily explicable, and the MN^{A}SZ results simply emphasise that some genetic relationship must be held to exist between these otherwise dissimilar groups.

Comparisons of red cell antigen and 'other loci' results

In Figure 3, rather different situations are represented. These 11 populations (listed in Table 1) were tested as part of the International Biological Programme for 12 polymorphic systems: 5 red cell antigen, 5 red cell enzyme, and 2 serum protein, as detailed on Figure 3. The results of analysis of blood groups are shown separately from those obtained with the other systems. This procedure was adopted because it had been noted (Booth, 1974) that the greater part (about 75 per cent) of the total variability encountered was attributable to the five blood group systems, with the other

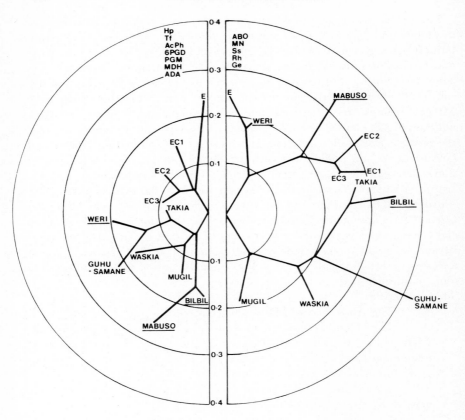

Figure 3 Minimum length genetic networks for 11 populations. derived from gene frequencies for systems as shown on each half of the diagram. The total net length for blood groups is 1·643, and for the other loci 1·245. The populations underlined are those whose positions alter significantly when the left and right-hand diagrams are compared.

systems giving distances showing very much less spread for the majority of pair-wise population comparisons. This suggested that for some loci balancing forces might be at work, and it was hoped that genetic distance analysis might provide some corroboration.

It will be noted (Figure 3) that blood group data give greater separation than is seen with the 'other loci' net, and put Weri and Mabuso, which may be regarded as Highland-affiliated populations, with the true Eastern Highlanders. On the other main branch of this net are found the Madang area populations, plus the Guhu-Samane from the mid-Waria River. It might have been thought the latter group occupied this position by virtue of their high Gerbich negative incidence, but their relationship to other groups is much the same on the 'other loci' net. The closely related Austronesian-speaking Takia and Bilbil groups are associated. Thus, on blood groups,

Table 1: Populations included in the analyses of Figure 3

Madang District	
Karkar Island	Takia
Karkar Island	Waskia
Coastal	Mugil
Coastal	Bilbil
Inland	Mabuso
Eastern Highlands	
Eastern Language Family:	Tairora, Agarabi. Auyana
East Central Family	1. Gahuku, Asaro, Bena Bena
East Central Family	2. Fore, Gimi
East Central Family	3. Kamano, Yagaria, Keiagana
Morobe District	
mid Waria	Guhu-Samane
upper Waria	Weri

there is a meaningful net in terms of linguistic, cultural and geographical information.

The other half of Figure 3, derived from serum protein and red cell enzyme data, is essentially similar, as might be expected because in fact blood group and 'other loci' data provide the same result in 90 per cent of the comparisons possible, as will be demonstrated later. The most significant alterations affect the groups underlined in Figure 3, namely Mabuso, Weri and Bilbil. It is striking that in each case the population has deserted the cultural and linguistic place occupied on the blood group net, to ally itself with its nearest geographical neighbour. Thus the Weri of the upper Waria River go with the Guhu-Samane of the mid-Waria, while the non-Austronesian Mabuso people of the mid-Gogol River are allied with the Austronesian Bilbil who live near its mouth.

This re-assortment suggested that in some of the serum protein and red cell enzyme systems an environmental effect might be sufficiently pronounced to off-set the variations due to drift. Analyses to ascertain in which particular systems the effect was most apparent were carried out, but without notable success.

Figure 4 shows the cluster analysis for enzymes, and this basic pattern of three main clusters remains in evidence through various permutations and combinations of the genetic data, with only insignificant variations within the Guhu-Samane, Weri, Takia, Mugil cluster. The striking feature is the association of Waskia with the Highland populations. This is so except when the acid phosphatase and 6PGD systems are examined on their own, when Takia joins with Waskia. (These two populations share Karkar Island.) The other relationships still hold.

Because of their known selective potential, it was thought that addition of the haptoglobin data might influence the clustering, but this turned out not to be the case (Figure 4), the enzyme pattern remaining almost unchanged. Incorporation of the transferrin data, however, placed Waskia with its mainland neighbour and linguistic associate, Mugil, as also shown in the figure.

There is no doubt that the blood groups provide, in these populations, a

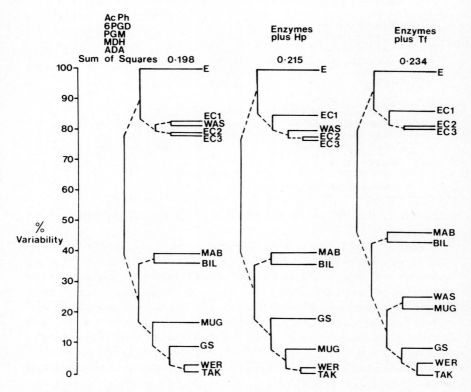

Figure 4   Cluster analyses for the 11 populations of Figure 3, using data on systems as indicated. Abbreviations are as follows: E = Eastern Family; E.C.I. = Gahuku, Asaro, Bena Bena; E.C.2 = Fore, Gimi; E.C.3 = Kamano, Yagaria, Keiagana; Was = Waskia, Mab = Mabuso, Bil = Bilbil, Mug = Mugil, GS = Guhu-Samane, Wer = Weri, Tak = Takia.

pattern of relationships more readily interpretable than do the 'other loci'. However, it is clear that the populations from the Eastern Highlands are similar, with the most easterly group well separated from their neighbours to the west, but the association of Waskia with this group can surely only be regarded as accidental in the present stage of our knowledge. The same might be said of Bilbil and Mabuso, except for their close geographical proximity. It is notable that the genetic similarities disclosed extend over most of the systems for which results were available, and thus a possible selective advantage in any system has not been discovered. The fact that Waskia and Takia are not associated, although sharing an off-shore island, militates against the suggestion that the environment may significantly influence the findings, except for the transferrins. The Tf^D frequencies in the Highland populations, and in the Highland-affiliated Weri, are at least double those found in other populations, and only in this system can such consistency be noted. This raised the faint possibility that the elevated frequency of Tf^D might be maintained by some selective advantage, but its nature remains obscure. For example, it does not seem to have been demonstrated that the transferrins vary in their ability to compete with micro-organisms for iron, and even if Tf^D were the most successful, whether the superior bacteriostatic or fungistatic activity resulting therefrom would be advantageous in the Highlands is quite unknown.

Time scales and blood group data

The third main aim of these distance analyses concerns their possible correlation with time scales. It had been noticed (Booth, 1974) that f_θ values derived from 12 polymorphic systems (ABO, MNSs, P, Rh, Gerbich, Hp, Tf, AcPh, 6PGD, PGM, MDH and ADA) corresponded well with time-scales resulting from lexico-statistical work, but because of the lesser variability found in systems other than blood groups, f_θ values for all 12 systems combined are usually less than those for blood groups alone.

It seemed quite likely that, in general, limited blood group gene frequencies might provide enough information for satisfactory distance estimates, and of course although there is a good deal of information available on the serum protein and red cell iso-enzyme systems for New Guinean populations, the body of blood group data is far more extensive. Cavalli-Sforza (1966) found it gratifying that doubling the number of markers employed in his genetic distance analyses reinforced most of the conclusions already reached. The converse would be similarly pleasing when dealing with New Guinean data, especially if distances derived from blood groups alone could be translated into time-scales. An attempt was therefore made to explore the possibilities.

The results from numerous I.B.P. surveys (Mourant, Booth, Hornabrook and Tills, in preparation) were utilised. From 11 population groups, as listed in Table 1, selected only by availability of data, the 55 pair-wise genetic distances were calculated from the gene frequencies, as $\sqrt{f_\theta}$ (see Cavalli-Sforza et al, 1969). Three distances were calculated for each comparison viz:

    1.   Blood groups (ABO, MN, Ss, Rh, Gerbich), counted here as five systems, 13 alleles.

    2.   Serum protein and red cell enzyme systems (as given above), seven systems, 15 alleles.

    3.   1. and 2. combined. twelve systems, 28 alleles.

As the populations included both closely-related and very distant groups, the spread of distance values was wide, ranging from $0\cdot038$ to $0\cdot556$ for blood groups, from $0\cdot057$ to $0\cdot334$ for other loci, and from $0\cdot063$ to $0\cdot425$ for the combined series.

As they are not independent, it is not surprising that distances 1 and 3 gave a high correlation coefficient $(0\cdot98)$ particularly as distances 1 and 2 correlate also $(r\ 0\cdot30\ p\ < 0\cdot05)$. The estimated equation best fitting these sets of calculated distances is $Y = 0\cdot051 + 0\cdot656\ X$ where $Y =$ the combined distance, and $X =$ the distance derived from blood groups alone. The regression line from this equation is shown in Figure 5, together with

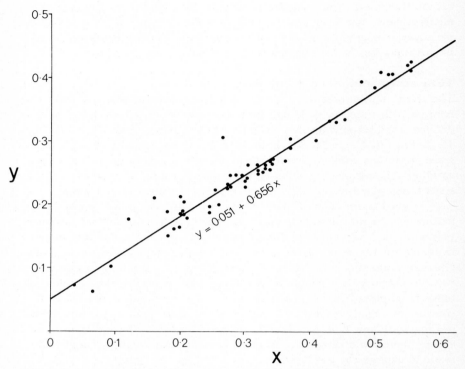

Figure 5 'Scatter diagram' showing relationship of points derived from genetic distances $(\sqrt{f_2})$ for blood groups (X) and blood groups plus 'other loci' (Y) to the 'regression line' of the equation shown. Points for 55 pair-wise population comparisons are included.

points indicating distances 1 and 3. The scatter of points about the line is narrow.

More recently, the effect of adding two more populations, making 13 in all, with 78 pair-wise comparisons, was tested. The two extras were Manus (Malcolm *et al*, 1972) and Jimi (I.B.P. results, in preparation). The correlation coefficient for distances 1 and 3 was $0 \cdot 97$, and the regression equation $Y = 0 \cdot 043 + 0 \cdot 677X$, which over the range of distances encountered does not differ significantly from that given earlier. For the 78 comparisons, the correlation coefficient for distances 1 and 2 was $0 \cdot 37$, making $p < 0 \cdot 001$.

In only seven comparisons, five of which involved one particular population group (Mabuso), did the distance as calculated from blood groups alone, by means of the equation, differ from the 'true' combined distance by more than 10 per cent. Thus out of 78 comparisons based on blood group systems 71 yielded 'correct' results. Where they did not, the distances derived from blood group data must differ greatly, of course, from those obtained from the proteins and enzymes. While this may arise from accidental sampling bias, selective possibilities have already been mentioned. Six of these seven discrepancies are covered by the Mabuso, Weri and Bilbil groups, while the last affects two closely related Eastern Highland populations. When the genetic distances are small, such discrepancies would be more likely to arise, with minor differences in gene frequencies having a proportionately greater effect than in more distantly related populations.

Population inter-relationships disclosed by limited blood group data are thus usually in accord with those derived from much more extensive genetic testing, which reinforces the findings of Cavalli-Sforza (1966) and Edwards (1969). If both blood groups and other systems have been investigated, the results should be assessed separately, as otherwise the greater variability in the blood group systems is likely to overwhelm and obscure discrepancies of possible significance. The lesser variability in serum protein and red cell enzyme systems may perhaps be attributable to the operation of normalising selection, such as is apparently absent in blood group systems. Directional selection similarly does not seem to affect blood groups, but further evidence for its occurrence in other systems should be sought.

It seems that, in general, the red cell antigens are subject only to the vicissitudes of life and time usually classed as random genetic drift, and must be affected thereby to much the same extent as are languages and cultures, for the association of populations by blood group data still corresponds to classifications using the other criteria. If random events and catastrophes really weighed as heavily upon small primitive groups as is often suggested, then surely by now genetic distance analysis might be expected to produce purely random groupings of populations, but this is evidently not the case. Between related populations, genetic and linguistic interchange appears to occur at similar rates, over a span of time extending to several millenia.

Special considerations apply to certain blood group systems. The common occurrence of Gerbich negative individuals in a few New Guinean populations and their virtual absence elsewhere resembles the occurrence of Rhesus negative subjects among many world populations and their absence in Melanesians. The genetically determined I^T weak state, common in coastal dwellers but absent in Highlanders and Caucasians, could conceivably be related to the environment, as evidence is accumulating to implicate foetal antigens, such as I^T, in disease (Garratty et al, 1974).

Glotto-chronological data on some languages of the Eastern Highlands, calculated by Wurm, were quoted by Watson et al (1961), and the figures representing 'time-depth' or number of years separating pairs of languages from their putative common origin are reproduced, in part, in Table 2, which also shows similar figures derived from data on five blood group systems. Gene frequencies for the blood group systems were calculated from the aggregated results of several surveys of each population, and each total population sample size varied from about 150–350 subjects. The standard error of f_θ (blood groups) was computed from its variation between loci. The value of Y^2 was arrived at via the regression equation given earlier and is tabulated $\times$ 100 to enable ready comparison with linguistic 'time-depths' (in millenia) to be made.

Table 2: Comparison of 'time-depths' derived from linguistic and from blood group data

Comparison	f_θ	S.E.	Y^2	t
Gimi-Auyana	$0 \cdot 0365 \pm 0 \cdot 0194$		$2 \cdot 9 \pm 1 \cdot 1$	$2 \cdot 6 \pm 0 \cdot 2$
Gimi-Tairora	$0 \cdot 0381 \pm 0 \cdot 0190$		$3 \cdot 0 \pm 1 \cdot 1$	$3 \cdot 75 \pm 0 \cdot 3$
Gimi-Agarabi	$0 \cdot 0530 \pm 0 \cdot 0240$		$3 \cdot 8 \pm 1 \cdot 3$	$2 \cdot 7 \pm 0 \cdot 25$
Auyana-Tairora	$0 \cdot 0136 \pm 0 \cdot 0081$		$1 \cdot 5 \pm 0 \cdot 5$	$2 \cdot 55 \pm 0 \cdot 2$
Auyana-Agarabi	$0 \cdot 0163 \pm 0 \cdot 0054$		$1 \cdot 7 \pm 0 \cdot 3$	$1 \cdot 65 \pm 0 \cdot 15$
Tairora-Agarabi	$0 \cdot 0285 \pm 0 \cdot 0077$		$2 \cdot 4 \pm 0 \cdot 5$	$2 \cdot 4 \pm 0 \cdot 2$

f_θ: derived from blood group data (5 systems, 13 alleles).
Y: see text (second equation).
t: separation times in millenia (Watson *et al* 1961).

Of the linguistic groups compared, Gimi is a member of the East-Central Family, whereas Auyana, Agarabi and Tairora belong to the Eastern Family. Four of the six comparisons made correspond rather well, when genetic and linguistic figures are considered, bearing in mind the speculative and tentative assumptions made. Both sets of data agree in placing Gimi further from the other three populations than they are from each other, and this separation is more marked with the blood groups. In the two discrepant comparisons, blood group data put Gimi/Agarabi further apart, and Auyana/Tairora closer together, than linguistic data would indicate, but which values are more likely to correspond with reality is impossible to say. The range indicated by blood group data is inevitably large, with the standard error computed from only five systems.

An indication that the linguistic-genetic correlations are not arising by chance is provided by the results of similarly comparing other Highland populations, selected at random to include one representative of the Eastern Language Family, and three from the East-Central Family. Unfortunately, linguistic 'time-depths' are lacking, but those derived from five blood group systems are shown in Table 3. It can be noted that the three East-Central languages, Kamano, Kanite and Fore, are more closely inter-related than any is to Agarabi, of the Eastern Family. Kamano, which borders on Agarabi, seems much less closely related to it than does the geographically more distant Fore group. It is of interest, though perhaps accidental, that the Agarabi/Fore blood group separation ($2 \cdot 6$) is similar to the Gimi/Agarabi linguistic separation ($2 \cdot 7$), because Fore and Gimi are classed in the same language sub-family.

Table 3: Possible 'time-depths' in millenia derived from blood group data, for four Eastern Highland populations

	Kamano	Kanite	Fore
Agarabi	$4 \cdot 0 \pm 0 \cdot 3$	$4 \cdot 3 \pm 1 \cdot 3$	$2 \cdot 6 \pm 0 \cdot 6$
Kamano		$1 \cdot 5 \pm 0 \cdot 3$	$1 \cdot 3 \pm 0 \cdot 3$
Kanite			$2 \cdot 0 \pm 0 \cdot 8$

In a symposium concerned with the origin of the Australians, mention should be made of the distance analysis reported by Kirk, Sanghvi and Balakrishnan (1972) on nine Aboriginal tribes of the Northern Territory. It was shown that the genetic distances correlated well with both the linguistic differences and the geographical distances separating the tribes. I have compared three of these groups, (the ones selected by Dr Lie-Injo for her paper), with each other and with four coastal Papuan populations, as shown in Table 4. The values shown are $Y^2 \times 100$ derived from blood group data as described previously. It is apparent that the Aranda and Nunggubuyu are quite close genetically—in the same range as are the Western and Gulf District Papuans—but that the Tiwi of Bathurst Island are nearly as distant from the mainland Aboriginals as all are from the coastal Papuans. The unusually large distance separating the Tiwi from their nearest neighbours was noted by Kirk *et al* (1972).

Populations separated by distances as great as some of these (i.e. above about $6 \cdot 0$) would generally be considered as unrelated. It is possibly of interest, though, that rising sea levels separated Australia from New Guinea 8000–10,000 years ago, and presumably Bathurst Island from the mainland at the same time. It can be noted that this is the indicated time of separation, using genetic distances, of the Australian Aboriginal from the Papuan populations.

However, the genetic distances separating the Austronesian-speaking Motu, living around Port Moresby, from the Australian Aboriginals are, by virtue of a shared high *M* frequency, slightly less than those separating the latter from the non-Austronesian Western and Gulf District Papuans. The similarity of genetic and geographical separation times is likely to be accidental.

The suggestion arising from the foregoing is simply that it seems not unreasonable to test linguistic and genetic data against each other, if possible times of separation of populations are sought. Both methods are at best crude approximations, but if the object is to explore unrecorded history, any method seems better than none, and any correlations established by using two different computations lend greater credence to the results. The exercise is perhaps like trying to establish what song the Sirens sang, but this puzzling question has been said to be not beyond all conjecture.

Table 4: Possible 'time-depths' in millenia, derived from blood group data for three Australian Aboriginal and four Papuan coastal populations

	Nunggubuyu	Tiwi	Kiwai	Kikori	Gogodara	Motu
Aranda	1·3	5·5	8·8	8·4	11·7	7·4
Nunggubuyu		7·6	9·3	9·4	12·5	7·8
Tiwi			10·6	9·7	11·1	8·6
Kiwai				1·1	1·7	2·6
Kikori					1·6	2·4
Gogodara						3·7

Comment and conclusions

It cannot be denied that genetic distance analysis is a form of classification. It is imperfect, and the inadequacies of much of the data fed in are evident. However, criticism seems often directed towards objectives which are not those sought, and such criticism is therefore invalid. The quotations which follow are taken from Birdsell (1972).

> The idea that a single figure can adequately summarize and measure biological variability between populations is unrealistic.

Now it is obvious that data do not exist on all possible polymorphisms, and therefore the figure only summarises the information available. Nevertheless such figures would seem to indicate non-random inter-relationships of populations, which frequently would be difficult or impossible to formulate from study of the raw data.

In New Guinea, and no doubt elsewhere, accidental convergences of gene frequencies may occur in populations which are widely disparate in language, culture or space. Much of the genetic data from New Guinea is derived from the sampling of small village groups and it is remarkable that the pooling of such heterogenous information to provide estimated gene frequencies for linguistic groups usually leads to analyses which associate populations in an evidently non-random fashion. The heterogeneity within a linguistic area must therefore generally be less than between such areas. The analyses themselves of course establish that this is so on a larger scale, when individual language groups of the same language family cluster together. Similar analyses could be applied to villages where sufficient data are available, as was done by Ward (1972) with the Yanomama Indians in South America.

> When the single figure of magnitude approaches are compounded with the necessary assumption that the degree of similitude is a measure of relationship by descent, the venture seems unsupportable.

The necessity of this assumption is questioned. Under certain circumstances, when there is independent supporting evidence, it may with reasonable justification be made, but of itself the genetic distance does not indicate whether two populations are diverging, converging or even running on parallel tracks. A genetic network shows relationships only of the populations included on the basis of whatever genetic data were available, and its relevance will depend largely on the common-sense or intuition of the programmer.

The point about convergence of populations appears to have been largely neglected, but in New Guinea, with increasing mobility of populations, it is surely a factor to be taken into consideration. The case of the non-Austronesian Waskia and the Austronesian Takia, who share Karkar Island, was discussed by Booth (1974). Elsewhere, the Highlands Highway, together with the people and the spirochaetes which travel it, may be producing incalculable effects in terms of gene flow. Perhaps we should be prepared to interpret genetic networks in either direction, and anyway resolve always to take them with a pinch of salt.

To assume that the varied and complex directive changes produced by selection can be ignored is to cut the heart out of adaptive evolution as a concept.

On the contrary, as we have shown, there is just a chance that distance analysis might indicate where selective adaptation has occurred, and if we could but pin it down, this of itself would be more than sufficient justification for using the method.

On the other hand, if system by system analysis did not provide evidence of selection, it could be assumed that the systems tested were not subject to detectable selection in the populations under review.

It is not advocated that distance analysis should replace other methods of assessment of inter-population relationships, but that it can usefully serve as an adjunct. Neither is it claimed that the method used here is of necessity the best or only one. It does, however, appear to give meaningful results, in that it correlates well with linguistic information, is sufficiently robust to provide worth-while results from relatively slender data, can reveal or confirm unexpected affinities between populations, can act as a cross-check on glotto-chronological estimates, and can suggest areas where selection may be operating.

No doubt the method is capable of refinement to take note of some of the complexities at present ignored. Meanwhile, critics could consider the bumble-bee, which, while disregarding the principles of aerodynamics, still manages to fly.

Acknowledgements: The authors are indebted to Dr A. W. F. Edwards for making available to them his computer programme TREE, and to Mr J. Brown for his assistance in adapting the programme.

References

BIRDSELL, J. B.   1972   The problem of the evolution of human races: classification or clines. *Social Biology*, 19:136–62.

BOOTH, P. B.   1974   Genetic distances between certain New Guinea populations studied under the International Biological Programme. *Philosophical Transactions of the Royal Society of London*, B 268:257–67.

—— and R. W. HORNABROOK   1973   The MNᴬSZ groups of some New Guinean populations. *Human Biology in Oceania*, 2:27–32.

BUCHBINDER, G. and P. CLARK   1971   The Maring people of the Bismarck Ranges of New Guinea. *Human Biology in Oceania*, 1:121–33.

CAVALLI-SFORZA, L. L.   1966   Population structure and human evolution. *Proceedings of the Royal Society*, Series B, 164:362–79.

——   1969   Human diversity. *Proceedings of the 7th International Congress of Genetics*, 3:405–17.

—— and A. W. F. EDWARDS   1967   Phylogenetic analyses, models and estimation procedures. *American Journal of Human Genetics*, 19:234–57.

——, L. A. ZONTA, E. NUZZO, L. BERNINI, W. W. W. DE JONG, P. MEERA KHAN, A. K. RAY, L. M. WENT, M. SINISCALCO, L. E. NIJENHUIS, E. VAN LOGHEM and G. MODIANO   1969   Studies on African Pygmies I. A pilot investigation of Babinga pygmies in the Central African Republic (with an analysis of genetic distance). *American Journal of Human Genetics*, 21:252–73.

EDWARDS, A. W. F.   1969   Genetic Taxonomy. In *Computer applications in genetics*, N. E. Morton (ed), pp. 140–46. University of Hawaii Press, Honolulu.

—— and L. L. CAVALLI-SFORZA   1965   A method for cluster analysis. *Biometrics*, 21:362–75.

GARRATTY, G., L. D. PETZ, R. O. WALLERSTEIN and H. H. FUDENBERG   1974 Auto-immune haemolytic anaemia in Hodgkin's Disease associated with anti-I[T]. *Transfusion*, 14:226–31.

KIRK, R. L., L. D. SANGHVI and V. BALAKRISHNAN   1972   A further study of genetic distances among Australian Aborigines: nine tribes of the Northern Territory. *Humangenetik*, 14:95–102.

MALCOLM, L. A., P. B. BOOTH and L. L. CAVALLI-SFORZA   1971   Intermarriage patterns and blood group gene frequencies of the Bundi people of the New Guinea Highlands. *Human Biology*, 43:187–99.

——, D. G. WOODFIELD, N. M. BLAKE, R. L. KIRK and E. M. McDERMID   1972 The distribution of blood, serum protein and enzyme groups on Manus Island. *Human Heredity*, 22:305–322.

WARD, R. H.   1972   The genetic structure of a tribal population, the Yanomama Indians, v. comparisons of a series of genetic networks. *Annals of Human Genetics, London*, 36:21–43.

WATSON, J. B., V. ZIGAS, O. KOOPTZOFF and R. J. WALSH   1961   The blood groups of natives in Kainantu, New Guinea. *Human Biology*, 33:25–41.

WURM, S. A.   1964   Australian New Guinea Highlands languages and the distribution of their typological features. *American Anthropology*, 66:77–97.

Authors

Abbie, A. A. Formerly, Department of Anatomy, University of Adelaide, South Australia, Australia.

Balakrishnan, V. Epidemiology Division, Cancer Research Institute, Tata Memorial Centre, Bombay, India.

Booth, P. B. Pathology Department, Christchurch Hospital, Christchurch, New Zealand.

Bowler, J. M. Department of Biogeography & Geomorphology, Research School of Pacific Studies, Australian National University, Canberra, Australia.

Brown, T. Department of Oral Biology, University of Adelaide, South Australia, Australia.

Calaby, J. H. CSIRO Division of Wildlife Research, Gungahlin, A.C.T. Australia.

Chappell, J. M. A. Department of Geography, School of General Studies, Australian National University, Canberra, Australia.

Curtain, C. C. CSIRO Division of Chemical Technology, South Melbourne, Victoria, Australia.

Doran, G. A. Department of Anatomy, University of Tasmania, Hobart, Australia.

Giles, E. University of Illinois, Urbana, Illinois, U.S.A.

Hope, G. S. Department of Biogeography & Geomorphology, Research School of Pacific Studies, Australian National University, Canberra, Australia.

Hope, J. H. Department of Prehistory, Research School of Pacific Studies, Australian National University, Canberra, Australia.

Howells, W. W. Department of Anthropology, Peabody Museum, Harvard University, Cambridge, Massachusetts, U.S.A.

Jacob, T. Department of Physical Anthropology, College of Medicine, Gadjah Mada University, Yogyakarta, Indonesia.

Keats, B. Department of Human Biology, John Curtin School of Medical Research, Australian National University, Canberra, Australia.

Kirk, R. L. Department of Human Biology, John Curtin School of Medical Research, Australian National University, Canberra, Australia.

Larnach, S. L. Department of Anatomy, University of Sydney, New South Wales, Australia.

Lie-Injo Luan Eng. The George Williams Hooper Foundation, University of California, San Francisco, U.S.A.

Macfarlane, W. V. Department of Animal Physiology, Waite Agricultural Research Institute, University of Adelaide, South Australia, Australia.

Macintosh, N. W. G. Department of Surgery, University of Sydney, New South Wales, Australia.

Misawa, S. Department of Legal Medicine, Tsukuba University, Tsukuba, Ibaragi Prefecture, Japan.

Morton, N. E. Population Genetics Laboratory, University of Hawaii at Manoa, Honolulu, U.S.A.

Omoto, K. Department of Anthropology, Faculty of Science, The University of Tokyo, Tokyo, Japan.

Parsons, P. A. Department of Genetics and Human Variation, La Trobe University, Victoria, Australia.

Prokopec, M. Institute of Hygiene and Epidemiology, Prague, Czechoslovakia.

Sanghvi, L. D. Epidemiology Division, Cancer Research Institute, Tata Memorial Centre, Bombay, India.

Schanfield, M. S. Transfusion Service and Reference Laboratory, Milwaukee Blood Center, Inc., Milwaukee, Wisconsin, U.S.A.

Sedivy, V. Institute of Hygiene and Epidemiology, Prague, Czechoslovakia.

Simmons, R. T. Formerly, Senior Consultant, National Blood Group Reference Laboratory, Commonwealth Serum Laboratories, Parkville, Victoria, Australia.

Taylor, H. W. Christchurch Hospital, Christchurch, New Zealand.

Thorne, A. G. Department of Prehistory, Research School of Pacific Studies, Australian National University, Canberra, Australia.

van Loghem, E. Central Laboratory of the Netherlands Red Cross Blood Transfusion Service, Amsterdam, The Netherlands.

Wallace, A. G. Department of Anatomy, University of Tasmania, Hobart, Australia.

White, N. G. Department of Genetics and Human Variation, La Trobe University, Victoria, Australia.

Wood, W. B. Department of Anatomy, University of Queensland, Brisbane, Queensland, Australia.

Wright, R. V. S. Department of Anthropology, University of Sydney, New South Wales, Australia.

Index of persons

Abbie, A. A. 1, 2, 141, 161, 171, 185, 192–3, 196–8, 200, 203–4, 208, 211, 213, 227, 239, 242, 247, 257, 261
Acheson, R. M. 259, 261–2
Adam, A. 295, 301
Adey, W. R. 247, 261
Akaishi, S. 376
Akerman, L. 26, 28
Albrey, J. A. 344
Allen, H. 59, 67, 69, 75, 124, 138, 171
Allen, J. 49, 52
Alpers, M. 328, 344–6, 356, 364, 398
Altland, K. 294, 301
Amarasingham, R. D. 280, 302
Amos, D. B. 344
Ananthakrishnan, R. 289, 301–2, 395
Andersen, B. G. 12, 20
Anderson, H. T. 193
Andrews, D. F. 146, 160
Andrews, J. T. 20
Arato, G. 274
Archbold, R. A. 40, 52
Arends, T. 345, 395
Arnold, K. 301
Ashton, C. J. 344
Atienze, R. Y. 328
Auricht, C. C. 344
Ayres, M. 396

Bada, J. 120–1
Baer, A. 281, 288, 291–2, 294–5, 301, 304
Bagby, G. F. 257, 263
Bailey, A. B. 77, 126
Baitsch, H. 398
Bajatzadeh, M. 398
Baker, L. L. 328
Balakrishnan, V. 243, 410, 427, 430
Banerjee, A. R. 315, 328
Barbetti, M. 59, 75, 134–5, 138
Barghoorn, E. S. 20

Barker, B. C. W. 113, 126, 173, 180, 182
Barnicot, N. A. 291, 301
Barrett, M. J. 197, 199, 205, 208, 269, 271, 274
Bartholomai, A. 27–8
Bartlett, A. S. 15, 20
Basedow, H. 1, 213–4
Bashir, H. V. 337, 344
Baumgarten, A. 364, 396
Bayani-Sioson, P. S. 337, 344
Baxi, A. J. 301
Beals, K. L. 204, 208
Bearn, A. G. 303, 333, 344–5, 397
Behar, M. 252, 262–3
Belkin, R. B. 328
Bennett, J. H. 4, 6, 243, 331, 344–5, 355, 364
Berger, R. 20
Bergman, R. A. M. 91–2
Berndt, C. H. 228, 242
Berndt, R. M. 228, 242
Bernini, L. 429
Berry, A. C. 90, 92, 236, 242
Berry, R. J. 90, 92, 236, 242
Berson, S. A. 206, 209
Bhagwan Singh, R. 305
Bhalla, V. 315, 327
Bhatia, H. M. 327, 346
Birdsell, J. B. 1–2, 24–5, 28, 141–2, 160–1, 171, 196, 208, 227, 231, 233, 238, 242–3, 319–20, 324, 327–8, 364, 374–5
Black, G. 165
Blagden, C. O. 278, 305
Blake, D. H. 50, 52
Blake, N. M. 289, 290–1, 301–5, 337–8, 340–1, 344–5, 376, 396–7, 430
Blake, W. 12, 22
Blackwell, R. Q. 287, 301
Bloom, A. L. 12–15, 20
Blumberg, B. S. 333, 345
Blumenthal, T. 262

Bodmer, W. F.   162, 171, 241–2, 396
Boettcher, B.   344
Bolton, J. M.   301, 303–4, 306
Bonazzi, L.   346
Bonne, C.   288, 301
Bonnevie, K.   215–6, 225
Boone, S. C.   301
Boopbhanirojana, P.   295, 301
Booth, P. B.   330, 344, 364, 415, 417,
    419, 423, 428, 430
Bowden, D. E. J.   270, 274
Bowler, J. M.   2, 19–20, 25–6, 28, 55,
    59, 61, 65, 69–70, 73, 75, 96,
    109–11, 121–2, 124, 127, 217–8,
    132, 134–6, 138, 161, 171
Bowman, J. E.   289–90, 301, 396
Boyd, W. C.   278, 301, 321–3, 327
Brace, C. L.   268, 274
Bradley, M. A.   327
Brandtzaeg, B.   396
Brass, L. J.   39–41, 49, 52
Brewer, C.   396
Broecker, W. S.   12, 19–20
Broca, P.   180
Brookfield, H. C.   32, 52
Brotherton, J. V. M.   344
Brown, P.   398
Brown, T.   4, 162, 171, 195, 197, 199,
    205, 208, 274
Brown, W. R.   71, 75
Brownlee, K. A.   101, 111
Bryson, R. A.   15, 20
Buchbinder, G.   417, 429
Buehl, C. C.   247, 261
Bulmer, R.   39, 42, 52
Bulmer, S.   39, 42, 44, 45, 52
Burch, T. A.   257, 263
Burston, R. S.   213–4
Butzer, K. W.   73, 75

Caine, N.   68, 75
Calaby, J. H.   23–4, 27–8
Campbell, T. D.   1, 72, 75, 105, 108,
    111, 197–8, 200–1, 208, 213–4
Capell, A.   229, 242, 350, 364
Cardini, L.   21
Carson, P. E.   301, 396
Carter, G.   121
Caseley-Smith, J. R.   192–3
Casey, D. A.   75, 124
Cavalli-Sforza, L. L.   162, 171, 238,
    241–2, 296, 298, 300, 302, 352,
    364, 371, 375, 383, 396, 416–7, 423,
    425
Chagnon, N.   396
Champion, I.   40, 52
Chan, K. L.   290, 302
Champness, L.   344
Chappell, J. M. A.   11–16, 20, 22, 24,
    28, 66, 76

Chen, S. H.   291, 302, 341, 344
Chetanasilpin, M.   301
Chin, J.   279, 302–3
Chopra, V. P.   396
Chown, B.   321, 327
Christensen, O. A.   45, 52
Churchward, H. M.   71, 76
Clapham, L. J.   327, 396
Clark, P.   242, 417, 429, 496
Clarke, W. C.   42, 52
Clegg, J. B.   302
Cleve, H.   303, 333, 344–5, 396–7
Cochrane, G. R.   27–8
Coe, M. J.   33, 52
Coetzee, J. A.   33, 37, 47, 52
Colombani, J.   344
Colbourne, M. J.   279, 302
Cole, F. C.   278, 299, 302
Cole, S.   302
Colwell, E. J.   301
Comas, J.   211, 214
Comstock, G.   259, 263
Connor, M. A.   225
Cooke, D. R.   303, 308, 328, 376
Coon, C. S.   119, 124, 142, 160, 374–5
Cooper, D. W.   243, 345, 355, 364
Costin, A. B.   25, 28, 50, 52, 68–70,
    72, 75
Cottingham, A. J.   301
Craig, R.   194, 209
Crane, G. G.   344
Crelin, E. S.   90, 93
Crook, K. A. W.   54
Cross, R.   344
Crow, J. F.   383, 397
Cummins, H.   215–6, 218, 221–2, 225,
    234, 242
Curr, E. M.   213–4
Currie, C.   261
Curray, J. R.   14, 20
Curtain, C. C.   331–2, 335, 344, 347,
    349, 351, 356, 358–9, 364, 396
Curtis, G. H.   81
Cutbush, M.   315–6, 322, 325, 327

Damon, A.   196, 208
Dahlberg, A. A.   270, 272, 274
Darlington, P. J.   23, 28
Darragh, T. A.   75
Dart, R.   117, 120
Das, S. K.   302
Das, S. R.   289–90, 302
Dausset, J.   344
Davies, H. W.   186, 188, 194
Davies, P. L.   105, 111
Davis, J. B.   1
Davivongs, V.   301
Day, M. H.   90, 93
Dean, R. F. A.   260, 262
De Garay, A. L.   396
De Jong, W. W. W.   429

Delbruck, H. 305
den Butter, 353
Denton, G. H. 47, 52
Detter, J. C. 291, 302
Dobzhansky, T. 265, 274
Dodson, J. 56, 76
Doherty, R. L. 364, 396
Domaniewska-Sobczak, K. 304, 327
Dominguez, S. 345
Doran, G. A. 122, 126, 173
Dortch, C. E. 56, 76, 121, 124
Douglas, R. 396
Doutch, H. F. 17, 20
Dreimannis, A. 12, 20
Dreizen, S. 252, 259–61
D'Sena, G. W. L. 328
Dubois, E. 90–1, 93
Duckworth, W. L. H. 116
Duncan, I. W. 398
Dunn, D. 328
Dunn, F. L. 277–8, 302
Duraisamy, G. 280, 302–3
Dury, G. H. 56, 75

Edmonds, R. 243
Edwards, A. W. F. 238, 241–2, 296,
    302, 352, 364, 371, 375, 416, 425
Edwards, F. M. 209
Edwards, S. M. 194
Efremov, G. D. 304
Ekstrand, V. 398
Eldridge, E. 193
Ellenberger, J. D. 39, 52
Elliot, M. 327
Elliot, O. 163, 171
Elliot, R. B. 194, 205–9
Elliot Smith, G. 118
Elsner, R. W. 193
Emery, K. O. 13–5, 21
Emiliani, C. 18–9, 21
Epple, F. 301

Fairbridge, R. W. 71, 76, 174, 182
Falkner, F. 196, 208, 262
Fanning, E. A. 197, 208
Farinaud, E. 278, 302
Fenner, F. J. 1, 100, 111, 114, 125,
    141, 213–4, 236, 242
Fessas, P. 288, 302
Fine, J. M. 346
Fisher, R. L. 270, 274
Fix, A. G. 279, 281, 299, 302, 304
Flatz, G. 285, 287, 295, 301–2, 305
Flenley, J. R. 32, 52
Flint, R. F. 12, 15, 17, 21, 47, 53
Flood, J. 74, 76
Flory, C. D. 247, 250, 261
Flory, L. L. 349–50, 355, 364
Foo, K. F. 304
Follis, R. H. 258, 261

Forbes, J. F. 335–6, 344
Fourquet. R. 280, 302
Francis, C. C. 247, 261
Franken, S. 327
Fraser, G. R. 302
Freedman, L. 4, 101, 104, 111, 115,
    125, 163, 172, 181–2
Friedlaender, J. S. 235, 242, 347,
    357–8, 364, 382, 396
Frisancho, A. R. 247, 262
Frischer, H. 301, 396
Froehlich, J. W. 197, 202, 208
Fry, E. I. 262
Fudenberg, H. H. 303, 364, 396, 430
Furuhata, T. 368, 375

Gajdusek, D. C. 328, 344–6, 353, 356,
    364, 380, 396, 398
Gall, P. 93
Gallango, M. L. 395
Galloway, R. W. 32, 47, 52, 55–6,
    68–9, 76
Gallus, A. 26, 59, 62, 76
Ganesan, J. 294, 306
Garn, S. M. 196, 208, 247, 251–3.
    257–60, 262
Gardner, C. A. 27–8
Garn, S. M. 374–5
Garratty, G. 425, 430
Garrison, L. E. 14–5, 21
Gates, R. R. 1
Gavan, J. A. 164, 171
Gershowitz, H. 396, 398
Ghiselin, M. T. 265, 274
Giblett, E. R. 289, 291–2, 294, 302,
    341, 344
Giles, E. 113, 125, 141, 161, 163, 167,
    171, 190, 193, 241–2, 310, 327,
    349, 353, 358, 364
Gill, E. D. 15, 21, 59, 62, 70, 76
Gillen, F. J. 213–4
Gilley, E. J. 261
Gillison, A. N. 40, 53
Gilman, R. H. 304
Girdany, B. R. 247, 262
Glaser, E. M. 190, 193
Glennie, R. 26, 28
Glick, S. M. 206, 209
Goddard, J. 20
Goedde, H. W. 301
Golab, T. 364, 396
Golden, R. 247, 262
Goldblum, R. 398
Goldman, H. M. 271, 274
Goldstein, M. S. 274
Golson, J. 30, 53, 185, 193
Gonzalez, E. 47, 53
Goose, D. H. 270, 274
Gorman, J. G. 344, 364, 396
Govindasamy, S. 304
Grave, K. C. 247, 262

Gray, A. J.   334
Gray, J. H.   7, 197, 208, 213–4
Graydon, J. J.   278–80, 305, 308, 318, 320–1, 324, 327–8, 376, 396 398
Green, R.   278, 302, 305, 328
Gregory, W. K.   268, 274
Greulich, W. W.   245, 252, 262
Groves, C.   117
Grub, R.   347, 364
Guiart, J.   396
Guha, B. S.   402, 410
Guinan, J. J.   344
Guzman, M. A.   262

Hackett, C. J.   7, 197, 208, 213–4
Haddon, A. C.   162, 171
Hagen, G.   162
Hainline, J.   396
Hall, D. G. E.   281, 302
Hamada, T.   73, 75
Hambly, W. D.   166, 171
Hammel, H. T.   191, 193–4
Harada, S.   331, 346, 365, 367, 370, 376
Harpending, J. M.   398
Harrer, H.   40, 46, 53
Harris, D. E.   394, 397
Harris, D. J.   329, 346
Harris, H.   301, 396
Harris, H. A.   258, 260, 262, 344
Harrison, R. S.   22
Harrisson, T.   327
Hatcher, L.   194, 209
Hatt, D.   225
Hawkins, B. R.   311, 313, 327
Hayashida, Y.   314, 327, 365, 368, 376
Hedberg, O.   33, 53
Hedegård, B.   197, 200–1, 203, 208
Heider, K. G.   39, 53
Hellmann, K.   194
Hemmer, H.   119
Hertzog, K. P.   253, 257–8, 262
Hewitt, D.   257, 259–60, 262
Hickey, G. C.   303
Hicks, C. S.   186, 190, 193
Hill, J. E.   23, 28
Hill, W. C. O.   316, 327
Hiser, W. W.   301
Hnatiuk, R.   37
Holt, S. B.   222, 224–5
Hoogland, R. D.   52
Hooton, E. A.   1, 153, 160
Hope, G. S.   3, 19, 21, 29, 32, 39–40, 47, 50, 52
Hope, J. H.   3, 29, 56, 76
Hopkins, D. M.   120
Hopkinson, D. A.   329, 340, 344, 394, 396
Hornabrook, R.   328, 364, 398, 417, 429
Horsfall, W. R.   294
Hoult, G. E.   396
Howard, B.   187, 194

Howells, W. W.   1, 3–4, 29, 53, 91, 93, 109, 111, 113–4, 118–9, 122, 125, 141, 145, 150, 160, 162–3, 166–7, 170–1, 213–4, 235, 239, 241, 243, 331, 342, 345, 373, 375
Hrdlicka, A.   1, 116, 165
Hrdy, D. B.   153, 160
Hsu, C.   327
Hughes, D. R.   195–6, 208, 295, 302
Hughes, I. M.   39, 53
Huisman, T. H. J.   304
Hulse, F. S.   205, 207, 208
Hursh, T. M.   167, 171
Huxley, T. H.   267, 274

Ikin, E. W.   279–81, 290, 302, 305, 327–8
Imaizumi, Y.   380, 387–8, 393, 396–7
Imbrie, J.   19, 21
Isaac, G. L.   75
Ishizaki, S.   376
Israel, H.   262
Ives, J. D.   20

Jacob, T.   81, 83–6, 90, 92–3, 95, 111, 117, 120, 125
Jacobs, J. J.   396
James, N. P.   12, 21
Jelinek, J.   119, 125
Jenkins, T.   396
Jennings, J. N.   17–19, 21, 68, 71, 75–6
Johnston, E.   346
Johnstone, J. M.   344
Jones, F. W.   213–4
Jones, P. R. M.   260, 262
Jones, R.   23, 25–6, 28, 62, 64–6, 69, 75–6, 114, 124–5, 138, 171, 173–4, 182
Jongsma, D.   13, 15, 17, 21
Jose, D. G.   205, 208, 376
Joseph, M. R.   186, 188, 194
Joshi, S. H.   327, 346

Kageyama, S.   398
Kalma, J. D.   24, 28–9, 32, 37, 46–8, 53, 74, 77
Kaplan, B. A.   202, 208
Kariks, J.   290, 303
Karlen, W.   47, 52
Karrow, P. F.   12, 20
Karsten, P.   91–2
Kay, M. P.   305
Keats, B. J. B.   5, 379
Keith, A.   1, 118, 125
Kellock, W. L.   118, 125, 162, 172, 235–8, 243
Kenrick, K. G.   333, 345
Kettle, E. S.   205, 208
Kershaw, A. P.   37, 47, 53, 56, 69, 73, 76

Kidd, K. K.   242
Kidson, C.   344, 364, 396
Kimura, K.   196, 208, 329, 345
Kipp, N. G.   19, 21
Kirk, R. L.   228, 233, 243, 286, 289–93,
    301–5, 307, 315–7, 323, 325, 327,
    329–33, 335, 337, 344–7, 349,
    351–3, 355, 364, 371, 376, 395–8,
    410, 427, 430
Kirke, D. K.   205–6, 208
Kirkman, H. N.   289, 303
Kitchin, F. D.   333–4, 345
Klaatsch, H.   1, 116, 125, 267–8, 274
Klatsky, M.   270, 274
Knauss, J. A.   17, 21
Kneebone G. M.   206, 208
Kodama, S.   328, 375–6, 398
Koganei, R.   373, 376
Konishi, K.   12, 21
Kooptzoff, O.   328, 430
Kopeć, A. C.   304, 327
Kosasih, E. N.   304, 327
Kotchetkova, V. I.   116
Kraus, E. B.   18–9, 21
Kreshover, S. J.   270, 274
Ku, T. L.   12, 20–1
Kudo, T.   376
Kullback, S.   383, 397
Kulunga, A.   53
Kuno, Y.   185, 193
Kurisu, K.   278–9, 303
Kurten, B.   124–5
Kwa, S. B.   290, 303

Ladell, W. S. S.   190, 193
Lai, L. Y. C.   242, 286, 290, 292, 303,
    305, 327, 331, 334–5
Lake, J. S.   69, 76
Lalouel, J. M.   380–1, 387, 396–8
Lampert, R. J.   65–6, 77
Lancaster, B.   90, 93
Langford-Smith, T. B.   66, 77
Larnach, S. L.   4, 98–101, 110–2,
    113–5, 117, 125–6, 131, 138, 141,
    159–60, 162–3, 165, 172, 181–2,
    274
Lasker, G. W.   252, 262
Latter, B. D. H.   386–7, 394, 397
Laurell, A.-B.   347, 364
Laurie, R.   23, 28
Lavelle, C. L. B.   197, 208
Layrisse, M.   329, 345, 396
Layrisse, Z.   396
Lee, J. R.   398
LeBar, F. M.   278, 303
Legters, L. J.   301
Lehmann, H.   279, 302, 315–6, 322,
    325, 327–8
Le Messurier, D. H.   193–4
Lendon, C.   52
Le Pichon, X.   15, 21

Lesson, A.   1
Lestrel, P. E.   86, 93
Lew, R.   397
Lewin, T.   197, 200–1, 203, 208
Lewis, A. J.   213–4
Lewis, A. N.   301, 304
Lewis, H. B. M.   243, 345, 355, 364
Lewis, P. H.   171
Lewis, W. H. P.   301, 344
Lewontin, R.   394, 397
Li, W. H.   329, 345
Lickiss, J. N.   205, 209
Lieberman, P.   90, 93
Lie-Injo, L. E.   277, 279, 285–94, 299,
    301–3, 305–6, 337, 340, 397
Lim, T. W.   305
Litchfield, W. H.   56, 77
Liu, C. S.   301
Livingstone, D. A.   46, 52
Livingstone, F. B.   235, 243, 287, 304
Loesch, D.   216, 226
Löffler, E.   19, 21, 32, 34, 49, 50, 52–3
Logan, B. W.   14, 21
Loo M.   304
Lopez, C. G.   280, 304
Ludloff, K.   258, 263
Lugg, J. W. H.   295, 304
Lynch, C.   398
Lyning, Y.   194

Macfarlane, W. V.   3, 183, 185–8, 190–4
MacDonald, J.   93
Macintosh, N. W. G.   1, 3–4, 70, 77,
    98–101, 109–12, 113–5, 117,
    120–2, 124–6, 131, 138, 141–2, 155,
    158–60, 162–3, 165, 172–3, 175,
    180–2, 215, 218, 222, 225, 274
MacIntyre, M. N.   259, 261
Mackay, D. H.   247, 251, 263
Macqueen, J. M.   344
Macumber, P. G.   26, 28, 96, 108–10,
    112, 268–9, 271, 274
Mader, M. K.   215, 218, 225, 232, 243
Mahalanobis, P. C.   228, 243, 383
Majumdar, D. N.   315, 327
Malcolm, L. A.   245, 247, 252–3, 260,
    263, 332, 338, 344–5, 397, 417,
    424, 430
Miki, C.   386, 397
Malécot, G.   379–80, 382, 386, 388,
    393, 397
Malina, R. M.   196, 208
Marshall, L. G.   26, 28, 56, 62, 77
Marshall, W. A.   259, 263
Martin, A. O.   387, 397
Martin, H. A.   56
Martin, R.   211, 214
Matsumoto, H.   366, 370, 376
Matthews, R. K.   20, 22
Matthews, R. S.   20
Mavalwala, J. D.   216, 225

Maxwell, G. M.   205–9
Mayeda, T.   21
May-May-Yi   304–5
Meera Khan, P.   429
Mermod, L. E.   398
Merrilees, D.   56, 62, 76–7
Mesolella, K. J.   20
McBurney, C. B. M.   21
McCann, M. B.   262
McClure, F. J.   270, 274
McDermid, E. M.   285–7, 289–94, 301,
   303–4, 333, 344–6, 397, 430
McDonald, B. C.   12, 21
McDougall, I.   54
McKay, D. A.   304
McNeish, M.   120
McPherson, R. K.   190, 194
McVean, D. N.   37, 53
Melartin, L.   333, 345
Midlo, C.   216, 218, 225, 234, 242
Milan, F. A.   193
Milbourne, J. D.   398
Mills, C. A.   252, 263
Miller, A. H.   27–8
Miller, E. B.   321, 325, 327
Miller, P. S.   196, 200–3, 209
Miller, R. L.   262
Milliman, J. D.   14, 21
Misawa, S.   314, 327, 343, 346, 365,
   368, 376
Mitton, R.   40
Miyazaki, T.   366, 370, 376
Modiano, G.   429
Moge, R.   53
Mohr, J.   396
Molleson, T. I.   90–1, 93
Molnar, S.   265, 274
Monn, E.   289, 304
Montagu, M. F. A.   211, 214, 313, 327
Moodie, P. M.   186, 192, 194, 205, 209,
   345, 376, 397
Moore, G. L.   304
Moore, H. O.   193
Moore, W. M.   196, 209
Morita, S.   197, 202, 204, 209
Morris, P. J.   344
Morrison, J.   1, 161, 172
Morrow, A.   294, 304
Morton, N. E.   5–6, 337, 379–83,
   386–7, 395–8
Mourant, A. E.   278–9, 289, 302, 304–5,
   316, 321, 323, 325, 327–8, 397
Mossberger, R. J.   304
Motulsky, A. G.   294, 302, 304
Mount, A. B.   27–8
Mountjoy, E. W.   21
Mukherjee, B. N.   302
Muller, H. J.   383, 397
Mulvaney, D. J.   75, 114, 118, 124, 126
Munro, A.   190, 194
Musgrave, J. K.   303

Mya-Tu, M.   281, 286, 290, 292, 304–6
Muangintra, J.   305

Nagy, J. M.   262
Nakajima, H.   368, 376
Na-Nakorn, S.   302, 306
Napier, J.   119, 126
Navratil, L.   216, 226
Neel, J. V.   346, 395,–6, 398
Nei, M.   397
Neumann, A. C.   15, 21
Newman, M. T.   218, 225
Newsome, A.   41, 53
Nguyen Van Hung   280, 286, 292–3,
   304
Nicholls, E. M.   228, 230, 243, 331,
   345, 349, 355, 364
Nicholls, K. D.   68, 77
Nicholson, M. K.   328
Niemann, L.   93
Niino, H.   21
Nijenhuis, L. E.   320, 324, 327, 429
Niswander, J. D.   398
Nix, H. A.   24, 28–9, 32, 37, 46–8, 53,
   74, 77
Nuzzo, E.   429
Nye, L. J. J.   192, 194

Oates, L. F.   233, 243
Oates, W. J.   233, 243
O'Brien, W. M.   257, 263
O'Connell, R. J.   13, 21
Odum, E. P.   40, 53
Ogan, E.   327, 349, 364
Ogawa, M.   376
Ohta, T.   329, 345
Ohtsuki, F.   197, 202, 204, 209
Olausson, E.   19, 22
Olivier, G.   211, 214
Olsson, I. U.   12, 22
Omakura, Y.   327
Omoto, K.   291, 299, 305, 331, 338,
   343–4, 346, 365, 367, 370–1, 374,
   376, 396–7
Omura, A.   21
Ong, Y. W.   301
Opdyke, N. D.   22
Ortali, V.   346
Oschinsky, L.   92–3
Oxnard, C. E.   146, 160
Ozols, I. V.   274

Paijmans, K.   49, 53
Panich, V.   289, 305–6
Park, E. A.   258, 260–1, 263
Parker, C.   344–5
Parker, G. S.   261
Parker, W. C.   303
Parkinson, R.   143
Parsons, P. A.   118, 125, 162, 173, 225,
   227–33, 235–8, 243

Paterson, W. S. B.   12, 22
Pederson, E. B.   186, 194
Pels, S.   110, 112
Penrose, L. S.   215–6, 218, 225
Perera, D. J. B.   327
Pereira, T. E.   345
Peron, F.   175, 182
Peters, T.   346
Peterson, J. A.   32, 47, 52, 68, 77
Peterson, R. F.   327
Petrakis, N. L.   305
Petrakis, S. J.   294, 305
Petrakis, S. L.   305
Petras, M. L.   234, 243
Petrini, C.   346
Petz, L. D.   430
Phansomboon, S.   280, 293, 305, 321,
    327
Phipps, C. V. G.   17, 22
Piazza, A.   335, 346
Pietrusewsky, M. 166, 172
Pingle, U.   305
Pinkerton, F. J.   398
Plane, M. D.   41–2, 53
Plato, C. C.   306
Platt, B. S.   260, 263
Poey-Oey, H. G.   291, 303–4, 397
Plomley, N. J. B.   166, 172
Polach, H. A.   12, 20, 59, 68–9, 75,
    111, 134–5, 138
Pollock, N.   380–1, 397
Polunin, I.   279–80, 287, 305, 320–1,
    324, 327, 397
Pons, J.   218, 226
Pono, C.   53
Pootrakul, P. 306
Popham, R. E.   218, 226
Porta, F.   346
Post, R. H.   295, 305
Poulianos, A. N.   119, 126
Powell, J. M.   32, 43, 49, 53–4
Powell, R. D.   301
Poznanski, A. K.   262
Prasad, C. H.   316, 323, 327
Prasad, P.   280
Pretty, G.   122
Pribadi, W.   304
Prokopec, M.   123, 215
Propert, D. N.   241, 243
Pyle, S. I.   245, 247, 261–3
Puenpatom, M.   301

Rao, P. P. D.   215, 218, 221–2, 226
Rand, A. L.   52
Ray, A. K.   429
Reynolds, C. A.   304
Read, D. W.   86, 93
Reid, J. L.   17, 22
Richardson, J. L.   75
Richkov, G.   295
Richter, C. P.   258, 260, 263

Ritter, H.   398
Rivat, L.   398
Roberts, D. F.   184, 186, 194
Roche, A. F.   257, 263
Rodrigue, R.   344
Rohmann, C. G.   247, 251, 262
Ropartz, C.   398
Rosenfield, R. E.   327
Roth, J. S.   206, 209
Rousseau, P. Y.   398
Rucknagel, D. L.   306
Ruffini, G.   346
Rutgers, C. F.   364, 396
Ruxton, B. P.   54
Ryan, P.   39, 54

Saave, J.   346, 364
Saengudom, C.   301
Saha, N.   315, 327, 337–8, 340, 344,
    346
Salzano, F. M.   398
Sandusky, S. T.   262
Sandground, J. H.   288, 301
Sanger, R.   279, 305, 344
Sanghvi, L. D.   243, 401, 403, 405, 407,
    410, 427, 430
Sanpitak, N.   285, 291, 305
Sarkar, S. S.   315, 328
Schaefer, O.   196, 206, 209
Schanfield, M. S.   335, 344, 347, 349
    351–2, 357–8, 364, 398
Schebesta, P.   328
Schipul, A.   301
Schlanger, S. O.   21
Schodde, R.   27–8
Schoetensack, O.   1
Scholander, P. F.   191, 194
Schultz, J.   395
Schwager, P. M.   258–60, 263
Scott, E. M.   398
Scott, N. M.   289
Scott, I. D.   346
Scrimshaw, N. S.   252, 263
Šedivý, V.   215, 218, 226
Selander, R. K.   234, 243
Seligman, B. Z.   189, 194
Seligman, C. G.   189, 194
Semple, N. M.   305, 327, 376, 396, 398
Setzler, F. M.   215, 218, 221–2, 225
Sgaramella-Zonta, L. A.   242
Shackleton, N. J.   19, 22
Shanbhag, Shaila   327, 346
Shows, T. B.   306
Shreffler, D. C.   346
Silverman, F. M.   262
Simmons, R. T.   234, 243, 278–80,
    305, 307–11, 314–16, 318, 320–1,
    323–5, 327–8, 352, 364, 367, 369,
    376, 396, 398
Simons, M. J.   301, 303–4, 313, 327
Simpson, G. G.   183, 194

440   INDEX OF PERSONS

Sinclair, D.   196, 209
Singh, S.   215, 218, 226
Singhprasert, P.   293, 305
Singleton, R.   398
Siniscalco, M.   429
Sinnett, P.   290, 305
Siregar, A.   304
Skeat, W. W.   278, 305
Smith, C. A. B.   236
Smith, G. E.   126
Smith, K. N.   77, 126
Smythe, R. B.   213–4
Sneath, P. H. A.   279–80, 287, 305,
    320–1, 324, 327, 387, 397–8
Snodgrasse, R. M.   261
Sokal, R. R.   387, 398
Sollas, W. J.   1
Sonn, E. B.   328
Sontag, L. W.   247, 258–9, 263
Spence, M.   93
Spencer, B.   213–4
Spies, T. D.   261
Sprigg, R. G.   71, 77
Sringam, S.   285, 302, 328
Stamatoyanopoulos, G.   302
Stavely, J. M.   396
Steinberg, A. G.   286, 293, 305, 335,
    346–7, 349, 351–8, 364, 396, 398
Steinen, R. P.   12, 22
Stern, J. T.   146, 160
Stettner, E.   258, 263
Stevens, P.   41, 54
Stewart, T. D.   116–7, 120–1, 126
Stewart, R. J. C.   260, 263
Stirling, E. C.   165, 172, 213–4
Strehlow, T. G. H.   233, 243
Streten, N. A.   17–8, 22, 24, 28
Strouhal, E.   196, 204, 209
Sullivan, B.   21
Sullivan, L. R.   278, 305
Sunahara, M.   366, 370, 376
Sungate, T.   305
Sutton, H. E.   346
Sutow, W. W.   251, 263

Takahashi, K.   376
Tanaka, T.   375–6
Tanis, R.   346
Tann, G.   304
Tanner, H. D.   327
Tanner, J. M.   196, 209, 245, 252, 263
Tashian, R. E.   291, 306
Taylor, C. N. D.   398
Taylor, H. W.   415
Tedford, R. H.   26, 28, 70, 77
Tepfenhart, M. A.   398
Thambipillai, V.   295, 306
Than-Than-Sint   286, 292, 306
Thein, H.   302
Thin-Thin-Hliang   304–5
Thom, B. G.   12, 22, 66, 77

Thoma, K. H.   271, 274
Thomas, B. H.   194
Thomas, D. W.   209
Thorne, A. G.   2, 4, 75, 95–6, 108–12,
    118, 121, 124, 126–7, 131, 138,
    171, 181–2, 268–71, 274
Thurber, D. L.   20
Thurstone, E.   402, 410
Ti, T. S.   303
Tibbs, G. J.   345, 397
Tills, D.   289, 304
Tindale, N. B.   1, 2, 231, 243, 320, 324,
    328, 364, 382, 396, 398
Ting, A.   344
Tobias, P. V.   117
Todd, D.   302
Tongiorgi, E.   21
Topinard, P.   1, 161, 172–3, 182
Tuchinda, S.   285, 289, 293, 306
Turner, W.   1

Undevia, J. V.   398
Urano, M.   376

van der Hammen, T.   47, 53
van der Hoeven, J. A.   320, 324, 327
van Deusen, H. M.   42–3, 54
van Donk. J.   12, 19–20
van Loghem, E.   335, 344, 347, 353,
    364, 396, 429
van Tets, G. F.   27
van Woerkom, A. J. J.   19
Veeh, H. H.   12–13, 15, 22
Veevers, J. J.   13, 15, 22
Veldkamp, J. F.   41, 54
Vella, F.   285, 306
Verstappen, H. T.   33–4, 54
Vickers Rich, P.   27
Vidyarthi, L. P.   345
Viganotti, C.   335, 346
Viteri, F.   262
Vogel, P.   327
von Baelz, E.   375
von Koenigswald, G. H. R.   81, 83, 93
Vos, G. H.   305, 327, 329–30, 333, 335,
    345–7, 349, 352–3, 355, 364, 396,
    398

Wakefield, N. A.   56, 77
Walcott, R. I.   13, 16, 22
Wallace, A. C.   122, 126, 173
Wallace, E. H.   327, 396
Wallerstein, R. O.   430
Walker, D.   32–3, 54
Walsh, R. J.   242, 305, 320, 327–8,
    430, 496
Wang, A. C.   331, 346
Wang, C. C.   301
Wangspa, S.   301
Ward, R. H.   428, 430
Wardlaw, H. S. H.   186, 188, 194

Wardle, P. 33, 54
Washbourn-Kamau, C. 75
Washburn, S. L. 171
Wasi, P. 288, 306
Watanabe, H. 375–6
Watanabe, S. 365, 376
Watson, J. B. 425–6, 430
Weatherall, D. J. 302
Webb-Peploe, H. 261
Webster, P. J. 17–18, 22, 24, 28
Weidenreich, F. 100, 109, 112, 114, 118, 126, 142
Weiner, J. S. 194
Weitkamp, L. R. 304, 333, 346, 395, 398
Welch, J. S. 205, 208
Welch, Q. B. 281, 289–91, 293, 301, 303–4, 306, 340, 343, 346
Wendland, W. M. 20
Weng, M. I. 301
Weninger, M. 216, 218, 226
Went, L. M. 429
Werle, P. P. 247, 261
Westendorp Boerma, F. 304
Westropp, C. K. 262
White, J. M. 295, 304
White, J. P. 30, 42–4, 53
White, N. G. 227–9, 230–3, 243
Whittaker, J. 344
Wickramasinghe, R. L. 316, 327–8, 345
Widdowson, E. M. 195, 209
Wiener, A. S. 280, 316, 323, 328
Wight, R. L. 303
Williams-Hunt, P. D. R. 278, 306
Wilson, I. B. 56, 75
Wilson, J. B. 304
Wilson, S. 93
Williams, G. E. 56, 68, 72, 77

Williams, P. W. 32, 42, 54
Winyar, B. 305
Wise, P. H. 191, 194, 207, 209
Woldstedt, P. 12, 22
Wood, W. 164
Wood, W. B. 245–6, 263
Woodfield, D. G. 345, 364, 397, 430
Wood Jones, F. 1, 116, 123, 126
Woods, J. D. 213–4
Wooster, W. S. 17, 22
Workman, P. L. 386, 398
WHO 348, 364
Wright, R. C. 398
Wright, R. V. S. 4, 265
Wright, S. 379–80, 383, 386, 398–9
Wunderly, J. 1, 166, 172
Wurm, S. A. 231, 243, 417, 430
Wyndham, C. H. 190, 194

Yalow, R. S. 206, 209
Yamaguchi, B. 120, 126, 162, 172, 365, 373, 376
Yamamoto, M. 397
Yang, H. J. 301
Yap, E. H. 303
Yasuda, N. 379, 397
Yee, S. 386, 397
Yengoyan, A. A. 382, 399
Yoshida, A. 344

Ziegler, E. 196, 206, 209
Zietze, F. R. 165
Zigas, V. 328, 430
Zimike, F. 53
Zonta, L. A. 429
Zoutendyk, A. 396

Index of subjects

Aboriginal Tribes
  Andilyaugwa   228, 233, 239
  Anmatjera   355
  Aranda   228, 231, 233, 239, 280,
    284, 286, 296–300, 340, 355, 427
  Burera   239
  Central Desert   351–2, 354
  Dalabon   187, 192
  Djauan   113
  Garawa   232
  Gunwinggu   228, 233
  Janjula   232
  Jarildekald   143
  Kaiadilt   234, 241
  Lardil   234
  Luridja   355
  Malag   337, 340
  Murngin   228, 231–4, 239
  Nangata   309
  Nangatara   309
  Ngalbun   113
  Njadjadjara   187, 192
  Nunggubuyu   280, 284, 286, 297–8,
    300, 340, 343, 427
  Pintubi   187, 228, 331, 355
  Pitjantjatjara   187, 228, 340, 355
  Rembarranga   215 ff
  Tiwi   228, 232–3, 279–80, 284, 286,
    296–300, 427
  Wailbri   197 ff, 228, 239, 335, 337,
    340–1, 355
  Warki-Korowalde   143
  Western Desert   330, 333–4, 349,
    352, 354–5, 359–60
Acclimatisation   190
Africans   5, 144–8, 218, 257–8, 279,
  291, 294, 318, 331 ff, 373
Ainu   5, 142, 148–9, 153–9, 313–5,
  317–8, 331, 343, 365 ff, 388
Allelic variability   411 ff

American Negroes   331, 333
Amerindians
  cranial relationships of   144, 148–9,
    153, 200, 203–4, 218, 257–8, 291,
    294, 309, 318, 329, 333, 373
Andamanese   142, 145, 159
Anson Bay   166, 168
  cranial relationships of   168
Apaches
  morphology of   200, 203–4
Arafura Sea   13, 15, 18, 25
  shelf   29–30, 37, 45
  plains   45
Arfak Mountains   30
Arnhem Land   25, 166, 168, 188, 191,
  221, 228 ff. 239, 337, 343, 371
  cranial relationships of   168
Aryans   315
Aru Island   24, 29
Atayal
  cranial relationships of   148–9, 153–4
Atherton Tableland   56, 69, 73
Atlantic Ocean   13
Australoid(s)   313, 388
Austronesians   352, 354
Baining
  cranial affinities of   155–6
Baliem River   30, 39
Banda Sea   30
Banks & Torres Islands   337
Barbados   12
Basal metabolic rate   184, 186, 192
Bass Strait   110
Batak   282, 286 ff, 311
Bathurst Islanders, see Aboriginal tribes,
  Tiwi
Behring Strait   120, 124
Bentinck Island   234, 308–9, 318, 352,
  359–61
Beswick   211

Bismarck Range 30, 43
Blood groups
  ABO 184, 234, 379–81, 296, 299,
    307 ff, 342, 366 ff, 375, 388, 390,
    402, 405 ff, 418–19, 423
  MNS 279–80, 296, 299, 308 ff, 330,
    366–8, 405 ff, 417 ff
  Rh 279–81, 296, 309 ff, 330. 366–8,
    388–90, 405 ff, 418–19
  P 309, 311 ff, 366–8
  Le 309, 311 ff, 366–8
  Lu 309, 311, 316, 324–6
  K 231, 309, 311, 324–6, 366–9, 390
  Jk 309, 311, 314, 366–8
  Fy 309, 311–14, 324–6, 366–8,
    388–90
  Di 279, 309, 324–6, 329, 366–8
  Ge 330, 417 ff
  I^T 425
Blood Pressure 186, 192
Borneo, see Kalimantan
Botany, see Flora
Bougainville Island 235, 310, 352,
  357–8
Brachymesophalangy 257–8
Brain
  increase in size of 183
Bruneis 312
Buchan 74
Buriats 149, 153
Burmese 281, 286. 290
Bushmen 142, 145, 152

Cairns 114, 116
Cambodia 313
Cancers 414
Cape York 213, 308, 318, 332–3, 350,
  352, 354–5, 359–61, 371, 407–8
Caroline Islands 380
Carpentarians 142
Carstenz, Mt, see Mount Jaya
Castaways 23–4
Caucasoid(s) 309, 343, 349, 354, 365,
  archaic 313, 317
  characteristics of 299
Central Australia 371, 407–8
Central Desert 188
Ceram 19–20
Ceylon, see Sri Lanka
Cham 284
Chamorros 291
Chinese 280 ff, 313, 318, 338, 371–3
  cranial relationships of 148–9, 152–4
Cladogram 387
Climate
  palaeo 3, 11, 17, 25, 57
Cloggs Cave 56
Conception
  seasonal variation 185, 192
Continental shelves 13, 15

Cranial series and analyses 81 ff, 95 ff,
  113 ff, 141 ff, 161 ff, 173 ff, 195 ff,
  211 ff, 227 ff
Cyclogenesis 18

Damil (Uhunduni) 39
Dampier Land 309
Darwin 215
  cranial series from 165, 168
Dating
  radiocarbon 12, 46, 50, 56, 59, 64,
    66, 96, 122–3, 134–8
  potassium-argon 81
  uranium/thorium 12
Dayak 279, 312
Deformation
  cranial 109, 116
Dendrogram 387
Derby 18
Dermatoglyphics 215 ff, 228 ff, 295
Devil's Lair 56, 121
Diabetes 207
Dingo 185
Dravidian
  pre 313, 315, 317–8
Dunes 18, 71

Earwax types 294, 366, 370
Elcho Island 228, 308, 337
Endogamy 232–3, 401
English 373
Environmental stress 4
Enzyme markers 329 ff
Eskimos 146, 149, 196, 206, 218, 373
Eurasia
  genetic links with 307 ff
Europeans
  cranial relationships of 144 ff

Fauna
  birds 27, 41–2
  extinct 25–7, 41–2, 62, 64
  fish 69
  mammal physiology 183 ff
  mammals 23, 40–2, 43 ff, 83, 122
  molluscs 19, 59, 65, 69
  reptiles 42
  use as charms 26
  Willandra Lakes 67
Fiji(ans) 158, 334, 341, 357–8
  affinities of 158
Filipinos 280, 294, 297
Finisterre Range 30
Fitzroy River 71
Flinders Ranges 68
Flora
  New Guinea 32 ff
  palaeo 19
  Snowy Mountains 68
Flores 23
Fluorine tests 91

Forests 33, 36, 39–42, 43–9, 51, 69
Fossils, *see* Human Fossils and Fauna

Gene-flow 231, 374
  frequencies, variation in 241
Genetic distance 4, 6, 277 ff, 279,
    296 ff, 371–3, 379 ff, 401 ff, 415 ff
  drift 299, 317, 374–5
  markers, *see* blood groups, serum pro-
    teins, red cell enzymes, etc.
  networks 416
  topology 386–8
Glaciation 12, 15, 17, 19, 25, 32–3,
    43–7, 51, 56, 65–8, 72, 74
Glottochronology 6, 425
Glucose tolerance 186, 191
Goulburn Island 221
Grasslands 33, 37, 39–42, 46–7, 49–51
  anthropogenic 32–3
Great Barrier Reef 13
Greater Australia 3, 23
Great Lakes 12
Groote Eylandt 228, 309
Growth of Aboriginals 205
  in New Guinea 245
Guam 148–9, 153–4
Gujurat 405, 411
Gulf of Carpentaria 17, 309

Haast's Bluff 211
Habituation 186, 190–1, 193
Haemoglobin 234, 287 ff, 296, 343
  Abnormal 282, 287–8, 299, 405 ff
Halmahera 19
Hamid Rock Shelter 40, 50
Harris' Lines 258 ff
Hawaiians
  cranial analysis of 148–9, 154
Heterozygosity 385 ff
Hidaka 367
Hokkaido 313, 365, 367
Human fossils
  Aitape 15, 114
  American 120–1, 123
  Australopithecus 83, 185
  Cape Flats 91
  Choukoutien 91–2, 120, 124
  Cohuna 3, 110, 114–7, 122
  Combe Capelle 118, 123
  Cro-magnon 119, 123
  Florisbad 91
  Green Gully 59, 110
  Grimaldi 118
  Homo erectus 4, 81 ff, 95, 100,
    114 ff, 265
  Kedungbrubus 83, 85
  Keilor 3, 26, 59, 62–3, 67, 74, 110,
    113–4, 122, 124, 158–9
  Kow Swamp 3–4, 96 ff, 116, 123,
    138, 181, 268 ff

Lake Mungo I 70, 96 ff, 121, 123,
    128 ff, 181, 268, 269, 271–2
Lake Mungo III 121, 127 ff
Lake Nitchie 110, 122
Liu-Kiang 120
Meganthropus 81, 83
Mojokerto 81, 85–6, 120
Mossgiel 110, 114, 122
Mt Cameron West 174 ff
Murrabit 117, 122
Neanderthal Man 1, 83–4, 90, 117,
    119, 121, 124, 267
Ngandong, *see* Solo
Niah 91–2, 95, 120, 123
Olduvai 117
Petralona 119
Piedmont 123
Pithecanthropus, see Homo erectus
Predmost 119, 123
Rhodesian 117
Saldanha 91
Sambungmachan 85–6
Solo 4, 81 ff, 109 ff
Steinheim 119
Swanscombe 119
Tabon 91, 95, 120, 124
Talgai 114, 122
Tartanga 114
Vertesszollos 119
Vestonice 123
Wajak 91–2, 95, 114, 120, 124
West Point 174
Humidity
  environmental importance of 57 ff,
    67, 72–3, 75
Huon Peninsula 14–15
Hybridity 385 ff

Ice-caps 11–12, 47
Immunoglobulins
  as indicators of affinities 347 ff
India(ns) 185, 192, 280–1, 286, 290 ff,
    313 ff, 329, 338, 401 ff
India
  Tribal populations 159, 315–6, 329,
    337–8, 340, 343, 405 ff
Indonesia(ns) 23, 29, 278, 291–2,
    279–80, 311, 313, 318, 371–3
Inthas 281
Irian Jaya 30, 39–41, 309 ff, 337–8,
    340, 343, 356, 358
Isolation
  by distance 381
Isoniazid metabolism 366, 370

Jakun 278, 281–2
Japan(ese) 313, 315, 317–8, 338,
    365 ff, 373
  cranial relationships of 148–9, 153–4.
    197, 202, 204

Java   4, 23, 81, 95
  Bali Passage   20
  Sea   20
Jayawijaya Range   30
Jews   289, 355
Jomon People   374

Kafiavana   42
Kalimantan   19, 312–3, 318
Kalamburu
  anthropometry at   211
Kedayans   312
Kemabu Plateau   35, 39, 40, 43
Keppel Islands   115–6
Kerowagi   39
Kidney   185, 192
Kimberley   25, 352, 355
  morphology in   213
Kinship   4
  and population structure   379 ff
Kiowa Rock Shelter   42
Kmer   284, 287, 290
Koreans   375
Koroba   42
Kosipe
  occupation of   30, 43
Kotan   375
Kraatke Range   30
Kubor Range   30
Kuru   333

Lachlan River   69, 71
Lake
  Albacutya   70
  Arumpo   71
  Corangamite   70
  Frome   72
  Garnpung   71
  George   68
  Glen Emu   70
  Habema   39–41
  Inle   281
  Keilambete   73
  Kow   96, 110
  Lind   288
  Menindee   26, 70
  Mungo   59, 64–5, 67, 69, 74
  Nitchie   70
  Paniai   30, 39, 46, 310
  Torrens   56, 72
  Tyson   70
  Victoria   56, 70
  Woods   68
Lancefield   26
Lae   331
Lahu   288–9
Language   3, 6, 90, 230, 233, 342,
  349 ff
Lapps   197, 200–4, 289, 373
Laos   313
Leucocyte antigens (HLA)   335–7

Lissu   288–9
Lombok Strait   20
Loyalty Islands   158

McEachern's Cave   56
Mahalanobis Distance   383
Maharashtra   405
Mainoru   215
Malaria
  Selection by   5
Malaya   29, 278–9
Malay Aborigines   5, 189, 277 ff, 312,
  340, 343
Malayo-Polynesians   289
Malays   277 ff, 311–13, 318, 371–3
Maningrida   241
  anthropometry   211
Manus Island   332, 338, 341
Mapala Rock Shelter   40–1, 43, 46, 49
Maribyrnong River   59, 62, 64
Markham Valley   30, 37, 310, 331
Marriage
  frequency of intertribal   231
Marshall Islands   380
Melanaus   312
Melanesia(ns)   5, 159, 342–3, 349, 388
Merauke (Moake) Range   30, 51
Miao   284, 286–7, 289, 295
Microevolution   317
Micronesia(ns)   158, 218, 258, 292,
  318, 338–42, 373, 380
Migration   381–2
  pleistocene   23 ff
  systematic pressure due to   383
Minangkabau   286
Miriwun   121
Mokil Atoll   380
Mon   290
Mongoloids   92, 218, 279, 294–5, 299,
  343, 349, 371–3
  cranial relationships   144, 149, 153–4,
  156, 159
Mon-Kmer   289
Mornington Island   234, 241, 308, 350,
  359–60
Mortality, Aboriginal infant   205
Mount
  Albert Edward   30, 32, 46
  Bangeta   32
  Cameron West   174
  Giluwe   32, 40–2, 50
  Jaya   30, 32, 39, 40, 46–7, 50
  Juliana, see Mandala
  Kosciusko   68, 70
  Mandala   30, 32–3, 40
  Muria   81
  Ngga Pulu   50
  Suckling   41
  Trikora   30, 39–41
  Wilhelm   32, 35–42, 46–7, 49–51
  Wilhelmina, see Trikora

Murray-Darling System   67, 71, 75
Murray Valley
  cranial remains from   107, 109, 116,
    123, 164–5, 168
  tribes   143
Muruts   288
Mutation   386
  neutral   394–5
  rate   395

Namu Atoll   380
Nassau Range, see Sudirman Range
Negrito(s)   5, 114, 116, 142, 152–3,
    159, 218, 222, 278 ff, 295–6, 318–9
Negroes see Africans or American
  Negroes
New Britain   143, 158, 166, 168, 170,
    310, 332, 351, 356–61, 363, 417,
    419
New Guinea(ns)   15, 117, 166, 168,
    170, 278, 294, 309 ff, 318, 333–4,
    337–41, 349, 371–3, 391–3
  Central District   356, 358, 361–2
  Eastern Highlands   310, 334, 356,
    358, 363
  Fly River   351, 357
  Gulf District   362
  Markham Valley   351, 357–8
  Milne Bay   362–3
  Morobe District   310, 363
  Northern District   362
  Sepik District   166, 168, 170, 363
  Southern Highlands   356, 362
  Western District   354–8, 361–2
  Western Highlands   351, 354, 356–8
New Guinea Populations
  Agarabi   426
  Asmat   340, 351, 358
  Atzera   417, 419
  Auyana   426
  Awin   351
  Baining   155–6, 359
  Balim   359–61
  Bilbil   420
  Bundi   39, 245 ff, 417
  Chimbu   39, 41–2, 47, 417
  Dani   39
  Eastern Highlands   422, 425
  Enga   417
  Fore   422
  Gimi (Jimi)   39, 417 ff
  Gogodara   351, 427
  Guhu-Samane   419–20
  Kanite   426
  Kamano   422, 426
  Kandawo   417
  Karkar   334, 341, 417
  Keiagana   422
  Kikori   427
  Kiwai   427
  Kopiago   417

  Kunimaipa   419
  Kutuba   419
  Mabuso   420, 422
  Managalese   419
  Maring   417
  Minj   359
  Motu   245, 359–60, 417–9, 427
  Narak   417
  Oksapmin   417
  Siane   417
  Simbai   417
  Sulka   351, 359
  Tairora   422
  Takia   417, 428
  Tari   419
  Telefolmin   417
  Waria   417, 420
  Waskia   422, 428
  Watut   41–2, 417, 419
  Yonngom   351
New Hebrides   310, 333
New Ireland   310
New South Wales   116
  coastal cranial series   163, 165
  cranial relationships of   168, 170
New Zealand Pass   40
Nilgiri Hills   315–6
Northern Territory   116, 308, 351
Nubians   204
Nutrition, in Aboriginals   205–7

Ocean currents   11, 17
Ochre   129–31
Oriomo Plateau   37
Ossification centres   247 ff
Otibanda Formation   41
Ovalocytosis   283–4, 288
Owen Stanley Ranges   30, 46
Oxygen
  isotopes in oceans   18–19

Palaeomagnetics   135
Palaeontology
  sampling problems   3
Palaeophysiology   183 ff
Papua New Guinea, see New Guinea
Papuo-Melanesians   142, 152, 155,
    158–60, 168, 170
Pathans   292
Philippines   23. 148–9, 153–4, 311.
    318. 337
Pingelap Atoll   380
Ple   278
Pollen analysis   32, 42, 50, 56
Polynesia(ns)   158, 258, 292, 342, 388
Population
  bottlenecks   380–1
  crashes   241–2
Proto Australoids   402
Pseudocholinesterase   294
PTC tasting   294–5, 366, 370, 405 ff

Pureni Swamp   42
Pygmies   142, 218, 278, 293, 310–11

Queensland
  cranial series   165
  cranial relationships of   168, 170

Race
  meaning of   227
  presapiens   6
Radiation
  solar   19
Radiography
  of hand and foot   245 ff
Rainfall   37
Ramu River   30, 37
Red cell enzyme groups
  esterases   234
  Na-K ATPase   183
  6PGD   283 ff, 296, 337, 370, 421, 423
  PGM   283 ff, 296, 338, 342, 366,
    369–70, 388, 390, 423
  AK   283, 285, 289, 343, 369–70
  Ac.Ph   290, 337, 342, 366, 369–70,
    390, 421, 423
  G6PD   281–4, 288–90, 299, 366, 402
  Pep B   283, 285, 291, 340–43, 366
  PHI   290, 366
  LDH   290, 366
  MDH   291, 423
  ADA   291, 366, 423
  PGK   291, 341, 366
  DIA   291, 366
  EsD   366
Red–green colour blindness   295, 366,
  370, 405 ff
Rennell and Bellona Islands   356
Rocky Cape   65
Roonka   122–3
Rhade   284
Robinson River   308
Roper River   308
Ryukyu Islands   12, 367, 369, 371–3
  relations with Ainu   375

Sakais   159
Sakhalin Islands   313, 365
Sahul Shelf   18, 24–5, 29, 74
Samoa   341
Sampung   124
Sangiran   81, 83, 85–6
Sarawak   279
Saruwaged Range   30, 39, 46–7, 50
Schouten Island   309 ff
Sea-Levels   11 ff, 65–7
Sedong   284
Selection pressure   386, 394
Semai   278 ff
Semang   159
Semelai   278, 282
Senoi   278 ff

Sepik River   30, 37
Serum protein groups
  Hp   286, 291, 296, 330, 366, 369–70
    390, 405 ff, 423
  Tf   286, 292, 296, 331, 341, 343, 366,
    369–70, 388, 390, 408, 422–3
  Gc   293, 332, 341, 366, 370, 408
  Alb   293, 333
  Cp   294, 366
  Pi   294, 334, 366
  Ag   366
  Gm and Inv   286, 292–3, 334, 342,
    347 ff, 366, 370, 388, 390, 407–8
  A2m   349 ff
Serum protein markers   329 ff
Siberia   295
Singapore   313
Skeletal series and analyses   246 ff (see
    also Cranial series and analysis)
Skin
  colour   239, 241
  reflectance   240
  temperature   191
Snowline   37
Snow (Sneeuw) Mountains see Merauke
    Range
Snowy Mountains   68, 70
Solomon Islands   310
South Australia   116
  skeletal remains from   143, 148
South East Asia
  genetic studies in   277 ff
Sowespac   144 ff
Sri Lanka   313, 316–7
Star Mountains   30
Stieng   284
Strandlines   12–13
Sudirman Range   30, 32, 39
Sula Island   19–20
Sulawesi   19–20, 23, 288
Sumatra   289–90, 294, 311, 337
Sumbawa-Flores   Passage   20, 23
Sunda Islands   20, 29
Sundaland   24
Swanport   113
  skeletal remains   143, 164–5
  affinities   168, 170
Sweat
  glands   185
  rate   188, 193
  suppression   186, 189–90, 193

Taiwan   291
Takasagos   371–3
Tamils   315–6
Tanimbar   19
Tari Gap   40
Taritatu River   37
Tasmania(ns)   25, 68, 73–4 110, 113,
    141–3, 148
  affinities   152 ff

crania in   166, 173 ff
cremation   174
population estimate   173
skeletal variation   122, 143, 145, 149
Tavoyans   281
Tectonics   11–12, 15
Teeth
    attrition of   265, 270
    evolution of   265 ff
    pathology of   271
    size   268–70
Tektites   81
Telegus   315
Temiar   278 ff
Temperature
    environmental importance of   57 ff, 67
    lowering of   69, 73
    of sea water   19
Temuan   278, 281–2, 287–8, 294, 296
Terraces
    submerged   14
Thais   279 ff, 291 ff, 313, 318, 373
Thalassaemia   287–8
Trade Winds   17
Traits   1
    habitus   4
    heritage   4
    non-metrical   4, 235 ff
Tree line   33, 37, 39, 40, 42, 43, 47, 51
Tribal size   231, 234
Tribe
    definition of   232
Trinil   81, 85, 90
Timor   15, 19, 23–4, 29
    Sea   20, 25
Tinne Range, see Jayawijaya Range
Tolais   113, 143, 145, 148–9
    affinities   153–4, 158–9, 170

Torres Strait   15
    affinities   168, 170
    cranial series   166
    Islanders   113
    landbridge   17–19
Tundra   33

Variation
    skeletal   4
Veddas   159, 278, 313 ff, 342–3, 402
Veddoids   185, 189, 315, 342–3
Vietnamese   279 ff, 290
Vitiaz Strait   14
Vogelkap   19

Wahgi Valley   49
Wajin   375
Walkabouts   381
Wallacea   12, 23, 29, 124
Wanni Castes   316
Water
    drinking   186, 188–9
    turnover   183, 187, 188–9
    volume in body   187, 191
Weipa   352, 359–60
Western Australia   17, 116, 308–9, 371
Western Desert   188, 407–8
West Irian see Irian Jaya
Willandra Lakes   59, 65, 67, 69–72, 110,
    127
Wissellakes, see Lake Paniai

Yaeo   286–7
Yalata, anthropometry   211
Yirrkala   221
Yuendumu
    morphology   197 ff
    anthropometry   211